DIES
IVNIVS

Being a collection of writings
about the Earth
in all its aspects;
with 64 pages of illustrations
in gravure,
and many line drawings.

Edited by A. C. Spectorsky

Appleton-Century-Crofts, Inc.
New York

THE BOOK OF THE

EARTH

Library of Congress Card Number: 57-12045

ACKNOWLEDGMENTS

The selections from the following books are reprinted by the kind permission of the publishers and copyright owners:

NAMES ON THE LAND *by George R. Stewart. Copyright, 1945, by George R. Stewart. Reprinted by permission of and arrangement with Houghton Mifflin Company, the authorized publishers.*

CRATERS OF FIRE *by Haroun Tazieff, Harper & Brothers. Copyright, 1952, by Haroun Tazieff.*

SCOTT'S LAST EXPEDITION *by Robert F. Scott. Copyright © 1913 by Dodd, Mead & Company. Also with the permission of John Murray (Publishers) Ltd., London.*

PHEASANT JUNGLES *by William Beebe, G. P. Putnam's Sons, copyright 1927 by William Beebe.*

ANIMAL TREASURE *by Ivan T. Sanderson. Copyright 1937 by Ivan T. Sanderson. Reprinted by arrangement with The Viking Press, Inc., New York.*

"Obituary of a Bone Hunter" *by Loren C. Eiseley, Harper's Magazine, October 1947. Copyright 1947 by Loren C. Eiseley. With the permission of the author.*

BEYOND THE HUNDREDTH MERIDIAN *by Wallace Stegner. Copyright, 1953, 1954, by Wallace E. Stegner. Reprinted by permission of and arrangement with Houghton Mifflin Company, the authorized publishers.*

THE GOOD EARTH *by Pearl S. Buck. Copyright © 1931 by Pearl S. Buck. Reprinted by permission of Harold Ober Associates Incorporated.*

"The Mystery of the Savage Sump" *by Sam Davis. Reprinted, by permission of the publisher, Vanguard Press, Inc., from* COMSTOCK BONANZA, *edited by Duncan Emrich. Copyright, 1950, by Duncan Emrich.*

TORTILLA FLAT *by John Steinbeck. Copyright 1935 by John Steinbeck. Reprinted by arrangement with The Viking Press, Inc., New York.*

"Land Grabbing and Uncle Mel" *by Jesse Stuart, The Commonweal, September 17, 1943. Copyright 1943 by the Commonweal Publishing Co., Inc. By permission of the publisher.*

"An Underground Episode" *by Edmund Ware Smith, Story Magazine, April 1934. Copyright 1934 by Story Magazine.*

THE BOGMAN *by Walter Macken. Copyright, 1952, by Walter Macken. With the permission of The Macmillan Company, New York, and The Macmillan Company of Canada Limited.*

REACH FOR THE MOON *by Royce Brier. Copyright, © 1934, by Royce Brier. With the permission of the author.*

"How Much Land Does a Man Need?" *by Leo Tolstoy. Reprinted from* TWENTY-THREE TALES *by Leo Tolstoy, translated by Louise and Aylmer Maude, with the permission of Oxford University Press, London.*

CRY, THE BELOVED COUNTRY *by Alan Paton, copyright 1948 by Alan Paton. Reprinted by permission of Charles Scribner's Sons.*

MY NAME IS ARAM *by William Saroyan, copyright, 1937, 1938, 1939, 1940, by William Saroyan. Reprinted by permission of Harcourt, Brace and Company, Inc.*

THE COUNTRY HEART *by H. E. Bates, published by Michael Joseph, Ltd. With the permission of the author.*

THE FIELDS *by Conrad Richter. Copyright 1945, 1946 by Conrad Richter. Reprinted by permission of Alfred A. Knopf, Inc.*

UNDER FIRE *by Henri Barbusse. Copyright, 1917, by E. P. Dutton & Co., Inc. Renewal, 1947, by J. M. Dent & Sons, Ltd., London, England. Reprinted by permission of the publishers, and J. M. Dent & Sons, Ltd., London.*

A STILLNESS AT APPOMATTOX *by Bruce Catton. Copyright 1953 by Bruce Catton, reprinted by permission of Doubleday & Company, Inc.*

LONDON CALLING *by Storm Jameson, Harper & Brothers. Copyright 1942, by Harper & Brothers.*

HIROSHIMA DIARY *by Michihiko Hachiya, translated and edited by Warner Wells, University of North Carolina Press. Copyright 1955 by University of North Carolina Press.*

ALL QUIET ON THE WESTERN FRONT *by Erich Maria Remarque. Copyright, 1929, by Little, Brown & Company. Copyright, 1957, by Erich Maria Remarque. By permission of the publishers, Little, Brown & Co., and Putnam & Co., Ltd., London.*

"Career," *from* THE WHITE HORSES OF VIENNA *by Kay Boyle, copyright, 1936, by Kay Boyle. Reprinted by permission of Harcourt, Brace and Company, Inc.*

THE CAVE OF THE CACAHUAMILPA *by Gabriela Mistral, from* THE GREEN CONTINENT, *edited by German Arciniegas. Copyright 1944 by Alfred A. Knopf, Inc. Reprinted by permission of Alfred A. Knopf, Inc.*

"mehitabel in the catacombs" *from* ARCHY AND MEHITABEL *by Don Marquis, Copyright 1927 by Doubleday & Company, Inc.*

MEN AND GARDENS *by Nan Fairbrother. Copyright 1956 by Nan Fairbrother. Reprinted by permission of Alfred A. Knopf, Inc. and The Hogarth Press, Ltd., London.*

"A Yard of Jungle," *by William Beebe, from* ADVENTURING WITH BEEBE. *Copyright 1918, 1921, 1932, 1934, 1938, 1942, 1946, 1949, 1955 by William Beebe. Reprinted by permission of Duell, Sloan & Pearce, Inc.*

LISTEN FOR A LONESOME DRUM *by Carl Carmer, copyright 1936, 1950 by Carl Carmer, by permission of William Sloane Associates, Inc.*

DON QUIXOTE *by Cervantes, translated by Samuel Putnam. Copyright 1949 by The Viking Press, Inc., New York.*

ALL AROUND THE TOWN *by Herbert Asbury. Copyright 1934 by Alfred A. Knopf, Inc. Reprinted by permission of Alfred A. Knopf, Inc.*

THE LATE GEORGE APLEY *by John P. Marquand. Copyright, 1936, 1937, by John P. Marquand. By permission of Little, Brown & Co.*

"Johnny Appleseed and Aunt Mattie," from PLEASANT VALLEY *by Louis Bromfield, Harper & Brothers. Copyright 1945, by Louis Bromfield.*

The seven photographs reproduced in the front of this volume are the work, respectively, of WILLIAM BELKNAP, JR.: *Rapho-Guillumette;* LANDAU: *Rapho-Guillumette;* LANDAU: *Rapho-Guillumette;* FRITZ HENLE: *Monkmeyer;* ANSEL ADAMS; FREDERIC LEWIS; ZACHARY FREYMAN; FPG.

Preface

THE WOMB AND THE HUB OF MAN'S APPARENT UNIVERSE IS THE EARTH, THE PLANET on which he dwells and which he has not yet succeeded in leaving, physically, though his imagination and the instruments of his sciences have probed outward beyond the measure of light years to the curved boundaries of space and time.

Man's home, this orb, this cosmic mote, is his only tangible contact with the universe of which he is but a minute and fleeting particle. His mind may soar, his imagination travel far beyond the range of Palomars and stellar spectroscopes. But it is Earth and Earth alone which man may touch, probe, pat, smell, work with—and upon which he may live and toil and dream.

Our spheroid, third planet from the sun, is in the midst of the most exhaustive study to which it has ever been exposed. For this International Geophysical Year, the combined resources of Earth's scientists will be pooled to delve her mysteries, the natural history of the earth as it is today, some two to five billion years since the solidification of the crust on which we walk. That thin envelope of gases which we call atmosphere will be ranged by men and missiles—and will be astonished by a second, brief satellite. The barosphere, the planet's dense, metallic heart of thousands of miles in diameter, may be reassayed. Yet, for all the searching and analyzing and despite the relative insignificance of man's only touchable specimen of the miracle of the universe, there will be, still, infinitely more to learn than will have become known when the IGY comes to an end. And there is much that will never be known fully about this our Earth, for among its most mysterious phenomena—utterly unique so far as we know—is sentient life, about which we have learned so much and know so little. The astronomer, home from a night of peering millions of miles into black space, sits across the kitchen table from his wife and knows less of the miracle of human life and feeling, as encompassed within the walls of his home, than he does of the motions of binaries or the chemistry of variables. As it is with this man in his home, so it is with mankind on Earth: we are held upon our planet not only physically, not only literally, not only experientially, but also emotionally. From pole to pole, from frozen waste to steaming tropic, from a farmer's field nestled in a valley to the shifting dunes of deserts, Earth is home.

So *The Book of the Earth,* the fourth and final volume in this series, which has attempted a compendium of man's literary response to the major phenomena of his apparent universe, concerns itself with man's creative writing about his ultimate home, his source and his resting place, the planet on which he is born, lives, loves, struggles, works, dreams and dies. It is, in a sense, a composite self-portrait by some seventy-odd artists, of man in his relation to his immediate environment.

The picture is not always a pretty one. The human race has not been at ease at home, it has been the aggressive, often surly, restless, questing youngest member of the family of Earth dwellers. It has treated its home like a mine rather than a garden, as rightful spoil to exploit and plunder. Regarded thus, as a destructive latecomer, humanity has little claim on its self-assumed role as having been created in the divine image. But man can also love and know, and can transmute his loving and his knowledge into art, so that they may both be shared.

Alfred Korzybski spoke of man as, uniquely, a "time-binder," that is, as being capable of the transmission of knowledge from generation to generation, so that each generation may proceed in knowledge from the point at which the previous generation left off. We have not always profited from our time-binding capacity—clearly—but thanks to it the storehouse of knowledge and of art which is man's self-created heritage has grown with each generation. That portion of it which constitutes literary expression concerning this our Earth and our life upon it was culled for the making of this book.

As with its predecessors, this volume follows no pattern of chronology or geography. Rather, its ordering is in terms of man himself as he has acted and reacted with Earth and its forces and manifold aspects. As in the previous books, too, the pictures were not selected to illustrate, but to visually supplement, the text. There are other similarities: literary excellence took precedence over subject matter; the fresh and the unfamiliar were deemed more suitable for inclusion than old favorites; short fragments were eschewed, and space limitations prevented the inclusion of longer works or of excerpts from them which would have done them less than justice. Finally, if one may return to the graphic analogy, this composite Earth portrait was conceived to be more impressionistic than anatomically faithful, in the belief that a truer picture of man in relation to his planet would result. For though the achievements of the International Geophysical Year will incalculably advance man's knowledge of his planet—at a time in human history when he is closer than ever to leaving it for other worlds, or destroying it—his relation to it is still more a matter of profound emotional involvement than of scientific inquiry, and its expression is more accurately revealed in art than in science. This is not to denigrate the scientific enlightenment the IGY will accomplish. It is suggested, however, that one of its most significant potentials has already been achieved: international co-operation. In a much smaller way and far less significantly this book, too, is international. But it not only crosses the man-made boundaries and the language boundaries which scotch the planet, it also roams freely over the time boundary, as only the work of man, the time-binder, can do. Thus, as with portraits in paint, in this impressionistic portrayal, the first brush stroke and the final one, however far apart in time, share simultaneously in the finished work.

Once again, the editor must express his very great indebtedness to Mr. Louis Lerman, whose literary scholarship and ranging curiosity did much to make the compilation of this volume possible, and to Miss Patricia Schartle of Appleton-Century-Crofts and her colleagues who have supervised, designed and published the four volumes of which this is the last. Special thanks, too, are due those readers and critics whose response to each succeeding book has provided incentive and inspiration for the editing of the next. It is the editor's hope that *The Book of the Earth* will meet as warm a welcome as its predecessors.

A. C. SPECTORSKY

Contents

(Titles in center column are sources of selections)

3 MEN AGAINST THE EARTH

4 MEN STUDY THE EARTH

5 MEN FIGHT ON THE EARTH

6 MEN WONDER AT THE EARTH

Illustrations

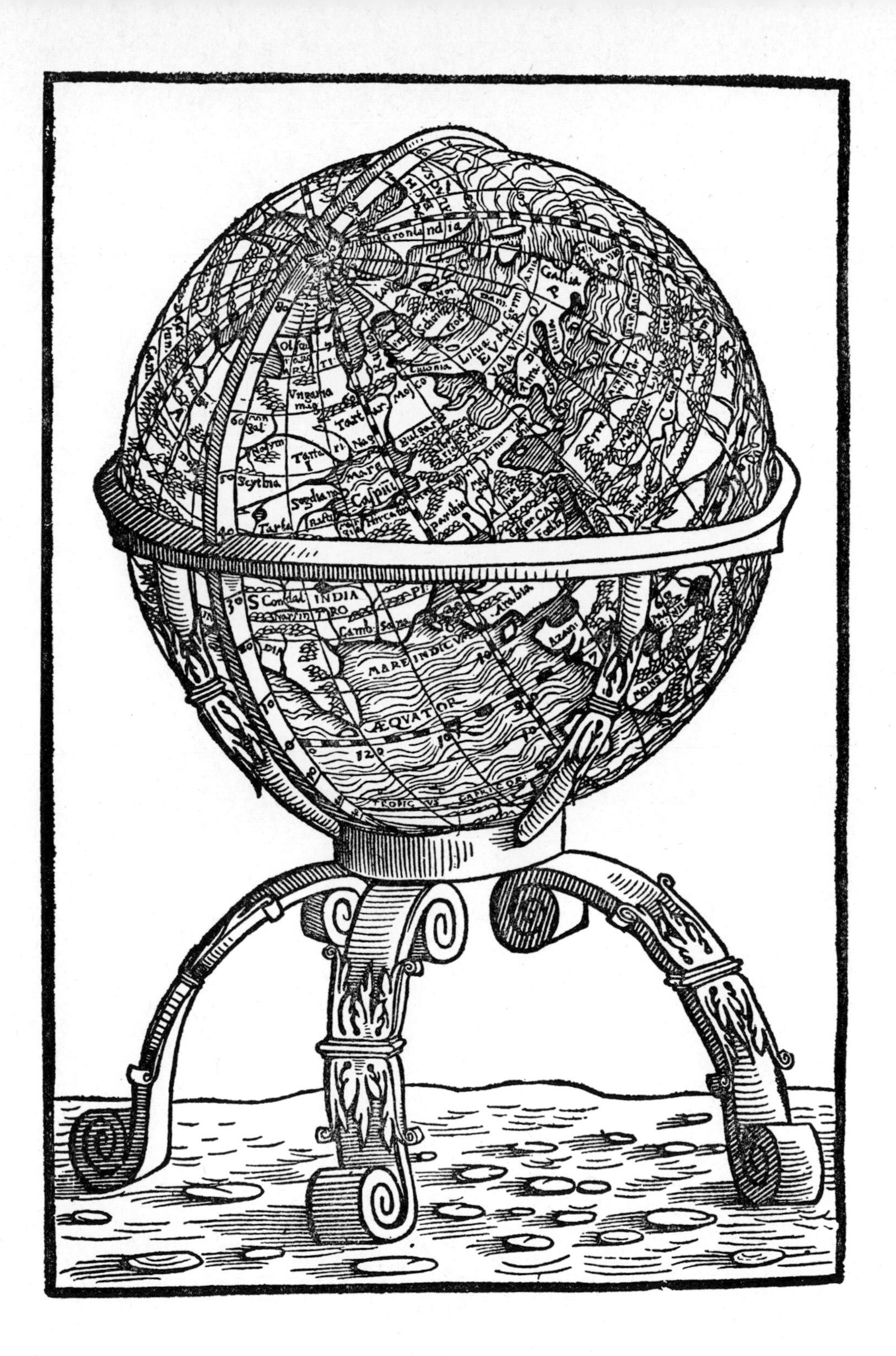

Gronlandia
Gallia
Scythia
Sogdiana
Caspiu
Parthia
INDIA
Arabia
MARE INDICV
ÆQVATOR
TROPICVS CAPRICOR

1

Men Venture on the Earth

The limits of our globe are known, but within the circumference of the great circles on our maps are vast, uncharted spaces, from the immense stretches of jungle on one surface of the earth to the five million square miles of ice which cover the Antarctic continent on another. Of the two hundred and sixty billion cubic miles inside this sphere, we know nothing. No man has yet penetrated beneath the thinnest and topmost crust of the lithosphere, except with fictional conjecture and scientific speculation.

In our time, men have moved outside the two dimensions of length and width which tie them to the earth. They have begun their exploration of the sky. In our time too, perhaps, there will be men to probe the core beneath us.

The record of man's exploration of his earth, both in fact and fiction, is an ancient and continuing one. It is a literature of restless, unquiet men driven to go where no others have gone before them. From that body of dramatic writing, we have chosen those selections which most eloquently picture the triumph and tragedy, the frustration and humor of man's exploration into the unknown realms of his planet.

ST. CHRISTOPHER, PATRON SAINT OF TRAVELERS

TOWARD A NEW COUNTRY

FROM *Names on the Land*

GEORGE R. STEWART

To write a novel in which a blizzard is the major character requires a thoroughgoing knowledge of meteorology and an inventive talent of a considerable order. George R. Stewart has both in more than sufficient degree. He repeated the performance in *Fire,* a novel in which a forest fire is hero, or villain, as you choose.

In this selection he combines geographic and historical research with skillful writing to give us the origin of place names.

IN THE DISTANT PAST, THEN, THE LAND WAS WITHOUT NAMES. YET THE NATURE OF the land itself prefigured something of what was to be. Where jagged mountains reared up along the horizon, many names would describe shapes, but in a flat country names of other meanings would be given. Where most streams were clear but one ran thick with reddish mud, a man coming to that stream would call it Red River, whether he said Río Colorado, or Rivière Rouge, or Bogue Homa, or blurted syllables in some now long-forgotten tongue. Since alders first grew close to water and desert-cedars clung to hillsides, they predestined Alder Creek and Cedar Mountain. Long Lake and Stony Brook, Blue Ridge and Grass Valley, lay deeper than tribe or language; the thing and the name were almost one.

No one knows when man came, or who gave the first names. Perhaps the streams still ran high from the melting ice-cap, and strange beasts roamed the forest. And since names—corrupted, transferred, re-made—outlive men and nations and languages, it may even be that we still speak daily some name which first meant "Saber-tooth Cave" or "Where-we-killed-the-ground-sloth."

There is no sure beginning. At the opening of history many and various tribes already held the land, and had given it a thin scattering of names. The names themselves can be made to reveal the manner of the earliest naming.

Once, let us say, some tribesmen moved toward a new country, which was unknown to them. Halting, they chose a good man, and sent him ahead. This scout went on, watching not to be ambushed or get lost, knowing he must report shrewdly when he returned. First he skulked along the edge of a big meadow, where he saw many deer. Then he came to a stream where he noted some oak trees, which were uncommon in that country. All this time he was skirting the slope of a great mountain, but because he was actually on it, and because the trees were so thick, he did not think of a mountain; and, besides, it made no difference to him one way or the other. So he went farther on—through a little swamp, and to a stream which he crossed on a beaver-dam. This stream was the same as the one where the oak trees grew, but he had no way of being certain, and besides it did not matter at all—each crossing was a thing in itself. He went on, through a narrow defile with many tall rocks, which he knew would be an ugly spot for an ambush. Going back, he noted all the places in reverse, but did not actually bestow any names on them.

When he told his story, however, he unconsciously gave names by describing places, such as the big meadow and the stream where the oak trees grew. He did not speak of the mountain, because the mountain was everywhere and the whole country was merely its slope; and he did not speak of the deer in the meadow, because he knew that deer are at one place for sun-up and another for nooning, so that only a fool would try to distinguish one meadow from another by mentioning them.

The others listened to his words, nodded and questioned and remembered; they knew that they would have no other knowledge of the next day's march, and that life and death might hang on how well they remembered his landmarks. So they thought to themselves, "big meadow," "stream where oak trees grow," "stream with a beaver-dam," and the rest. When they went ahead into that country, they recognized each place as they came to it.

Then, when they lived there, they used the descriptions first, saying, "There is good fishing in the stream where oak trees grow." But soon they said, "stream-where-oak-trees-grow" in one breath, and it had become a name.

The first simple names were like sign-posts, noting something permanent and easily recognized, something to distinguish one place from other places—size, or shape, or color, or the kind of rocks or trees found there. After the tribe grew familiar with the region, such sign-post names were no longer much needed, and as the people began to have memories of what had happened here or there, names of another kind sprang up.

At some stream, perhaps, a hunter saw a panther drinking in broad daylight, and killed it with a single arrow. This was a matter of wonder, and people began to say: "the stream where the panther was killed." After a few generations the actual story may have been forgotten, but the name retained. In the old Choctaw country there is still a Quilby Creek, from their words *koi-ai-albi,* "panther-there-killed." Far in the Southwest a ruined pueblo is Calle-mongue, "where-they-hurled-down-stones." But the name is the only testimony; no man knows the story of that desperate siege, or who hurled down stones at what besiegers.

Not all these adventures need have been real. If a young man saw a vision, what happened to him then may have been as vivid as the killing of a panther. Or he may have thought that his dream made manifest the world of spirits. So in the country of the Sioux many places had the suffix *-wakan,* and among the Algonquians *-manito,* to show that a presence haunted them. The Cherokees had a belief in a race of huge snakes. Each was great as a tree-trunk, horned, with a bright blazing crest. Even to see one was sure death. Where they were thought to lurk, in deep river-pools and lonely passes in high mountains, the Cherokees called *Where-the-Uktena-stays.*

From visions or from often-told and much-distorted exploits came a few mythological names, although sometimes the story arose later to explain an unusual name. The Abnaki of the far Northeast told of the giant Glooscap. Once he pursued an enormous moose, killing it finally close to the shore of the ocean. There they pointed out a ledge of rock which at one stage of tide looked much like a moose's rump, and so was called Moos-i-katch-ik. To reward his dog, Glooscap threw him the entrails. These became a reddish rock known as Osquoon, "the liver," and a vein of white quartz, Oolaghesee, "the gut."

If a tribe lived in the same region for many generations, the name-pattern grew more complex. The land itself might change. Stream-with-a-Beaver-Dam might fill with silt and become a mere swamp, so that the beavers no longer lived there. The dam itself would be grown over with trees and bushes. After the dam became indistinguishable, the name was actually misleading. Then it might be changed entirely, but a traditional-minded tribe would sometimes keep the old name, as in a modern city Canal Street may remain after the canal has long been filled in.

Language also changed with the generations, and names more rapidly than the rest of language. A lengthy descriptive name of an important place was said so often that it was likely to be clipped and slurred. Before long, it sounded like words having some other meaning, or else like meaningless syllables. The tribe had no written records to show what the name should be. Eventually some story-teller might build up a tale to explain the new name. Thus Allegheny seems most likely to have meant "fine river" in the language of the Delawares, but they later told a story of a mythical tribe called the Allegewi who had lived on that river until defeated by the all-conquering Delawares. More often, when a common name became meaningless, the Indians, like other people, merely accepted it—"Just a name!"

A tribe entering a new country also faced, unconsciously, the problem of what to name. In even a small area there were thousands of "places." But the Indians had no written records, and the ordinary man could not well burden his memory with more than some few hundreds of names. The corn-growing Pueblos, who seldom wandered far from their villages, placed their names thickly. In a nomadic tribe, like the Pawnee, the ordinary man may not have known very many more names than a Pueblo farmer, and they were scattered thinly over a range of several hundred miles.

The more distinct a place was, the more likely an Indian was to name it. A small lake set cleanly in the forest was a thing in itself, as individual as a person; so was a small island, or a single up-standing rock.

Also, the more useful a place was, the more it was frequented, and the more it needed a name. If a bay had a mud-flat with a fine oyster-bed and another without any, there was no need of wasting a name on the useless one.

On both counts, mountains generally went unnamed. They were huge and vague; they mingled one with another, and faded off into their own shoulders; no one was really sure just where a mountain began. Some high peaks served as landmarks, but most mountains in themselves were of little use. An Indian might have names for the game-haunted glades on the slope, and for the lakes and streams where he fished—but no name for the mountain itself. Most of the resonant Indian names of high peaks were placed there later by white men.

Rivers were closest of all to the life of primitive man. In a dry country they supplied the water of life itself. If a tribe knew the use of canoes, the rivers were the highways. To nomads wandering across country, rivers were barriers to be crossed. Everywhere they furnished food—clams, turtles, and frogs; catfish and perch; in their season the salmon and shad and alewives crowding up from the sea. Game trails led to the water, and the hunter lay in wait by the drinking place. First of all, any tribe named the rivers.

But a well-known river seldom had the same name throughout its course. Crossways, a river was cleanly set off, but lengthways it was like a mountain in having no limits. A tribe often had no idea where its rivers came from or went to. In thick forest country a primitive Indian knew the river only at the spots where trails touched or crossed it. Each of these spots was for him a place in itself, and the flowing of the water from one to another was of no importance. If later he learned to use canoes, he was then likely to name every reach and rapid and bend—a very practical procedure, since a single word then identified both the river and the place on the river.

Anything as large and vaguely marked off as a region or territory, most

Indians did not name at all. The place where a certain tribe lived was known after that tribe, and if they shifted ground, the name shifted with them.

Names also were affected by the absence of any "Indian language." To say that a name is Indian is even less than to say that it is European, for among the tribes the languages differed much more than English from French, Dutch, or Russian. Because of this multiplicity of languages a large river or lake usually had several totally different names, which might or might not have the same meaning in translation. This was also true of tribal names.

When the white men arrived, the pattern of Indian naming had grown somewhat complex. Here and there, as with the pueblo-dwellers of the Southwest and the Iroquois of the Northeast, tribes had lived for many generations in the same country. With them, many names had become meaningless, or referred to some forgotten incident. Most tribes, however, were apparently newcomers in the regions where they lived. Their legends told of migrations; their names were simple and understandable. Many tribes shifted during historical times. Far from being universally very old, many Indian place-names are recent. Some make reference to pigs, cattle, gunpowder, drunkenness, or something else of which they were ignorant before the coming of the whites.

The Europeans constantly made mistakes about Indian names, in form, and in application. They thought in terms of kingdoms and provinces, and failed to realize that Indians thought in terms of tribes. They assumed that a river or a lake had the same name everywhere. They failed to conceive the vast differences between languages of near-by tribes. They were used to names like Cadiz and Bristol which had long since lost literal meaning, and so they were likely to use a name as a mere counter, applying that of a river to a bay, or that of a tribe to a lake.

Our heritage of Indian names is rich and treasured—twenty-six states, eighteen of the greatest cities, most of the larger lakes and longer rivers, a few of the highest mountains, and thousands of smaller towns and natural features. Other names are translations of the Indian words. But merely to tell what such names mean literally or may possibly have meant to some long-vanished tribe is to miss most of the flavor. The meaning of a name is more than the meaning of the words composing it.

OUT OF THE BOWELS OF THE EARTH

FROM *Craters of Fire*

HAROUN TAZIEFF

Having climbed many of the world's mountain peaks, traversed the little-explored areas of the Belgian Congo, and ventured undersea with Jacques-Yves Cousteau, Haroun Tazieff turned his attention to the earth's interior.

Tazieff has earned the title of "daredevil geologist" and this selection, an account of a descent into the interior of an active volcano, is evidence that he has earned it the hard way.

STANDING ON THE SUMMIT OF THE GROWLING CONE, EVEN BEFORE I GOT MY breath back after the stiff climb, I peered down into the crater.

I was astonished. Two days previously the red lava had been boiling up to the level of the gigantic lip; now the funnel seemed to be empty. All that incandescent magma had disappeared, drawn back into the depths by the reflux of some mysterious ebb and flow, a sort of breathing. But there, about fifty feet below where I was standing, was the glow and the almost animate fury of the great throat which volcanologists call the conduit or chimney. It was quite a while before I could tear my eyes away from that lurid, fiery centre, that weird palpitation of the abyss. At intervals of about a minute, heralded each time by a dry clacking, bursts of projectiles were flung up, running away up into the air, spreading out fan-wise, all aglare, and then falling back, whistling, on the outer sides of the cone. I was rather tense, ready to leap aside at any moment, as I watched these showers, with their menacing trajectories.

Each outburst of rage was followed by a short lull. Then heavy rolls of brown and bluish fumes came puffing out, while a muffled grumbling, rather like that of some monstrous watch-dog, set the whole bulk of the volcano quivering. There was not much chance for one's nerves to relax, so swiftly did each follow on the other—the sudden tremor, the burst, the momentary intensification of the incandescence, and the outbreak of a fresh salvo. The

AN OLD WOMAN JOINS THE GOOD FRIDAY PROCESSION IN JERUSALEM

Rapho-Guillumette

A FATHER LEADS HIS SONS DOWN A LONELY ROAD IN ARIZONA

Esther Henderson: Rapho-Guillumette

Ewing Galloway

A BRIDGE OF GRASS ROPE SPANS THE INDUS RIVER IN WESTERN TIBET

RAILROAD TRACKS SPLIT A TEXAS PRAIRIE

Ewing Galloway

FPG

AN OIL DERRICK RISES FROM AN EXPANSE OF DESERT SAND

George Harrison: Monkmeyer

A PARTY OF SPELUNKERS, WHOSE ONLY LIGHT IS PROVIDED BY CARBIDE LAMPS, EXPLORES A CAVE

GAS PITS ON THE LAKE MEAD, COLORADO, DELTA, FORMED AS THE MARSH GAS BUBBLED UP THROUGH MUD WHEN THE BAR WAS UNDER WATER

William Belknap, Jr.: Rapho-Guillumette

Black Star

left: SERGEANT FRANCIS LONG, HUNTER FOR A NINETEENTH-CENTURY ARCTIC EXPEDITION

below: THE BASE CAMP OF A TWENTIETH-CENTURY ANTARCTIC EXPEDITION

Black Star

THE HEREFORD MAP, 1280

above: JOHN MANDEVILLE, PROFESSED TO BE AN ENGLISH KNIGHT AND TRAVELER WHO DEPARTED ON HIS JOURNEYS IN 1322, WRITING HIS ACCOUNT OF THEM AT LIÈGE IN 1356, AS A RELIEF FROM THE PANGS OF GOUT

below: MARCO POLO ARRIVES AT CATHAY

Culver Service

Frank Hurley: Rapho-Guillumette

THE RIVER JORDAN, ON THE BANKS OF WHICH, IN ALL RECORDED HISTORY, NO TOWN HAS BEEN BUILT. IT WINDS ITS SINUOUS WAY FOR A COURSE OF 120 MILES, AT TIMES AS MANY AS 1,280 FEET BELOW SEA LEVEL bombs went roaring up, the cone of fire opening out overhead, while I hung in suspense. Then came the hissing and sizzling, increasing in speed and intensity, each "whoosh" ending up in a muffled thud as the bomb fell. On their black bed of scoriae, the clots of molten magma lay with the fire slowly dying out of them, one after the other growing dark and cold.

Some minutes of observation were all I needed. I noted that today, apart from three narrow zones to the west, north, and north-east, the edges of the crater had scarcely been damaged at all by the barrage from underground. The southern point where I stood was a mound rising some twelve or fifteen feet above the general level of the rim, that narrow, crumbling lip of scoriae nearer to the fire, where I had never risked setting foot. I looked at this rather alarming ledge all round the crater, and gradually felt an increasing desire to do something about it . . . It became irresistible. After all, as the level of the column of lava had dropped to such an exceptional degree, was this not the moment to try what I was so tempted to do and go right round the crater?

Still, I hesitated. This great maw, these jaws sending out heat that was like the heavy breathing of some living creature, thoroughly frightened me. Leaning forward over that hideous glow, I was no longer a geologist in search of information, but a terrified savage.

"If I lose my grip," I said aloud, "I shall simply run for it."

The sound of my own voice restored me to normal awareness of myself. I got back my critical sense and began to think about what I could reasonably risk trying. "De l'audace, encore de l'audace. . . ." That was all very well, of course, but one must also be careful. Past experience whispered a warning not to rush into anything blindly. Getting the upper hand of both anxiety and impatience, I spent several minutes considering, with the greatest of care, the monster's manner of behaving. Solitude has got me into the habit of talking to myself, and so it was more or less aloud that I gave myself permission to go ahead.

"Right, then. It can be done."

I turned up my collar and buttoned my canvas jacket tight at the throat—I didn't want a sly cinder down the back of my neck! Then I tucked what was left of my hair under an old felt hat that did service for a helmet. And now for it!

Very cautiously indeed, I approach the few yards of pretty steep slope separating the peak from the rim I am going to explore. I cross, in a gingerly manner, a first incandescent crevasse. It is intense orange in colour and quivering with heat, as though opening straight into a mass of glowing embers. The fraction of a second it takes me to cross it is just long enough for it to scorch the thick cord of my breeches. I get a strong whiff of burnt wool.

A promising start, I must say!

Here comes a second break in the ground. Damn it, a wide one, too! I can't just stride across this one: I'll have to jump it. The incline makes me thoughtful. Standing there, I consider the unstable slope of scoriae that will have to serve me for a landing-ground. If I don't manage to pull up . . . if I go rolling along down this funnel with the flames lurking at the bottom of it . . . My little expedition all at once strikes me as thoroughly rash, and I stay where I am, hesitating. But the heat under my feet is becoming unbearable. I can't endure it except by shifting around. It only needs ten seconds of standing still on this enemy territory, with the burning gases slowly and steadily seeping through it, and the soles of my feet are already baking hot. From second to second the alternative becomes increasingly urgent: I must jump for it or retreat.

Here I am! I have landed some way down the fissure. The ashes slide underfoot, but I stop without too much trouble. As so often happens, the anxiety caused by the obstacle made me over-estimate its importance.

Step by step, I set out on my way along the wide wall of slag-like debris that forms a sort of fortification all round the precipice. The explosions are still going on at regular intervals of between sixty and eighty seconds. So far no projectile has come down on this side, and this cheers me up considerably. With marked satisfaction I note that it is pretty rare for two bombs of the same salvo to fall less than three yards apart: the average distance between them seems to be one of several paces. This is encouraging. One of the great advantages of this sort of bombardment, compared with one by artillery, lies in the relative slowness with which the projectiles fall, the eye being able to follow them quite easily. Furthermore, these shells don't burst. But what an uproar, what an enormous, prolonged bellowing accompanies their being hurled out of the bowels of the earth!

I make use of a brief respite in order to get quickly across the ticklish north-eastern sector. Then I stop for a few seconds, just long enough to see yet another burst gush up and come showering down a little ahead of me, after which I start out for the conquest of the northern sector. Here the crest narrows down so much that it becomes a mere ridge, where walking is so difficult and balancing so precarious that I find myself forced to go on along the outer slope, very slightly lower down. Little by little, as I advance through all this tumult, a feeling of enthusiasm is overtaking me. The immediate imperative necessity for action has driven panic far into the background. And under the hot, dry skin of my face, taut on forehead and cheekbones, I can feel my compressed lips parting, of their own accord, in a smile of sheer delight. But look out!

A sudden intensification of the light warns me that I am approaching a point right in the prolongation of the fiery chimney. In fact, the chimney is not vertical, but slightly inclined in a north-westerly direction, and from here one can look straight down into it. These tellurian entrails, brilliantly yellow, seem to be surging with heat. The sight is so utterly amazing that I stand there, transfixed.

Suddenly, before I can make any move, the dazzling yellow changes to white, and in the same instant I feel a muffled tremor all through my body and there is a thunderous uproar in my ears. The burst of incandescent blocks is already in full swing. My throat tightens as, motionless, I follow with my gaze the clusters of red lumps rising in slow, perfect curves. There is an instant of uncertainty. And then down comes the hail of fire.

This time the warning was too short: I am right in the middle of it all. With my shoulders hunched up, head drawn back, chin in air, buttocks as much tucked in as possible, I peer up into the vault of sinister whining and whizzing there above me. All around bombs are crashing down, still pasty and soft, making a succession of muffled *plops*. One dark mass seems to have singled me out and is making straight for my face. Instinctively I take a leap to one side, and *feel* the great lump flatten itself out a few inches from my left foot. I should like to have a look, but this is not the moment! Here comes another projectile. I take another leap to dodge it. It lands close beside me. Then suddenly the humming in the air begins to thin out. There are a few more whizzing sounds, and then the downpour is over.

Have you ever tried to imagine a snail's state of mind as it creeps out of its shell again, the danger past? That was the way my head, which had been drawn back between hunched-up shoulders, gradually began to rise up again on my neck, and my arched back began to straighten, my arms to loosen, my hands to unclench. Right, then—it's better not to hang about in this sector! So I set out again. By this time I have got round three-quarters of the crater, and am in the gap between the northern and western zones, which are those that get the worst pounding. From here I can get back on to the ridge proper.

I am now almost directly over the roaring chasm, and my gaze goes straight down into it like a stone dropping into the pit. After all, it's nothing but a tunnel. That's all. It's a vertical tunnel, ten or fifteen yards across, its walls heated to such a degree that they stretch and "rise" like dough, and up from its depths every now and then enormous drops of liquid fire spurt forth, a great splashing sweat that falls and vanishes, golden flash upon flash, back into the dazzling gulf. Even the brownish vapours emanating from the pit cannot quite veil its splendour. It is nothing but a tunnel running down into viscous copper-coloured draperies; yet it opens into the very substance of another world. The sight is so extraordinary that I forget the insecurity of my position and the hellish burning under the soles of my feet. Quite mechanically, I go on lifting first the left foot, then the right. It is as though my mind were held fast in a trap by the sight of this burning well from which a terrifying snore continually rises, interrupted by sharp explosions and the rolling of thunder.

Suddenly I hurl myself backwards. The flight of projectiles has whizzed past my face. Hunched up again, instinctively trying to make as small a target of myself as I can, I once more go through the horrors that I am beginning to know. I am in the thick of this hair's-breadth game of anticipation and dodging.

And now it's all over; I take a last glance into the marvellous and terrible abyss, and am just getting ready to start off on the last stage of this burning circumnavigation, all two hundred yards of it, when I get a sudden sharp blow in the back. A delayed-action bomb! With all the breath knocked out of me, I stand rigid.

A moment passes. I wonder why I am not dead. But nothing seems to have happened to me—no pain, no change of any sort. Slowly I risk turning my head, and at my feet I see a sort of huge red loaf with the glow dying out of it.

I stretch my arms and wriggle my back. Nothing hurts. Everything seems to be in its proper place. Later on, examining my jacket, I discovered a brownish scorch-mark with slightly charred edges, about the size of my hand, and I drew from it a conclusion of immense value to me in future explorations: so long as one is not straight in the line of fire, volcanic bombs, which fall in a still pasty state, but already covered with a kind of very thin elastic skin, graze one without having time to cause a deep burn.

I set off at a run, as lightly as my 165 pounds allow, for I must be as quick as I can in crossing this part of the crater-edge, which is one of the most heavily bombarded. But I am assailed by an unexpected blast of suffocating fumes. My eyes close, full of smarting tears. I am caught in a cloud of gas forced down by the wind. I fight for breath. It feels as if I were swallowing lumps of dry, corrosive cotton-wool. My head swims, but I urge myself at all costs to get the upper hand. The main thing is not to breathe this poisoned air. Groping, I fumble in a pocket. Damn, not this one. How about this other one, then? No. At last I get a handkerchief out and, still with my eyes shut, cover my mouth with it. Then, stumbling along, I try to get through the loathsome cloud. I no longer even bother to pay any attention to the series of bursts from the volcano, being too anxious to get out of this hell before I lose grip entirely. I am getting pretty exhausted, staggering . . . The air filtered through the handkerchief just about keeps me going, but it is still too poisonous, and there is too little of it for the effort involved in making this agonising journey across rough and dangerous terrain. The gases are too concentrated, and the great maw that is belching them forth is too near.

A few steps ahead of me I catch a glimpse of the steep wall of the peak, or promontory, from the other side of which I started about a century ago, it seems to me now. The noxious mists are licking round the peak, which is almost vertical and twice the height of a man. It's so near! But I realise at once that I shall never have the strength to clamber up it.

In less than a second, the few possible solutions to this life-and-death problem race through my mind. Shall I turn my back to the crater and rush away down the outer slope, which is bombarded by the thickest barrages? No. About face and back along the ledge? Whatever I do, I must turn back. And then make my escape. By sliding down the northern slope? That is also under too heavy bombardment. And the worst of it would be that in making a descent of that sort there would be no time to keep a watch for blocks of lava coming down on one.

Only one possibility is left: to make my way back all along the circular ridge, more than a hundred yards of it, till I reach the eastern rim, where neither gas nor projectiles are so concentrated as to be necessarily fatal.

I swing round. I stumble and collapse on all fours, uncovering my mouth for an instant. The gulp of gas that I swallow hurts my lungs, and leaves me gasping. Red-hot scoriae are embedded in the palms of my hands. I shall never get out of this!

The first fifteen or twenty steps of this journey back through the acrid fumes of sulphur and chlorine are a slow nightmare; no step means any progress and no breath brings any oxygen into the lungs. The threat of bombs no longer counts. Only these gases exist now. Air! Air!

I came to myself again on the eastern rim, gasping down the clean air borne by the wind, washing out my lungs with deep fresh gulps of it, as though I could never get enough. How wide and comfortable this ledge is! What a paradise compared with the suffocating, torrid hell from which I have at last escaped! And yet this is where I was so anxious and so tense less than a quarter of an hour ago.

Several draughts of the prevailing breeze have relieved my agony. All at once, life is again worth living! I no longer feel that desire to escape from here as swiftly as possible. On the contrary, I feel a new upsurge of explorer's curiosity. Once more my gaze turns towards the mouth, out of which sporadic bursts of grape-shot are still spurting forth. Now and then there are bigger explosions and I have to keep a look-out for what may come down on my head, which momentarily interrupts the dance I keep up from one foot to the other, that *tresca* of which Dante speaks—the dance of the damned, harried by fire. True, I have come to the conclusion that the impact of these bombs is not necessarily fatal, but I am in no hurry to verify the observation.

The inner walls of the crater do not all incline at the same angle. To the north, west and south, they are practically vertical, not to say overhanging, but here on the east the slope drops away at an angle of no more than fifty degrees. So long as one moved along in a gingerly way, this might be an incline one could negotiate. It would mean going down into the very heart of the volcano. For an instant I am astounded by my own foolhardiness. Still, it's really too tempting . . .

Cautiously, I take a step forward . . . then another . . . and another . . . seems all right . . . it *is* all right. I begin the climb down, digging my heels as deep as I can into the red-hot scoriae. Gradually below me, the oval of the enormous maw comes nearer, growing bigger, and the terrifying uproar becomes more deafening. My eyes, open as wide as they will go, are drunken with its monstrous glory. Here are those ponderous draperies of molten gold and copper, so near—so near that I feel as if I, human being that I am, had entered right into their fabulous world. The air is stifling hot. I am right in the fiery furnace.

I linger before this fascinating spectacle. But then, by sheer effort, I tear myself away. It's time to get back to being "scientific" and measure the temperatures, of the ground, and of the atmosphere. I plunge the long spike of the thermometer into the shifting scoriae, and the steel of it glitters among these brownish and grey screes with their dull shimmer. At a depth of six inches the temperature is two hundred and twenty degrees centigrade. It's amusing to think that when I used to dream it was always about polar exploration!

Suddenly, the monster vomits out another burst; so close that the noise deafens me. I bury my face in my arms. Fortunately almost every one of the projectiles comes down outside the crater. And now all at once I realise that it is I who am here—*alive* in this crater, surrounded by scorching walls, face to face with the very mouth of the fire. Why have I got myself into this trap, alone and without the slightest chance of help? Nobody in the world has any suspicion of the strange adventure on which I have embarked, and nobody, for that matter, could now do the slightest thing about it. Better not think about it . . .

Without a break the grim, steady growling continues to rise from the depths of that throat, only out-roared at intervals by the bellowing and belching of lava. It's too much; I can feel myself giving up. I turn my back on it, and try, on all fours, to scramble up the slope, which has now become incredibly steep and crumbles and gives way under my weight, which is dragging me down, down . . . "Steady, now," I say to myself. "Keep calm for a moment. Let's work it out. Let's work it out properly. Or else, my boy, this is the end of *you*."

Little by little, by immense exertions, I regain control of my movements, as well as the mental steadiness I need. I persuade myself to climb *calmly* up this short slope, which keeps crumbling away under my feet. When I reach the top, I stand upright for just a moment. Then, crossing the two glowing fissures that still intersect my course, I reach the part of the rim from where there is a way down to the world of ordinary peaceful things.

DISCOVERY OF THE PACIFIC

GOD HELP US, WE CAN'T KEEP UP THIS PULLING

FROM *Personal Journals of Captain Robert F. Scott on His Journey to the South Pole*

ROBERT F. SCOTT

There are few records in the history of the exploration of the unknown surfaces of the earth that are so moving as these last entries in the diary which Captain Robert Scott wrote in the hours before the pen dropped from his frozen fingers. And few men in any great endeavor with his courage. Scott led two expeditions to the Antarctic continent. On the second, he tried to reach the South Pole by sledge, a long and murderous journey. The party fought weather, terrain, illness, accident with unbelievable and hopeless tenacity. The diary was found alongside his frozen body by a rescue party from the base camp.

Sunday, February 26.—Lunch Temp. —17°. Sky overcast at start, but able see tracks and cairn distinct at long distance. Did a little better, 6½ miles to date. Bowers and Wilson now in front. Find great relief pulling behind with no necessity to keep attention on track. Very cold nights now and cold feet starting march, as day footgear doesn't dry at all. We are doing well on our food, but we ought to have yet more. I hope the next depôt, now only 50 miles, will find us with enough surplus to open out. The fuel shortage still an anxiety.

R. 40. Temp. —21°. Nine hours' solid marching has given us 11½ miles. Only 43 miles from the next depôt. Wonderfully fine weather but cold, very cold. Nothing dries and we get our feet cold too often. We want more food yet and especially more fat. Fuel is woefully short. We can scarcely hope to get a better surface at this season, but I wish we could have some help from the wind, though it might shake us up badly if the temp. didn't rise.

Monday, February 27.—Desperately cold last night: —33° when we got up, with —37° minimum. Some suffering from cold feet, but all got good rest. We *must* open out on food soon. But we have done 7 miles this morning and hope for some 5 this afternoon. Overcast sky and good surface till now, when sun shows again. It is good to be marching the cairns up, but there is still much to be anxious about. We talk of little but food, except after meals. Land disappearing in satisfactory manner. Pray God we have no further set-backs. We are naturally always discussing possibility of meeting dogs, where and when, &c. It is a critical position. We may find ourselves in safety at next depôt, but there is a horrid element of doubt.

Camp R. 41. Temp. –32°. Still fine clear weather but very cold–absolutely calm tonight. We have got off an excellent march for these days (12.2) and are much earlier than usual in our bags. 31 miles to depôt, 3 days' fuel at a pinch, and 6 days' food. Things begin to look a little better; we can open out a little on food from tomorrow night, I think.

Very curious surface–soft recent sastrugi which sink underfoot, and between, a sort of flaky crust with large crystals beneath.

Tuesday, February 28.–Lunch. Thermometer went below –40° last night; it was desperately cold for us, but we had a fair night. I decided to slightly increase food; the effect is undoubtedly good. Started marching in –32° with a slight north-westerly breeze–blighting. Many cold feet this morning; long time over foot gear, but we are earlier. Shall camp earlier and get the chance of a good night, if not the reality. Things must be critical till we reach the depôt, and the more I think of matters, the more I anticipate their remaining so after that event. Only 24½ miles from the depôt. The sun shines brightly, but there is little warmth in it. There is no doubt the middle of the Barrier is a pretty awful locality.

Camp 42. Splendid pony hoosh sent us to bed and sleep happily after a horrid day, wind continuing; did 11½ miles. Temp. not quite so low, but expect we are in for cold night (Temp. –27°).

Wednesday, February 29.–Lunch. Cold night. Minimum Temp. –37.5°; –30° with north-west wind, force 4, when we got up. Frightfully cold starting; luckily Bowers and Oates in their last new finnesko; keeping my old ones for present. Expected awful march and for first hour got it. Then things improved and we camped after 5½ hours marching close to lunch camp–22½. Next camp is our depôt and it is exactly 13 miles. It ought not to take more than 1½ days; we pray for another fine one. The oil will just about spin out in that event, and we arrive 3 clear days' food in hand. The increase of ration has had an enormously beneficial result. Mountains now looking small. Wind still very light from west–cannot understand this wind.

Thursday, March 1.–Lunch. Very cold last night–minimum –41.5°. Cold start to march, too, as usual now. Got away at 8 and have marched within sight of depôt; flag something under 3 miles away. We did 11½ yesterday and marched 6 this morning. Heavy dragging yesterday and *very* heavy this morning. Apart from sledging considerations the weather is wonderful. Cloudless days and nights and the wind trifling. Worse luck, the light airs come from the north and keep us horribly cold. For this lunch hour the exception has come. There is a bright and comparatively warm sun. All our gear is out drying.

Friday, March 2.—Lunch. Misfortunes rarely come singly. We marched to the [Middle Barrier] depôt fairly easily yesterday afternoon, and since that have suffered three distinct blows which have placed us in a bad position. First we found a shortage of oil; with most rigid economy it can scarce carry us to the next depôt on this surface [71 miles away]. Second, Titus Oates disclosed his feet, the toes showing very bad indeed, evidently bitten by the late temperatures. The third blow came in the night, when the wind, which we had hailed with some joy, brought dark overcast weather. It fell below −40° in the night, and this morning it took 1½ hours to get our foot gear on, but we got away before eight. We lost cairn and tracks together and made as steady as we could N. by W., but have seen nothing. Worse was to come—the surface is simply awful. In spite of strong wind and full sail we have only done 5½ miles. We are in a *very* queer street since there is no doubt we cannot do the extra marches and feel the cold horribly.

Saturday, March 3.—Lunch. We picked up the track again yesterday, findourselves to the eastward. Did close on 10 miles and things looked a trifle better; but this morning the outlook is blacker than ever. Started well and with good breeze; for an hour made good headway; then the surface grew awful beyond words. The wind drew forward; every circumstance was against us. After 4¼ hours things so bad that we camped, having covered 4½ miles. [R. 46.] One cannot consider this a fault of our own—certainly we were pulling hard this morning—it was more than three parts surface which held us back—the wind at strongest, powerless to move the sledge. When the light is good it is easy to see the reason. The surface, lately a very good hard one, is coated with a thin layer of woolly crystals, formed by radiation no doubt. These are too firmly fixed to be removed by the wind and cause impossible friction on the runners. God help us, we can't keep up this pulling, that is certain. Amongst ourselves we are unendingly cheerful, but what each man feels in his heart I can only guess. Putting on foot gear in the morning is getting slower and slower, therefore every day more dangerous.

Sunday, March 4.—Lunch. Things looking *very* black indeed. As usual we forgot our trouble last night, got into our bags, slept splendidly on good hoosh, woke and had another, and started marching. Sun shining brightly, tracks clear, but surface covered with sandy frost-rime. All the morning we had to pull with all our strength, and in 4½ hours we covered 3½ miles. Last night it was overcast and thick, surface bad; this morning sun shining and surface as bad as ever. One has little to hope for except perhaps strong dry wind—an unlikely contingency at this time of year. Under the immediate surface crystals is a hard sastrugi-surface, which must have been excellent for pulling a week or two ago. We are about 42 miles from the next depôt and have a week's food, but only about 3 to 4 days' fuel—we are as economical of the latter as one can possibly be, and we cannot afford to save food and pull as we are pulling. We are in a very tight place indeed, but none of us despondent *yet*, or at least we preserve every semblance of good cheer, but one's heart sinks as the sledge stops dead at some sastrugi behind which the surface sand lies thickly heaped. For the moment the temperature is on the −20°—an improvement which makes us much more comfortable, but a colder snap is bound to come again soon. I fear that Oates at least will weather such an event very poorly. Providence to our aid! We can expect little from man now except the possibility of extra food at the next depôt. It will be real bad if we get there and find the same shortage of oil. Shall we get there? Such a short distance it would have appeared to us on the summit! I don't know what I should do if Wilson and Bowers weren't so determinedly cheerful over things.

Monday, March 5.—Lunch. Regret to say going from bad to worse. We got a slant of wind yesterday afternoon, and going on 5 hours we converted our wretched morning run of 3½ miles into something over 9. We went to bed on a cup of cocoa and pemmican solid with the chill off. (R. 47.) The result is telling on all, but mainly on Oates, whose feet are in a wretched condition. One swelled up tremendously last night and he is very lame this morning. We started march on tea and pemmican as last night—we pretend to prefer the pemmican this way. Marched for 5 hours this morning over a slightly better surface covered with high moundy sastrugi. Sledge capsized twice; we pulled on foot, covering about 5½ miles. We are two pony marches and 4 miles about from our depôt. Our fuel dreadfully low and the poor Soldier nearly done. It is pathetic enough because we can do nothing for him; more hot food might do a little, but only a little, I fear. We none of us expected these terribly low temperatures, and of the rest of us Wilson is feeling them most; mainly, I fear, from his self-sacrificing devotion in doctoring Oates' feet. We cannot help each other, each has enough to do to take care of himself. We get cold on the march when the trudging is heavy, and the wind pierces our warm garments. The others, all of them, are unendingly cheerful when in the tent. We mean to see the game through with a proper spirit, but it's tough work to be pulling harder than we ever pulled in our lives for long hours, and to feel that the progress is so slow. One can only say "God help us!" and plod on our weary way, cold and very miserable, though outwardly cheerful. We talk of all sorts of subjects in the tent, not much of food now, since we decided to take the risk of running a full ration. We simply couldn't go hungry at this time.

Tuesday, March 6.—Lunch. We did a little better with help of wind yesterday afternoon, finishing 9½ miles for the day, and 27 miles from depôt. [R. 48.] But this morning things have been awful. It was warm in the night and for the first time during the journey I overslept myself by more than an hour; then we were slow with foot gear; then, pulling with all our might (for our lives) we could scarcely advance at rate of a mile an hour; then it grew thick and three times we had to get out of harness to search for tracks. The result is something less than 3½ miles for the forenoon. The sun is shining now and the wind gone. Poor Oates is unable to pull, sits on the sledge when we are track-searching—he is wonderfully plucky, as his feet must be giving him great pain. He makes no complaint, but his spirits only come up in spurts now, and he grows more silent in the tent. We are making a spirit lamp to try and replace the primus when our oil is exhausted. It will be a very poor substitute and we've not got much spirit. If we could have kept up our 9-mile days we might have got within reasonable distance of the depôt before running out, but nothing but a strong wind and good surface can help us now, and though we had quite a good breeze this morning, the sledge came as heavy as lead. If we were all fit I should have hopes of getting through, but the poor Soldier has become a terrible hindrance, though he does his utmost and suffers much I fear.

Wednesday, March 7.—A little worse I fear. One of Oates' feet *very* bad this morning; he is wonderfully brave. We still talk of what we will do together at home.

We only made 6½ miles yesterday. [R. 49.] This morning in 4½ hours we did just over 4 miles. We are 16 from our depôt. If we only find the correct proportion of food there and this surface continues, we may get to the next depôt [Mt. Hooper, 72 miles farther] but not to One Ton Camp. We hope against hope that the dogs have been to Mt. Hooper; then we might pull through. If there is a shortage of oil again we can have little hope. One feels that for poor Oates the crisis is near, but none of us are improving, though we are wonderfully fit considering the really excessive work we are doing. We are only kept going by good food. No wind this morning till a chill northerly air came ahead. Sun bright and cairns showing up well. I should like to keep the track to the end.

Thursday, March 8.—Lunch. Worse and worse in morning; poor Oates' left foot can never last out, and time over foot gear something awful. Have to wait in night foot gear for nearly an hour before I start changing, and then am generally first to be ready. Wilson's feet giving trouble now, but this mainly because he gives so much help to others. We did 4½ miles this morning and are now 8½ miles from the depôt—a ridiculously small distance to feel in difficulties, yet on this surface we know we cannot equal half our old marches, and that for that effort we expend nearly double the energy. The great question is, What shall we find at the depôt? If the dogs have visited it we may get along a good distance, but if there is another short allowance of fuel, God help us indeed. We are in a very bad way, I fear, in any case.

Saturday, March 10.—Things steadily downhill. Oates' foot worse. He has rare pluck and must know that he can never get through. He asked Wilson if he had a chance this morning, and of course Bill had to say he didn't know. In point of fact he has none. Apart from him, if he went under now, I doubt whether we could get through. With great care we might have a dog's chance, but no more. The weather conditions are awful, and our gear gets steadily more icy and difficult to manage. At the same time of course poor Titus is the greatest handicap. He keeps us waiting in the morning until we have partly lost the warming effect of our good breakfast, when the only wise policy is to be up and away at once; again at lunch. Poor chap! it is too pathetic to watch him; one cannot but try to cheer him up.

Yesterday we marched up the depôt, Mt. Hooper. Cold comfort. Shortage on our allowance all round. I don't know that anyone is to blame. The dogs which would have been our salvation have evidently failed. Meares had a bad trip home I suppose.

This morning it was calm when we breakfasted, but the wind came from the W.N.W. as we broke camp. It rapidly grew in strength. After travelling for half an hour I saw that none of us could go on facing such conditions. We were forced to camp and are spending the rest of the day in a comfortless blizzard camp, wind quite foul. [R. 52.]

Sunday, March 11.—Titus Oates is very near the end, one feels. What we or he will do, God only knows. We discussed the matter after breakfast; he is a brave fine fellow and understands the situation, but he practically asked for advice. Nothing could be said but to urge him to march as long as he could. One satisfactory result to the discussion; I practically ordered Wilson to hand over the means of ending our troubles to us, so that any one of us may know how to do so. Wilson had no choice between doing so and our ransacking the medicine case. We have 30 opium tabloids apiece and he is left with a tube of morphine. So far the tragical side of our story. [R. 53.]

The sky completely overcast when we started this morning. We could see nothing, lost the tracks, and doubtless have been swaying a good deal since—3.1 miles for the forenoon—terribly heavy dragging—expected it. Know that 6 miles is about the limit of our endurance now, if we get no help from wind or surfaces. We have 7 days' food and should be about 55 miles from One Ton

Camp tonight, 6 × 7 =42, leaving us 13 miles short of our distance, even if things get no worse. Meanwhile the season rapidly advances.

Monday, March 12.—We did 6.9 miles yesterday, under our necessary average. Things are left much the same, Oates not pulling much, and now with hands as well as feet pretty well useless. We did 4 miles this morning in 4 hours 20 min.—we may hope for 3 this afternoon, 7 × 6 = 42. We shall be 47 miles from the depôt. I doubt if we can possibly do it. The surface remains awful, the cold intense, and our physical condition running down. God help us! Not a breath of favourable wind for more than a week, and apparently liable to head winds at any moment.

Wednesday, March 14.—No doubt about the going downhill, but everything going wrong for us. Yesterday we woke to a strong northerly wind with temp. —37°. Couldn't face it, so remained in camp [R. 54] till 2, then did 5¼ miles. Wanted to march later, but party feeling the cold badly as the breeze (N.) never took off entirely, and as the sun sank the temp. fell. Long time getting supper in dark. [R. 55.]

This morning started with southerly breeze, set sail and passed another cairn at good speed; half-way, however, the wind shifted to W. by S. or W.S.W., blew through our wind clothes and into our mits. Poor Wilson horribly cold, could [not] get off ski for some time. Bowers and I practically made camp, and when we got into the tent at last we were all deadly cold. Then temp. now midday down —43° and the wind strong. We *must* go on, but now the making of every camp must be more difficult and dangerous. It must be near the end, but a pretty merciful end. Poor Oates got it again in the foot. I shudder to think what it will be like tomorrow. It is only with greatest pains rest of us keep off frostbites. No idea there could be temperatures like this at this time of year with such winds. Truly awful outside the tent. Must fight it out to the last biscuit, but can't reduce rations.

Friday, March 16 *or Saturday* 17.—Lost track of dates, but think the last correct. Tragedy all along the line. At lunch, the day before yesterday, poor Titus Oates said he couldn't go on; he proposed we should leave him in his sleeping-bag. That we could not do, and we induced him to come on, on the afternoon march. In spite of its awful nature for him he struggled on and we made a few miles. At night he was worse and we knew the end had come.

Should this be found I want these facts recorded. Oates' last thoughts were of his Mother, but immediately before he took pride in thinking that his regiment would be pleased with the bold way in which he met his death. We can testify to his bravery. He has borne intense suffering for weeks without complaint, and to the very last was able and willing to discuss outside subjects. He did not—would not—give up hope till the very end. He was a brave soul. This was the end. He slept through the night before last, hoping not to wake; but he woke in the morning—yesterday. It was blowing a blizzard. He said, "I am just going outside and may be some time." He went out into the blizzard and we have not seen him since.

I take this opportunity of saying that we have stuck to our sick companions to the last. In case of Edgar Evans, when absolutely out of food and he lay insensible, the safety of the remainder seemed to demand his abandonment, but Providence mercifully removed him at this critical moment. He died a natural death, and we did not leave him till two hours after his death. We knew that poor Oates was walking to his death, but though we tried to dissuade him, we knew it was the act of a brave man and an English gentleman. We all hope to meet the end with a similar spirit, and assuredly the end is not far.

I can only write at lunch and then only occasionally. The cold is intense, —40° at midday. My companions are unendingly cheerful, but we are all on the verge of serious frostbites, and though we constantly talk of fetching through I don't think any one of us believes it in his heart.

We are cold on the march now, and at all times except meals. Yesterday we had to lay up for a blizzard and today we move dreadfully slowly. We are at No 14 pony camp, only two pony marches from One Ton Depôt. We leave here our theodolite, a camera, and Oates' sleeping-bags. Diaries, &c., and geological specimens carried at Wilson's special request, will be found with us or on our sledge.

Sunday, March 18.—Today, lunch, we are 21 miles from the depôt. Ill fortune presses, but better may come. We have had more wind and drift from ahead yesterday; had to stop marching; wind N.W., force 4, temp. —35°. No human being could face it, and we are worn out *nearly*.

My right foot has gone, nearly all the toes—two days ago I was proud possessor of best feet. These are the steps of my downfall. Like an ass I mixed a small spoonful of curry powder with my melted pemmican—it gave me violent indigestion. I lay awake and in pain all night; woke and felt done on the march; foot went and I didn't know it. A very small measure of neglect, and have a foot which is not pleasant to contemplate. Bowers takes first place in condition, but there is not much to choose after all. The others are still confident of getting through—or pretend to be—I don't know! We have the last *half* fill of oil in our primus and a very small quantity of spirit—this alone between us and thirst. The wind is fair for the moment, and that is perhaps a fact to help. The mileage would have seemed ridiculously small on our outward journey.

Monday, March 19.—Lunch. We camped with difficulty last night, and were dreadfully cold till after our supper of cold pemmican and biscuit and a half a pannikin of cocoa cooked over the spirit. Then, contrary to expectation, we got warm and all slept well. Today we started in the usual dragging manner. Sledge dreadfully heavy. We are 15½ miles from the depôt and ought to get there in three days. What progress! We have two days' food but barely a day's fuel. All our feet are getting bad—Wilson's best, my right foot worst, left all right. There is no chance to nurse one's feet till we can get hot food into us. Amputation is the least I can hope for now, but will the trouble spread? That is the serious question. The weather doesn't give us a chance—the wind from N. to N.W. and −40° temp. today.

Wednesday, March 21.—Got within 11 miles of depôt Monday night; had to lay up all yesterday in severe blizzard. Today forlorn hope, Wilson and Bowers going to depôt for fuel.

Thursday, March 22 *and* 23.—Blizzard bad as ever—Wilson and Bowers unable to start—tomorrow last chance—no fuel and only one or two of food left—must be near the end. Have decided it shall be natural—we shall march for the depôt with or without our effects and die in our tracks.

Thursday, March 29.—Since the 21st we have had a continuous gale from W.S.W. and S.W. We had fuel to make two cups of tea apiece and bare food for two days on the 20th. Every day we have been ready to start for our depôt *11 miles* away, but outside the door of the tent it remains a scene of whirling drift. I do not think we can hope for any better things now. We shall stick it out to the end, but we are getting weaker, of course, and the end cannot be far.

It seems a pity, but I do not think I can write more.

R. Scott.

Last entry.

For God's sake look after our people.

BY THIS OUR DONATION, CONCESSION AND ASSIGNMENT

FROM *The Bull "Intercaetera" of May 4, 1493*

POPE ALEXANDER VI

This title deed to the newly discovered continent of America is undoubtedly the largest realty transaction ever made and one which provided religious and legal sanction for two centuries of bloody conflict. Like less illustrious real estate transactions of history it had a reason in contemporary European politics which was somewhat less than religious. Pope Alexander VI, Rodrigo Borgia of notorious memory, with filial concern for the future of his four children, traded half a world which he did not own for Spain's support in carving out a fief for his son Goffredi.

Pope Alexander VI was one of the less spiritual pontiffs with which the Renaissance church was blessed. One of the wealthiest men of his time, he won his office by buying up the largest number of votes in the College of Cardinals. He is perhaps the only pope who has never found an apologist among Catholic historians.

ALEXANDER, BISHOP, SERVANT OF THE SERVANTS OF GOD, TO OUR MOST BELOVED son in Christ, Ferdinand, King, and to our most beloved daughter in Christ, Elizabeth, Queen, most illustrious [Princes] of Castile, Leon, Aragon, *Sicily* and Granada, greeting and the apostolic blessing.

Among other works agreeable to the Divine Majesty and desirable to our heart this is certainly the most important, that the Catholic Faith and the Christian Religion, particularly in our times, shall be exalted and everywhere amplified and spread, [and] that the salvation of souls may be provided for and barbarous nations subjugated and brought to the very true faith. And whereas we are called to this Holy Seat of Peter by the favour of Divine clemency, though not with like merits, and recognizing that you as true Catholic

Kings and Princes, such as we know you have ever been, and as your famous deeds already well known to almost the entire world prove, not merely desired this, but with every possible effort, study and diligence, sparing no labours, no expenses, no dangers, shedding even your own blood, are accomplishing it and have devoted to this aim already for a long time your entire mind and all your efforts, such as attests the recovery of the kingdom of Granada from the tyranny of the Saracens, achieved in these very times with such great glory to the Divine name. . . . Yet we are informed that you who for a long time had purposed to search and find some *islands and mainlands,* remote and unknown and hitherto not found by others, in order to bring their natives and inhabitants to worship our Redeemer and to profess the Catholic faith, having been hitherto chiefly occupied in the conquest and recovery of this same Kingdom of Granada, have been unable to bring this your sacred and praiseworthy purpose to the issue desired. But at last, as it has pleased the Lord, the aforenamed Kingdom having been recovered, wishing to fulfil your desire, you have appointed our beloved son Christopher Columbus, *a so worthy man [and] highly to be commended and suitable for so great an undertaking,* with ships and men equipped for such purpose not without greatest labours and perils and expenses, to seek diligently such remote and unknown *mainlands and islands* by seas, which had not been navigated before, who at last by the help of God, with utmost foresight, navigating *in the Ocean,* found certain far remote islands and also mainlands, which had not been discovered by others before, in which dwell very many tribes, peacefully living and, as it is asserted, going naked and not eating meat; and so far as your said messengers are able to conjecture, these nations living in the said islands and lands believe that there is one God and Creator in the heavens and seem sufficiently well fitted to embrace the Catholic faith and to be imbued with good manners; and hope is entertained that, if they should be taught, the name of our Saviour and Lord Jesus Christ would be easily introduced into the said islands and lands: and the aforenamed Christopher has already caused to be constructed and built in one of the principal aforementioned islands one sufficiently well fortified tower, in which he has placed certain Christians who had gone with him, as garrison and for the purpose that they might seek other remote and unknown islands and *mainlands:* in which already discovered islands and lands are found gold, spices and very many other precious things of sundry kind and sundry quality. Wherefore all this having been carefully considered and particularly the exaltation and propagation of the Catholic faith as it is seemly for Catholic kings and princes, following the practice of your predecessors, kings of glorious memory, you have purposed to subdue to us with the aid of God's clemency and to lead to the Catholic faith the aforesaid *mainlands and islands,* their natives and inhabitants. . . . And in order that you may undertake the assignment of so great a task, generously endowed with the Apostolic favour, more freely and boldly, we of our own motion, not at your instance or that of a petition of any other presented to us to such effect on your behalf, but of our own sheer liberality and certain knowledge and of the plenitude of Apostolic power, give, concede and assign *all islands and mainlands found and to be found, discovered and to be discovered towards west and south, [by] establishing and constituting one line from the Arctic pole, that is the north, to the Antarctic pole, that is the south, whether the mainlands and islands found and to be found are towards India or [towards] any other part whatever; which line shall be distant from any of the islands, which are commonly called the Azores and Cape Verde, one hundred leagues towards west and south, in such way that all islands and mainlands found and to be found, discovered and to be discovered from the said line towards west and south have not been actually possessed by any other Christian King and prince until to the day of the Nativity of Our Lord Jesus Christ last passed, from which begins the present year fourteen hundred and ninety three, when some of the said islands have been found by your messengers and captains,* by the authority of the omnipotent God granted to us in Saint Peter and of the vicariate of Jesus Christ which we are exercising on earth, with all their dominions, states, camps, places and villages, with all right and jurisdictions and everything else belonging thereto, to you and your heirs and to your successors, Kings of Castile and Leon, to all eternity in the tenor of these presents, make, constitute and depute you and the aforesaid heirs and successors as the Lords of these with full, free and every sort of power, authority and jurisdiction. Decreeing nevertheless that by this our donation, concession and assignment, the acquired right of no Christian Prince *who has actually possessed the aforesaid islands and mainlands up to the aforementioned day of the Nativity of Our Lord Jesus* could be understood as annulled or should be allowed to be taken away. And, moreover, we command you by virtue of holy obedience, as you have also promised, and we do not doubt you will perform from your very great devotion and royal magnanimity, to delegate to the said *mainlands* and islands honest, God-fearing, learned, skilled men with experience, to instruct the aforenamed natives and inhabitants in the Catholic faith and to imbue them with good morals, applying all due diligence in the mentioned work; and we strictly inhibit all persons whatever of whatever rank, *whether imperial or royal, or* state, degree, order or condition, under pain of excommunication late sententie, which they shall incur by the fact itself, if they have acted contrary, *that they presume to go to the* islands *and mainlands found and to be found, discovered and to be discovered towards west and south* [by] *establishing and constituting a line from the Arctic Pole to the Antarctic Pole, whether the mainlands and islands found and to be found are towards India or towards any other part whatever, which line shall be distant from any of the islands which are commonly called the Azores and Cape Verde; one hundred leagues towards west and south as before stated,* for getting goods or for any other purpose whatever without special license of yourself and of your aforesaid heirs and successors: notwithstanding the apostolic constitutions and ordinances and all other contradictions whatever, confiding in Him from whom empires and dominions and everything good comes, that the Lord directing your acts, if you prosecute such sacred and praiseworthy *purpose* in short time to the felicity and glory of the whole Christian world your labours and efforts will find a most happy issue.

But since it would be difficult for these letters to be carried to all such places as might be expedient, We wish and of like motion and knowledge decree, that to transcripts of these, signed by the hand of a public notary thereunto required and provided with the seal of any person constituted in ecclesiastical dignity or of an ecclesiastical court the same credence in the law-court and beyond, and in whatever other places shall be given, as would be given to the presents, if they were exhibited or shown.

It shall therefore be lawful for no man at all to infringe or to resist with daring presumption this page of our *commendation,* exhortation, requisition, donation, concession, assignation, constitution, deputation, decree, command, inhibition and will, and if any one should presume to attempt it, let him know that he shall incur the indignation of the omnipotent God and of his holy Apostles Peter and Paul.

Given at Rome at St. Peter's in the year of the incarnation of the Lord, 1493, the *4th* of May, in the first year of Our Pontificate.

Gratis. By order of our most sacred Lord and Pope.

I PLUNGED INTO DARKNESS

FROM *Pheasant Jungles*

WILLIAM BEEBE

Adventuring with William Beebe is always a quickening and alluring experience. It is the *whyness* of things that interests him, he says, not the *isness*. His search for the *whyness* takes him to new and far-flung places on the earth and below it. He led the first expedition into the unexplored regions of Mexico, he went down in a bathysphere deeper than any man had gone before him, he studied animals and plants in the country of the head-hunters.

In this selection from his *Pheasant Jungles* he explores a cavern that stretches into the heart of a tropical mountain range.

I MOTORED OUT TO A BUKIT, OR MOUNTAIN, IN WHICH WERE SOME INTERESTING limestone caves.

My day with these caves was unforgettable. Gulliver and Alice and Seumas might have accompanied me and would not have been bored, so strange were the great caverns. Even the approach held something of mystery, for while they were etched into the base of a high precipitous mountain, this was invisible until one stood suddenly before it. After passing along roads beaded with thatched coolie huts and little Chinese shops, the purring motor turned into a lane-like path and I drove past all the rubber trees in the world—thousands and thousands of them. Like the rows of pulque plants on the Mexican uplands, the trunks of the rubber trees seemed to revolve as I passed, like the spokes of some gigantic horizontal wheel. Then we stopped suddenly, and looking up I saw a great cliff looming high overhead. It was clothed in green, except where it was out at elbow with patches of raw, white limestone. Before I left the car, a strong scent—unpleasant, exciting, and entirely strange—was wafted down on some current of air from the cave.

A stiff climb of a hundred yards brought me to the mouth of the dark cave—a great, gaping, black hole, the edges draped with graceful vines. I entered and, after going a hundred feet, looked back and saw an exquisite bit of the tropical landscape: palms, distant blue mountains, and white clouds framed in the jet-black, jagged aperture.

The great height was overwhelming; the graceful dome-like summit of the cavern stretched up and up into the very vitals of the mountain. Then I plunged into darkness and lighted my electric searchlight, which seemed at first the merest bit of light ray. On and on I went, and at last, far in the distance, perceived a faint glimmer from high overhead. A rustling sound at my feet drew my light downward, and there were untold thousands of great brown cockroaches, all striving to bury themselves out of sight in the soft, sawdust-like flooring, the century-old guano of the bats. I had to go with great care, for huge jagged rocks and deformed stalagmites obstructed the path in every direction.

I reached the rift in the lofty roof, and the glare blinded me for the moment, although it was tempered with a tracery veil of green. I had already begun to adapt myself to the everlasting darkness. At my feet the light fell softened, diluted with a subterranean twilight. In the centre of this part of the cave, directly under the cleft in the roof, was a curious, gigantic stalagmite, still forming from the constant dripping two hundred feet overhead—a stalagmite of great size and extreme irregularity. The first casual glance showed it vividly to the eye as two weird, unnamable beasts struggling with each other. No feature or limb was distinct, and yet the suggestiveness of the whole was irresistible. Virile with the strength of a Rodin, the lime-saturated water had splashed it into visibility, depositing the swell of muscles and the tracery of veins through all the passing years, to the musical tapping of the falling drops. And in all the great extent of the passage of the cavern, the statue had been brought into being in the only spot where it would be visible by the light of the outer world.

For a long time I sat here, finding the odor of the bats less pungent than elsewhere, and here I watched the ghostly creatures dash past. From the inky darkness of some hidden fissure they dropped almost to my face; then, with a whip of their leathery wings, they turned and vanished in the dark cavern ahead. The noise their wings made was incredibly loud; sometimes a purring, as fifty small ones whirred past together, then a sharp singing, and finally an astonishing whistling twang as a single giant bat twisted and flickered on his frightened way.

Another sound was the musical, hollow dripping of slowly falling drops on some thin resonant bit of stone, a metronome marking the passing of inky black hours and years and centuries; for in this cavern there are no days. Every noise I made, whether of voice or footfall, was taken up and magnified and passed upward from ledge to ledge, until it reached the roof and returned again to me. It was changed, however—wholly altered; for it seemed that no sound of healthy creature could remain pure in this durable darkness, the sepulchre of unburied bats, the underworld of hateful, bleached things, of sunless, hopeless blackness. The obscurity seemed, by reason of its uninterrupted ages of persistence, to have condensed, the ebony air to have liquefied. There was no twilight of imagination, inspired by knowledge of coming day. Only quiet, eternal night.

From the black gulf ahead came, now and then, low distant mumblings, mingled with the shrill squeak of the bats, and into this vocal void I now plunged, with the searchlight playing at my feet to avoid tripping and falling. I found that I had entered a veritable Dante's Inferno, and pictured to myself some still more dreadful round as presently to open out ahead. The sighing, gibbering, squeaking spirits or devils were there in multitudes, brushing my face or fighting among themselves as they clung to the slippery fissures high, high overhead. More than once my light led me down a small, blind side lane, into which I stumbled as far as possible. At the end of one such corridor was a roundish hole leading irregularly downward, far beyond the rays of my light. Another contracted very slowly, until the damp walls touched my head and sides and I drew nervously back, glad to escape from the sense of suffocation—as if the walls were actually closing about me, inevitably, irrevocably.

Every stone I overturned revealed numbers of tall, slender spirals—the homes of dark-loving snails; and ever the roaches in their myriads hurried away from my light. Then I came upon tragedy—fitly staged in this black hell. A commotion on the black mould directed me to where a poor bat had recently fallen, having by some accident broken his shoulder, and lay, like fallen Lucifer, gnashing his teeth and helplessly turning from side to side. More than this, two horrible gnomes fled at my approach—a long, sinuous serpent, white from its generations of life within the cave, and a huge centipede, pale, translucent green, sinister as death itself. I shuddered as I beheld this ghastly tableau—serpent and centipede both emblematic of poisonous death, preparing to feast upon a yet living bat, devil-winged and devil-faced.

The predatory ones escaped me, though I wanted the snake. I put the bat out of his misery, his evil squeaking rage at fate remaining undiminished to the very last breath. On his nose were the great leaves of skin which aided him in dodging the obstacles in his path of darkness—organs which had failed him for a fatal moment.

Farther on I turned sharp corners and wound my path around strange angles, disturbing unending hosts of bats and finding many recently dead, together with innumerable skeletons half buried in the guano. Now and then a centipede fled from my tiny pencil of light, and once I broke open a nest of stinging ants, blind but ferocious, which attacked me and made me flee for several yards headlong, heedless of bruising, jagged obstacles.

Then my feet sank suddenly in ooze and water, and, flashing the light ahead, I saw it reflected from the ripples of an underground river flowing with no more than a murmur out of one yawning hole into the opposite wall of the cavern, mysterious as the Styx. Beyond this I might not pass. The current was swift and it was far over my depth. I had no wish to be swept deep into the bowels of these mighty Malay mountains, although the Nibelungs might well have chosen such a place for their labors.

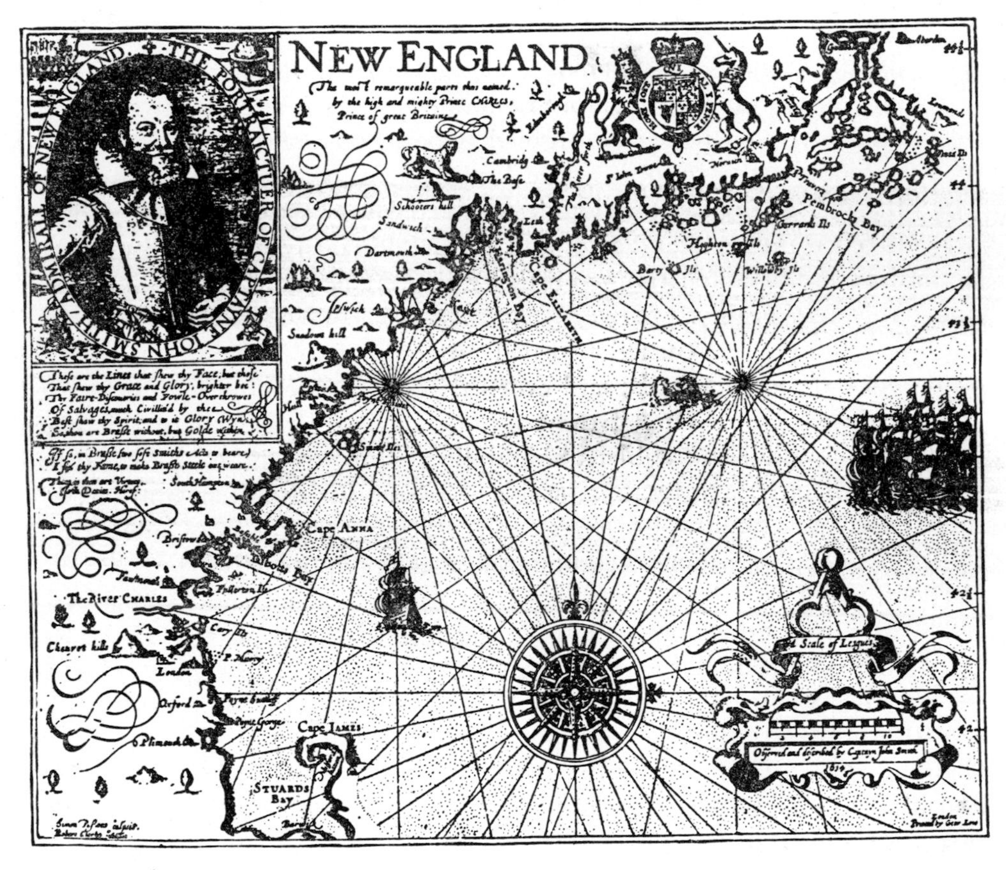

JOHN SMITH'S MAP OF NEW ENGLAND

A VOYAGE OF DISCOVERY

FROM *Les Misérables*

VICTOR HUGO

During his lifetime Victor Hugo was hailed by his contemporaries as the greatest man born since the death of Shakespeare—a writer with the lyric inspiration of Shelley, the prophetic inspiration of Dante, the satiric inspiration of Juvenal. This prodigal judgment has been much tempered since, but his *Les Misérables* has admirably stood the test of time and Jean Valjean's flight from the police agent Jouvert will probably continue to thrill as many generations of future readers as it has of past ones. This selection on the exploration of the Paris sewers is one of the historical asides with which Hugo intersperses his action.

THE POPULAR IMAGINATION SEASONED THE SOMBRE PARISIAN SINK WITH SOME indescribably hideous intermixture of the infinite. The sewer had no bottom. The sewer was the lower world. The idea of exploring these leprous regions did not even occur to the police. To try that unknown thing, to cast the plummet into that shadow, to set out on a voyage of discovery in that abyss—who would have dared? It was alarming. Nevertheless, some one did present himself. The cess-pool had its Christopher Columbus.

One day, in 1805, during one of the rare apparitions which the Emperor made in Paris, the Minister of the Interior, some Decrès or Crétet or other, came to the master's intimate levee. In the Carrousel there was audible the clanking of swords of all those extraordinary soldiers of the great Republic, and of the great Empire; then Napoleon's door was blocked with heroes; men from the Rhine, from the Escaut, from the Adige, and from the Nile; companions of Joubert, of Desaix, of Marceau, of Hoche, of Kléber; the aérostiers of Fleurus, the grenadiers of Mayence, the pontoon-builders of Genoa, hussars whom the Pyramids had looked down upon, artillerists whom Junot's cannon-ball had spattered with mud, cuirassiers who had taken by assault the fleet lying at anchor in the Zuyderzee; some had followed Bonaparte upon the bridge of Lodi, others had accompanied Murat in the trenches of Mantua, others had preceded Lannes in the hollow road of Montebello. The whole army of that day was present there, in the courtyard of the Tuileries, represented by a squadron or a platoon, and guarding Napoleon in repose; and that was the splendid epoch when the grand army had Marengo behind it and Austerlitz before it.—"Sire," said the Minister of the Interior to Napoleon, "yesterday I saw the most intrepid man in your Empire."—"What man is that?" said the Emperor brusquely, "and what has he done?"—"He wants to do something, Sire."—"What is it?"—"To visit the sewers of Paris."

This man existed and his name was Bruneseau.

The visit took place. It was a formidable campaign; a nocturnal battle against pestilence and suffocation. It was, at the same time, a voyage of discovery. One of the survivors of this expedition, an intelligent workingman, who was very young at the time, related curious details with regard to it, several years ago, which Bruneseau thought himself obliged to omit in his report to the prefect of police, as unworthy of official style. The processes of disinfection were, at the epoch, extremely rudimentary. Hardly had Bruneseau crossed the first articulations of that subterranean network, when eight laborers out of the twenty refused to go any further. The operation was complicated; the visit entailed the necessity of cleaning; hence it was necessary to cleanse and at the same time, to proceed; to note the entrances of water, to count the gratings and the vents, to lay out in detail the branches, to indicate the currents at the point where they parted, to define the respective bounds of the divers basins, to sound the small sewers grafted on the principal sewer, to measure the height under the key-stone of each drain, and the width, at the spring of the vaults as well as at the bottom, in order to determine the arrangements with regard to the level of each water-entrance, either of the bottom of the arch, or on the soil of the street. They advanced with toil. The lanterns pined away in the foul atmosphere. From time to time, a fainting sewerman was carried out. At certain points, there were precipices. The soil had given away, the pavement had crumbled, the sewer had changed into a bottomless well; they found nothing solid; a man disappeared suddenly; they had great difficulty in getting him out again. . . . They lighted large cages filled with tow steeped in resin, from time to time, in spots which had been sufficiently disinfected. In some places, the wall was covered with misshapen fungi—one would have said, tumors; the very stone seemed diseased within this unbreathable atmosphere.

Bruneseau, in his exploration, proceeded down hill. At the point of separation of the two water-conduits of the Grand-Hurleur, he deciphered upon a projecting stone the date of 1550; this stone indicated the limits where Philibert Delorme, charged by Henri II with visiting the subterranean drains of Paris, had halted. This stone was the mark of the sixteenth century on the sewer; Bruneseau found the handiwork of the seventeenth century once more in the Ponceau drain of the old Rue Vielle-du-Temple, vaulted between 1600 and 1650; and the handiwork of the eighteenth in the western section of the collecting canal, walled and vaulted in 1740. These two vaults, especially the less ancient, that of 1740, were more cracked and decrepit than the masonry of the belt sewer, which dated from 1412, an epoch when the brook of fresh water of Ménilmontant was elevated to the dignity of the Grand Sewer of Paris, an advancement analogous to that of a peasant who should become first *valet de chambre* to the King; something like Gros-Jean transformed into Lebel.

Here and there, particularly beneath the Court-House, they thought they recognized the hollows of ancient dungeons, excavated in the very sewer itself. Hideous *in-pace*. An iron neck-collar was hanging in one of these cells. They walled them all up. Some of their finds were singular; among others, the skeleton of an ourang-outan, who had disappeared from the Jardin des Plantes in 1800, a disappearance probably connected with the famous and indisputabe apparition of the devil in the Rue des Bernardins, in the last year of the eighteenth century. The poor devil had ended by drowning himself in the sewer.

Beneath this long, arched drain which terminated at the Arche-Marion, a perfectly preserved rag-picker's basket excited the admiration of all connoisseurs. Everywhere, the mire, which the sewermen came to handle with intrepidity, abounded in precious objects, jewels of gold and silver, precious stones, coins. If a giant had filtered this cesspool, he would have had the riches of centuries in his lair. At the point where the two branches of the Rue du Temple and of the Rue Sainte-Avoye separate, they picked up a singular Huguenot medal in copper, bearing on one side the pig hooded with a cardinal's hat, and on the other, a wolf with a tiara on his head.

The most surprising rencounter was at the entrance to the Grand Sewer. This entrance had formerly been closed by a grating of which nothing but the hinges remained. From one of these hinges hung a dirty and shapeless rag which, arrested there in its passage, no doubt, had floated there in the darkness and finished its process of being torn apart. Bruneseau held his lantern close to this rag and examined it. It was of very fine batiste, and in one of the corners, less frayed than the rest, they made out a heraldic coronet and embroidered above these seven letters: LAVBESP. The crown was the coronet of a Marquis, and the seven letters signified *Laubespine*. They recognized the fact, that what they had before their eyes was a morsel of the shroud of Marat. Marat in his youth had had amorous intrigues. This was when he was a member of the household of the Comte d'Artois, in the capacity of physician to the Stables. From these love affairs, historically proved, with a great lady, he had retained this sheet. As a waif or a souvenir. At his death, as this was the only linen of any fineness which he had in his house, they buried him in it. Some old women had shrouded him for the tomb in that swaddling-band in which the tragic Friend of the people had enjoyed voluptuousness. Bruneseau passed on. They left that rag where it hung; they did not put the finishing touch to it. Did this arise from scorn or from respect? Marat deserved both. And then, destiny was there sufficiently stamped to make them hesitate to touch it. Besides, the things of the sepulchre must be left in the spot which they select. In short, the relic was a strange one. A Marquise had slept in it; Marat had rotted in it; it had traversed the Pantheon to end with the rats of the sewer. This chamber rag, of which Watteau would formerly have joyfully sketched every fold, had ended in becoming worthy of the fixed gaze of Dante.

The whole visit to the subterranean stream of filth of Paris lasted seven years, from 1805 to 1812. As he proceeded, Bruneseau drew, directed, and completed considerable works: in 1808 he lowered the arch of the Ponceau, and, everywhere creating new lines, he pushed the sewer, in 1809, under the Rue Saint-Denis as far as the fountain of the Innocents; in 1810, under the Rue Froidmanteau and under the Salpêtrière; in 1811 under the Rue Neuve-des-Petits-Pères, under the Rue du Mail, under the Rue de l'Écharpe, under the Place Royale; in 1812, under the Rue de la Paix, and under the Chaussée d'Antin. At the same time, he had the whole net-work disinfected and rendered healthful. In the second year of his work, Bruneseau engaged the assistance of his son-in-law Nargaud.

It was thus that, at the beginning of the century, ancient society cleansed its double bottom, and performed the toilet of its sewer. There was that much clean, at all events.

THE ENTRANCE WAS CHOKED

FROM *Animal Treasure*

IVAN T. SANDERSON

In a pleasantly laconic note on himself, Ivan T. Sanderson says, "No claim made to title of author. Rather is recognition sought in fields of experimental zoology, natural history, and possibly, art of animal illustration." Booklovers fortunately, have not permitted Sanderson the luxury of obscurity as an author. *Animal Treasure,* from which this selection on a cave exploration is taken, was a book club selection, and a similarly pleasant, even if unlooked-for, fate met his second book which was born as by-product of a zoological expedition financed by royalties from his first book. Mr. Sanderson is still a relatively young man and both readers of his scientific papers and those equally demanding people who are taken with his sympathetic prose may look forward hopefully to a cycle of widely read books to finance expeditions which will result in more widely read books.

AS I BEGAN EXPLORING THE LEVEL, SANDY FLOORS OF THE STREET-LIKE PASSAGEways between the great chunks of rock, the light became fainter and fainter. There was practically no bare rock at all, every inch of its surface where there was any light being covered with smooth, soft, bright-green moss. The place was like a buried city, silent, mysterious, and eerie.

Turning an abrupt corner, I came upon a wide sunken arena overhung by a tall cliff. In the very dim light under this natural arch I saw an endless stream of bats passing to and fro from the mouth of a cave at one end to a monstrous horizontal crack at the other. The whole roof of this archway was a dense mass of sleeping bats, suspended upside down in serried ranks. The ground below was covered to a depth of more than a foot with their excrement, which had disintegrated under the influence of the weather and resulted in a mass of broken remains of uncountable millions of insects.

In this stream of bat guano, I found a number of peculiar insects and a small bright-red millepede that I have never seen anywhere else.

By a mere fluke I had a torch in my collecting bag; with its aid I entered the cave. Though the mouth was just wide enough to permit my squeezing through, it expanded somewhat within and rose to a great height above. On both walls, as far as the light of the torch penetrated, bats were hanging or crawling about. The air was literally filled with them. The floor here was covered with guano to such a depth that I could not reach the earth below even by digging with a trapper's friend!

I was so amazed at the whole place and its denizens that I forgot all time and scrambled onwards into the depths, following the endless streams of bats that hurried along and round the corners just as busy traffic does in the streets of a great city.

Turning a corner, I was confronted by a blank wall. The bats were all passing upwards and disappearing over the top of a miniature cliff. I clambered up with some difficulty, to find that I was on top of one of the great blocks of rock. The next one above it was held away by a third block's edge far to the right. This left a horizontal gallery that stretched far ahead, beyond which I could see a large chamber. Into this I eventually emerged complete with gun and all other equipment, after a few uncomfortable minutes of wriggling through, all the time obsessed with that ridiculous but persistent impression that the roof would suddenly cave in and pin me in a not quite dead condition where nobody would ever in any circumstances find me.

The place I now found myself in was much larger than any that I had previously passed through. It was nearly the size of one whole block and almost exactly cubic in shape. The air was as dry as a desert sandstorm; whether it was due to this or the pungent smell of the bats I do not know, but my lips became hard and cracked in a surprisingly short time and my eyes began to water. The roof was altogether free from resting bats, but on the walls were what I at first supposed to be a great number of them. Some being very low down, I put down my collecting bag and gun, and advanced with the torch and a net only, to try to effect a capture.

As I approached the side, however, these things that I had supposed to be bats vanished as if by magic. One minute they were there; the next they were gone. By the time that I was close enough to the rock face to be able to see what they were, had they still been there, there was not one in sight. This was most perplexing.

Deciding that the light must disturb them, if they were not mere shadows, I put out the torch and crept forward to another wall. When I judged that I was close enough, I suddenly flashed on the torch again. A perfectly horrible vision met my eyes. The whole wall was covered with enormous whip-scorpions, crouching and leering at me. Only for a second did they remain, then, like a flash, they all shot out and away in all directions, disappearing into paper-thick crevices with a loathsome rustle.

Their behaviour and appearance are, as I have remarked before, revolting in the extreme, but they were of such unusual size and colour that for the sake of science I steeled myself to a systematic hunt with all the low cunning of a cave man in search of food. Eventually I captured a few after many misses, once being subjected to the nerve-shattering odiousness of having one of them scuttle over my bare arm in escaping from the net.

After this experience I deemed science had sufficient material to gloat over, and I devoted my attention to an examination of the ground for other invertebrates. The bats were entering by the same route as I had done. After crossing the gallery diagonally, they disappeared through one of three vertical fissures, though most of them streamed into and out of the left-hand one, which was the widest. Across the floor below the line of their flight stretched a ridge of their droppings, showing that they excrete while on the wing. Elsewhere the floor was covered with silver sand and spotlessly clean. Only in one corner of the room, remote from the bat highway, was there a pile of small, pellet-like dung.

Examining this, I at once noticed that it was not composed of the crushed remains of insects as was that of the other bats. It resembled more the droppings of a rabbit, although there seemed to be a few small bones projecting from it. This prompted me to search the ceiling above to ascertain where this might be descending from. All I could see, however, was a small cleft above; so, taking the shotgun, I managed by degrees to lever myself up the sharp angle of the corner and eventually peered over the brink into the cleft.

As I switched on the torch, I went cold all over and felt as if my skin were wrinkling up everywhere preparatory to splitting and falling off in one piece. The only alternative to looking into the crevice a second time was falling down backwards. Therefore, after summoning up courage, I switched on the torch again and took a second look. The result was just as bad.

In the mouth of the hole not eighteen inches from my face, four large greenish-yellow eyes stared unblinkingly at me. They were so large that I thought involuntarily of some dead human thing, but the face that projected in front of them soon dispelled this impression. That face is indescribable. . . . In addition there were clammy groping fingers all muddled up with endless flaps of wrinkled naked skin. I pushed in the net and made a random scoop; then I slipped and crashed to the bottom of the cave.

The gun, luckily, fell in the soft sand, and I retained hold of the net in which a huge hammer-headed bat (*Hypsignathus monstrosus*) was struggling.

My left leg was emitting piercing pains and both wrists were quite numbed. There followed an awful period during which I tried to kill the bat in the net and nursed my leg and arms, making, I am afraid, a great deal of noise about it. At last I got the animal under control and chloroformed in the "killer," and then set about gathering together the wreckage. When I came to the gun, my wrists were still numb, but being anxious to make sure that there was no sand choking the barrel, I foolishly tried to open the breech. I am not exactly certain what happened; anyway, both barrels went off almost at once and the gun shot partly out of my hand.

At the same moment the light went out.

There was a period of tremendous echoing, then the whole of this eerie subterranean world seemed to give way, starting with a gentle "swussssh" and culminating in a rattling roar. Things fell down on all sides; choking dust filled the air; while I groped for the torch, hundreds of bats wheeled around my head screaming and twittering.

The torch would not light; for some maddening reason it was not forming a proper contact. I had to sit down and take the batteries out in the dark. I pulled out the metal strips on the ends and procured a flash of light by holding on the screw cap at the back of the container. In my excitement I could not for the life of me get this screw onto the thread. Finally I had to light a match, but before I could see anything, the flame went greenish-blue and quickly died. Other matches did the same.

I had just discovered that they burnt better at a higher level when, with an awful crash, a shower of earth cascaded down from my right side and covered my feet and most of my equipment, which was lying on the floor. There was a wild scramble to retrieve all my possessions and move to a bit of clearer ground, but every time I bent down, the match went out. There was obviously some gas or lack of gas that killed a flame near the floor. I therefore concentrated on fixing the torch. At long last it lit up.

It was less use than a car headlight in a dense mist, because the air was filled with clouds of billowing dust from which a very much startled bat periodically emerged. Groping forward, festooned with gun, collecting bag, net, and torch, I tried to locate the wall with the cleft through which I had gained an entrance, but I soon lost my sense of direction. Then I stumbled across the ridge of bats' dung. This I followed up until it disappeared under a great scree of fine dry earth which was still being added to from above. After further fumbling I found the cleft; the dust was so dense that I could not see more than a few feet into it. This was, however, quite sufficient really to disturb me.

The cleft was choked with earth and rubble. Slowly it dawned on me that the percussion of the shots had released all kinds of pent-up things and perhaps even shifted the roof, as I had imagined might happen through natural causes.

By this time the dust had begun to clear considerably and the rumblings and droppings had ceased. I trekked back to the other side of the cave and tried each of the three exits. The largest, upon which I based my hopes, narrowed quickly, then plunged downward into a low, uninviting crevice. One of the others was too narrow to permit the passage of my head, while the third, although very small, seemed to continue endlessly. Its floor descended rapidly, however, and I soon discovered that the air was very bad a few feet down—matches hardly lit at all. I had therefore to return to the central cave from which I felt almost certain there were no other exits. As the dust was by now less thick, I determined to go all round and make certain.

There proved to be a hopeful-looking chimney in one corner, but try as I would, my left leg steadfastly refused to assist me to climb! This was rendered more exasperating by the fact that a piece of burning paper thrown upwards to its mouth was instantly sucked up out of sight never to return, which all went to show that the passage had some connexion with the outer world. Burning bits of note-book were then applied to the three exits. In one the flame promptly went out, in another it just wilted, and only in the narrowest one did it sail away into the distance, burning merrily. Such a result might, of course, have been predicted!

It then struck me that the choked entrance might not be all choked, so, scrambling along the ledge formed by the long horizontal mouth of this, I peered among the piles of earth that now clogged it, pushing small pieces of burning paper into any gaps or hole that remained. About two-thirds of the way down to the right the paper left my hand and blew straight into my face. I could feel a small draught. The hole was very low and descended towards the right, whereas the part of this gigantic crack through which I had come further up had distinctly sloped upwards out of the square chamber. There was fresh air coming in, so, provided it was not too small, it seemed the only feasible exit. I accordingly packed everything into the collecting bag, including the stock of the gun, wrapped the gun-barrel in the muslin bag of the net to prevent its getting scratched, crammed my felt hat onto my head for the same reason, and, holding the torch in my right hand, committed myself to the depths and the will of Allah.

Progress was slow and at one period extremely painful, for the ceiling—being the flat underside of a giant tilted cube—gradually descended until there was room for me to squeeze through only with the greatest difficulty. This effort I had to make, because I could reach for and feel the angular edge of the ceiling cube just beyond. This edge was as sharp as the angle on a small pack of cigarettes, though the block of rock above must have weighed thousands of tons. Through this slit I must get, and it was a struggle in no way made easier by having a now more or less useless left leg and also having to get the collecting bag over my head in order to push it through before me. How I envied those beastly *Amblypygi!*

Once through, I found myself in a long wide corridor again immaculately carpeted with silver sand. Having by now lost all sense of direction, I set off to the left, where I was soon involved in a tumbled mass of immense angular boulders. To climb over them was a little more than I felt prepared to attempt, so I dived in and tried to find a way through. This led me into a tunnel that smelt strongly and vaguely familiar. Before I had time to think what the cause of it could be, a rasping grunt echoed out from its depths; realizing at once that I had walked voluntarily into a leopard's private quarters, I lost absolutely no time at all in passing back through those boulders as if I were a sandworm brought up to perform such feats. The only course now was to try the other way, as I had no desire to meet a leopard, and even less to fire at one with a shotgun in the depths of the earth, considering what had occurred after the last cannonade.

The other end was a perfectly smooth blank wall. I began to feel rather desperate, a thing one should not do in well-regulated adventures. The feeling was nevertheless sufficiently insistent to call for a cigarette. How I thanked everything, not least myself, that I had cigarettes!

While seated on the sand smoking, feeling sorry for myself, and recounting a lot of things I should like to have done, I played my torch hither and thither over the opposite wall. It was only after a long time that it dawned on me that I was gazing at great patches of green moss. Even after this it was a long time, during which I repacked my equipment, bandaged a knee, and smoked another cigarette, before my idiot brain put two and two together and arrived at the simple fact that green moss meant sunlight. Then all at once this fact penetrated my silly head and I realized that I had never yet looked at the roof. I flashed my torch upwards and saw a line of green branches dangling down into the cleft. During my subterranean meanderings night had come—I was actually standing in the open air.

I'M THE GUY WHO DIDN'T FIND THE SKULL

FROM *Obituary of a Bone Hunter*

LOREN C. EISELEY

In this irreverent anthropological paper, Loren C. Eiseley explains some of the difficulties which beset those who search for human origins, and also such learned distinctions as the difference between big bone hunters and little bone hunters.

Professor Eiseley is chairman of the bone hunting department at the University of Pennsylvania—laymen would call it the anthropology department. He writes of his ventures underground in search of glory and fossil man with a genial and sprightly humor.

THE PAPERS AND THE MAGAZINES HAVE BEEN FULL OF IT THESE PAST FEW DAYS. I mean that business of the skull at Tepexpan and how it was found by sound devices and nobody had to guess at all and they brought the skull home and everybody was famous overnight.

I'm the guy who didn't find the skull. I'm the guy who'd just been looking twenty years for something like it. This isn't sour grapes. It's their skull and welcome to it. What made me sigh was the geophysics equipment. The greatest gambling game in the world—the greatest wit-sharpener—and now they do it with amplifiers. An effete age, gentlemen, and the fun gone out of it.

There are really two kinds of bone hunters—the big bone hunters and the little bone hunters. The little bone hunters may hunt big bones, but they're little bone hunters just the same. They are the consistent losers in the most difficult game of chance that men can play: the search for human origins. Dubois, the discoverer of the Java Ape Man, hit the jackpot in a gamble with such stupendous odds that the most devoted numbers enthusiast would have had better sense than to stake his life on them.

I am a little bone hunter. I've played this game for a twenty-year losing streak. I used to think it all lay in the odds—that it was luck that made the difference between the big and little bone hunters. Now I'm not so sure any longer. Maybe it's something else.

Maybe sometimes an uncanny clairvoyance is involved, and if it comes you must act or the time goes by. Anyhow I've thought about it a lot in these later years. You think that way as you begin to get grayer and you see pretty plainly that the game is not going to end as you planned.

With me I think now that there were three chances: the cave of spiders, and that matter of the owl's egg, and the old man out of the Golden Age. I muffed them all. And maybe the old man just came to show me I'd sat in the big game for the last time.

In that first incident of the spiders, I was playing a hunch, a long one, but a good one still. I wanted to find Neanderthal man, or any kind of Ice-Age man, in America. One or two of the big authorities were willing to admit he *might* have got in before the last ice sheet; that he *might* have crossed Bering Straits with the mammoth. He might have, they said, but it wasn't likely. And if he had, it would be like looking for humming birds in the Bronx to find him.

Well, the odds were only a hundred to one against me, so I figured I'd look. That was how I landed in the cave of spiders. It was somewhere west out of Carlsbad, in the Guadalupe country. Dry. With sunlight that would blister cactus. We were cavehunting with a dynamiter and a young Harvard assistant. The dynamiter was to blow boulders away from fallen entrances so we could dig what lay underneath.

We found the cave up a side canyon, the entrance blocked with fallen boulders. Even to my youthful eyes it looked old, incredibly old. The waters and the frosts of centuries had eaten at the boulders and gnawed the cave roof. Down by the vanished stream bed a little gleam of worked flints caught our eye.

We stayed there for days, digging where we could, and leaving the blasting till the last. We got the Basket Maker remains we had come to get—the earliest people that the scientists of that time would concede had lived in the Southwest. Was there anything more? We tamped a charge under one huge stone that blocked the wall of the cave and scrambled for the outside. A dull boom echoed down the canyon and the smoke and dust slowly blew away.

Inside the cave mouth the shattered boulder revealed a crack behind it. An opening that ran off beyond our spot lights. The hackles on my neck crawled. This might be the road to—something earlier? There was room for only one man to worm his way in. The dynamiter was busy with his tools.

"It's probably nothing," I said to the assistant. "I'll just take a quick look."

As I crawled down that passage on my belly I thought once or twice about rattlesnakes and what it might be like to meet one on its own level where it could look you in the eye. But after all I had met snakes before in this country, and besides I had the feeling there was something worth getting to beyond.

I had it strong—too strong to turn back. I twisted on and suddenly dropped into a little chamber. My light shot across it. It was low and close, and this was the end of the cave. But there was earth on the floor beneath me, the soft earth that must be dug, that might hold something more ancient than the cave entrance. I couldn't stand up; the roof was too low. I would have to dig on hands and knees. I set the light beside me and started to probe the floor with a trench shovel. It was just then that the fear got me.

The light lay beside me shining on the ceiling—a dull, velvety looking ceiling different from the stone around. I don't know when I first sensed something was wrong, that the ceiling was moving, that waves were passing over it like the wind in a stand of wheat. But suddenly I did, suddenly I dropped the shovel, and thrust the light closer against the roof. Things began to detach themselves and drop wherever the light touched them. Things with legs. I could hear them plop on the soft earth around me.

I shut off the light. The plopping ceased. I sat on my knees in the darkness, listening. My mind was centered on just one thing—escape. I knew what that wavering velvet wall was. Millions upon millions of daddy-long-legs—packed in until they hung in layers. Daddy-long-legs, the most innocent and familiar of all the spider family. I wish I could say I had seen black widows there among them. It would help now, in telling this.

But I didn't. I didn't really see anything. If I turned on the light that hideous dropping and stirring would commence again. The light awoke them. They disliked it.

If I could have stood up it would have been different. If they had not been overhead it would have been different. But they had me on my knees and they were above and all around. Millions upon millions. How they got there I don't know. All I know is that up out of the instinctual well of my being flowed some ancient, primal fear of the crawler, the walker by night. One clambered over my hand. And above they dangled, dangled. . . . What if they all began to drop at once?

I did not light the light. I had seen enough. I buttoned my jacket close, and my sleeves. I plunged blindly back up the passage down which I had wriggled and which, luckily, was free of them.

Outside the crew looked at me. I was sweating, and a little queer. "Close air," I gasped; "a small hole, nothing there."

We went away then in our trucks. I suppose in due time the dust settled, and the fox found his way in. Probably all that horrible fecund mass eventually crept, in its single individualities, back into the desert where it frightened no one. What it was doing there, what evil unknown to mankind it was plotting, I do not know to this day. The evil and the horror, I think now, welled out of my own mind, but somehow that multitude of ancient life in a little low dark chamber touched it off. It did not pass away until I could stand upright again. It was a fear out of the old, four-footed world that sleeps within us still.

Neanderthal man? He might have been there. But I was young and that was only a first chance gone. Yes, there were things I might have done, but I didn't do them. You don't tell your chief dynamiter that you ran from a daddy-long-legs. Not in that country. But do you see, it wasn't *one* daddy-long-legs? That's what I can't seem to make clear over the cigars. It wasn't just one daddy-long-legs. It was millions of them. Enough to bury you. And have you ever thought of being buried under spiders? I thought not. You begin to get the idea?

I had a second chance and again it was in a cave I found. This time I had been alone, tramping up a canyon watching for bones, and I had just happened to glance upward in the one place where the cave could be seen. I studied it a long time—until I could feel the chill crawling down my back. This might be it; this might be the place. . . . This time I would know. This time there would be no spiders.

Through the glasses I could make out a fire-blackened roof, a projecting ledge above the cave mouth, and another one below. It was a small, strange hide-out, difficult to reach, but it commanded the valley on which the canyon opened. And there was the ancient soot-impregnated cave roof. Ancient men had been there.

I made that climb. Don't ask me how I did it. Probably there had been an easier route ages ago. But I came up a naked chimney of rock down which I lost my knapsack and finally the geologist's pick that had helped me hack out a foothold in the softening rock.

When I flung myself over the ledge where the cave mouth opened, I was shaking from the exhausting muscle tension and fear. No one, I was sure, had come that way for a thousand years, and no one after me would come again. I did not know how I would get down. It was enough momentarily to be safe. In front of me the cave mouth ran away darkly into the mountain.

I took the flashlight from my belt and loosened my sheath knife. I began to crawl downward and forward, wedging myself over sticks and fallen boulders. It was a clean cave and something was there, I was sure of it. Only, the walls were small and tight. . . .

They were tighter when the voice and the eyes came. I remember the eyes best. I caught them in my flashlight the same instant that I rammed my nose into the dirt and covered my head. They were big eyes and coming my way.

I never thought at all. I just lay there dazed while a great roaring buffeting thing beat its way out over my body and went away.

It went out into the silence beyond the cave mouth. A half minute afterward, I peered through my fingers and rolled weakly over. Enough is enough. But this time I wasn't going back empty-handed. Not I. Not on account of a mere bird. Not if I *had* thought it was a mountain lion, which it could just as well have been. No owl was going to stop me, not even if it was the biggest owl in the Rocky Mountains.

I twitched my ripped shirt into my pants and crawled on. It wasn't much farther. Over the heap of debris down which the great owl had charged at me, I found the last low chamber, the place I was seeking. And there in a pile of sticks lay an egg, an impressive egg, mottled and full of potentialities, fraught, if I may say so, with destiny. It was almost an insolent egg.

I affected at first to ignore it. I was after the buried treasures that lay beneath its nest in the cave floor. The egg was simply going to have to look after itself. Its parent had gone, and in a pretty rude fashion, too. I was no vandal, but I was going to be firm. If an owl's egg stood in the path of science. . . . But suddenly the egg seemed very helpless, very much alone. I probed the earth around the nest. The nest got in the way. This was a time for decision.

I know a primatologist who will lift a rifle and shoot a baby monkey out of its mother's arms for the sake of science. He is a good man, too, and goes home nights to his wife. I tried to focus on this thought as I faced the egg.

I knew it was a rare egg. The race of its great and lonely mother was growing scant in these mountains and would soon be gone. Under it might lie a treasure that would make me famed in the capitals of science; but suppose there was nothing under the nest after all and I destroyed it? Suppose. . . .

Here in this high, sterile silence with the wind crying over frightful precipices, myself and that egg were the only living things. That seemed to me to mean something. Well, at last I backed quietly out of the cave and slipped down into the chasm out of which I had come. By luck I did not fall.

Sometimes in these later years I think perhaps the skull was there, the skull that could have made me famous. It is not so bad, however, when I think that the egg became an owl. I had had charge of it in the universe's sight for a single hour, and I had done well by life.

It is not the thought of the skull that torments me sometimes on winter evenings. Suppose the big, unutterably frightened bird never came back to its egg? A feeling of vast loss and desolation sweeps over me then. I begin to perceive what it is to doubt.

It was years later that I met the old man. He was waiting in my office when I came in. It was obvious from the timid glances of my secretary that he had been passed from hand to hand and that he had outwitted everybody. Someone in the background made a twisting motion at his forehead.

The old man sat, a colossal ruin, in the reception chair. The squirrel-like twitterings of the office people did not disturb him.

As I came forward he fished in a ragged wallet and produced a clipping. "You made this speech?" he asked.

"Why, yes," I said.

"You said men came here late? A few thousand years ago?"

"Yes, you see—"

"Young man," he interrupted, "you are frightfully wrong."

I was aware that his eyes were contracted to pin points and seemed in some danger of protruding on stalks.

"You have ignored," he rumbled, "the matter of the Miocene period—the Golden Age. A great civilization existed then, far more splendid than this—degenerate time." He struck the floor fiercely with his cane.

"But," I protested, "that period is twenty million years ago. Man wasn't even in existence. Geology shows—"

"Nothing!" said the massive relic. "Geology has nothing to do with it. Sit down. I know all about the Golden Age. I will prove to you that you are wrong."

I collapsed doubtfully into a chair. He told me that he was from some little town in Missouri, but I never believed it for a moment. He smelled bad, and it was obvious, if he brought news of the Golden Age, as he claimed, that he had come by devious and dreadful ways from that far era.

"I have here," he said, thrusting his head forward and breathing heavily into my face, "a human jaw. I will unwrap it a little and you can see. It is from a cave I found."

"It is imbedded in stalactite drippings," I murmured, hypnotized against my will. "That might represent considerable age. Where did you find it?"

He raised a protesting hand. "Later, son, later. You admit then—?"

I strained forward. "Those teeth," I said, "they are large—they look primitive." The feeling I had had at the mouth of the owl's cave came to me again overpoweringly. "Let me see a little more of the jaw. If the mental eminence should be lacking, you may have something important. Just let me handle it a moment."

With the scuttling alacrity of a crab, the old man drew back and popped the papers over his find. "You admit, then, that it is important? That it proves the Golden Age was real?"

Baffled, I looked at him. He eyed me with an equal wariness.

"Where did you find it?" I asked. "In this light it seemed—it might be—a fossil man. We have been looking a long time. If you would only let me see—"

"I found it in a cave in Missouri," he droned in a rote fashion. "You can never find the cave alone. If you will make a statement to the papers that the Golden Age is true, I will go with you. You have seen the evidence."

Once more I started to protest. "But this has nothing to do with the Golden Age. You may have a rare human fossil there. You are denying science—"

"Science," said the old man with frightening dignity, "is illusion." He arose. "I will not come back. You must make a choice."

For one long moment we looked at each other across the fantastic barriers of our individual minds. Then, on his heavy oakwood cane, he hobbled to the door and was gone. I watched through the window as he crossed the street in a patch of autumn sunlight as phantasmal and unreal as he. Leaves fell raggedly around him until, a tatter among tatters, he passed from sight.

I rubbed a hand over my eyes, and it seemed the secretary looked at me strangely. How was it that I had failed this time? By unbelief? But the man was mad. I could not possibly have made such a statement as he wanted.

Was it pride that cost me that strange jaw bone? Was it academic dignity? Should I have followed him? Found where he lived? Importuned his relatives? Stolen, if necessary, that remarkable fragment?

Of course I should! I know that now. Of course I should.

Ten years have passed since the old man came to see me. I have crawled in many caverns, stooped with infinite aching patience over the bones of many men. I have made no great discoveries.

I think now that in some strange way that old man out of the autumn leaf-fall was the last test of the inscrutable gods. There will be no further chances. The egg and the spiders and the madman—in them is the obituary of a life dedicated to the folly of doubt, the life of a small bone hunter.

CANYON VOYAGE

FROM *Beyond the Hundredth Meridian*

WALLACE STEGNER

Major John Wesley Powell was the larger than life-sized figure who led a party of nine men on the first exploration of the Colorado River. Neither the killing rapids, nor the impossible portages stopped this one-armed man. He somehow managed to push and pull his much less resolute party through all the dangers and accidents that beset them.

This selection is from the narrative of the expedition by Wallace Stegner, author of the best-selling novel of some years ago, *The Big Rock Candy Mountain.*

AT NOON ON MAY 24, 1869, THE POPULATION OF GREEN RIVER GATHERED ON the bank, and an hour later they watched the four boats of the Powell Expedition spin out into the current—the *Emma Dean,* the *Maid of the Canyon,* the *Kitty Clyde's Sister,* and the *No-Name,* all but the pilot boat heavy and low in the water with their loads. The men jumped to oars and sweeps, the Major swung his hat from the *Emma Dean.* In two or three minutes the current carried them left, then right, and one after another they disappeared around the bend. The crowd stood around a little, squinted at the rising river, passed predictions, and dispersed. . . .

For a while the river flirts with the great mountain table rising east and west across its course. It cuts in through Flaming Gorge, emerges into a little park where today there are three or four remote ranches, and then wheels left into the mountain. But it does not cut through. The red walls turn it in a half circle, forcing it through a complete U out into the valley again, barely a half mile from where it entered. Powell named this stretch Horseshoe Canyon. In the part of it now called Hideout Canyon there is a footbridge across the Green to accommodate pack trains and deer hunters and sheep bands headed for the back country. This canyon gave the expedition its first real thrill—a curving rapid where the water plunged down among rocks. They ran it, at first scared and then exhilarated.

The walls widened out to make another little valley, pinched in to make another canyon. The river was broad and quiet here, and kingfishers playing along a tributary stream gave valley and canyon and stream a name. Just beyond their May 30 camp came a great domed point eroded into thousands of holes where swallows nested. They called it Beehive Point and followed the river around it, changing course from south to east as the river, having cut in close to the heart of the range, turned and ran along it lengthwise.

By now the walls were close to a half mile high, stepping backward in terraces, clean cliff and wooded slope and clean cliff again, to remote rims. Red Canyon they called it; it is one of the spectacular chasms of the Green. Today a tourist can look down into it from several spots on the rim, notably from Green Lake. But the tourist from that height sees only a thread of river, green in low water, reddish in high. He will not see the rapids that for the first time gave Powell and his men a touch of danger and exhausting work, and he will not hear what is perhaps the most nerve-wearing accompaniment of any voyage in these canyons: the incessant, thundering, express-engine roar of the water. In many parts of the canyons it never ceases, day or night. It speeds the heartbeat and deafens the ears and shakes the ground underfoot. It comes from every side, echoed and multiplied by the walls. A man's voice is lost, shouting in it.

The expedition would have plenty of experience with that roar of rapids. What they had of it here was a mere preliminary, for this was still a small river, unaugmented by the large tributaries. The rapids in Red Canyon, though bad enough to force them to line their boats down several times, were not such rapids as they would meet later, and there were stretches of wonderfully fast exciting water. Powell records that they made in one hour, including stops, twelve miles. Some of the men guessed that at times they were doing a mile a minute. . . .

Powell was not thinking of history as he camped in Brown's Hole, resting after the canyons, restoring the ears of his party with silence and birdsong, measuring the country he could reach or see. Some history had not happened yet, and some of it he did not know. He might glance up the Vermillion where Frémont had gone, but he glanced more frequently at the frowning gateway where the river, after miles of running down the east-west axis of the Uintas, turned south again and cut straight in. For him this was the real beginning. Up to here he had been anticipated by trappers and prospectors. Brown's Hole itself was a vast cattle ranch, there were cabins and herds, and the place had been known years back by trappers on the Seedskeedee. But from here on was something else. Two thousand feet above the Hole, hanging his feet over the cliff, Powell sat and wrote a letter, dated June 7, 1869, which he would send out to the Chicago *Tribune* if and when he had the chance.

While I write [he concluded], I am sitting on the same rock where I sat last spring, with Mrs. Powell, looking down into this cañon. When I came down at noon, the sun shone in splendor on its vermilion walls shaded into green and gray when the rocks are lichened over. The river fills the channel from wall to wall. The cañon opened like a beautiful portal to a region of glory. Now, as I write, the sun is going down, and the shadows are settling in the cañon. The vermilion gleams and the rosy hues, the green and gray tints, are changing to sombre brown above, and black shadows below. Now 'tis a black portal to a region of gloom.

And that is the gateway through which we enter [on] our voyage of exploration tomorrow—and what shall we find?

He dramatized himself somewhat, this one-armed major, and he had perhaps been reading eloquent and rhetorical travelers of the school of Mungo Park. Circumstances would conspire to assist in the dramatization. Though he would not know it for months, the rumor of his death and the death of his whole party but one would shortly go out from the mountains, and the place of his reported death . . . was this same canyon beneath his feet.

The rapids Powell saw from the walls had not looked too bad, but they turned out to be sharp, fierce pitches in the riverbed, filled with boulders fallen from the cliffs. Powell went ahead, waving the boats ashore at every bad spot, reconnoitering on foot. Until noon they had short stretches of navigable water broken by rapids so furious that Andy Hall, remembering some schoolboy lesson, was led to exclaim, "Oh how the waters come down at Lodore!" They named it the Canyon of Lodore, to Sumner's disgust. Sumner's reason for carping, confided a little later to his journal, is not only a sharp reminder of the difference between leader and men, but has a quaintly modern sound: "The idea of diving into musty trash to find names for new discoveries on a new continent is un-American, to say the least."

Just at noon on June 7 Powell's boat pulled ashore at the head of a bad place, and signaled the freight boats to land. Powell went along shore to scout a practicable portage. Over his shoulder he saw one of the boats pulling in, but when he looked again he saw the *No-Name,* with the two Howlands and Frank Goodman struggling at oars and sweep. Either they had not seen the signal, or had not started digging for shore in time. O. G. Howland later said he could have made shore if he had not been half full of water from running the rapids above. But now the experience Hawkins and Hall had had in easy water the first day was repeated without the laughs.

Powell saw the boat hang for a breath at the head of the rapid and then sweep into it. He leaped onto a rock to signal frantically at the last boat, and after a long minute saw it pulling heavily toward shore well above the tongue. The moment he saw that one safe, he ran after the *No-Name.*

It had shot the first fall, only a few feet high, and was rearing down a steep rapid. He saw it strike a boulder and heave up like a bucking horse. All three men were thrown out, but when the boat jammed briefly against the rocks they managed to grab the gunwale, and as she slipped off and started down again Powell watched the dripping boatmen frantically haul themselves in. The boat was full of water; though her watertight compartments kept her afloat, she was unmanageable in the fierce current. She wallowed down through the rapid, pounded into the tail waves and on two hundred yards to a second rapid as wild as the first. There she struck solidly, broadside, and broke completely in two. For a moment the tiny dark heads of the swimming men were visible in the foam, and then the water swept them out of sight.

Powell ran, bursting his lungs, with the other men behind him. Around the bend he came in sight of a swimmer being washed and pounded on a rock to which he clung for his life. O. G. Howland, recognizable by his draggled beard, had made a stony island in mid-rapid and was scrambling out to stretch a pole to the man on the rock, who turned out to be Goodman. Goodman let go the rock, seized the pole, and was hauled out. Further down the island Seneca Howland was dragging himself to the safety of the boulders.

They were safe for the time, but marooned in the middle of a bad rapid. Now the lightness and maneuverability of the *Emma Dean* proved out. The others lined her down to the foot of the first rapid, and Sumner, a brave man and by now a good boatman, was shoved off from there. Angling across the tail waves that swept almost to the tongue of the second rapid, he made the tip of the island. Then the four men pulled the boat upriver as high as they could go. Standing in water to his shoulders, one held it there while the others climbed in. Then a straining push, a scramble, the men in the stern hauling the pusher aboard, Sumner pulling furiously on the oars, and they made it in to where those on shore could reach them. There was a good deal of handshaking and thumping on the back—as much rejoicing, Powell wrote, "as if they had been on a voyage around the world and wrecked on a distant coast." . . .

Lodore was not a succession of rapids such as they had passed before, but as Bradley wrote in his journal, one continuous rapid. The shores were cluttered boulders, without level ground on which to camp. Bitching like a good army man, Bradley remarked on June 11 that the Major had as usual chosen the worst campsite available. "If I had a dog," Bradley said, "that would lie where my bed is made tonight I would kill him and burn his collar and swear I never owned him." That same day, to give him better cause to grouse, he fell on the portage and cut his eye badly, so that thereafter, down the canyon where the river "roars and foams like a wild beast," he went sullenly with a notable black eye. Bedraggled, soaked, muddy, their shirttails dragging and their drawers clinging to their goosepimpled legs, they were all in Bradley's mood.

There are characteristic discomforts on a river voyage. Not the least is the incessant wetting and the sharp alternation of heat and cold. On a bright day a boatman swiftly sunburns the backs of his hands, the insteps of his feet if they are bare, every unexpected spot exposed by long sitting in one position. In the shade, in soaked clothes, the wind is often icy. And worse than either sun or wind is the irritation of sitting long hours on a hard wet board in sopping pants or drawers. The water is full of silt and sand, and so, consequently, are the clothes one wears. After a few hours there grows a sensation as if one has been gently coasting his seat back and forth across fine sandpaper. After a few more hours a boatman likes to stand whenever the river will let him.

Their clothes, even in the valises and carpetbags stowed under the cabin decks, were soaked. Their flour was wet and souring, their bacon gritty with silt, their coffee damp, their beans sprouting. Their muscles were sore and their bodies bruised and their tempers tried. When they took a rest on June 13 the saturnine Bradley commented that it was the first Sunday they had paid any attention to and he was inclined to believe that nobody but himself even knew it was the Sabbath. As they spread the spoiling rations out to dry on the rocks he prophesied dourly that they would soon be sorry they had taken no better care of them. "If we succeed," he said, "it will be *dumb luck,* not good judgment that will do it."

Thus the enlisted man about his commander, *ad infinitum.*

Lodore continued to rub its lessons in. They had barely started from their enforced rest camp on June 15 before the *Maid of the Canyon,* allowed to swing a little too far out into the current in the tongue of a rapid, smoked her line through the palms of the men holding her and broke clean away down the rapid and out of sight. Their spirits went down with her, for with only two boats they would be badly overloaded and underrationed. But they chased along shore, hoping against probability, and found her rotating with dignity in an eddy, unharmed except for a bruise or two.

Still that was not enough. Accidents it seemed must happen by threes. A day after the breaking loose of the *Maid,* Powell climbed with Howland up the cliff above camp, which was pitched in willows and cedars on a bar. A few minutes later he looked down on pandemonium. With characteristic carelessness Hawkins had built his cooking fire too close to the dead willows. A whirlwind swept upriver, tore across the bar, and scattered burning sticks in every direction. Willow and cedar smoldered and burst into flame which in the stiff wind grew almost instantly into a conflagration. Trapped on the bar, the men had no escape except the river as the wind swooped tongues of flame across the camp. They jumped for the boats. Hawkins grabbed what he could carry of the mess kit, and ran with his arms full of kettles and bake ovens, but at the bank he stubbed his toe, and without a pause or a cry dove head first into the Green. He came up strangling and cussing, and without the mess kit.

By that time the whole point was ablaze. Their hair and beards were singed and the boats in danger. There was nothing to do but cut loose. From up on the cliff Powell watched the boats full of smoking, slapping men pour down the river and through a stiff rapid for almost a mile before they got under control and made shore. Their knives, forks, spoons, tin plates, and some of their kettles remained behind them in Lodore, along with the cryptic wreckage they themselves had found, to be a warning to careless travelers.

As if the lessons were now finished, the river relented, and on the morning of June 18 they floated down into a cliff-walled park where the Yampa flowed smoothly in, carrying more water at this stage than the Green. In a grassy, sunny bottom "the size of a good farm" they camped and rested and sent their voices against the cliffs that sent them back in diminishing echoes, six or eight echoes, or echoes of echoes. Behind them, as Powell now wrote in a fourth letter to the Chicago *Tribune,* lay "a chapter of disasters and toils," but Lodore was "grand beyond the power of pen to tell. Its waters poured unceasingly from the hour we entered it until we landed here. No quiet in all that time; but its walls and cliffs, its peaks and crags, its amphitheaters and alcoves, told a story that I hear yet, and shall hear, and shall hear. . . ." With an ear cocked for the public sound of his voice, he could still sound perilously like Mungo Park. . . .

Looking upon the unknown, they found reasons for its being so. On both sides of the river an increasingly barren and broken land closed in, topped with fantastic towers. On July 7 they were deep in an entrenched, meandering canyon, swinging in great bends and amphitheaters. By evening they had come again to bad water, the walls much broken by side canyons, sometimes so close together that holes had eroded out between them leaving natural bridges. On the high rims they could see pine forests, but down on the river there was little but baking broken rock. It reminded them all of the arid plateau around Green River and Fort Bridger; they were agreeably surprised to be in tune with science when the Major found fossil fish teeth that told him these rocks were in fact the same lacustrine formations.

Wanting to know as much as he could about the unexplored land back from the river, Powell took Bradley and climbed up a steep, ledgy wall in blistering sun. Somewhere on the cliff he made the mistake of jumping from one foothold to another, grabbing a projection of rock with his one hand. Then he found himself "rimmed," unable to go forward or back. Standing on tiptoe and clinging to the knob, he shouted to Bradley, above him, but Bradley could not reach him with his hand, and there was no halfway foothold to which he could descend. The cliff had neither brush nor pole; they had carried no rope with them.

Below his feet was a hundred-foot drop, a terrace, and then a longer drop. If he let himself go he might fall clear to the river's edge. By now his legs were trembling, his strength beginning to waver. As a desperation measure Bradley sat down on his ledge and yanked off his long drawers, which he lowered to Powell. With nice timing, Powell let go the knob, and half falling away from the cliff, grabbed the dangling underwear. That was the first, but by no means the only time he had cause to thank his stars for Bradley's presence on the party.

That day, and for several successive days, Powell scanned from the rims a country even more wild and desolate than the canyon through which the boats felt their careful way. A great plateau was cut completely in two by the river. From a tower which he climbed he looked across the high pine forest clothing the summits, and across dozens of canyons heading in mid-plateau and deepening toward their confluence with the Green or with the White and Uinta to the north. But he could see little that told him what lay to the south, only the widening gray and brown lips of canyons cutting down toward unknown junctions. He took barometric measurements of the depth of strata, height of walls, fall of river. He taught Jack Sumner to use a sextant. He came down from the cliffs, groping dangerously after dark, and stayed up nearly all night making observations, and with an hour or two of sleep pushed off to run a while and tie up for more climbing, more observations.

They met headwinds so hot and strong they could not run against them. Even in mid-river, soaking wet, they panted with the heat, and on shore the sand of their campsite blew over them so that they covered their heads with blankets and sweltered. And when the wind subsided enough so that they could run, they hit twenty miles of continuous cataracts that made them revise some of the superlatives they had applied to Lodore. Sometimes running, sometimes (to the men's disgust) cautiously lining, they got through forty-five miles of what they named the Canyon of Desolation and thought the country ahead looked favorable for a break. Andy Hall, rising above sandstorms and headwinds and the grinding labor of the portages, lay on his back that night and sang to the glum Bradley in a voice like a crosscut saw:

When he put his arm around her
She bustified like a forty-pounder,
Look away, look away, look away, Dixie land.

All the way down the river Bradley had been griping in his diary about the Major's habit of ignoring the Sabbath. Now he had a chance to crow. On Sunday, July 11, Powell started the *Emma Dean* down a brisk rapid and saw too late that it was a dogleg with a sharp kick to the left and a heavy pile-up of water against the wall at the turn. Earlier, two of their oars had been broken; the boat had only two now, not enough to pull them out of danger. All they could do was to point her nose downstream, wave frantically to the following boats to pull ashore, and hang on. They shot past a rock and were caught in a reflex wave that rolled the boat like a spinning log. Powell was thrown a boat's length away, Sumner and Dunn managed to cling to the gunwales. In a pneumatic life preserver, and in water so swift, Powell could not sink. He struck out one-armed for the boat, wallowing swamped through the tail waves. The three of them, swimming and pulling at the waterlogged boat, managed to get her against a pile of driftwood before she could be swept over a second rapid below. But to Bradley's satisfaction they had lost two rifles, some blankets, a barometer, and both remaining oars, and the Major had had his comeuppance for laboring on Sunday. That day they made a half mile, most of it swimming, and spent the remaining hours of daylight whipsawing oars out of a driftwood log.

Next day Bradley got his own comeuppance for gloating. Coming to a long, curving fall between broken rocks and an overhanging cliff, the Major looked the rapid over and concluded to run it, keeping as close to the rocks on the left as possible to avoid the great waves and the overhang along the cliff. The *Emma Dean* made it, half full of water, but as Bradley's boat swept down out of the tongue a wave broke over his stern and knocked him overboard. His foot caught under the thwart, and head down, now contorting himself upward enough to get a hand on the gunwale, now dragging clear under, he rushed with the swamped boat through a series of battering waves before Walter Powell, pulling like a madman away from the threatening cliff, made it past the danger and could reach his strangling companion a hand.

The river played no favorites, and it showed no sign of conforming to their united wish for a letup. Beyond the Canyon of Desolation they ran directly into another, which they called Coal Canyon from the seams of lignite in the walls. It is now called Gray Canyon. And Gray Canyon was more of the same. In one bad rapid the river filled the channel from cliff to cliff, leaving not even the bare toehold of a portage. They had to let one boat down the full length of its line, then push off the second attached to it, and the third attached to the second, until all three were stretched out straining in the rapid, when the third was pulled in, then the second loosed and snubbed in, then the first. Then Bill Dunn, left on a rock in mid-stream, had to swim for it and be yanked in by those on shore.

It was bone-wrenching labor. Below that difficult lining job lay a portage, and below that a camp on a sandbeach in a hurricane of wind that blew all night and filled blankets, kettles, food, hair, eyes, ears, mouths, with sand. Desolation and Coal Canyons had been pretty continuous strain. Tempers were short, the rapids apparently endless. And then in a blink the unpredictable river gave them precisely what they craved: swift water, exhilarating little riffles and rapids that sped them along without labor and with a great lift of the spirit. They ran nineteen rapids in eighteen miles without the necessity of getting out of the boats, and at the end of Coal Canyon they burst out into open country again, a shimmering, blistered desert broken by circumeroded buttes of buff and gray and brown and slaty blue. Behind them, stretching in a long line east and west, were the Roan and Book Cliffs, cut to their base by the river's gorge, and meandering away in long wavy lines distorted by heat haze and the smoke of forest fires. To the northeast they saw snow mountains, the Uncompahgre Range in western Colorado. Across the valley the buttes lifted on the heat waves and hung dreamlike above the earth.

The river was deep, broad, quiet. Two hours below the mouth of Coal Canyon they found an Indian crossing where crude rafts were moored against the bank, and knew it for another of the very few practicable crossings in the canyon wilderness. At this point, now the site of Greenriver, Utah, where both Highway 50 and the Denver and Rio Grande cross, the old Spanish Trail, route of mule drivers between Taos and California, route of traveling mountain men and supply trains, found a way across the canyons. To this same point Captain Gunnison, surveying for the Pacific Railroad in 1853, had been compelled like water in a funnel. The Powell party knew that Gunnison and seven of his men had been massacred by the Pahvant Indians a little farther west. When they landed and found evidence that Indians had recently crossed, they did not linger. Even such half-spoiled rations and depleted outfits as they had might be a temptation.

Beyond their brief meeting with the tracks of Indian and white they pushed on down the quiet river, one day, two days. At the mouth of the San Rafael, trickling from the west through a deep canyon, they found much Indian sign. Out from the river the buttes were evenly banded, brilliantly colored: pink, purple, brown, gray. As the river dug again into the rock and the walls rose higher around them they kept climbing out to look over the dunes of colored sand, maroon and orange and creamy white. The river began to pursue another entrenched meander, locked and baffled in the deep rock, swinging on itself in great bends under walls of homogeneous orange sandstone domed and hollowed into immense caves.

By now they had left behind them all familiarity; the country was such as none of them had ever seen. On the broken plains stretching away from rimrock there was no vegetation, only worn rock and sand and the bizarre forms of desert erosion; in the distance the Roan Cliffs were pale azure, the flat and tabular outlines of mesas and buttes were evenly bedded, colored like the rainbow. It *looked* like unknown country, and its heat fried their skins and beat on their heads and sucked the sweat from their pores as they rowed down the slow baffled current around bends that showed always more alcoves, more amphitheaters. The strangeness excited them to horseplay; they shot off their guns and loosed sharp yells to hear the confused echoes in the bowknot tangles of the river. They named it Labyrinth Canyon.

Like a teasing woman the river dawdled, meandered, surprised them with new forms, new colors, delayed and delayed and delayed the expected union with the Grand, now marked on the maps as the Colorado, at that point which on all the maps was frank guess work. They watched, and rowed, and waited, and expected the rapids and cataracts that should accompany the junction in such a wild and moonlike landscape, but the river swept them on serenely through July 14, 15, 16. Again and again they climbed out, but they looked in vain for any canyon that could mean the incoming Grand. They walked over pavements of jasper and heard their foreign voices in painted amphitheaters and tracked the sand in the bottoms of lateral gorges and saw the Orange Cliffs flame under the harsh sun, but still their objective escaped them, and still the Green went smooth and quiet around more bends.

Late in the afternoon of the 16th the river broke into hurrying waves, became again a swift steep pouring on which the boats rode like coasting sleds. Stillwater Canyon was behind them. In another hour they broke without warning on the junction, the Grand coming in "in a calm strong tide" from the left. No falls, no cataracts, no tumult to mark the union. Lesser canyons, wet-weather streams, almost always meant rapids, for they bore down flood-washed boulders and left them at their mouths. But the Grand came secretly out of the concealing rock, clearer and colder than the Green and at this time of year with a greater flow. Below the junction for a thousand yards, as far as they could see, the doubled river went unrippled, undangerous.

From Green River, Wyoming, they had come, by Powell's computation, 538 miles. Caution had held their losses to one boat and its contents. Of the crew only one, the weakest, had given up. They were tightly knit, an expedition, camped on a spot probably no white man and perhaps no man of any kind had ever seen.

2

Men Live and Work on the Earth

At first, by making use of its resources, man sought to free himself from his environment, the earth. Later, it was not freedom he sought, but improvident dominion. He dug out great areas of the earth's surface to house and feed him. He tore down its forests, scooped out its ores for his cities. He squandered much of the substance of the earth, left it gullied and eroded for nature to fill and cover again. But the earth keeps a cruel reckoning. It may be that one day there will be too much stripped, too much dug, and this once green and pleasant earth will no longer suffer our spendthrift mastery. For in this struggle we have won no balance with nature, nor any harmony with ourselves.

Man's challenge of the earth for his livelihood is an oft-repeated theme in our literature. Its heroes are those who have established our squatter sovereignty—the men who farm the earth, mine the coal, dig the tunnels.

JULY, THE MONTH OF PLENTY

THE HARVEST IS IN SIGHT

FROM *The Good Earth*

PEARL BUCK

In *The Good Earth,* from which we have taken this selection, Pearl Buck gave a great body of American readers more than a word picture of the older Chinese peasant life: she caught some of its taste and touch and smell.

Pearl Buck was brought up in China, the daughter of missionaries, and was married to one. She has written a number of books with western settings, but it is her novels on China with which she has made her large contribution to both racial understanding and world literature.

IT SEEMED TO HIM THAT DURING THESE NEXT MONTHS HE DID NOTHING EXCEPT watch this woman of his. In reality he worked as he always had. He put his hoe upon his shoulder and he walked to his plots of land and he cultivated the rows of grain, and he yoked the ox to the plow and he ploughed the western field for garlic and onions. But the work was luxury, for when the sun struck the zenith he could go to his house and food would be there ready for him to eat, and the dust wiped from the table, and the bowls and the chopsticks placed neatly upon it. Hitherto he had had to prepare the meals when he came in, tired though he was, unless the old man grew hungry out of time and stirred up a little meal or baked a piece of flat, unleavened bread to roll about a stem of garlic.

Now whatever there was, was ready for him, and he could seat himself upon the bench by the table and eat at once. The earthen floor was swept and the fuel pile replenished. The woman, when he had gone in the morning, took the bamboo rake and a length of rope and with these she roamed the countryside, reaping here a bit of grass and there a twig or a handful of leaves, returning at noon with enough to cook the dinner. It pleased the man that they need buy no more fuel.

In the afternoon she took a hoe and a basket and with these upon her shoulder she went to the main road leading into the city where mules and donkeys and horses carried burdens to and fro, and there she picked the droppings from the animals and carried it home and piled the manure in the dooryard for fertilizer for the fields. These things she did without a word and without being commanded to do them. And when the end of the day came she did not rest herself until the ox had been fed in the kitchen and until she had dipped water to hold to its muzzle to let it drink what it would.

And she took their ragged clothes and with thread she herself had spun on a bamboo spindle from a wad of cotton she mended and contrived to cover the rents in their winter clothes. Their bedding she took into the sun on the threshold and she ripped the coverings from the quilts and washed them and hung them upon a bamboo to dry, and the cotton in the quilts that had grown hard and grey from years she picked over, killing the vermin that had flourished in the hidden folds, and sunning it all. Day after day she did one thing after another, until the three rooms seemed clean and almost prosperous. The old man's cough grew better and he sat in the sun by the southern wall of the house, always half-asleep and warm and content. . . .

But there is not that about three rooms and two meals a day to keep busy a woman who has been a slave in a great house and who has worked from dawn until midnight. One day when Wang Lung was hard pressed with the swelling wheat and was cultivating it with his hoe, day after day, until his back throbbed with weariness, her shadow fell across the furrow over which he bent himself, and there she stood, with a hoe across her shoulder.

"There is nothing in the house until nightfall," she said briefly, and without speech she took the furrow to the left of him and fell into steady hoeing.

The sun beat down upon them, for it was early summer, and her face was soon dripping with her sweat. Wang Lung had his coat off and his back bare, but she worked with her thin garment covering her shoulders and it grew wet and clung to her like skin. Moving together in a perfect rhythm, without a word, hour after hour, he fell into a union with her which took the pain from his labor. He had no articulate thought of anything; there was only this perfect sympathy of movement, of turning this earth of theirs over and over to the sun, this earth which formed their home and fed their bodies and made their gods. The earth lay rich and dark, and fell apart lightly under the points of their hoes. Sometimes they turned up a bit of brick, a splinter of wood. It was nothing. Some time, in some age, bodies of men and women had been buried there, houses had stood there, had fallen, and gone back into the earth. So would also their house, some time, return into the earth, their bodies also. Each had his turn at this earth. They worked on, moving together—together—producing the fruit of this earth—speechless in their movement together.

When the sun had set he straightened his back slowly and looked at the woman. Her face was wet and streaked with the earth. She was as brown as the very soil itself. Her wet, dark garments clung to her square body. She smoothed a last furrow slowly. Then in her usual plain way she said, straight out, her voice flat and more than usually plain in the silent evening air,

"I am with child."

Wang Lung stood still. What was there to say to this thing, then! She stooped to pick up a bit of broken brick and threw it out of the furrow. It was as though she had said, "I have brought you tea," or as though she had said, "We can eat." It seemed as ordinary as that to her! But to him—he could not say what it was to him. His heart swelled and stopped as though it met sudden confines. Well, it was their turn at this earth!

He took the hoe suddenly from her hand and he said, his voice thick in his throat, "Let be for now. It is a day's end. We will tell the old man."

They walked home, then, she half a dozen paces behind him as befitted a woman. The old man stood at the door, hungry for his evening's food, which, now that the woman was in the house, he would never prepare for himself. He was impatient and he called out,

"I am too old to wait for my food like this!"

But Wang Lung, passing him into the room, said,

"She is with child already."

He tried to say it easily as one might say, "I have planted the seeds in the western field today," but he could not. Although he spoke in a low voice it was to him as though he had shouted the words out louder than he would.

The old man blinked for a moment and then comprehended, and cackled with laughter.

"Heh-heh-heh—" he called out to his daughter-in-law as she came, "so the harvest is in sight!" . . .

She would have no one with her when the hour came. It came one night, early, when the sun was scarcely set. She was working beside him in the harvest field. The wheat had borne and been cut and the field flooded and the young rice set, and now the rice bore harvest, and the ears were ripe and full after the summer rains and the warm ripening sun of early autumn. Together they cut the sheaves all day, bending and cutting with short-handled scythes. She had stooped stiffly, because of the burden she bore, and she moved more slowly than he, so that they cut unevenly, his row ahead, and hers behind. She began to cut more and more slowly as noon wore on to afternoon and evening, and he turned to look at her with impatience. She stopped and stood up then, her scythe dropped. On her face was a new sweat, the sweat of a new agony.

"It is come," she said. "I will go into the house. Do not come into the room until I call. Only bring me a newly peeled reed, and slit it, that I may cut the child's life from mine."

She went across the fields toward the house as though there were nothing to come, and after he had watched her he went to the edge of the pond in the outer field and chose a slim green reed and peeled it carefully and slit it on the edge of his scythe. The quick autumn darkness was falling then and he shouldered his scythe and went home.

When he reached the house he found his supper hot on the table and the old man eating. She had stopped in her labor to prepare them food! He said to himself that she was a woman such as is not commonly found. Then he went to the door of their room and he called out,

"Here is the reed!"

He waited, expecting that she would call out to him to bring it in to her. But she did not. She came to the door and through the crack her hand reached out and took the reed. She said no word, but he heard her panting as an animal pants which has run for a long way. . . .

And then, almost before one could realize anything, the woman was back in the fields beside him. The harvests were past, and the grain they beat out upon the threshing floor which was also the dooryard to the house. They beat it out with flails, he and the woman together. And when the grain was flailed they winnowed it, casting it up from great flat bamboo baskets into the wind and catching the good grain as it fell, and the chaff blew away in a cloud with the wind. Then there were the fields to plant for winter wheat again, and when he had yoked the ox and ploughed the land the woman followed behind with her hoe and broke the clods in the furrows.

She worked all day now and the child lay on an old torn quilt on the ground, asleep. When it cried the woman stopped and uncovered her bosom to the child's mouth, sitting flat upon the ground, and the sun beat down upon them both, the reluctant sun of late autumn that will not let go the warmth of summer until the cold of the coming winter forces it. The woman and the child were as brown as the soil and they sat there like figures made of earth. There was the dust of the fields upon the woman's hair and upon the child's soft black head.

But out of the woman's great brown breast the milk gushed forth for the child, milk as white as snow, and when the child suckled at one breast it flowed like a fountain from the other, and she let it flow. There was more than enough for the child, greedy though he was, life enough for many children, and she let it flow out carelessly, conscious of her abundance. There was always more and more. Sometimes she lifted her breast and let it flow out upon the ground to save her clothing, and it sank into the earth and made a soft, dark, rich spot in the field. The child was fat and good-natured and ate of the inexhaustible life his mother gave him.

Winter came on and they were prepared against it. There had been such harvests as never were before, and the small, three-roomed house was bursting. From the rafters of the thatched roof hung strings and strings of dried onions and garlic, and about the middle room and in the old man's room and in their own room were mats made of reeds and twisted into the shapes of great jars and these were filled full of wheat and rice. Much of this would be sold, but Wang Lung was frugal and he did not, like many of the villagers, spend his money freely at gambling or on foods too delicate for them, and so, like them, have to sell the grain at harvest when the price was low. Instead he saved it and sold it when the snow came on the ground or at the New Year when people in the towns will pay well for food at any price. . . .

In the midst of all this plenty they sat in the house, therefore, when the winds of winter came out of the desert to the northeast of them, winds bitter and biting. Soon the child could almost sit alone. They had had a feast of noodles, which mean long life, on his month birthday, when he was a full moon of age, and Wang Lung had invited those who came to his wedding feast and to each he had given a round ten of the red eggs he had boiled and dyed, and to all those who came from the village to congratulate him he gave two eggs. And every one envied him his son, a great, fat, moony-faced child with high cheek bones like his mother. Now as winter came on he sat on the quilt placed on the earthen floor of the house instead of upon the fields, and they opened the door to the south for light, and the sun came in, and the wind on the north beat in vain against the thick earthen wall of the house.

The leaves were soon torn from the date tree on the threshold and from the willow trees and the peach trees near the fields. Only the bamboo leaves clung to the bamboos in the sparse clump to the east of the house, and even though the wind wrenched the stems double, the leaves clung.

With this dry wind the wheat seed that lay in the ground could not sprout and Wang Lung waited anxiously for the rains. And then the rains came suddenly out of a still grey day when the wind fell and the air was quiet and warm, and they all sat in the house filled with well-being, watching the rain fall full and straight and sink into the fields about the dooryard and drip from the thatched ends of the roof above the door. The child was amazed and stretched out his hands to catch the silver lines of the rain as it fell, and he laughed and they laughed with him and the old man squatted on the floor beside the child and said,

"There is not another child like this in a dozen villages. Those brats of my brother notice nothing before they walk."

And in the fields the wheat seed sprouted and pushed spears of delicate green above the wet brown earth.

At a time like this there was visiting, because each farmer felt that for once Heaven was doing the work in the fields and their crops were being watered without their backs being broken for it, carrying buckets to and fro, slung upon a pole across their shoulders; and in the morning they gathered at this house and that, drinking tea here and there, going from house to house barefoot across the narrow path between the fields under great oiled paper umbrellas. The women stayed at home and made shoes and mended clothes, if they were thrifty, and thought of preparations for the feast of the New Year.

But Wang Lung and his wife were not frequent at visiting. There was no house in the village of small scattered houses, of which theirs was one of a half dozen, which was so filled with warmth and plenty as their own, and Wang Lung felt that if he became too intimate with the others there would be borrowing. New Year was coming and who had all the money he wanted for the new clothes and the feasting? He stayed in his house and while the woman mended and sewed he took his rakes of split bamboo and examined them, and where the string was broken he wove in new string made of hemp he grew himself, and where a prong was broken out he drove in cleverly a new bit of bamboo.

And what he did for the farm implements, his wife, O-lan, did for the house implements. If an earthen jar leaked she did not, as other women did, cast it aside and talk of a new one. Instead she mixed earth and clay and welded the crack and heated it slowly and it was as good as new.

They sat in their house, therefore, and they rejoiced in each other's approval, although their speech was never anything more than scattered words such as these:

"Did you save the seed from the large squash for the new planting?" Or, "We will sell the wheat straw and burn the bean stalks in the kitchen." Or perhaps rarely Wang Lung would say, "This is a good dish of noodles," and O-lan would answer in deprecation, "It is good flour we have this year from the fields."

THE HOLE IN THE LAKE

FROM *The Mystery of the Savage Sump*

SAM DAVIS

Sam Davis was a reporter in Carson City during the Comstock silver days. It was a wild, fantastic period of boom and bust, when a man could beg or borrow a stake on Monday, be a millionaire on Tuesday, a pauper on Wednesday. Fiction was a little less incredible than fact and newspapermen like Sam Davis moved from fact to fiction, fiction to fact with so ready an ease that the line between them must frequently have blurred. If he had not labeled it fiction, this selection from "The Mystery of the Savage Sump," could as easily have appeared as a news story in the Carson City *Morning Appeal* when Sam Davis was editor.

IT WAS MORE THAN TWENTY YEARS AGO THAT VIRGINIA CITY, NEVADA, FIRST wrestled with what was known as the "Mystery of the Savage Sump."

The sump of the Savage Mine is an excavation at the foot of the incline where the hot water of the mine collects in volume, and from whence it is pumped into the Sutro Tunnel, steaming, scalding hot. The Sutro Tunnel strikes the great Comstock Ledge 1,750 feet below the surface, and is the drain pipe through which all the water in the Comstock mines is discharged. It runs through the boxes in the tunnel nearly five miles before it reaches the lower mouth of the tunnel, and from thence finds its way into the Carson River. The sump is more than three thousand feet below the surface, and when this point was reached it marked the limit of man's ability to pierce the depths of the earth on the Comstock Ledge.

The water came in so fast that the big pumps had to be kept constantly at work to prevent the flooding of the lower levels.

One morning the miners who came off the three-o'clock shift reported the finding of the body of a man in the sump. It was a horrible, shapeless thing, with the flesh cooked in the hot water and the features unrecognizable. The body, what was left of it, was exposed in the morgue for more than a week, but not identified. Several thousand men were working in the mines at the time, but the roll of the Miners' Union and the tally sheet of the Savage Mine showed no one missing.

Besides this it was noticed that the corpse had on fine boots with high heels. It also had on remnants of clothes, and portions of a broadcloth coat were fished up from the sump. It could not have been a miner, and those who had charge of the incline leading to the sump were positive that no such man had ever gone down. There was but one way of reaching it, and that was by riding down on a sort of cage known as the "giraffe," let down and pulled up by a cable working by machinery running in the hoisting works above ground.

The men who were employed in the responsible positions about the mine were all of the most trustworthy character, and had been employed there for years. No one could enter the mine without a permit from the superintendent, and even then no visitor ever went into the lower levels, where the hot water dripped from the rocks and the heat was sometimes as high as 140 degrees in places where the half-naked men worked with cold water playing from a hose on their bodies.

If it was murder, who could possibly be implicated? The authorities and the newspapers and the officers of the Miners' Union and the superintendents of the mines investigated the mystery on separate lines, and after a year of probing it was as much a mystery as on the day the body was discovered floating about, swollen and distorted, in the foul and steaming waters of the sump.

As years passed the incident was well-nigh forgotten, but now, at this remote time, I am able to furnish the world with a complete solution.

If the reader will take the pains to look over the files of the San Francisco papers during the latter part of 1869 and the spring of '70, some of the most violent fluctuations that ever occurred in the mining stock market will be noticed. One and the same narration tells the story of the death of the unknown man found in the Savage sump and the rise and fall of mining stock at the time mentioned.

In the fall of '69, a San Francisco stock speculator was spending a few weeks at Lake Tahoe, the summer resort in the Sierra Nevada mountains, which lie partly in Nevada and partly in California. Wishing to be out of the way of the world as much as possible, he engaged quarters at a little secluded place on the Nevada side of the lake, known as Carnelian Bay. It was a cheap and out-of-the-way place, and not over a dozen guests were there at a time, but the fishing was excellent and the surroundings pleasant. The tourist's name was William Meeker, and he had lost a large fortune in the whirl of stock speculations on California Street.

One morning, while fishing about a mile from the hotel, he noticed that his boat began slowly turning, and in a few minutes described a complete circle in the water. Some chips and debris were collected about the boat and they seemed to stay there. He studied the situation carefully and reached the conclusion that there was a subterranean outlet which caused the eddy.

He was a man of quick action, and that night he carved the initials W. M. on a piece of pine and next morning rigged up a weight, rowed out, and lowered it into the water where his boat had been affected by the currents. It went down in about a hundred feet of water, and then something began bearing it down. There was a succession of tugs, and the line began spinning over the edge of the boat with rapidly increasing speed. Then the line caught in the boat and snapped with the strain. This made it clear to him that the water was surging through an outlet in the lake bottom. That night he settled his bill and started for San Francisco.

He took but one man into his confidence and that was Colonel Clair, one of the heaviest and most unscrupulous operators in the market and a member of the biggest firm on the street. They figured for more than a week, with maps and surveys, and reached the conclusion that the water making its exit from the lake was finding its outlet in the lower levels of the Comstock mines.

They pored over statistical tables showing how the lake had been, on an average, at least one foot higher before the mines in Virginia City had encountered water in the lower levels, and to them the mystery of the fall in the water of the lake was explained.

It was decided to send a man into the Savage to watch for the piece of pine with Meeker's initials on. But why trust it to a third party? Meeker himself went into Virginia City, and on a letter of recommendation from Colonel Clair was given work in the Savage and placed at the foot of the incline as a station tender.

He had not been long at his post when the little piece of wood with the initials W. M. came up on the surface of the water of the sump, and his heart gave a great bound of joy. That night he was flying to San Francisco on a fast train, and next morning was closeted with Colonel Clair, the mining operator and millionaire.

The plan these two men fixed on was the boldest ever conceived in the annals of stock speculation. It was nothing less than a method by which the hole in the bottom of Tahoe might be stopped by a mechanical contrivance and then opened and closed at will. By this means the mine might be cleared of water or flooded to suit the convenience of the two operators, and this condition, having its influence on the stock market, would make millions for the men who had conceived the bold design.

Before the week was over, Meeker, backed by the money of Colonel Clair, was back at Lake Tahoe. He ordered a large flatboat built, ostensibly for fishing purposes. It was completed in a couple of weeks and fitted with a good cabin, and here he took up his abode. From then on a lot of mysterious consignments reached Tahoe for Meeker, and he received them on his flatboat at Tahoe City and moved the boat from place to place by the aid of a small steam launch.

To all intents and purposes it was an angler's craft, the mere pastime of a man who had the money at his disposal to catch Tahoe trout in his own way.

It proved really a simple matter to stop the hole in the lake. Careful investigation showed it to be nearly circular and about four feet across. The dimensions of the hole being known approximately was sufficient. The butt of a log about five feet in diameter was given a conical shape, and bolts were sunk in the end, to which a heavy chain was attached. This was connected with a windlass and let down through the "well" in the bottom of the rough board house built on the boat; and on a calm day, when the water was still, Clair and Meeker could see a long distance into the depths of the water by the aid of a large mirror and the sunlight—which came in through a hole in the roof of the house—reflected down the "well."

Then came the grand test, when they let down the big plug. Slowly it was lowered until it was caught in the suction and the chain showed the enormous strain. Then down, deeper and deeper it went into the mighty current, taking the handles of the windlass from the hands of the men and sending it whirling. It revolved like a buzz saw for a few seconds and then came to a standstill. It was evident the plug had settled into the hole as far as it would go and that the pressure of the water was keeping it there. The deflected light thrown down by the large mirror on the boat showed that such was the case.

Could the plug be lifted back? The fate of their plot depended upon their answer. The two men threw their weight on the handles of the windlass, but they could not budge it an inch. That night they bored holes in the windlass shaft and inserted long crowbars. With this improved leverage, they succeeded with comparatively little trouble in drawing the plug out of the hole and lifting it beyond the influence of the suction. Several times they lowered and raised it again. That night Colonel Clair was on his way to San Francisco, leaving Meeker to guard the boat.

During the next ten days, brokers who watched the market noticed that the firm of Goodman and Crowley was buying Savage in any lots offered. There was nothing special in the way of developments in the mine, and those who had become tired of holding Savage began to unload on a rising market. Presently the brokers who had the handling of the deal were active bidders on the stock. The tall form of Joe Goodman was soon noticeable in the center of a gesticulating crowd, bidding up Savage. The price rose gradually, and still he stood calm and serene, as was his wont, and taking in all the Savage offered.

"Five thousand at twenty-six, buyer thirty."

Goodman took them and more at the same figure.

A little man rose and flung twenty thousand shares at Goodman. He took them without blinking.

There was a pause, and a swirl of speculation seemed for a moment to have lost its momentum.

Thirty-five thousand shares inside a minute, and snapped up by one man, was not a usual thing. They waited to see what the calm, blue-eyed man would do, as if he would dare bid higher. Then his voice rang out:

"Twenty-seven for twenty-five thousand shares, buyer thirty."

In an instant the cry of "sold" was shouted at him from all sides of the Board room.

"Take 'em all," he cried, "and will give twenty-eight for fifty thousand more."

Not a sale was offered at those figures. Something was on. The brokers scented a big deal in Savage and no one dared to take his offer.

The session closed and in a few minutes the street was a scene of extraordinary excitement. The wires were hot between San Francisco and Virginia City with cipher dispatches, but no one could report anything extraordinary in Savage. There was no development, and the water in the lower levels required the full working capacity of the big Cornish pumps to hold it in control.

Goodman was a commission broker and evidently not speculating on his own hook, and Colonel Clair's brokers were selling Savage—but in mighty small lots.

Colonel Clair was moving about the street in front of the Exchange building deprecating the idea of a rise in stocks not based on actual merit.

"My son," he said to one of the curbstone brokers, "there can never be anything in buying Savage until the water is out of the lower levels."

Within a week the water was nearly all out of the Savage, and also out of the adjoining mines, and stocks began to soar. The pumps all along the big lead were slowing down and the word went out that the water had been conquered at last and now the big bonanzas were going to be uncovered. Virginia City was happy, and the Stock Exchange in San Francisco was a whirl of speculation.

Then Colonel Clair began shorting everything in the midst of flurry. He had sold and realized a cool million, and was now a bear. It seemed odd that this should be the case when the pumps had drained the lower levels almost dry and no water was coming in. Then unexpectedly the waters came into the lower levels in a great flood and caught the miners napping with the pumps barely moving. There was a crash in stocks when the news reached Pine Street, San Francisco, and everything went by the board. Colonel Clair cleaned up another million.

"I didn't think it could be permanent," he said.

Then came a series of rises and breaks in the market and Colonel Clair always "hit them just right." No man seemed so shrewd as he, and so the deals went on and his wealth accumulated. William Meeker had but to raise or lower the plug in Lake Tahoe, according to advices.

One night as Meeker was raising the plug with the big windlass, he became aware of a figure behind him. It was Colonel Clair, who had reached the spot by a boat.

"How is she working?"

"Never better."

"I have your share deposited in the Nevada bank and it is now over two million."

Meeker smiled and his heart bounded when he heard these words.

"How big the moon looks over yonder!" exclaimed the Colonel.

Meeker turned his head, and a heavy iron bar crushed in his skull. Colonel Clair tied a weight to the body and lowered it into the depths. Down and down it slowly sank, and then the swirl sucked it into the hole and it was gone. Colonel Clair lowered the plug.

PLOUGHING, SOWING, MOWING AND GLEANING CORN IN THE TENTH CENTURY

"I AM DIGGING THIS TREASURE FOR DANNY"

FROM *Tortilla Flat*

JOHN STEINBECK

Tortilla Flat, the setting for John Steinbeck's captivating assortment of unconventional characters, is Monterey where in the earlier, much less affluent time before his books became best sellers, he and his wife lived on $25 a month and what fish they could catch. There he met the people of *Cannery Row, Tortilla Flat,* and *Sweet Thursday,* whose deviations from strictly orthodox behavior he treats with humorous affection and jovial clemency.

AFFECTION AND A DESIRE TO SEE HIS FRIENDS CAME TO BIG JOE. IN THE EVENING he wandered up toward Tortilla Flat to find Danny and Pilon. It was dusk as he walked up the street, and on the way he met Pilon, hurrying by in a businesslike way.

"Ai, Pilon. I was just coming to see you."

"Hello, Joe Portagee," Pilon was brusque. "Where you been?"

"In the army," said Joe.

Pilon's mind was not on the meeting. "I have to go on."

"I will go with you," said Joe.

Pilon stopped and surveyed him. "Don't you remember what night it is?" he asked.

"No. What is it?"

"It is St. Andrew's Eve."

Then the Portagee knew; for this was the night when every paisano who wasn't in jail wandered restlessly through the forest. This was the night when all buried treasure sent up a faint phosphorescent glow through the ground. There was plenty of treasure in the woods, too. Monterey had been invaded many times in two hundred years, and each time valuables had been hidden in the earth.

The night was clear. Pilon had emerged from his hard daily shell, as he did now and then. He was the idealist tonight, the giver of gifts. This night he was engaged in a mission of kindness.

"You may come with me, Big Joe Portagee, but if we find any treasure I must decide what to do with it. If you do not agree, you can go by yourself and look for your own treasure."

Big Joe was not an expert at directing his own efforts. "I will go with you, Pilon," he said. "I don't care about the treasure."

The night came down as they walked into the forest. Their feet found the pine-needle beds. Now Pilon knew it for a perfect night. A high fog covered the sky, and behind it, the moon shone so that the forest was filled with a gauze-like light. There was none of the sharp outline we think of as reality. The tree trunks were not black columns of wood, but soft and unsubstantial shadows. The patches of brush were formless and shifting in the queer light. Ghosts could walk freely tonight, without fear of the disbelief of men; for this night was haunted, and it would be an insensitive man who did not know it.

Now and then Pilon and Big Joe passed other searchers who wandered restlessly, zig-zagging among the pines. Their heads were down and they moved silently and passed no greeting. Who could say whether all of them were really living men? Joe and Pilon knew that some were shades of those old folk who had buried the treasures; and who, on Saint Andrew's Eve, wandered back to the earth to see that their gold was undisturbed. Pilon wore his saint's medallion, hung around his neck, outside his clothes; so he had no fear of the spirits. Big Joe walked with his fingers crossed in the Holy Sign. Although they might be frightened, they knew they had protection more than adequate to cope with the unearthly night.

The wind arose as they walked, and drove the fog across the pale moon like a thin wash of gray water color. The moving fog gave shifting form to the forest, so that every tree crept stealthily along and the bushes moved soundlessly, like great dark cats. The tree-tops in the wind talked huskily, told fortunes and foretold deaths. Pilon knew it was not good to listen to the talking of the trees. No good ever came of knowing the future; and besides, this whispering was unholy. He turned the attention of his ears from the trees' talking.

He began a zig-zag path through the forest, and Big Joe walked beside him like a great alert dog. Lone silent men passed them, and went on without a greeting, and the dead passed them noiselessly, and went on without a greeting.

The fog siren began its screaming on the Point, far below them; and it wailed its sorrow for all the good ships that had drowned on the iron reef, and for all those others that would sometime die there.

Pilon shuddered and felt cold, although the night was warm. He whispered a Hail Mary under his breath.

They passed a gray man who walked with his head down, and who gave them no greeting.

An hour went by, and still Pilon and Big Joe wandered as restlessly as the dead who crowded the night.

Suddenly Pilon stopped. His hand found Big Joe's arm. "Do you see?" he whispered.

"Where?"

"Right ahead there."

"Ye-s—I think so."

It seemed to Pilon that he could see a soft pillar of blue light that shone out of the ground ten yards ahead of him.

"Big Joe," he whispered, "find two sticks about three or four feet long. I do not want to look away. I might lose it."

He stood like a pointing dog while Big Joe scurried off to find the sticks. Pilon heard him break two small dead limbs from a pine tree. And he heard the snaps as Big Joe broke the twigs from the sticks. And still Pilon stared at the pale shaft of nebulous light. So faint it was that sometimes it seemed to disappear altogether. Sometimes he was not sure he saw it at all. He did not move his eyes when Big Joe put the sticks in his hands. Pilon crossed the sticks at right angles and advanced slowly, holding the cross in front of him. As he came close, the light seemed to fade away, but he saw where it had come from, a perfectly round depression in the pine needles

Pilon laid his cross over the depression, and he said, "All that lies here is mine by discovery. Go away, all evil spirits. Go away, spirits of men who buried this treasure. *In Nomen Patris et Filius et Spiritu Sancti,*" and then he heaved a great sigh and sat down on the ground.

"We have found it, oh my friend, Big Joe," he cried. "For many years I have looked, and now I have found it."

"Let's dig," said Big Joe.

But Pilon shook his head impatiently. "When all the spirits are free? When even to be here is dangerous? You are a fool, Big Joe. We will sit here until morning; and then we will mark the place, and tomorrow night we will dig. No one else can see the light now that we have covered it with the cross. Tomorrow night there will be no danger."

The night seemed more fearful now that they sat in the pine needles, but the cross sent out a warmth of holiness and safety, like a little bonfire on the ground. Like a fire, however, it only warmed the front of them. Their backs were to the cold and evil things that wandered about in the forest.

Pilon got up and drew a big circle around the whole place, and he was inside when he closed the circle. "Let no evil thing cross this line, in the Name of the Most Holy Jesus," he chanted. Then he sat down again. Both he and Big Joe felt better. They could hear the muffled footsteps of the weary wandering ghosts; they could see the little lights that glowed from the transparent forms as they walked by; but their protecting line was impregnable. Nothing bad from this world or from any other world could cross into the circle.

"What are you going to do with the money?" Big Joe asked.

Pilon looked at him with contempt. "You have never looked for treasure, Big Joe Portagee, for you do not know how to go about it. I cannot keep this treasure for myself. If I go after it intending to keep it, then the treasure will dig itself down and down like a clam in the sand, and I shall never find it. No, that is not the way. I am digging this treasure for Danny."

All the idealism in Pilon came out then. He told Big Joe how good Danny was to his friends.

"And we do nothing for him," he said. "We pay no rent. Sometimes we get drunk and break the furniture. We fight with Danny when we are angry with him, and we call him names. Oh, we are very bad, Big Joe. And so all of us, Pablo and Jesus Maria and the Pirate and I talked and planned. We are all in the woods, tonight, looking for treasure. And the treasure is to be for Danny. He is so good, Big Joe. He is so kind; and we are so bad. But if we take a great sack of treasure to him, then he will be glad. It is because my heart is clean of selfishness that I can find this treasure?"

"Won't you keep any of it?" Big Joe asked, incredulous. "Not even for a gallon of wine?"

Pilon had no speck of the Bad Pilon in him this night. "No, not one scrap of gold! Not one little brown penny! It is all for Danny, every bit."

Joe was disappointed. "I walked all this way, and I won't even get a glass of wine for it," he mourned.

"When Danny has the money," Pilon said delicately, "it may be that he will buy a little wine. Of course I shall not suggest it, for this treasure is Danny's. But I think maybe he might buy a little wine. And then if you were good to him, you might get a glass."

Big Joe was comforted, for he had known Danny a long time. He thought it possible that Danny might buy a great deal of wine.

The night passed on over them. The moon went down and left the forest in muffled darkness. The fog siren screamed and screamed. During the whole night Pilon remained unspotted. He preached a little to Big Joe as recent converts are likely to do.

"It is worth while to be kind and generous," he said. "Not only do such actions pile up a house of joy in Heaven; but there is, too, a quick reward here on earth. One feels a golden warmth glowing like a hot enchilada in one's stomach. The Spirit of God clothes one in a coat as soft as camel's hair. I have not always been a good man, Big Joe Portagee. I confess it freely."

Big Joe knew it perfectly well.

"I have been bad," Pilon continued ecstatically. He was enjoying himself thoroughly. "I have lied and stolen. I have been lecherous. I have committed adultery and taken God's name in vain."

"Me too," said Big Joe happily.

"And what was the result, Big Joe Portagee? I have had a mean feeling. I have known I would go to Hell. But now I see that the sinner is never so bad that he cannot be forgiven. Although I have not yet been to confession, I can feel that the change in me is pleasing to God, for His grace is upon me. If you, too, would change your ways, Big Joe, if you would give up drunkenness and fighting and those girls down at Dora Williams' House, you too might feel as I do."

But Big Joe had gone to sleep. He never stayed awake very long when he was not moving about.

The grace was not quite so sharp to Pilon when he could not tell Big Joe about it, but he sat and watched the treasure place while the sky grayed and the dawn came behind the fog. He saw the pine trees take shape and emerge out of obscurity. The wind died down and the little blue rabbits came out of the brush and hopped about on the pine needles. Pilon was heavy-eyed but happy.

When it was light he stirred Big Joe Portagee with his foot. "It is time to go to Danny's house. The day has come." Pilon threw the cross away, for it was no longer needed, and he erased the circle. "Now," he said, "we must make no mark, but we must remember this by trees and rocks."

"Why don't we dig now?" Big Joe asked.

"And everybody in Tortilla Flat would come to help us," Pilon said sarcastically.

They looked hard at the surroundings, saying, "Now there are three trees together on the right, and two on the left. That patch of brush is down there, and here is a rock." At last they walked away from the treasure, memorizing the way as they went.

At Danny's house they found tired friends. "Did you find any?" the friends demanded.

"No," said Pilon quickly, to forestall Joe's confession.

"Well, Pablo thought he saw the light, but it disappeared before he got to it. And the Pirate saw the ghost of an old woman, and she had his dog with her."

The Pirate broke into a smile. "That old woman told me my dog was happy now," he said.

"Here is Big Joe Portagee, back from the army," announced Pilon.

"Hello, Joe."

"You got a nice place here," said the Portagee, and let himself down easily into a chair.

"You keep out of my bed," said Danny, for he knew that Joe Portagee had come to stay. The way he sat in a chair and crossed his knees had an appearance of permanence.

The Pirate went out, and took his wheelbarrow and started into the forest to cut his kindlings; but the other five men lay down in the sunshine that broke through the fog, and in a little while they were asleep.

It was mid-afternoon before any of them awakened. At last they stretched their arms and sat up and looked listlessly down at the bay below, where a brown oil tanker moved slowly out to sea. The Pirate had left the bags on the table, and the friends opened them and brought out the food the Pirate had collected.

Big Joe walked down the path toward the sagging gate. "See you later," he called to Pilon.

Pilon anxiously watched him until he saw that Big Joe was headed down the hill to Monterey, not up toward the pine forest. The four friends sat down and dreamily watched the evening come.

At dusk Joe Portagee returned. He and Pilon conferred in the yard, out of earshot of the house.

"We will borrow tools from Mrs. Morales," Pilon said. "A shovel and a pick-ax stand by her chicken house."

When it was quite dark they started. "We go to see some girls, friends of Joe Portagee's," Pilon explained. They crept into Mrs. Morales' yard and borrowed the tools. And then, from the weeds beside the road, Big Joe lifted out a gallon jug of wine.

"Thou hast sold the treasure," Pilon cried fiercely. "Thou art a traitor, oh dog of a dog."

Big Joe quieted him firmly. "I did not tell where the treasure was," he said with some dignity. "I told like this, 'We found a treasure,' I said. 'But it is for Danny. When Danny has it, I will borrow a dollar and pay for the wine.' "

Pilon was overwhelmed. "And they believed, and let you take the wine?" he demanded.

"Well—" Big Joe hesitated. "I left something to prove I would bring the dollar."

Pilon turned like lightning and took him by the throat. "What did you leave?"

"Only one little blanket, Pilon," Joe Portagee wailed. "Only one."

Pilon shook at him, but Big Joe was so heavy that Pilon only succeeded in shaking himself. "What blanket," he cried. "Say what blanket it was you stole."

Big Joe blubbered. "Only one of Danny's. Only one. He has two. I took only the little tiny one. Do not hurt me, Pilon. The other one was bigger. Danny will get it back when we find the treasure."

Pilon whirled him around and kicked him with accuracy and fire. "Pig," he said, "dirty thieving cow. You will get the blanket back or I will beat you to ribbons."

Big Joe tried to placate him. "I thought how we are working for Danny," he whispered. "I thought, 'Danny will be so glad, he can buy a hundred new blankets.' "

"Be still," said Pilon. "You will get that same blanket back or I will beat you with a rock." He took up the jug and uncorked it and drank a little to soothe his frayed sensibilities; moreover he drove the cork back and refused the Portagee even a drop. "For this theft you must do all the digging. Pick up those tools and come with me."

Big Joe whined like a puppy, and obeyed. He could not stand against the righteous fury of Pilon.

They tried to find the treasure for a long time. It was late when Pilon pointed to three trees in a row. "There!" he said.

They searched about until they found the depression in the ground. There was a little moonlight to guide them, for this night the sky was free of fog.

Now that he was not going to dig, Pilon developed a new theory for uncovering treasure. "Sometimes the money is in sacks," he said, "and the sacks are rotted. If you dig straight down you might lose some." He drew a generous circle around the hollow. "Now, dig a deep trench around, and then we will come *up* on the treasure."

"Aren't you going to dig?" Big Joe asked.

Pilon broke into fury. "Am I a thief of blankets?" he cried. "Do I steal from the bed of my friend who shelters me?"

"Well, I ain't going to do all the digging," Big Joe said.

Pilon picked up one of the pine limbs that only the night before had

THE SEWER HUNTERS

FROM *London Labour and the London Poor*

HENRY MAYHEW

An England far removed from the Victorian elegancies is that which Henry Mayhew shows us. Mayhew was one of the founders of the English comic magazine *Punch* and edited the first of the digest magazines. His avocation was sociological research and his study, *London Labour and the London Poor,* from which we have chosen this selection, is a gallery of occupational portraits drawn from a less familiar but undoubtedly more universal aspect of English nineteenth-century life than the one most of us know.

THE SEWER-HUNTERS, LIKE THE STREET-PEOPLE, ARE ALL KNOWN BY SOME peculiar nickname, derived chiefly from some personal characteristic. It would be a waste of time to inquire for them by their right names, even if you were acquainted with them, for none else would know them, and no intelligence concerning them could be obtained; while under the title of Lanky Bill, Long Tom, One-eye George, Short-armed Jack, they are known to every one.

My informant, who is also dignified with a title, or as he calls it a "handle to his name," gave me the following account of himself: "I was born in Birmingham, but afore I recollects anythink, we came to London. The first thing I remembers is being down on the shore at Cuckold's P'int, when the tide was out and up to my knees in mud, and a gitting down deeper and deeper every minute till I was picked up by one of the shore-workers. I used to git down there every day, to look at the ships and boats a sailing up and down; I'd niver be tired a looking at them at that time. At last father 'prenticed me to a blacksmith in Bermondsey, *and then I couldn't get down to the river when I liked, so I got to hate the forge and the fire, and blowing the bellows, and couldn't stand the confinement no how—at last I cuts and runs.* After some time they gits me back ag'in, but I cuts ag'in. I was determined not to stand it. I wouldn't go home for fear I'd be sent back, so I goes down to Cuckold's P'int and there I sits near half the day, when who should I see but the old un as had picked me up out of the mud when I was a sinking. I tells him all about it, and he takes me home along with hisself, and gits me a bag and an o, and takes me out next day, and shows me what to do, and shows me the dangerous places, and the places what are safe, and how to rake in the mud for rope, and bones, and iron, and that's the way I comed to be a shore-worker. Lor' bless you, I've worked Cuckold's P'int for more nor twenty year. I know places where you'd go over head and ears in the mud, and jist alongside on 'em you may walk as safe as you can on this floor. But it don't do for a stranger to try it, he'd wery soon git in, and it's not so easy to git out agin, I can tell you. I stay'd with the old un a long time, and we used to git lots o' tin, specially when we'd go to work the sewers. I liked that well enough. I could git into small places where the old un couldn't, and when I'd got near the grating in the street, I'd search about in the bottom of the sewer; I'd put down my arm to my shoulder in the mud and bring up shillings and half-crowns, and lots of coppers, and plenty other things. I once found a silver jug as big as a quarter pot, and often found spoons and knives and forks and every thing you can think of. Bless your heart the smells nothink; it's a roughish smell at first, but nothink near so bad as you thinks, 'cause, you see, there's sich lots o' water always a coming down the sewer, and the air gits in from the gratings, and that helps to sweeten it a bit. There's some places, 'specially in the old sewers, where they say there's foul air, and they tells me the foul air 'ill cause instantious death, but I niver met with anythink of the kind, and I think if there was sich a thing I should know somethink about it, for I've worked the sewers, off and on, for twenty year. When we comes to a narrow place as we don't know, we takes the candle out of the lantern and fastens it on the hend of the o, and then runs it up the sewer, and if the light stays in, we knows as there a'n't no danger. We used to go up the city sewer at Blackfriars-bridge, but that's stopped up now; it's boarded across inside. The city wouldn't let us up if they knew it, 'cause of the danger, they say, but they don't care if we hav'n't got nothink to eat nor a place to put our heads in, while there's plenty of money lying there and good for nobody. If you was caught up it and brought afore the Lord Mayor, he'd give you fourteen days on it, as safe as the bellows, so a good many on us now is afraid to wenture in. We don't wenture as we used to, but still it's done at times. There's a many places as I knows on where the bricks has fallen down, and that there's dangerous; it's so delaberated that if you touches it with your head or with the hend of the o, it 'ill all come down atop o' you. I've often seed as many as a hundred rats at once, and they're woppers in the sewers, I can tell you; them there water rats, too, is far more ferociouser than any other rats, and they'd think nothink of tackling a man, if they found they couldn't get away no how, but if they can why they runs by and gits out o' the road. I knows a chap as the rats tackled in the sewers; they bit him hawfully: you must ha' heard on it; it was him as the watermen went in arter when they heard him a shouting as they was a rowin' by. Only for the watermen the rats would ha' done for him, safe enough. Do you recollect hearing on the man as was found in the sewers about twelve year ago?—oh you must—the rats eat every bit of him, and left nothink but his bones. I knowed him well, he was a rig'lar shore-worker.

"The rats is wery dangerous, that's sartain, but we always goes three or four on us together, and the varmint's too wide awake to tackle us then, for they know they'd git off second best. You can go a long way in the sewers if you like; I don't know how far. I niver was at the end on them myself, for a cove can't stop in longer than six or seven hour, 'cause of the tide; you must be out before that's up. There's a many branches on ivery side, but we don't go into all; we go where we know, and where we're always sure to find somethink. I know a place now where there's more than two or three hundred weight of metal all rusted together, and plenty of money among it too; but it's too heavy to carry it out, so it 'ill stop there I s'pose till the world comes to an end. I often brought out a piece of metal half a hundred in weight, and took it under the harch of the bridge, and broke it up with a large stone to pick out the money. I've found sovereigns and half sovereigns over and over ag'in, and three on us has often cleared a couple of pounds apiece in one day out of the sewers. But we no sooner got the money than the publican had it. I only wish I'd back all the money I've guv to the publican, and I wouldn't care how the wind blew for the rest of my life."

"EACH RING IS A YEAR'S GROWTH"

FROM *Land Grabbing and Uncle Mel*

JESSE STUART

The Uncle Mel in Jesse Stuart's story about land thievery is very likely the somewhat toned-down prototype of his very real grandfather, Mitch Stuart, who moved to W-Hollow in Kentucky to get away from belligerent neighbors. He served in the Civil War and then came home to start his own. "I can be fairly sure," says his grandson a little smugly, "that he did away with four of his enemies."

Jesse Stuart still lives in W-Hollow. He owns 723 acres of land, all with clear title, and writes more short stories that are reprinted in secondary and college English textbooks than, he reports, "any American author living or dead."

WE HAD JUST MOVED ONTO THE FIRST FARM WE HAD EVER OWNED WHEN JAKE Timmins walked down the path to the barn where Pa and I were nailing planks on a barn-stall. Pa stood with a nail in one hand and his hatchet in the other while I stood holding the plank. We watched this small man with a beardy face walk toward us. He took short steps and jabbed his sharpened sourwood cane into the ground as he hurried down the path.

"Wonder what he's after?" Pa asked as Jake Timmins came near the barn.

"Don't know," I said.

"Howdy, Mick," Jake said as he leaned on his cane and looked over the new barn that we had built.

"Howdy, Jake," Pa grunted, since he had heard how Jake Timmins had taken men's farms. Pa was nervous when he spoke, for I watched the hatchet shake in his hand.

"I see ye're still a-putting improve-ments on yer barn," Jake said.

"A-trying to get it fixed for winter," Pa told him.

"I'd advise ye to stop now, Mick," he said. "Jist want to be fair with ye so ye won't go ahead and do a lot of work fer me fer nothing."

"How's that, Jake?" Pa asked.

"Ye've built yer barn on my land, Mick," he said with a little laugh.

"Ain't you a-joking, Jake?" Pa asked him.

"Nope, this is my land by rights," he told Pa as he looked our new barn over. "I hate to take this land with this fine barn on it, but it's mine and I'll haf to take it."

"I'm afraid not, Jake," Pa said. "I've been around here since I was a boy. I know where the lines run. I know that ledge of rocks with that row of oak trees a-growing on it is the line!"

"No it hain't," Jake said. "If it goes to court, ye'll find out. The line runs from that big dead chestnut up there on the knoll, straight across this holler to the top of the knoll up there where the twin hickories grow."

"But that takes my barn, my meadow, my garden," Pa said. "That takes ten acres of the best land I have. It almost gets my house!"

The hatchet quivered in Pa's hand and his lips trembled when he spoke.

"Tim Mennix sold ye land that belonged to me," Jake said.

"But you ought to a-said something about it before I built my house and barn on it," Pa told Jake fast as the words would leave his mouth.

"Sorry, Mick," Jake said, "but I must be a-going. I've given ye fair warning that ye air a-building on my land!"

"But I bought this land," Pa told him. "I'm a-going to keep it."

"I can't hep that," Jake told Pa as he turned to walk away. "Don't tear this barn down fer it's on my property!"

"Don't worry, Jake," Pa said. "I'm not a-tearing this barn down. I'll be a-feeding my cattle in it this winter!"

Jake Timmins walked slowly up the path the way he had come. Pa and I stood watching him as he stopped and looked our barn over; then he looked at our garden that we had fenced and he looked at the new house that we had built.

"I guess he'll be a-claiming the house too," Pa said.

And just as soon as Jake Timmins crossed the ledge of rocks that separated our farms Pa threw his hatchet to the ground and hurried from the barn.

"Where are you a-going, Pa?" I asked.

"To see Tim Mennix."

"Can I go too?"

"Come along," he said.

We hurried over the mountain path toward Tim Mennix's shack. He lived two miles from us. Pa's brogan shoes rustled the fallen leaves that covered the path. October wind moaned among the leafless treetops. Soon as we reached the shack we found Tim cutting wood near his woodshed.

Underwood and Underwood

SPRING ON A MISSOURI FARM

Underwood and Underwood

PLOUGHING AN IOWA FIELD

Frederic Lewis

PLANTING A TREE

PLOUGHING MATCH OF THE BALLYLANE AND DISTRICT PLOUGHING SOCIETY, ON THE FARM OF J. A. KILPATRICK, BALLYLANE, MOWHAN, COUNTY ARMAGH, NORTHERN IRELAND

Underwood and Underwood

Owen: Black Star

AN OLD WOMAN DRAWS WATER IN THE TENNESSEE VALLEY

Underwood and Underwood

SIPHON IRRIGATION ON A COLORADO CORNFIELD

MAINE WATER

Roger Flint: FPG

R. W. Wolfe: FPG

WHEAT FIELD IN WASHINGTON

GATHERING HAY

Thomas E. Styles: FPG

JAPANESE RICE HARVEST

Underwood and Underwood

FPG

LORNE MOFFITT OF ONTARIO HARROWS A FIELD AFTER SEEDING

"What's the hurry, Mick?" Tim asked Pa who stood wiping sweat from his October-leaf colored face with his blue bandanna.

"Jake Timmins is a-trying to take my land," Pa told Tim.

"Ye don't mean it?"

"I do mean it," Pa said. "He's just been to see me and he said the land where my barn, garden and meadow were belonged to him. Claims about ten acres of the best land I got. I told him I bought it from you and he said it didn't belong to you to sell."

"That ledge of rocks and the big oak trees that grow along the backbone of the ledge has been the line fer seventy years," Tim said. "But lissen, Mick, when Jake Timmins wants a piece of land, he takes it."

"People told me he's like that," Pa said. "I was warned against buying my farm because he's like that. People said he'd steal all my land if I lived beside him ten years."

"He'll have it before then, Mick," Tim Mennix told Pa in a trembling voice. "He didn't have but an acre to start from. That acre was a bluff where three farms jined and no one fenced it in because it was worthless and they didn't want it. He had a deed made fer this acre and he's had forty lawsuits when he set his fence over on other people's farms and took their land, but he goes to court and wins every time."

"I'll have the County Surveyor, Finn Madden, to survey my lines," Pa said.

"That won't hep any," Tim told Pa. "There's been more people kilt over the line fences that he's surveyed than has been kilt over any other one thing in this county. Surveyor Finn Madden's a good friend to Jake."

"But he's the County Surveyor," Pa said. "I'll haf to have him."

"Jake Timmins is a dangerous man," Tim Mennix warned Pa. "He's dangerous as a loaded double-barrel shotgun with both hammers cocked."

"I've heard that," Pa said. "I don't want any trouble. I'm a married man with a family."

When we reached home, we saw Jake upon the knoll at the big chestnut tree sighting across the hollow to the twin hickories on the knoll above our house. And as he sighted across the hollow, he walked along and drove stakes into the ground. He set one stake in our front yard, about five feet from the corner of our house. Pa started out on him once but Mom wouldn't let him go. Mom said let the law settle the dispute over the land.

And that night Pa couldn't go to sleep. I was awake and heard him a-walking the floor when the clock struck twelve. I knew that Pa was worried, for Jake was the most feared man among our hills. He had started with one acre and now had over four hundred acres that he had taken from other people.

Next day Surveyor Finn Madden and Jake ran a line across the hollow just about on the same line that Jake had surveyed with his own eyes. And while Surveyor Finn Madden looked through the instrument, he had Jake to set the stakes and drive them into the ground with a pole ax. They worked at the line all day. And when they had finished surveying the line, Pa went up on the knoll at the twin hickories behind our house and asked Surveyor Finn Madden if his line was right.

"Surveyed it right with the deed," he told Pa. "Tim Mennix sold you land that didn't belong to him."

"Looks like this line would've been surveyed before I built my barn," Pa said.

"Can't see why it wasn't," he told Pa. "Looks like you're a-losing the best part of your farm, Mick."

Then Surveyor Finn Madden, a tall man with a white beard, and Jake Timmins went down the hill together.

"I'm not so sure that I'm a-losing the best part of my farm," Pa said. "I'm not a-going to sit down and take it! I know Jake's a land thief and it's time his stealing land is stopped."

"What are you a-going to do, Pa?" I asked.

"Don't know," he said.

"You're not a-going to hurt Jake over the the land, are you?"

He didn't say anything but he looked at the two men as they turned over the ledge of rocks and out of sight.

"You know Mom said the land wasn't worth hurting anybody over," I said.

"But it's my land," Pa said.

And that night Pa walked the floor. And Mom got out of bed and talked to him and made him go to bed. And that day Sheriff Eif Whiteapple served a notice on Pa to keep his cattle out of the barn that we had built. The notice said that the barn belonged to Jake Timmins. Jake ordered us to put our chickens up, to keep them off his garden when it was our garden. He told us not to let anything trespass on his land and his land was on the other side of the stakes. We couldn't even walk in part of our yard.

"He'll have the house next if we don't do something about it," Pa said.

Pa walked around our house in a deep study. He was trying to think of something to do about it. Mom talked to him. She told him to get a lawyer and fight the case in court. But Pa said something had to be done to prove that the land belonged to us; though we had a deed for our land in our trunk. And before Sunday came, Pa dressed in his best clothes.

"Where're you a-going, Mick?" Mom asked.

"A-going to see Uncle Mel," he said. "He's been in a lot of line-fence fights and he could give me some good advice!"

"We hate to stay here and you gone, Mick," Mom said.

"Just don't step on property Jake laid claim to until I get back," Pa said. "I'll be back soon as I can. Some time next week you can look for me."

Pa went to West Virginia to get Uncle Mel. And while he was gone, Jake Timmins hauled wagon loads of hay and corn to the barn that we had built. He had taken over as if it were his own and that he would always have it. We didn't step beyond the stakes where Surveyor Finn Madden had surveyed. We waited for Pa to come. And when Pa came, Uncle Mel came with him carrying a long-handled double-bitted ax and a turkey of clothes across his shoulder. Before they reached the house, Pa showed Uncle Mel the land Jake Timmins had taken.

"Land hogs air pizen as copperhead snakes," Uncle Mel said, then he fondled his long white beard in his hand. Uncle Mel was eighty-two years old, but his eyes were keen as sharp pointed briars and his shoulders were broad and his hands were big and rough. He had been a timber-cutter all his days and he was still a-cutting timber in West Virginia at the age of eighty-two. "He can't do this to ye, Mick!"

Uncle Mel was madder than Pa when he looked over the new line that they had surveyed from the dead chestnut on one knoll to the twin hickories on the other knoll.

"Anybody would know the line wouldn't go like that," Uncle Mel said. "The line would follow the ridge.'"

"Looks that way to me too," Pa said.

"He's a-stealing yer land, Mick," Uncle Mel said. "I'll hep ye get yer land back. He'll never beat me. I've had to fight too many squatters a-trying to take my land. I know how to fight 'em with the law."

That night Pa and Uncle Mel sat before the fire and Uncle Mel looked over Pa's deed. Uncle Mel couldn't read very well and when he came to a word he couldn't read, I told him what it was.

"We'll haf to have a court order first, Mick," Uncle Mel said. "When we get the court order, I'll find the line."

I didn't know what Uncle Mel wanted with a court order, but I found out after he got it. He couldn't chop on a line tree until he got an order from the court. And soon as Pa got the court order and gathered a group of men for witnesses, Uncle Mel started work on the line fence.

"Sixteen rods from the dead chestnut due north," Uncle Mel said, and we started measuring sixteen rods due north.

"That's the oak tree, there," Uncle Mel said.

It measured exactly sixteen rods from the dead chestnut to the blackoak tree.

"Deed said the oak was blazed," Uncle Mel said, for he'd gone over the deed until he'd memorized it.

"See the scar, men," Uncle Mel said.

"But that was done seventy years ago," Pa said.

"Funny about the testimony of trees," Uncle Mel told Pa, Tim Mennix, Orbie Dorton and Dave Sperry. "The scar will allus stay on the outside of a tree well as on the inside. The silent trees will keep their secrets."

Uncle Mel started chopping into the tree. He swung his ax over his shoulder and bit out a slice of wood every time he struck. He cut a neat block into the tree until he found a dark place deep inside the tree.

"Come, men, and look," Uncle Mel said. "Look at that scar. It's as pretty a scar as I ever seen in the heart of a tree!"

And while Uncle Mel wiped sweat with his blue bandanna from his white beard, we looked at the scar.

"It's a scar, all right," Tim Mennix said, since he had been a timber-cutter most of his life and knew a scar on a tree.

"Think that was cut seventy years ago," Orbie Dorton said. "That's when the deed was made and the old survey was run."

"We'll see if it's been seventy years ago," Uncle Mel said as he started counting the rings in the tree. "Each ring is a year's growth."

We watched Uncle Mel pull his knife from his pocket, open the blade and touch each ring with his knife blade point as he counted the rings across the square he had chopped into the tree. Uncle Mel counted exactly seventy rings from the bark to the scar.

"Ain't it the line tree, boys?" Uncle Mel asked.

"Can't be anything else," Dave Sperry said.

And then Uncle Mel read the deed which called for a mulberry thirteen rods due north from the blackoak. We measured to the mulberry and Uncle Mel cut his notch to the scar and counted the rings. It was seventy rings from the bark to the scar. Ten more rods we came to the poplar the deed called for, and he found the scar on the outer bark and inside the tree. We found every tree the deed called for but one, and we found its stump. We surveyed the land from the dead chestnut to the twin hickories. We followed it around the ledge.

"We have the evidence to take to court," Uncle Mel said. "I'd like to bring the jurymen right here to this line fence to show 'em."

"I'll go right to town and put this thing in court," Pa said.

"I'll go around and see the men that have lost land to Jake Timmins," Uncle Mel said. "I want 'em to be at the trial."

Before our case got to court, Uncle Mel had shown seven of our neighbors how to trace their lines and get their land back from Jake Timmins. And when our trial was called, the courthouse was filled with people who had lost land and who had disputes with their neighbors over line fences, attending the trial to see if we won. Jake Timmins, Surveyor Finn Madden and their lawyer, Henson Stapleton, had produced their side of the question before the jurors and we had lawyer Sherman Stone and our witnesses to present our side, while all the landowners Jake Timmins had stolen land from listened to the trial. The foreman of the jury asked the members of the jury to be taken to the line fence.

"Now here's the way to tell where a line was blazed on saplings seventy years ago," Uncle Mel said as he showed them the inner mark on the line oak; then he showed them the outward scar. Uncle Mel took them along the line fence and showed them each tree that the deed called for all but the one that had fallen.

"It's plain as the nose on your face," Uncle Mel would say every time he explained each line tree. "Too many land thieves in this county and a county surveyor the devil won't have in hell."

After Uncle Mel had explained the line fence to the jurors, they followed Sheriff Whiteapple and his deputies back to the courtroom. Pa went with them to get the decision. Uncle Mel waited at our house for Pa to return.

"That land will belong to Mick," Uncle Mel told us. "And the hay and corn in that barn will belong to him."

When Pa came home, there was a smile on his face.

"It's yer land ain't it, Mick?" Uncle Mel asked.

"It's still my land," Pa said, "and sixteen men are now filing suits to recover their land. Jake Timmins won't have but an acre left."

"Remember the hay and corn he put in yer barn is yourn," Uncle Mel said.

Uncle Mel got up from his chair, stretched his arms. Then he said, "I must be back on my way to West Virginia."

"Can't you stay longer with us, Uncle Mel?" Pa said.

"I must be a-getting back to cut timber," he said. "If ye have any more land troubles write me."

We tried to get Uncle Mel to stay longer. But he wouldn't stay. He left with his turkey of clothes and his long-handled, double-bitted ax across his shoulder. We waved goodby to him as he walked slowly down the path and out of sight on his way to West Virginia.

THE DIGGERS IN CLAY

FROM *An Underground Episode*

EDMUND WARE

Edmund Ware's story of the pick and shovel men, the deep trench gangs who shift the mountains of mud and earth to make room for subways, cables, gas mains, sewers—all the complex underground accessories of a modern city—has the stamp of reported personal experience. It was selected as one of the best short stories of the year when it originally appeared in *Story* Magazine.

THREE FIGURES LEANED AGAINST THE SLANTING RAIN—ALAMO LASKA, NICK Christopher, and the boy who had run away from home. They rested on their long-handled shovels and, as they gazed into the crater which by their brawn they had hollowed in the earth, the blue clay oozed back again, slowly devouring the fruits of their toil.

Laska, the nomad, thought of the wild geese winging southward to warm bayous. Nick's heart, under the bone and muscle of his great chest, swelled with sweet thoughts of his wife and child who lived in a foreign city across an ocean. The boy felt the sting of rain against his cheeks and dreamed of his mother who seemed lovely and far away.

It was Sunday. The regular deep-trench gang lounged in their warm boarding house and drank dago red, while out on the job the three men toiled alone. They breathed heavily, and the gray steam crawled upon their backs, for it was cold.

"Look at 'er filling in," growled Laska, "faster than a man could dig."

"Mud's get inna pipe," said Nick. "The Inspector make us tear him out if she fill any more."

Backed close to the edge of the crater stood a giant trench-digging machine. In the dusk it appeared as a crouched and shadowy animal—silent, gloomy, capable. But a broken piston had crippled its engines and they were swathed in tarpaulin.

A long gray mound stretched away from the crater opposite the machine.

Buried thirty feet below the mound was the new-laid sewer pipe. From the bottom of the pit at the machine, the pipe ran a hundred yards horizontally under the surface, opening in a manhole. The hundred yards of new-laid pipe was the reason for the three men digging in the rain. They had dug eleven hours trying to uncover the open end of the pipe in order to seal it against the mud. But rain and ooze and storm had bested them. The bank had caved, and the mud had crawled into the mouth of the pipe, obstructing it.

"It's getting dark fast," said Laska, "an' we're licked."

"We can't do nothing more," said the boy.

Nick Christopher scraped the mud from his shovel. He looked up into the whirlpools of the sky. "In a year I go old country. I see my wife. I see my kid."

"Nick," said Laska, "go over to the shanty and get a couple of lanterns and telephone Stender. Tell him if he don't want the Inspector on our tail to get out here quick with a gang."

Nick stuck his shovel in the mud and moved away across the plain toward the shanty.

The cold had crept into the boy. It frightened him, and in the darkness his eyes sought Laska's face. "How could we clean out the pipe, even when the gang got down to it?"

"Maybe we could flush her out with a fire hose," said Laska.

"There's no water plug within a mile."

Laska said nothing. The boy waited for him to reply, but he didn't. Picking up his damp shirt, the boy pulled it on over his head. He did not tuck in the tails, and they flapped in the wind, slapping against him. He looked like a gaunt, serious bird, striving to leave the ground. He was bare-headed, and his yellow hair was matted and stringy with dampness. His face was thin, a little sunken, and fine drops of moisture clung to the fuzz on his cheeks. His lips were blue with cold. He was seventeen.

Laska stared into the pit. It was too dark to see bottom, but something in the black hole fascinated him. "If we could get a rope through the pipe we could drag sandbags through into the manhole. That would clean her out in good shape."

"How could we get a rope through?"

"I dunno. Stender'll know." Laska walked over to the digging machine and leaned against its towering side. The rain had turned to sleet. "It's cold," he said.

The boy followed Laska, and went close to him for warmth and friendship. "How *could* we get a rope through?"

Laska's shoulders lifted slowly. "You'll see. You'll see when Stender gets here. Say, it's freezing."

After a long time of waiting, a yellow light flamed into being in the shanty, and they heard the muffled scraping of boots on the board floor. The shanty door opened. A rectangle of light stood out sharply.

Swart figures crossed and re-crossed the lighted area, pouring out into the storm.

"Ho!" called Laska.

"Ho!" came the answer, galloping to them in the wind.

They heard the rasping of caked mud on dungarees, the clank of shovels, the voice of Stender, the foreman. Lanterns swung like yellow pendulums. Long-legged shadows reached and receded.

The diggers gathered about the rim of the pit, staring. Stender's face showed in the lantern light. His lips were wrinkled, as if constantly prepared for blasphemy. He was a tall, cursing conqueror. Orders shot from his throat, and noisily the men descended into the pit and began to dig. They drew huge, gasping breaths like mired beasts fighting for life.

The boy watched, his eyes bulging in the dark. Hitherto he had thought very briefly of sewers, regarding them as unlovely things. But Laska and Nick and Stender gave them splendor and importance. The deep-trench men were admirable monsters. They knew the clay, the feel and pattern of it, for it had long been heavy in their minds and muscles. They were big in three dimensions and their eyes were black and barbarous. When they ate it was with rough and tumble relish, and as their bellies fattened, they spoke tolerantly of enemies. They played lustily with a view to satiation. They worked stupendously. They were diggers in clay, transformed by lantern light into a race of giants.

Through the rain came Stender, his black slicker crackling. "They're down," he said. "Angelo just struck the pipe."

Laska grunted.

Stender blew his nose with his fingers, walked away and climbed down into the hole. They lost sight of him as he dropped over the rim. The sound of digging had ceased and two or three men on the surface rested on their shovels, the light from below gleaming in their flat faces. Laska and the boy knew that Stender was examining the pipe. They heard him swearing at what he had found.

After a moment he clambered up over the rim and held up a lantern. His cuddy, gripped firmly between his teeth, was upside down to keep out the wet.

"Someone's got to go through the pipe," he said, raising his voice. "There's fifty bucks for the man that'll go through the pipe into the manhole with a line tied to his foot. Fifty bucks!"

There was a moment of quiet. The men thought of the fifty dollars, and furtively measured themselves against the deed at hand. It seemed to the boy that he was the only one who feared the task. He did not think of the fifty dollars, but thought only of the fear. Three hundred feet through a rathole, eighteen inches in diameter. Three hundred feet of muck, of wet black dark, and no turning back. But, if he did not volunteer, they would know that he was afraid. The boy stepped from behind Laska and said uncertainly: "I'll go, Stender," and he wished he might snatch back the words; for, looking about him, he saw that not a man among those present could have wedged his shoulders into the mouth of an eighteen-inch pipe. He was the only volunteer. They had known he would be the only one.

Stender came striding over holding the lantern above his head. He peered into the boy's face. "Take off your clothes," he said.

"Take off my clothes?"

"That's what I said."

"You might get a buckle caught in a joint," said Laska. "See?"

The boy saw only that he had been trapped very cunningly. At home he could have been openly fearful, for at home everything about him was known. There, quite simply, he could have said: "I won't do it. I'm frightened. I'll be killed." But here the diggers in clay were lancing him with looks. And Laska was bringing a ball of line, one end of which would be fastened to his ankle.

"Just go in a sweater," said Laska. "A sweater an' boots over your woolens. We'll be waiting for you at the manhole."

He wanted so desperately to dive off into the night that he felt his legs bracing for a spring, and a tight feeling in his throat. Then, mechanically, he began to take off his clothes. Nick had gone clumping off to the shanty and shortly he returned with a pair of hip boots. "Here, kid. I get 'em warm for you inna shanty."

He thrust his feet into the boots, and Laska knelt and tied the heavy line to his ankle. "Too tight?"

"No. It's all right, I guess."

"Well—come on."

They walked past Stender who was pacing up and down among the men. They slid down into the crater, deepened now by the diggers. They stood by the partly covered mouth of the pipe. They were thirty feet below the surface of the ground.

Laska reached down and tugged at the knot he had tied in the line, then he peered into the mouth of the tube. He peered cautiously, as if he thought it might be inhabited. The boy's glance wandered up the wet sides of the pit. Over the rim a circle of bland yellow faces peered at him. Sleet tinkled against lanterns, spattered down and stung his flesh.

"Go ahead in," said Laska.

The boy blanched.

"Just keep thinking of the manhole, where you'll come out," said Laska.

The boy's throat constricted. He seemed to be bursting with a pressure from inside. He got down on his belly in the slush-ice and mud. It penetrated slowly to his skin, and spread over him. He put his head inside the mouth of the pipe, drew back in horror. Some gibbering words flew from his lips. His voice sounded preposterously loud. Laska's voice was already shopworn with distance. "You can make it! Go ahead."

He lay on his left side, and reaching out with his left arm, caught a joint and drew himself in. The mud oozed up around him, finding its way upon him, welling up against the left side of his face. He pressed his right cheek against the ceiling of the pipe to keep the muck from covering his mouth and nose. Laska's voice was far and muffled. Laska was in another world—a sane world of night, of storm, and the mellow glow of lanterns.

"Are you makin' it all right, kid?"

The boy cried out, his ears ringing with his cry. It re-echoed from the sides of the pipe. The sides hemmed him, pinned him, closed him in on every side with their paralyzing circumference.

There is no darkness like the darkness underground that miners know. It borrows something from night, from tombs, from places used by bats. Such fluid black can terrify a flame, and suffocate, and drench a mind with madness. There is a fierce desire to struggle, to beat one's hands against the prison. The boy longed to lift his pitiful human strength against the walls. He longed to claw at his eyes in the mad certainty that more than darkness curtained them.

He had moved but a few feet on his journey when panic swept him. Ahead of him the mud had built into a stolid wave. Putting forth his left hand, he felt a scant two inches between the wave's crest and the ceiling of the pipe. There was nothing to do but go back. If he moved ahead, it meant death by suffocation. He tried to back away, but caught his toe in a joint of the pipe. He was entombed! In an hour he would be a body. The cold and dampness would kill him before they could dig down to him. Nick and Laska would pull him from the muck, and Laska would say: "Huh, his clock's stopped."

He thrashed with delirious strength against his prison. He felt the skin tearing from the backs of his hands as he flailed the rough walls. And some gods must have snickered, for above the walls of the pipe were thirty feet of unyielding clay, eight thousand miles of earth below. A strength, a weight, a night, each a thousand times his most revolting dream, leaned upon the boy, depressing, crushing, stamping him out. The ground gave no cry of battle. It did no bleeding, suffered no pain, uttered no groans. It flattened him silently. It swallowed him in its foul despotism. It dropped its merciless weight upon his mind. It was so inhuman, so horribly incognizant of the God men swore had made it.

In the midst of his frenzy, when he had beaten his face against the walls until it bled, he heard a ringing voice he knew was real, springing from human sympathy. It was Laska, calling: "Are you all right, kid?"

In that instant the boy loved Laska as he loved his life. Laska's voice sheered the weight from him, scattered the darkness, brought him new balance and a hope to live.

"Fine!" he answered in a cracking yell. He yelled again, loving the sound of his voice, and thinking how foolish yelling was in such a place.

With his left hand he groped ahead and found that the wave of mud had settled, levelled off by its own weight. He drew his body together, pressing it against the pipe. He straightened, moved ahead six inches. His fingers found a loop of oakum dangling from a joint, and he pulled himself on, his left arm forward, his right arm behind over his hip, like a swimmer's.

He had vanquished panic, and he looked ahead to victory. Each joint brought him twenty inches nearer his goal. Each twenty inches was a plateau which enabled him to vision a new plateau—the next joint. The joints were like small deceitful rests upon a march.

He had been more than an hour on the way. He did not know how far he had gone, a third, perhaps even a half of the distance. He forgot the present, forgot fear, wet, cold, blackness; he lost himself in dreaming of the world of men outside the prison. It was as if he were a small superb island in hell.

He did not know how long he had been counting the joints, but he found himself whispering good numbers: "Fifty-one, fifty-two, fifty-three. . . ." Each joint, when he thought of it, appeared to take up a vast time of squirming in the muck, and the line dragged heavily behind his foot.

Suddenly, staring into the darkness so that it seemed to bring a pain to his eyes, he saw a pallid ray. He closed his eyes, opened them, and looked again. The ray was real, and he uttered a whimper of relief. He knew that the ray must come from Stender's lantern. He pictured Stender and a group of the diggers huddled in the manhole, waiting for him. The men and the manhole grew magnificent in his mind, and he thought of them worshipfully.

"Seventy-six, seventy-seven, seventy-eight. . . ."

The ray grew slowly, like a worthwhile thing. It took an oval shape, and the oval grew fat, like an egg, then round. It was a straight line to the manhole, and the mud had thinned.

Through the pipe, into the boy's ears, a voice rumbled like half-hearted thunder. It was Stender's voice: "How you makin' it?"

"Oh, just fine!" His cry came pricking back into his ears like a shower of needles.

There followed a long span of numbness. The cold and wet had dulled his senses, so that whenever the rough ceiling of the pipe ripped his face, he did not feel it; so that struggling in the muck became an almost pleasant and normal thing, since all elements of fear and pain and imagination had been removed. Warmth and dryness became alien to him. He was a creature native to darkness, foreign to light.

The round yellow disk before him gave him his only sense of living. It was a sunlit landfall, luring him on. He would close his eyes and count five joints, then open them quickly, cheering himself at the perceptible stages of progress.

Then, abruptly, it seemed, he was close to the manhole. He could hear men moving. He could see the outline of Stender's head as Stender peered into the mouth of the pipe. Men kneeled, pushing each other's heads to one side, in order to watch him squirm toward them. They began to talk excitedly. He could hear them breathing, see details—and Stender and Laska reached in. They got their hands upon him. They hauled him to them, as if he were something they wanted to inspect scientifically. He felt as if they thought he was a rarity, a thing of great oddness. The light dazzled him. It began to move around and around, and to dissolve into many lights, some of which danced locally on a bottle. He heard Stender's voice: "Well, he made it all right. What do you know?"

"Here, kid," said Laska, holding the bottle to his mouth. "Drink all of this that you can hold."

He could not stand up. He believed calmly that his flesh and bones were constructed of putty. He could hear no vestige of the song of victory he had dreamed of hearing. He looked stupidly at his hands, which bled painlessly. He could not feel his arms and legs at all. He was a vast sensation of lantern light and the steam of human beings breathing in a damp place.

Faces peered at him. The faces were curious, and surprised. He felt a clouded, uncomprehending resentment against them. Stender held him up on one side. Laska on the other. They looked at each other across him. Suddenly Laska stooped and gathered him effortlessly into his arms.

"You'll get covered with mud," mumbled the boy.

"Damn if he didn't make it all right," said Stender. "Save us tearing out the pipe."

"Hell with the pipe," said Laska.

The boy's wet head fell against Laska's chest. He felt the rise and fall of

Laska's muscles, and knew that Laska was climbing with him up the iron steps inside the manhole. Night wind smote him. He buried his head deeper against Laska. Laska's body became a mountain of warmth. He felt a heavy sighing peace, like a soldier who has been comfortably wounded and knows that war for him is over.

A METHOD OF MINING, 1621

LIKE AN ETERNAL SPONGE

FROM *The Bogman*

WALTER MACKEN

Walter Macken is an actor, playwright, theatre director and novelist, who has eminent distinction in each of these demanding roles. He is a mainstay of Dublin's famed Abbey Theatre, having written, acted in, and staged many of its productions since 1948. His novels, like *The Bogman,* from which we have made this selection, reflect the mood and sensibility of the Irish land and its people, a green and lovely land, but harsh and unyielding for those who must dig a spare and bitter living out of its potato fields and its turf bogs.

AS YOU KNOW, THE FACE OF IRELAND IS VERY BEAUTIFUL WHEN IT IS GREEN. IT is shaped like a saucer with the mountains all around the edges and the great plains in the dip. The plains are not all fertile. Many of them are bogs laid down thousands of years ago, quivering quaking bog that is hundreds of feet deep in places. These bogs have been very useful to the people since the first one put his foot in the country. They have provided fuel for fires, and hiding-places for men pursued by implacable enemies, who gained a measure of safety by travelling the lonely places on pathways they alone knew. Men have died in them and have never been heard of again until one day a turf-cutter may disclose their bodies to the gaze of the sky. Generally they will have been well preserved and will only crumble at the kiss of the air. And butter has been preserved in bogs, and all sorts of things have come to light from them, but they can be frightening places, so expansive and treacherous, in their own big way somewhat like the sea, that can be placid and beautiful until it turns on you, or until you have learned to know its ways.

The fertile places in the village of Caherlo were those fields that bounded the great bends of the river. Inside the bends for about half a mile, the land was good but it became less good as the foetid breath of the bogs withered it. It was a great stretch of bog, reaching as far as the eye could see until it joined itself with the unfathomable Bog of Allen in the middle of the country.

Cahal came clattering down towards the bog on a spring morning.

He was driving the jennet and standing up in the cart, swaying and balancing to its leaping like a sailor on a ship at sea. The jennet didn't like Cahal. Cahal liked the jennet, mainly because he was sorry for him. Barney had asserted himself over the jennet. It was an amazing thing to see. Anybody else in the world could drive that jennet, and he would be sluggish and recalcitrant and as lazy as possible, avoiding work just as if he was a hired hand, but as soon as old Barney put the tackle on him and climbed on the cart, that jennet always set off as if he had the devil on his back, and he would never slacken until the journey was done.

It was fear drove him. Barney had beaten him into fear with the knobby stick he owned. It was as old as the jennet. The jennet was fourteen years of age, and when he got him young Barney had beaten him for six months, every time he drove him. Now all he had to do was raise the stick in the air, and the jennet responded. But if Cahal beat him it did no good. Maybe because he sensed that Cahal's heart wasn't in the beating. So the animal was master of the man. Cahal smiled ruefully at the thought.

They came out of the lane into the plain and crossed over the little bridge. . . . From there the road deteriorated sadly. It wasn't a proper road, but a cutting made in the bog by collective labour, branches of trees laid down on the raw bog and thick scraws thrown over them so that they barely supported the heavy carts. They were terribly rutted so that sometimes one wheel went in to the axle while the other remained solid, and you had to be part acrobat to remain aboard. It was hard on the animals. They had to use every muscle they possessed, straining mightily against the harness, so that their eyes became wild. It was much worse on them coming back with a load. The bog road stretched away half a mile in front of them until it petered out in the heavy virgin bog that had been uncut for generations. On their right was reclaimed bog, that had been cut over and after that drained and sprinkled with coarse pasture seed and clover. This was divided up by drains and ash poles with wire strung on them; and the cattle were driven here sometimes to graze. They took a sad view of it all. They had to graze twice as hard as a real field, and no matter how much they ate, it only took the edge off their hunger. On their right were the turf banks, and already Cahal could see the small figures high up against the sky, pausing to look at the approaching carts, and then going back to work, the blades of the sleans shining and glinting in the dull sunshine.

There was a cold cutting wind across the bog, so he pulled his tattered coat across his shirt. He wore very old clothes, as did everyone else, because the brown bog seemed to be part acid and would eat its way through iron. Old, old trousers, patched behind so that they hung slackly down, tied with twine below the knee to keep the ends of them out of the eternal water. So as the two carts went on with the men high on them, clucking their tongues at the animals, they looked like two scarecrows that had miraculously acquired flesh-and-blood bodies. It was odd driving a cart on the bog. There was no noise of the iron-shod wheels grating on the stones. Silenced they were, and the only noise was the dull club-club of the wooden hubs of the wheels hitting against the powerful iron axle, or if a man had neglected to put car-grease on it squeaked as well.

Cahal waved a hand at Mary Cassidy and her daughter Jennie and her son Tommy. They were cutting the first bank. Mary Cassidy was a tall grey-haired woman with a flat stomach and strong tendons standing out on her arms like a man's. She was cutting and she leaned on the slean, her heavy-shod foot resting on the nub. Her two children were fetching for her, catching the wet sods as she cut them and flung them and placing them symmetrically on the wooden wheelbarrow with the heavy thick wheel. They were no light weight. A barrow could hold twelve or twenty of those sods, but if a grown man could push a barrow with twelve he was fine and strong. . . .

He took the cart as close as he could to the bank, but then the ground became very soggy, so he dismounted, untackled the jennet, let the shafts of the cart rest on the ground, tied the jennet to one of the wheels with the rope reins and threw it a bag of hay from the cart.

Then he mounted his own bank. It was raised about eight foot off the ground below, from the years of cutting. As you approached, the ground became wetter and wetter, like an eternal sponge, until at the foot of the bank there was a rectangular boghole from last year. Brown dirty water, inhabited by nothing except the water spiders who ran backwards and forwards over it, making a peculiarly broken wake, or occasionally the small yellow and gold bog-lizards. These intrigued Cahal. He often bent over one of them for some time, taking one into the palm of his hand, watching the belly in and out, in and out, and if you lay down and got it on an eye level you could believe all those things you read in the geography books about the strange animals that peopled the bogs of Ireland, incredible monsters of great size and ferocity, and all that remained of them was this tiny two-inch lizard that one time might have been as big as the whole village.

He didn't take off his coat. It was too bitter, the wind from behind him. He had already prepared the bank for cutting, having been two days with the spade clearing away the top of it to a depth of two feet, two feet of heather and gorse and the tangled roots of the ferns. A hard job, dragging away at nature like that, and she only doing a good job of covering the top of the bog, trying desperately to make it into good land.

He spat on his hands and started to dig with the slean. He liked the way it cut into the bog. Cut and thrust and lift with the knee and you had a grand-shaped sod of bog like jelly, only firmer, and you threw this away on the dry parts one side you and it rested there and you cut again and pitched so that it lay beside the other, and it was part white and part brown and the deeper you dug into the layer of the bog the browner and blacker it became. Poor turf on top, brown cooking turf in the middle and the black brittle coal turf below.

All right at first, but you got tired of it. It was hard work. He soon had the spaces within reach of his throw well covered with the sods. Then he had to slow up, because every sod he dug, he had to walk away with it in order to place it on the ground. Oul Barney should be here by this with the barrow to catch them and spread them on the dry ground.

He wiped his forehead, leaving a big brown streak across it, and looked over towards the road. The sky was grey, veiling the sun. He saw the figure of Barney then turning off the road by the bridge and crossing into the by-road of the bog pastures. He could even see the glint of the sun on the can he was carrying. Good job too. He tightened the belt holding up his ragged trousers. He was as hungry as a hawk. That's what the bog did to you. It blew an appetite into you. Hungry as a hawk. He saw one over his head, hardly visible against the peculiar spring sky. Hovering. They were always there. You were always flushing the larks and watching the curlews away from you flying low and the snipe zig-zagging as if there was a gun eternally behind them. Not that you would be bothered here shooting snipe. They were too bloody small. There wasn't the fill of a tooth in one.

Another cart coming now and that was Tom Creel and his son Gob. They were his neighbours at home and his neighbours on the bog. . . .

"Ha, ye lazy bees!" he shouted at them now. "It's the middle of the day yeer comin' on the bog. Have ye no shame in ye?"

"The devil a bit," Gob shouted at him.

"Aren't we being after taunted be every scarecrow on the bog?" Tom Creel said. "And we cut more in two hours than the whole lot of them put together."

"Includin' yerself," added Gob.

"What's the need to be talkin' to us now?" Tom asked. "Isn't it oney dodgin' the work you are? Look at the brave Murphys beyant. You don't get honest men like them raising their heads and jeerin' at Christians passin' by."

"Hup our that," said Gob, hitting the jennet and turning her into the cut-away.

Cahal laughed and spat on his hands and went back to work.

Old Barney reached him after crossing the bog. It was high noon by this, so they sat in the shelter of the seat they had cut on the away wind side of the bank and ate their lunch. It tasted very sweet to Cahal. A pint bottle of tea with the sugar and milk in it, wrapped in a cloth to keep the heat in it. And thick sandwiches with fried eggs and scallions in them. The grease had congealed but it was nourishing and the bread was fresh, and Barney could make a cake.

They didn't talk. They rarely talked. He wondered what went on in Barney's mind or if anything at all went on in it. He had a big nose and his cheeks were deeply engraved with lines. It made him look like something that was carved out of granite. The collie dog haunched in front of them with his head on one side, watching every bit that went into their mouths. Sometimes Barney bit into a sandwich and then threw the crust to the collie, and he would grab it and wag his silky tail. If Cahal threw him a bit, he accepted it, but had no thanks for it. Only Barney's bit seemed to give him complete satisfaction. Cahal wondered again at Barney's power over animals. He could make any animal come to him. Cahal trying to catch the horse and jennet in the pasture of a morning with a tin basin with oats in it. It was the only way he could get his hands on them. Barney just went into the field and whistled and they came to him and he would catch a clump of mane in his big hand and walk the animal back to the stable. Even with the oats Cahal had to get the blinkers on them and strap them before he could lead them home. Was it because they felt dominated, as he himself sometimes felt? Dominated by what? By unconscious ruthlessness. . . . He could see why Barney was left alone, but he could feel sorry for him.

They went to work.

Cahal cut and Barney fetched and filled the barrow and went away and spread the sods and came back for more. It went on all day. Mechanically. Unfailing. Nothing to break the monotony. Except Peder coming in his creel cart, and waving at them all and shouting as he passed to his bog. They jeered at him too. What an hour of the day to be coming on the bog! Oh, ye whores, ye, and me after going the long road to the town with a load of turf this very day. Up at six I was and on the way at seven without a bite in the belly. Ha, Mary, how about an oul cuddle? Go on, you randy lecher, you, and your wife waitin' up beyond. Begod, Jamesey Jordan, you'll never be as good a man as your oul fella. That's right, Spray, you have him worked to a standstill, the lout. Lo, Barney. Nice day. An oul bar of a song now, Cahal Kinsella, to raise me heart before I tear at the turf. G'wan, y'oul bags. Ho-ho, Tom. Have the Gob with you? Work him hard. Keep down his temperature. Stop him rousing after the women. (You could nearly see Gob blushing.) Good day, Mister Murphy, grand day for the work, God bless it. We'll be all dead at Christmas. Cahal chuckled. An obscure blow under the belt. The Murphys let him pass without a word so he took up his song and sang it to the larks. It was like a royal procession. Cahal felt he would like to be like Peder. Let the world pass over your head. An independent clot of blood in the body parochial.

The sky was red and raw with the going of the sun, as if it was suffering from a burst appendix. Only then they straightened their tired backs and rubbed their bog-encrusted hands on the heather. Skeleton heather it was now, all stalk, the brush just beginning to grow like the fuzz on the face of a sixteen-year-old boy.

They tackled the jennet and they loaded some of last year's dried turf from the tight clamp near the road.

They started off home.

Cahal was leading the jennet when it bogged.

One minute its four hooves were pulling at the road and next minute it was up to its belly in the bog. It had hit a soft patch. The jennet reared and the harness clinked as it tore itself free. Almost free, but it went to its belly again. It was maybe Cahal's fault. He should have supported the weight of the cart by holding the shaft over the bad patch so that the jennet might have skipped it. It was too late now. The jennet was struggling and roaring trying to pull itself out of the bog. One leg out and then it sank again.

Cahal felt his shoulder being taken in a hand and then he was pulled and propelled. He heard Barney shouting at him, but he lost his footing and went slithering towards the drain on the side of the road. It was a fat drain, pregnant, with the placid water scummed over with green slime. He fell on his back and his head and shoulders went under it. It went into his eyes and pained them and it went into his open mouth and he nearly vomited straight away. His hands were clawing, digging into the ground that had no hold, that came away in his hand. Then he felt his legs caught in two hands and he was pulled out of it.

Barney hauled him to his feet and left him there, spluttering, his hands up to his face rubbing at his eyes, dry vomiting tightening his stomach.

He cleared his eyes sufficiently to see Barney bending over the shafts and raising them in his hand, his shoulders hunched. He saw the cart come up and he saw the jennet come up with them. It was a terrible feat on the part of one man. The jennet sought harder ground and stood there, its slender grey legs shaking and dirty.

THE GREAT PIT IN ALDGATE CHURCHYARD

FROM *A Journal of the Plague Year*

DANIEL DEFOE

There is a touch of reality in everything that Daniel Defoe wrote, from his fictionalized biographies, like *Roxana,* to this account of the great pits in London, which we have selected from his *Journal of the Plague Year.* The *Journal* is so terrifyingly vivid, so appallingly particular that it is hard to accept the fact that Defoe was only six years old when the plague decimated London.

I WENT ALL THE FIRST PART OF THE TIME FREELY ABOUT THE STREETS, THOUGH not so freely as to run myself into apparent danger, except when they dug the great pit in the churchyard of our parish of Aldgate. A terrible pit it was, and I could not resist my curiosity to go and see it; as near as I may judge, it was about forty feet in length, and about fifteen or sixteen feet broad; and, at the time I first looked at it, about nine feet deep; but it was said, they dug it near twenty feet deep afterwards, in one part of it, till they could go no deeper for the water; for they had, it seems, dug several large pits before this; for, though the plague was long a coming to our parish, yet, when it did come, there was no parish in or about London where it raged with such violence as in the two parishes of Aldgate and Whitechapel.

I say they had dug several pits in another ground when the distemper began to spread in our parish, and especially when the dead-carts began to go about, which was not in our parish till the beginning of August. Into these pits they had put perhaps fifty or sixty bodies each, then they made larger holes, wherein they buried all that the cart brought in a week, which, by the middle to the end of August, came to from two hundred to four hundred a week; and they could not well dig them larger, because of the order of the magistrates, confining them to leave no bodies within six feet of the surface; and the water coming on at about seventeen or eighteen feet, they could not well, I say, put more in one pit; but now, at the beginning of September, the plague raging in a dreadful manner, and the number of burials in our parish increasing to more than was ever buried in any parish about London, of no larger extent, they ordered this dreadful gulf to be dug, for such it was rather than a pit.

They had supposed this pit would have supplied them for a month or more, when they dug it, and some blamed the churchwardens for suffering such a frightful thing, telling them they were making preparations to bury the whole parish, and the like; but time made it appear the churchwardens knew the condition of the parish better than they did; for the pit being finished the 4th of September, I think they began to bury in it the 6th, and by the 20th, which was just two weeks, they had thrown into it 1114 bodies, when they were obliged to fill it up, the bodies being then come to lie within six feet of the surface. I doubt not but there may be some ancient persons alive in the parish, who can justify the fact of this, and are able to show even in what place of the churchyard the pit lay better than I can; the mark of it also was many years to be seen in the churchyard on the surface, lying in length, parallel with the passage which goes by the west wall of the churchyard, out of Houndsditch, and turns east again, into Whitechapel, coming out near the Three-Nuns inn.

It was about the 10th of September, that my curiosity led, or rather drove me to go and see this pit again, when there had been near four hundred people buried in it; and I was not content to see it in the day time, as I had done before, for then there would have been nothing to have been seen but the loose earth; for all the bodies that were thrown in were immediately covered with earth, by those they called the buriers, which at other times were called bearers; but I resolved to go in the night, and see some of them thrown in.

There was a strict order to prevent people coming to those pits, and that was only to prevent infection; but, after some time, that order was more necessary, for people that were infected, and near their end, and delirious also, would run to those pits wrapt in blankets, or rugs, and throw themselves in, and, as they said, bury themselves. I cannot say that the officers suffered any willingly to lie there; but I have heard, that in a great pit in Finsbury, in the parish of Cripplegate, it lying open then to the fields, for it was not then walled about, many came and threw themselves in, and expired there, before they threw any earth upon them; and that when they came to bury others, and found them there, they were quite dead, though not cold.

This may serve a little to describe the dreadful condition of that day, though it is impossible to say anything that is able to give a true idea of it to those who did not see it, other than this; that it was indeed, very, very, very dreadful, and such as no tongue can express.

I got admittance into the churchyard by being acquainted with the sexton who attended, who, though he did not refuse me at all, yet earnestly persuaded me not to go: telling me very seriously, for he was a good religious and sensible man, that it was, indeed, their business and duty to venture, and to run all hazards, and that in it they might hope to be preserved; but that I had no apparent call to it but my own curiosity, which, he said, he believed I would not pretend, was sufficient to justify my running that hazard. I told him I had been pressed in my mind to go, and that, perhaps, it might be an instructing sight, that might not be without its uses. Nay, says the good man, if you will venture upon that score, 'Name of God, go in; for, depend upon it, it will be a sermon to you, it may be, the best that ever you heard in your life. It is a speaking sight, says he, and has a voice with it, and a loud one, to call us all to repentance; and with that he opened the door, and said, Go, if you will.

His discourse had shocked my resolution a little, and I stood wavering for a good while, but, just at that interval, I saw two links come over from the end of the Minories, and heard the bellman, and then appeared a dead-cart, as they called it, coming over the streets; so I could no longer resist my desire of seeing it, and went in. There was nobody as I could perceive at first, in the churchyard, or going into it, but the buriers, and the fellow that drove the cart, or rather led the horse and cart, but when they came up to the pit, they saw a man go to and again, muffled up in a brown cloak, and making motions with his hands, under his cloak, as if he was in great agony; and the buriers immediately gathered about him, supposing he was one of those poor delirious, or desperate creatures, that used to pretend, as I have said, to bury themselves; he said nothing as he walked about, but two or three times groaned very deeply, and loud, and sighed as he would break his heart.

When the buriers came up to him, they soon found he was neither a person infected and desperate, as I have observed above, or a person distempered in mind, but one oppressed with a dreadful weight of grief indeed, having his wife and several of his children, all in the cart, that was just come in with him, and he followed in an agony and excess of sorrow. He mourned heartily, as it was easy to see, but with a kind of masculine grief, that could not give itself vent by tears; and, calmly desiring the buriers to let him alone, said he would only see the bodies thrown in, and go away, so they left importuning him; but no sooner was the cart turned round, and the bodies shot into the pit, promiscuously, which was a surprise to him, for he at least expected they would have been decently laid in, though indeed, he was afterwards convinced that was impracticable; I say, no sooner did he see the sight, but he cried out aloud, unable to contain himself. I could not hear what he said, but he went backward two or three steps, and fell down in a swoon; the buriers ran to him and took him up, and in a little while he came to himself, and they led him away to the Pye-tavern, over-against the end of Houndsditch, where, it seems, the man was known, and where they took care of him. He looked into the pit again, as he went away, but the buriers had covered the bodies so immediately with throwing in earth, that, though there was light enough, for there were lanthorns and candles in them, placed all night round the sides of the pit, upon the heaps of earth, seven or eight, or perhaps more, yet nothing could be seen.

This was a mournful scene indeed, and affected me almost as much as the rest; but the other was awful, and full of terror; the cart had in it sixteen or seventeen bodies, some were wrapt up in linen sheets, some in rugs, some little other than naked, or so loose, that what covering they had fell from them, in the shooting out of the cart, and they fell quite naked among the rest; but the matter was not much to them, or the indecency much to any one else, seeing they were all dead, and were to be huddled together into the common grave of mankind, as we may call it, for here was no difference made, but poor and rich went together.

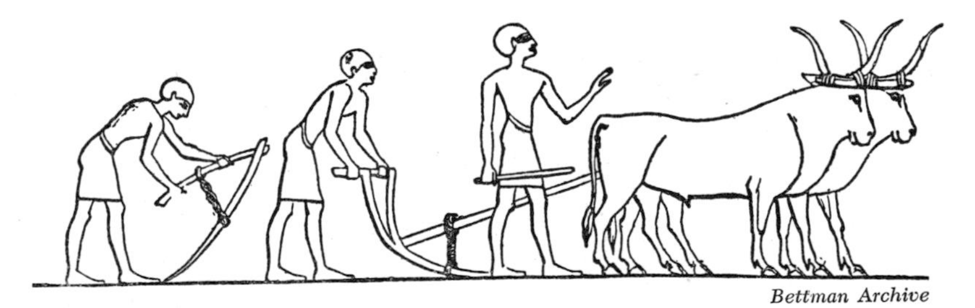

Bettman Archive

EARLY EGYPTIAN FARMERS

''IT'S A GREAT DISASTER''

FROM *Reach for the Moon*

ROYCE BRIER

People who have lived through a major earthquake talk of the Apocalypse, a vision of the last day of judgment, with the earth opening under a city and swallowing men and their small monuments. It remains a memory of mixed terror and awe.

There are not many writers who have captured this memory with the sure touch of Royce Brier in this selection from his novel of the San Francisco earthquake of 1906.

POOLE WAS AWAKENED BY A GENTLE JOGGLING, WHICH HAD THE OUTLANDISH property of amusing him. He thought in his first half-conscious moment that some celebrating reporters had got into his room and were shaking the foot of his bed.

He opened his eyes, but the reporters were not there, and he saw the gray-green light of dawn, soft and furtive. The joggling persisted, about five movements a second, with a rhythmic rise and fall, and he thought of the earthquake last year. . . .

Ten seconds had gone, and the movement died abruptly. Poole looked up at the chandelier, observing that it trembled slightly, that one of the bell-shaped shades was sounding with some high note which was sensuously almost imperceptible. He had one more instant for thought, that an earthquake was the deepest experience man knew in his outer world, freeing him from the dull prison of his ego. Poole had always vaguely delighted in them.

As he watched the shade, trying to understand its singing, almost forgetting the twelve seconds past, the chandelier leaped sidewise, and insanely started swinging like the clapper of a bell. His bed moved with a whip of vicious life, his whole room swayed sickeningly, as though it were pendent, some car of a ferris wheel.

He had one flash of supernal incredulity. The sway, the lightning sense of being caught in a cosmic and ungovernable power, preceded by a twinkling in his perception, the sound.

There was a ripping, like lightning at close quarters, and above it the tinkle of falling glass, which had the quality of pattering rain, and there was a creaking and crying of wood and steel on wood and steel, as though a thousand wagons with dry wheels were in the street. Pitched lower than these sounds was a measured grinding, like a hand coffee-mill magnified a thousand times, and beneath it all was a booming like big guns, yet deeper than any possible massing of man-made ordnance.

The totality of this sound, motion, stupendous and ravening violence was in steady crescendo. Each moment it seemed to have attained its uttermost limit, and yet the next moment was more convulsive. The hotel bounced four times, as though a titanic hand in the basement lifted it; then it moved like a piston, horizontally, for a full ten seconds, with a despairing groan of timbers and occasional gunshot sounds of parting joists.

The violence and the sound ceased abruptly, and there was a gentle rocking which to Poole was inertia. He was out of bed now, pulling on his underwear and his socks. He was shaking with excitement and he was afraid. . . .

He was putting one leg into his trousers, when he was hurled across the room. He stumbled over a chair, plunging headlong to the radiator in the bow window. From the radiator pipe came lukewarm water, tickling his outspread fingers like crawling insects. He lay prone, and the floor beneath him boomed with sledge-hammer blows. He had a thread of thought that there was no hope for the world. The earth had collided with another body in space.

From where he lay, pondering this with a critical faculty of which he was inordinately proud, having lost his fear of personal death, he saw through half-opened eyes a crack from the lower sill of the window to the floor, a wedge-shaped crack with the green light of morning beyond.

Astounded at light in chaos, he got to his knees, biting his lip as nausea came to him. There was a cut on the back of his hand, and he smeared the blood on his underwear. He looked up the street.

A church steeple a block away was disintegrating like brown sugar in a pan of water. Sections of the steeple fell away, one after another, leaving a stark skeleton against the pale sky. The mound of bricks below was growing, and a white dust, like a big balloon at a county fair, hovered before the church.

And all this disintegration was from movement less violent than had been; some peculiar tortion was demolishing the church façade at this stage, and it was all in silence, because deeper sounds smothered the sound of falling material, and the silence made it seem unreal. He had seen such destruction in a moving picture, and this also seemed contrived.

As he knelt there the subterranean booming, to which he had become inured, ended. The shocks fell away to a violent trembling, which seemed anodyne to Poole. He had no hope for it, however, he was confident the next shock would make an end of things. . . . He blinked in some wonder to see the ranks of buildings still standing in Sutter Street. One had a gap in a brick wall, exposing a white bedstead, but most of them were unchanged save for sheered cornices and staring windows without panes.

The trembling continued at an even tenor; there were several hammer-blow shocks, and then the independent undercurrent of trembling grew steadily feebler. Poole crossed the room, clinging to the foot of the bed and awaiting another great impact. The one shade of the chandelier resumed its singing vibration. Poole sat in a chair, putting on his shirt, looking idly at the cut on the back of his hand.

In the sixty-five seconds of the earthquake he had not heard a human voice, and now he heard a voice whimpering beyond his open window.

"It's—it's a great disaster," he muttered aloud, to himself. "By golly, it's come," as though he had foreseen it.

A shock knocked any further words from him, and again came a shuttle-like movement of the hotel building. He stopped buttoning his shirt, with a kind of fortitude awaiting the outcome of this temblor, as though it were useless to button a shirt if the task were never to be completed.

He heard the clang of a fire-engine bell, and he laughed. He supposed fire bells were ringing all over the world. Of what use, he wondered, were fire departments. He gave thought again to a planetary collision, perhaps a body had upset the earth's orbital movement, or there had fallen some vast meteor. He could not conceive this as casual fault-slipping; the orbital deflection seemed the most logical. The earth was shaking now like jelly. There were occasional lulls, and one came to dislike them, and to prefer the steadfast agitation.

Four or five minutes had passed. Poole had resumed dressing, and he methodically hunted a clean collar in the commode, which was covered with plaster from the ceiling. Beside the commode was a Chinese chest, and he suddenly jerked open the lid and peered quizzically at his manuscripts.

The sound of stirring life came to him. He heard running in the hall and muffled pounding on a door. There was a distant shout, and the high music of a hammer on iron, and the far clanging of a church bell, and the fairly irritating toots of a factory whistle. A small dog yelped. An automobile horn honked.

At first Poole could not relate these sounds to the earthquake, each had an origin both obscure and aberrant. Perhaps a demented sexton rang the bell, a drunken night-watchman blew the whistle, the dog was being bully-ragged by a boy. Then Poole was arrested by the sound of an approaching horse. He stepped to the window. It was coming at breakneck speed, trailing a fragment of harness, its bay shoulders flecked with foam. It fled as though all the world but it had stiffened in death. It passed, and far down Sutter Street its shoes rang with a terrible periodicity.

Poole related all the sounds to the earthquake, and he knew how completely he had been dominated by a sense-world for seven or eight minutes. He was delivered suddenly into a world which had a touch of rationality. He knew himself for a newspaper man, and he knew it was hell to pay for him. . . .

He looked at his watch. It was twenty-one minutes past five o'clock.

He tried to open his door, but the floor had sunk, the door-frame was splintered, and each panel bellied outward like a full sail. As he crossed the room for a chair, he saw a woman in a bathrobe descending a fire escape across the street. He suspected that every door in town was jammed. This, he thought, grinning over his sagacity, was not so sublime a conception as one of colliding planets.

When he struck his door with the chair, the panels exploded into the hallway. Exploding doors were the greatest hazard of the morning, he concluded, having wholly forgotten the fallen church. He stepped into the corridor. A woman waddled by, speaking to herself with the curious abstraction of the White Rabbit.

The hotel lobby was already filled with guests, some in absurd garb or lack of it, all in obtrusive emotional states, calm being the most obtrusive of them all. Many of the resident guests, knowing Poole, rushed to him for information. He shook his head, but such trust cleared his thought. He took the receiver from the desk telephone. The clerk spread his hands, and Poole spread his own and replaced the receiver.

There was a heavy shock, and a rolling motion of the hotel building. The clatter of voices ceased. A wisp of thought drifted in Poole's head: he loved cigars at a three-alarm fire.

"Gimme a few cigars."

"Cigars?" The clerk's face was like whitewashed stone.

Poole raised the glass lid of the cigar case and chose ten Owls and gave the clerk fifty cents. A man who wore no necktie, and who had pinned to his lapel a slip of paper bearing his name, gazed at Poole.

"You—buy—cigars?" he muttered.

"Sure—have one," and Poole thrust a cigar into the other's vest pocket. The man stared down at it.

"Thanks."

Poole nodded and went to the front steps of the hotel. He felt the jelly trembling of the boards beneath his feet, but he didn't mind it. After all great earthquakes came after-shocks; he foresaw a score of them in a few hours. Feeling wise, he lighted a cigar.

"Now, for a hack," he spoke aloud, and then he laughed at himself for it.

He cocked his cigar at a Speaker Cannon angle. There were no hacks to be had. He sauntered up the street. A small crowd was gathering at the wrecked church, and some boys were poking about among the bricks, looking for copper. Down the street, as Poole looked, there was débris from cornices, and glass littered the sidewalk as far as he could see, like spume along a straight beach.

He looked again at the church, at the gold cross askew on its steeple skeleton, gleaming in the first rays of the rising sun. The air was soft and warm, and hazy with dust. The sunlight lay in pale bronze squares against the higher buildings, but had not yet reached into the street. A trace of green dawn still lingered in the sky.

As Poole glanced east again, his eye caught a white mushroom, almost perfect in symmetry beyond the skyline. He was certain it had not been there a moment before. At first he thought it was a cloud, but it seemed to throb like a heart, and it was licked by a long tongue of darker smoke.

Poole noted that several others had espied this splendid plume in the morning sky, and he waited for them to say something, but they said nothing.

He went down the street, watching for a fire-engine which would take him across town. The street was filled with increasing traffic, which was beginning to snarl at intersections. There were shouting drivers, but the sidewalks were deserted. People had already learned to walk in the street. A sharp shock at this moment confirmed them, but they were going downtown anyway. Some were laughing and some were grave. Some made jokes and some stared stupidly at the jesters, but excepting these interludes, they were all gabbling like fowls.

A little old woman in a deaconess's cap plucked Poole's sleeve. She pulled him down, as though he, too, were deaf.

"It hain't much," she shouted.

Poole shook his head and smiled. "No—not much."

"That's what I said!" She triumphantly marched away.

Poole thought perhaps she was right. The entire city was thoroughly frightened, but it would be forgotten in a week. It was a great morning for plate-glass setters. Oh, it was a good story—the best story to crack in this town in five years. . . .

In a vacant store in Polk Street was a long drygoods counter bearing fourteen typewriters. The reporters sat behind the counter on high stools and boxes. All, including Poole, groused over the height of the counter. It was apparently the foremost concern of their lives.

A lantern hung from each gas light fixture. There was a bright maroon light in the room. Beyond the counter was a surge of men. A policeman was stationed at the door to keep them out, but he availed little. In the street were more friends of the paper, subscribers who had read the *Scimitar* since 1871, and said so interminably. To this throng Old Broom, standing on a box, was reading bulletins under an acetylene light.

Poole could hear their shouts to Broom, and the clatter of conversation in the long room like the drone of bees. Now and again, absurdities leaped out and battered through his concentration.

He wrote:

> The flames, disregarding the puny efforts of thousands, marched like an invincible army up all the streets north of Market—Jackson, Clay, Washington, Sacramento, Pine, California, Bush, Sutter. Dynamite accomplished nothing.
>
> The increasing scope of the fire was so astounding that areas thought safe at noon were untenable three hours later, and in another hour were devastated.
>
> The Mechanics' Pavilion was the first clearing house for casualties. Five hundred lay there in pain and death. Police and Red Cross would have laughed at anyone who doubted its security in the morning.

"Hey," he yelled, "where is she now?"

"Powell," some one shouted back.

This was not truth, but Poole knew he could attain small truth even in the world of phenomena. He could not write the inner truth of the people, save in paltry fragments. Long afterward, he knew, they would talk of the heroism of the people, and they would strive to shape drama from this heroism. Men would be heroes individually, and the people would be heroic.

But heroism was not the basic stuff of this day, Poole thought. The basic stuff was bewilderment. The lifelong bewilderment of men was compressed into a few hours, a few days. The little problems and the little longings strung through a life like endless beads, were merged into one problem and one longing.

What was it, this problem and this longing?—There was the question. Certainly it was no matter of a burning building. He did not forget those children playing hop-scotch out in Post Street. They knew they were of no account—their elders told them so—but there had been no one to tell the elders that elders were of no account, and they were incredulous to see it told in the sky. Well, no use to seek to draw philosophy from a fire, however big, or to be caught up, like the people, in the incomprehensible. You had to write the facts, the fire did this and the fire did that; many were dead and more were injured, and the price in round numbers was ten million dollars an hour.

Clack paused before him, rolling a cigarette.

"Buildings," he said, "pick out the biggest buildings destroyed. Let's have one fat paragraph on that, with the Mint and the Postoffice saved. You're getting worlds of drama and color into your copy, Harp. It's a classic."

"How much have I written?"

"Five thousand, maybe. Don't know how much we can set up in Oakland tonight, but we'll write as long as you can sit there. It's one of the greatest dramas the world's ever seen, my boy. By God, with this staff I could cover the Deluge! You could write an eye-witness story from the Ark—heh, heh."

Poole smiled sourly.

"Can't you get some typewriter tables? I've got a hell of a cramp in my shoulder."

Clack leaned on the counter. "Take a rest, take a five-minute rest. . . . Well, keep up the destruction element, the cataclysm words. You've got some great similes in that yarn, Harp. . . ."

Reports that the Cliff House has slipped into the sea are unfounded. The Cliff House was little damaged by the quake.

The greatest loss of life was in the Valencia Hotel. At least sixty were crushed when the frail building fell in. No one could help them.

Steel buildings were little damaged by the earthquake, excepting for X-cracks.

The Committee of Fifty was driven out of the Hall of Justice almost as soon as it convened. In Portsmouth Square the members sat about on boxes of dynamite. Last night they moved to the Fairmont.

Stanford University is wrecked. Scientists say it is close to the San Andreas fault.

In the Western Addition yesterday children were playing hop-scotch while their parents waited amidst their possessions. On Sutter Street, Chinese laundrymen were ironing shirts across the street from a fallen church.

Chinatown and the Barbary Coast are wiped out.

The fire moved with elephantine deliberation. Like the pachyderm it was almost benign, but it was also inexorable, in appearance and in fact, irresistible. Men were beetles, waving their antennae in warning at the elephant.

Poole smiled, wondering if beetles have antennae. A copy boy put a bottle of coffee before him, and he slowly drank it and ate the entire ham sandwich content of a paper bag. He, too, found a morning paper. It was full of the railroad rate measure President Roosevelt was planning to give the Congress.

A CIRCUIT OF THIRTY-FIVE MILES

FROM *How Much Land Does a Man Need?*

LEO TOLSTOY

In 1880, when Turgenev, the great man of Russian letters, visited Yasnaya Polyana, the ancestral estate which Count Leo Tolstoy had converted into a school for peasant children, he bewailed Tolstoy's desertion of art. "I, for instance," Turgenev wrote, "am considered an artist, but what am I compared with him? In contemporary European literature he has no equal. . . . But what is one to do with him. He has plunged headlong in another sphere."

Tolstoy, in his writing and in the practice of his own life, was working to develop a system of ethics based upon "moral instincts." Of all great literature of the past two centuries, his is perhaps the most didactic, and at the same time the most faithful to reality, being independent of that artifice which some assume to be the foundation on which fiction is built. His writing, as one critic has put it, "is simply the unaltered process of life itself," as is evident in this short story of peasants and the land, a theme to which he returned again and again.

AN ELDER SISTER CAME TO VISIT HER YOUNGER SISTER IN THE COUNTRY. THE elder was married to a shopkeeper in town, the younger to a peasant in the village. As the sisters sat over their tea talking, the elder began to boast of the advantages of town life, saying how comfortably they lived there, how well they dressed, what fine clothes her children wore, what good things they ate and drank, and how she went to the theater, promenades, and entertainments.

The younger sister was piqued, and in turn disparaged the life of a shopkeeper, and stood up for that of a peasant.

"I wouldn't change my way of life for yours," said she. "We may live roughly, but at least we're free from worry. You live in better style than we do, but though you often earn more than you need, you're very likely to lose all you have. You know the proverb, 'Loss and gain are brothers twain.' It often happens that people who're wealthy one day are begging their bread the next. Our way is safer. Though a peasant's life is not a rich one, it's long. We'll never grow rich, but we'll always have enough to eat."

The elder sister said sneeringly:

"Enough? Yes, if you like to share with the pigs and the calves! What do you know of elegance or manners! However much your good man may slave, you'll die as you live—on a dung heap—and your children the same."

"Well, what of that?" replied the younger sister. "Of course our work is rough and hard. But on the other hand, it's sure, and we need not bow to anyone. But you, in your towns, are surrounded by temptations; today all may be right, but tomorrow the Evil One may tempt your husband with cards, wine, or women, and all will go to ruin. Don't such things happen often enough?"

Pahom, the master of the house, was lying on the top of the stove and he listened to the women's chatter.

"It is perfectly true," thought he. "Busy as we are from childhood tilling mother earth, we peasants have no time to let any nonsense settle in our heads. Our only trouble is that we haven't land enough. If I had plenty of land, I shouldn't fear the Devil himself!"

The women finished their tea, chatted a while about dress, and then cleared away the tea things and lay down to sleep.

But the Devil had been sitting behind the stove, and had heard all that had been said. He was pleased that the peasant's wife had led her husband into boasting, and that he had said that if he had plenty of land he would not fear the Devil himself.

"All right," thought the Devil. "We'll have a tussle. I'll give you land enough; and by means of that land I'll get you into my power."

Close to the village there lived a lady, a small landowner who had an estate of about three hundred acres. She had always lived on good terms with the peasants until she engaged as her manager an old soldier, who took to burdening the people with fines. However careful Pahom tried to be, it happened again and again that now a horse of his got among the lady's oats, now a cow strayed into her garden, now his calves found their way into her meadows—and he always had to pay a fine.

Pahom paid up, but grumbled, and, going home in a temper, was rough with his family. All through that summer Pahom had much trouble because of this manager, and he was actually glad when winter came and the cattle had to be stabled. Though he grudged the fodder when they could no longer graze on the pasture land, at least he was free from anxiety about them.

In the winter the news got about that the lady was going to sell her land

and that the keeper of the inn on the high road was bargaining for it. When the peasants heard this they were very much alarmed.

"Well," thought they, "if the innkeeper gets the land, he'll worry us with fines worse than the lady's manager. We all depend on that estate."

So the peasants went on behalf of their village Council and asked the lady not to sell the land to the innkeeper, offering her a better price for it themselves. The lady agreed to let them have it. Then the peasants tried to arrange for the village Council to buy the whole estate, so that it might be held by them all in common. They met twice to discuss it, but could not settle the matter; the Evil One sowed discord among them and they could not agree. So they decided to buy the land individually, each according to his means; and the lady agreed to this plan as she had to the other.

Presently Pahom heard that a neighbor of his was buying fifty acres, and that the lady had consented to accept one half in cash and to wait a year for the other half. Pahom felt envious.

"Look at that," thought he, "the land is all being sold, and I'll get none of it." So he spoke to his wife.

"Other people are buying," said he, "and we must also buy twenty acres or so. Life is becoming impossible. That manager is simply crushing us with his fines."

So they put their heads together and considered how they could manage to buy it. They had one hundred rubles laid by. They sold a colt and one half of their bees, hired out one of their sons as a farm hand, and took his wages in advance; borrowed the rest from a brother-in-law, and so scraped together half the purchase money.

Having done this, Pahom chose a farm of forty acres, some of it wooded, and went to the lady to bargain for it. They came to an agreement, and he shook hands with her upon it and paid her a deposit in advance. Then they went to town and signed the deeds, he paying half the price down, and undertaking to pay the remainder within two years.

So now Pahom had land of his own. He borrowed seed, and sowed it on the land he had bought. The harvest was a good one, and within a year he had managed to pay off his debts both to the lady and to his brother-in-law. So he became a landowner, plowing and sowing his own land, making hay on his own land, cutting his own trees, and feeding his cattle on his own pasture. When he went out to plow his fields, or to look at his growing corn, or at his grass meadows, his heart would fill with joy. The grass that grew and the flowers that bloomed there seemed to him unlike any that grew elsewhere. Formerly, when he had passed by that land, it had appeared the same as any other land, but now it seemed quite different.

So Pahom was well contented, and everything would have been right if the neighboring peasants would only not have trespassed on his wheatfields and meadows. He appealed to them most civilly, but they still went on: now the herdsmen would let the village cows stray into his meadows, then horses from the night pasture would get among his corn. Pahom turned them out again and again, and forgave their owners, and for a long time he forebore to prosecute anyone. But at last he lost patience and complained to the District Court. He knew it was the peasants' want of land, and no evil intent on their part, that caused the trouble, but he thought:

"I can't go on overlooking it, or they'll destroy all I have. They must be taught a lesson."

So he had them up, gave them one lesson, and then another, and two or three of the peasants were fined. After a time Pahom's neighbors began to bear him a grudge for this, and would now and then let their cattle on to his land on purpose. One peasant even got into Pahom's wood at night and cut down five young lime trees for their bark. Pahom, passing through the wood one day, noticed something white. He came nearer and saw the stripped trunks lying on the ground, and close by stood the stumps where the trees had been. Pahom was furious.

"If he'd only cut one here and there it would have been bad enough," thought Pahom, "but the rascal has actually cut down a whole clump. If I could only find out who did this, I'd get even with him."

He racked his brains as to who it could be. Finally he decided: "It must be Simon—no one else could have done it." So he went to Simon's homestead to have a look around, but he found nothing, and only had an angry scene. However, he now felt more certain than ever that Simon had done it, and he lodged a complaint. Simon was summoned. The case was tried, and retried, and at the end of it all Simon was acquitted, there being no evidence against him. Pahom felt still more aggrieved, and let his anger loose upon the Elder and the Judges.

"You let thieves grease your palms," said he. "If you were honest folks yourselves you wouldn't let a thief go free."

So Pahom quarreled with the judges and with his neighbors. Threats to burn his hut began to be uttered. So though Pahom had more land, his place in the community was much worse than before.

About this time a rumor got about that many people were moving to new parts.

"There's no need for me to leave my land," thought Pahom. "But some of the others may leave our village and then there'd be more room for us. I'd take over their land myself and make my estate somewhat bigger. I could then live more at ease. As it is, I'm still too cramped to be comfortable."

One day Pahom was sitting at home, when a peasant, passing through the village, happened to drop in. He was allowed to stay the night, and supper was given him. Pahom had a talk with this peasant and asked him where he came from. The stranger answered that he came from beyond the Volga, where he had been working. One word led to another, and the man went on to say that many people were settling in those parts. He told how some people from his village had settled there. They had joined the community there and had had twenty-five acres per man granted them. The land was so good, he said, that the rye sown on it grew as high as a horse, and so thick that five cuts of a sickle made a sheaf. One peasant, he said, had brought nothing with him but his bare hands, and now he had six horses and two cows of his own.

Pahom's heart kindled with desire.

"Why should I suffer in this narrow hole, if one can live so well elsewhere?" he thought. "I'll sell my land and my homestead here, and with the money I'll start afresh over there and get everything new. In this crowded place one is always having trouble. But I must first go and find out all about it myself."

Toward summer he got ready and started out. He went down the Volga on a steamer to Samara, then walked another three hundred miles on foot, and at last reached the place. It was just as the stranger had said. The peasants had plenty of land: every man had twenty-five acres of communal land given him for his use, and anyone who had money could buy, besides, at a ruble-and-a-half an acre, as much good freehold land as he wanted.

Having found out all he wished to know, Pahom returned home as autumn came on, and began selling off his belongings. He sold his land at a profit, sold his homestead and all his cattle, and withdrew from membership in the village. He only waited till the spring, and then started with his family for the new settlement.

As soon as Pahom and his family reached their new abode, he applied for admission into the Council of a large village. He stood treat to the Elders and obtained the necessary documents. Five shares of communal land were given him for his own and his sons' use: that is to say—125 acres (not all together, but in different fields) besides the use of the communal pasture. Pahom put up the buildings he needed and bought cattle. Of the communal land alone he had three times as much as at his former home, and the land was good wheat-land. He was ten times better off than he had been. He had plenty of arable land and pasturage, and could keep as many head of cattle as he liked.

At first, in the bustle of building and settling down, Pahom was pleased with it all, but when he got used to it he began to think that even here he hadn't enough land. The first year he sowed wheat on his share of the communal land and had a good crop. He wanted to go on sowing wheat, but had not enough communal land for the purpose, and what he had already used was not available, for in those parts wheat is sown only on virgin soil or on fallow land. It is sown for one or two years, and then the land lies fallow till it is again overgrown with steppe grass. There were many who wanted such land, and there was not enough for all, so that people quarreled about it. Those who were better off wanted it for growing wheat, and those who were poor wanted it to let to dealers, so that they might raise money to pay their taxes. Pahom wanted to sow more wheat, so he rented land from a dealer for a year. He sowed much wheat and had a fine crop, but the land was too far from the village—the wheat had to be carted more than ten miles. After a time Pahom noticed that some peasant-dealers were living on separate farms and were growing wealthy, and he thought:

"If I were to buy some freehold land and have a homestead on it, it would be a different thing altogether. Then it would all be fine and close together."

The question of buying freehold land recurred to him again and again.

He went on in the same way for three years, renting land and sowing wheat. The seasons turned out well and the crops were good, so that he began to lay by money. He might have gone on living contentedly, but he grew tired of having to rent other people's land every year, and having to scramble for it. Wherever there was good land to be had, the peasants would rush for it and it was taken up at once, so that unless you were sharp about it you got none. It happened in the third year that he and a dealer together rented a piece of pasture land from some peasants, and they had already plowed it up, when there was some dispute and the peasants went to law about it, and things fell out so that the labor was all lost.

"If it were my own land," thought Pahom, "I should be independent, and there wouldn't be all this unpleasantness."

So Pahom began looking out for land which he could buy, and he came across a peasant who had bought thirteen hundred acres, but having got into difficulties was willing to sell again cheap. Pahom bargained and haggled with him, and at last they settled the price at fifteen hundred rubles, part in cash and part to be paid later. They had all but clinched the matter when a passing dealer happened to stop at Pahom's one day to get feed for his horses. He drank tea with Pahom, and they had a talk. The dealer said that he was just returning from the land of the Bashkirs, far away, where he had bought thirteen thousand acres of land, all for a thousand rubles. Pahom questioned him further, and the dealer said:

"All one has to do is to make friends with the chiefs. I gave away about one hundred rubles' worth of silk robes and carpets, besides a case of tea, and I gave wine to those who would drink it; and I got the land for less than three kopecks an acre." And he showed Pahom the title deed, saying:

"The land lies near a river, and the whole steppe is virgin soil."

Pahom plied him with questions, and the dealer said:

"There's more land there than you could cover if you walked a year, and it all belongs to the Bashkirs. They're as simple as sheep, and land can be got almost for nothing."

"There, now," thought Pahom, "with my one thousand rubles, why should I get only thirteen hundred acres, and saddle myself with a debt besides? If I take it out there, I can get more than ten times as much for my money."

Pahom inquired how to get to the place, and as soon as the grain dealer had left him, he prepared to go there himself. He left his wife to look after the homestead, and started on his journey, taking his hired man with him. They stopped at a town on their way and bought a case of tea, some wine, and other presents, as the grain dealer had advised.

On and on they went until they had gone more than three hundred miles, and on the seventh day they came to a place where the Bashkirs had pitched their round tents. It was all just as the dealer had said. The people lived on the steppe, by a river, in felt-covered tents. They neither tilled the ground nor ate bread. Their cattle and horses grazed in herds on the steppe. The colts were tethered behind the tents, and the mares were driven to them twice a day. The mares were milked, and from the milk kumiss was made. It was the women who prepared the kumiss, and they also made cheese. As far as the men were concerned, drinking kumiss and tea, eating mutton, and playing on their pipes was all they cared about. They were all stout and merry, and all the summer long they never thought of doing any work. They were quite ignorant, and knew no Russian, but were good-natured enough.

As soon as they saw Pahom, they came out of their tents and gathered around their visitor. An interpreter was found, and Pahom told them he had come about some land. The Bashkirs seemed very glad; they took Pahom and led him into one of the best tents, where they made him sit on some down cushions placed on a carpet, while they sat around him. They gave him some tea and kumiss, and had a sheep killed, and gave him mutton to eat. Pahom took presents out of his cart and distributed them among the Bashkirs, and divided the tea amongst them. The Bashkirs were delighted. They talked a great deal among themselves, and then told the interpreter what to say.

"They wish to tell you," said the interpreter, "that they like you, and that it's our custom to do all we can to please a guest and to repay him for his gifts. You have given us presents, now tell us which of the things we possess please you best, that we may present them to you."

"What pleases me best here," answered Pahom, "is your land. Our land is crowded and the soil is worn out, but you have plenty of land, and it is good land. I never saw the likes of it."

The interpreter told the Bashkirs what Pahom had said. They talked among themselves for a while. Pahom could not understand what they were saying, but saw that they were much amused and heard them shout and laugh. Then they were silent and looked at Pahom while the interpreter said:

"They wish me to tell you that in return for your presents they will gladly give you as much land as you want. You have only to point it out with your hand and it is yours."

The Bashkirs talked again for a while and began to dispute. Pahom asked what they were disputing about, and the interpreter told him that some of them thought they ought to ask their Chief about the land and not act in his absence, while others thought there was no need to wait for his return.

While the Bashkirs were disputing, a man in a large fox-fur cap appeared on the scene. They all became silent and rose to their feet. The interpreter said: "This is our Chief himself."

Pahom immediately fetched the best dressing gown and five pounds of tea, and offered these to the Chief. The Chief accepted them, and seated himself in the place of honor. The Bashkirs at once began telling him something. The Chief listened for a while, then made a sign with his head for them to be silent, and addressing himself to Pahom, said in Russian:

"Well, so be it. Choose whatever piece of land you like; we have plenty of it."

"How can I take as much as I like?" thought Pahom. "I must get a deed to make it secure, or else they may say: 'It is yours,' and afterward may take it away again."

"Thank you for your kind words," he said aloud. "You have much land, and I only want a little. But I should like to be sure which portion is mine. Could it not be measured and made over to me? Life and death are in God's hands. You good people give it to me, but your children might wish to take it back again."

"You are quite right," said the Chief. "We will make it over to you."

"I heard that a dealer had been here," continued Pahom, "and that you gave him a little land, too, and signed title deeds to that effect. I should like to have it done in the same way."

The Chief understood.

"Yes," replied he, "that can be done quite easily. We have a scribe, and we will go to town with you and have the deed properly sealed."

"And what will be the price?" asked Pahom.

"Our price is always the same: one thousand rubles a day."

Pahom did not understand.

"A day? What measure is that? How many acres would that be?"

"We do not know how to reckon it out," said the Chief. "We sell it by the day. As much as you can go around on your feet in a day is yours, and the price is one thousand rubles a day."

Pahom was surprised.

"But in a day you can get around a large tract of land," he said.

The Chief laughed.

"It will all be yours!" said he. "But there is one condition: If you don't return on the same day to the spot whence you started, your money is lost."

"But how am I to mark the way that I have gone?"

"Why, we shall go to any spot you like, and stay there. You must start from that spot and make your round, taking a spade with you. Wherever you think necessary, make a mark. At every turning, dig a hole and pile up the turf; then afterward we will go around with a plow from hole to hole. You may make as large a circuit as you please, but before the sun sets you must return to the place you started from. All the land you cover will be yours."

Pahom was delighted. It was decided to start early next morning. They talked a while, and after drinking some more kumiss and eating some more mutton, they had tea again, and then the night came on. They gave Pahom a feather bed to sleep on, and the Bashkirs dispersed for the night, promising to assemble the next morning at daybreak and ride out before sunrise to the appointed spot.

Pahom lay on the feather bed, but could not sleep. He kept thinking about the land.

"What a large tract I'll mark off!" thought he. "I can easily do thirty-five miles in a day. The days are long now, and within a circuit of thirty-five miles what a lot of land there will be! I'll sell the poorer land, or let it to peasants, but I'll pick out the best and farm it myself. I'll buy two ox teams and hire two more laborers. About a hundred and fifty acres shall be plowland, and I'll pasture cattle on the rest."

Pahom lay awake all night, and dozed off only just before dawn. Hardly were his eyes closed when he had a dream. He thought he was lying in that same tent and heard somebody chuckling outside. He wondered who it could be, and rose and went out, and he saw the Bashkir Chief sitting in front of the tent holding his sides and rolling about with laughter. Going nearer to the Chief, Pahom asked: "What are you laughing at?" But he saw that it was no longer the Chief, but the grain dealer who had recently stopped at his house and had told him about the land. Just as Pahom was going to ask: "Have you been here long?" he saw that it was not the dealer, but the peasant who had come up from the Volga, long ago, to Pahom's old home. Then he saw that it was not the peasant either, but the Devil himself with hoofs and horns, sitting there and chuckling, and before him lay a man, prostrate on the ground, barefooted, with only trousers and a shirt on. And Pahom dreamed that he looked more attentively to see what sort of man it was lying there, and he saw that the man was dead, and that it was himself. Horror-struck, he awoke.

"What things one dreams about!" thought he.

Looking around he saw through the open door that the dawn was breaking.

"It's time to wake them up," thought he. "We ought to be starting."

He got up, roused his man (who was sleeping in his cart), bade him harness, and went to call the Bashkirs.

"It's time to go to the steppe to measure the land," he said.

The Bashkirs rose and assembled, and the Chief came, too. Then they began drinking kumiss again, and offered Pahom some tea, but he would not wait.

"If we are to go, let's go. It's high time," said he.

The Bashkirs got ready and they all started: some mounted on horses and some in carts. Pahom drove in his own small cart with his servant and took a spade with him. When they reached the steppe, the red dawn was beginning to kindle. They ascended a hillock (called by the Bashkirs a *shikhan*) and, dismounting from their carts and their horses, gathered in one spot. The Chief came up to Pahom and, stretching out his arm toward the plain:

"See," said he, "all this, as far as your eye can reach, is ours. You may have any part of it you like."

Pahom's eyes glistened: it was all virgin soil, as flat as the palm of your hand, as black as the seed of a poppy, and in the hollows different kinds of grasses grew breast-high.

The Chief took off his fox-fur cap, placed it on the ground, and said:

"This will be the mark. Start from here, and return here again. All the land you go around shall be yours."

Pahom took out his money and put it on the cap. Then he took off his outer coat, remaining in his sleeveless undercoat. He unfastened his girdle and tied it tight below his stomach, put a little bag of bread into the breast of his coat, and, tying a flask of water to his girdle, he drew up the tops of his boots, took the spade from his man, and stood ready to start. He considered for some moments which way he had better go—it was tempting everywhere.

"No matter," he concluded, "I'll go toward the rising sun."

He turned his face to the east, stretched himself, and waited for the sun to appear above the rim.

"I must lose no time," he thought, "and it's easier walking while it's still cool."

The sun's rays had hardly flashed above the horizon when Pahom, carrying the spade over his shoulder, went down into the steppe.

Pahom started walking neither slowly nor quickly. After having gone a thousand yards he stopped, dug a hole, and placed pieces of turf one on another to make it more visible. Then he went on; and now that he had walked off his stiffness he quickened his pace. After a while he dug another hole.

Pahom looked back. The hillock could be distinctly seen in the sunlight, with the people on it, and the glittering iron rims of the cartwheels. At a rough guess Pahom concluded that he had walked three miles. It was growing warmer; he took off his undercoat, slung it across his shoulder, and went on again. It had grown quite warm now; he looked at the sun—it was time to think of breakfast.

"The first shift is done, but there are four in a day, and it's too soon yet to turn. But I'll just take off my boots," said he to himself.

He sat down, took off his boots, stuck them into his girdle, and went on. It was easy walking now.

"I'll go on for another three miles," thought he, "and then turn to the left. This is so fine that it would be a pity to lose it. The further one goes, the better the land seems."

He went straight on for a while, and when he looked around, the hillock was scarcely visible and the people on it looked like black ants, and he could just see something glistening there in the sun.

"Ah," thought Pahom, "I have gone far enough in this direction; it's time to turn. Besides, I'm in a regular sweat, and very thirsty."

He stopped, dug a large hole, and heaped up pieces of turf. Next he untied his flask, had a drink, and then turned sharply to the left. He went on and on; the grass was high, and it was very hot.

Pahom began to grow tired: he looked at the sun and saw that it was noon.

"Well," he thought, "I must have a rest."

He sat down, and ate some bread and drank some water; but he did not lie down, thinking that if he did he might fall asleep. After sitting a little while, he went on again. At first he walked easily; the food had strengthened him; but it had become terribly hot and he felt sleepy. Still he went on, thinking: "An hour to suffer, a lifetime to live."

He went a long way in this direction also, and was about to turn to the left again, when he perceived a damp hollow: "It would be a pity to leave that out," he thought. "Flax would do well there." So he went on past the hollow and dug a hole on the other side of it before he made a sharp turn. Pahom looked toward the hillock. The heat made the air hazy: it seemed to be quivering, and through the haze the people on the hillock could scarcely be seen.

"Ah," thought Pahom, "I have made the sides too long; I must make this one shorter." And he went along the third side, stepping faster. He looked at the sun: it was nearly halfway to the horizon, and he had not yet done two miles of the third side of the square. He was still ten miles from the goal.

"No," he thought, "though it will make my land lopsided, I must hurry back in a straight line now. I might go too far, and as it is I have a great deal of land."

So Pahom hurriedly dug a hole and turned straight toward the hillock.

Pahom went straight toward the hillock, but he now walked with difficulty. He was exhausted from the heat, his bare feet were cut and bruised, and his legs began to fail. He longed to rest, but it was impossible if he meant to get back before sunset. The sun waits for no man, and it was sinking lower and lower.

"Oh, Lord," he thought, "if only I have not blundered trying for too much! What if I am too late?"

He looked toward the hillock and at the sun. He was still far from his goal, and the sun was already near the rim of the sky.

Pahom walked on and on; it was very hard walking, but he went quicker and quicker. He pressed on, but was still far from the place. He began running, threw away his coat, his boots, his flask, and his cap, and kept only the spade which he used as a support.

"What am I to do?" he thought again. "I've grasped too much and ruined the whole affair. I can't get there before the sun sets."

And this fear made him still more breathless. Pahom kept on running; his soaking shirt and trousers stuck to him, and his mouth was parched. His breast was working like a blacksmith's bellows, his heart was beating like a hammer, and his legs were giving way as if they did not belong to him. Pahom was seized with terror lest he should die of the strain.

Though afraid of death, he could not stop.

"After having run all that way they will call me a fool if I stop now," thought he.

And he ran on and on, and drew near and heard the Bashkirs yelling and shouting to him, and their cries inflamed his heart still more. He gathered his last strength and ran on.

The sun was close to the rim of the sky and, cloaked in mist, looked large, and red as blood. Now, yes, now, it was about to set! The sun was quite low, but he was also quite near his goal. Pahom could already see the people on the hillock waving their arms to make him hurry. He could see the fox-fur cap on the ground and the money in it, and the Chief sitting on the ground holding his sides. And Pahom remembered his dream.

"There's plenty of land," thought he, "but will God let me live on it? I have lost my life, I have lost my life! Never will I reach that spot!"

Pahom looked at the sun, which had reached the earth: one side of it had already disappeared. With all his remaining strength he rushed on, bending his body forward so that his legs could hardly follow fast enough to keep him from falling. Just as he reached the hillock it suddenly grew dark. He looked up—the sun had already set!

He gave a cry: "All my labor has been in vain," thought he, and was about to stop, but he heard the Bashkirs still shouting, and remembered that though to him, from below, the sun seemed to have set, they on the hillock could still see it. He took a long breath and ran up the hillock. It was still light there. He reached the top and saw the cap. Before it sat the Chief, laughing and holding his sides. Again Pahom remembered his dream, and he uttered a cry: his legs gave way beneath him, he fell forward and reached the cap with his hands.

"Ah, that's a fine fellow!" exclaimed the Chief. "He has gained much land!"

Pahom's servant came running up and tried to raise him, but he saw that blood was flowing from his mouth. Pahom was dead.

The Bashkirs clicked their tongues to show their pity.

His servant picked up the spade and dug a grave long enough for Pahom to lie in, and buried him in it.

Six feet from his head to his heels was all he needed.

THE HILLS STAND DESOLATE

FROM *Cry, The Beloved Country*

ALAN PATON

Wherever men are stripped of the land, the land dies and then the men, Alan Paton says in this prologue to his deeply moving novel of South African life, *Cry, the Beloved Country*. The novel, undoubtedly the finest to come out of that explosive continent in many years, was transferred into an opera and then produced as a film. It awoke many to a first realization of the tragedy that is being played out in Malan's South Africa. Paton, by virtue of his leadership in the liberal opposition party, and even more by virtue of his novels, has become the leading white spokesman challenging the theory of white supremacy which governs South Africa.

THERE IS A LOVELY ROAD THAT RUNS FROM IXOPO INTO THE HILLS. THESE HILLS are grass-covered and rolling, and they are lovely beyond any singing of it. The road climbs seven miles into them, to Carisbrooke; and from there, if there is no mist, you look down on one of the fairest valleys of Africa. About you there is grass and bracken and you may hear the forlorn crying of the titihoya, one of the birds of the veld. Below you is the valley of the Umzimkulu, on its journey from the Drakensberg to the sea; and beyond and behind the river, great hill after great hill; and beyond and behind them, the mountains of Ingeli and East Griqualand.

The grass is rich and matted, you cannot see the soil. It holds the rain and the mist, and they seep into the ground, feeding the streams in every kloof. It is well-tended, and not too many cattle feed upon it; not too many fires burn it, laying bare the soil. Stand unshod upon it, for the ground is holy, being even as it came from the Creator. Keep it, guard it, care for it, for it keeps men, guards men, cares for men. Destroy it and man is destroyed.

Where you stand the grass is rich and matted, you cannot see the soil. But the rich green hills break down. They fall to the valley below, and falling, change their nature. For they grow red and bare; they cannot hold the rain and mist, and the streams are dry in the kloofs. Too many cattle feed upon the grass, and too many fires have burned it. Stand shod upon it, for it is coarse and sharp, and the stones cut under the feet. It is not kept, or guarded, or cared for, it no longer keeps men, guards men, cares for men. The titihoya does not cry here any more.

The great red hills stand desolate, and the earth has torn away like flesh. The lightning flashes over them, the clouds pour down upon them, the dead streams come to life, full of the red blood of the earth. Down in the valleys women scratch the soil that is left, and the maize hardly reaches the height of a man. They are valleys of old men and old women, of mothers and children. The men are away, the young men and the girls are away. The soil cannot keep them any more.

A HARVEST CYCLE

THE WORST FARMER THAT EVER LIVED

FROM *My Name Is Aram*

WILLIAM SAROYAN

When literary systematizers argued with William Saroyan that his stories ought not by the rules to be called stories, he answered, "What the hell difference does it make what you call it, so long as it breathes." He had a point and he makes it in this very Saroyanesque story about his Uncle Melik's venture into fruit farming.

Whatever literary judgments have been made about Saroyan since the *Daring Young Man on the Flying Trapeze* and its author burst on the literary scene—and they have been various—his stories do breathe. They have a quality and character very much their own. He has never been afflicted with doubts about his place in American literature, but, as one commentator said, after digging through Saroyan's innumerable productions, one feels "uneasily, that perhaps after all, even though he does admit it, he really is a genius."

MY UNCLE MELIK WAS JUST ABOUT THE WORST FARMER THAT EVER LIVED. HE was too imaginative and poetic for his own good. What he wanted was beauty. He wanted to plant it and see it grow. I myself planted over one hundred pomegranate trees for my uncle one year back there in the good old days of poetry and youth in the world. I drove a John Deere tractor too, and so did my uncle. It was all pure esthetics, not agriculture. My uncle just liked the idea of planting trees and watching them grow.

Only they wouldn't grow. It was on account of the soil. The soil was desert soil. It was dry. My uncle waved at the six hundred and eighty acres of desert he had bought and he said in the most poetic Armenian anybody ever heard, Here in this awful desolation a garden shall flower, fountains of cold water shall bubble out of the earth, and all things of beauty shall come into being.

Yes, sir, I said.

I was the first and only relative to see the land he had bought. He knew I was a poet at heart, and he believed I would understand the magnificent impulse that was driving him to glorious ruin. I did. I knew as well as he that what he had purchased was worthless desert land. It was away over to hell and gone, at the foot of the Sierra Nevada Mountains. It was full of every kind of desert plant that ever sprang out of dry hot earth. It was overrun with prairie dogs, squirrels, horned toads, snakes, and a variety of smaller forms of life. The space over this land knew only the presence of hawks, eagles, and buzzards. It was a region of loneliness, emptiness, truth, and dignity. It was nature at its proudest, dryest, loneliest, and loveliest.

My uncle and I got out of the Ford roadster in the middle of his land and began to walk over the dry earth.

This land, he said, is my land.

He walked slowly, kicking into the dry soil. A horned toad scrambled over the earth at my uncle's feet. My uncle clutched my shoulder and came to a pious halt.

What is that animal? he said.

That little tiny lizard? I said.

That mouse with horns, my uncle said. What is it?

I don't know for sure, I said. We call them horny toads.

The horned toad came to a halt about three feet away and turned its head.

My uncle looked down at the small animal.

Is it poison? he said.

To eat? I said. Or if it bites you?

Either way, my uncle said.

I don't think it's good to eat, I said. I think it's harmless. I've caught many of them. They grow sad in captivity, but never bite. Shall I catch this one?

Please do, my uncle said.

I sneaked up on the horned toad, then sprang on it while my uncle looked on.

Careful, he said. Are you sure it isn't poison?

I've caught many of them, I said.

I took the horned toad to my uncle. He tried not to seem afraid.

A lovely little thing, isn't it? he said. His voice was unsteady.

Would you like to hold it? I said.

No, my uncle said. You hold it. I have never before been so close to such a thing as this. I see it has eyes. I suppose it can see us.

I suppose it can, I said. It's looking up at you now.

My uncle looked the horned toad straight in the eye. The horned toad looked my uncle straight in the eye. For fully half a minute they looked one another straight in the eye and then the horned toad turned its head aside and looked down at the ground. My uncle sighed with relief.

A thousand of them, he said, could kill a man, I suppose.

They never travel in great numbers, I said. You hardly ever see more than one at a time.

A big one, my uncle said, could probably bite a man to death.

They don't grow big, I said. This is as big as they grow.

They seem to have an awful eye for such small creatures, my uncle said. Are you sure they don't mind being picked up?

I suppose they forget all about it the minute you put them down, I said.

Do you really think so? my uncle said.

I don't think they have very good memories, I said.

My uncle straightened up, breathing deeply.

Put the little creature down, he said. Let us not be cruel to the innocent creations of Almighty God. If it is not poison and grows no larger than a mouse and does not travel in great numbers and has no memory to speak of, let the timid little thing return to the earth. Let us be gentle toward these small things which live on the earth with us.

Yes, sir, I said.

I placed the horned toad on the ground.

Gently now, my uncle said. Let no harm come to this strange dweller on my land.

The horned toad scrambled away.

These little things, I said, have been living on soil of this kind for centuries.

Centuries? my uncle said. Are you sure?

I'm not sure, I said, but I imagine they have. They're still here, anyway.

My uncle looked around at his land, at the cactus and brush growing out of it, at the sky overhead.

What have they been eating all this time? he shouted.

I don't know, I said.

What would you say they've been eating? he said.

Insects, I guess.

Insects? my uncle shouted. What sort of insects?

Little bugs, most likely, I said. I don't know their names. I can find out tomorrow at school.

We continued to walk over the dry land. When we came to some holes in the earth my uncle stood over them and said, what lives down there?

Prairie dogs, I said.

What are *they?* he said.

Well, I said, they're something like rats. They belong to the rodent family.

What are all these things doing on my land? my uncle said.

They don't know it's your land, I said. They've been living here a long while.

I don't suppose that horny toad ever looked a man in the eye before, my uncle said.

I don't think so, I said.

Do you think I scared it or anything? my uncle said.

I don't know for sure, I said.

If I did, my uncle said, I didn't mean to. I'm going to build a house here some day.

I didn't know that, I said.

Of course, my uncle said. I'm going to build a magnificent house.

It's pretty far away, I said.

It's only an hour from town, my uncle said.

If you go fifty miles an hour, I said.

It's not fifty miles to town, my uncle said. It's thirty-seven.

Well, you've got to take a little time out for rough roads, I said.

I'll build me the finest house in the world, my uncle said. What else lives on this land?

Well, I said, there are three or four kinds of snakes.

Poison or non-poison? my uncle said.

Mostly non-poison, I said. The rattlesnake is poison, though.

Do you mean to tell me there are *rattlesnakes* on this land? my uncle said.

This is the kind of land rattlesnakes usually live on, I said.

How many? my uncle said.

Per acre? I said. Or on the whole six hundred and eighty acres?

Per acre, my uncle said.

Well, I said, I'd say there are about three per acre, conservatively.

Three per acre? my uncle shouted. Conservatively?

Maybe only two, I said.

How many is that to the whole place? my uncle said.

Well, let's see, I said. Two per acre. Six hundred and eighty acres. About fifteen hundred of them.

Fifteen hundred of them? my uncle said.

An acre is pretty big, I said. Two rattlesnakes per acre isn't many. You don't often see them.

What else have we got around here that's poison? my uncle said.

I don't know of anything else, I said. All the other things are harmless. The rattlesnakes are pretty harmless too, unless you step on them.

All right, my uncle said. You walk ahead and watch where you're going.

If you see a rattlesnake, don't step on it. I don't want you to die at the age of eleven.

Yes, sir, I said. I'll watch carefully.

We turned around and walked back to the Ford. I didn't see any rattlesnakes on the way back. We got into the car and my uncle lighted a cigarette.

I'm going to make a garden of this awful desolation, he said.

Yes, sir, I said.

I know what my problems are, my uncle said, and I know how to solve them.

How? I said.

Do you mean the horny toads or the rattlesnakes? my uncle said.

I mean the problems, I said.

Well, my uncle said, the first thing I'm going to do is hire some Mexicans and put them to work.

Doing what? I said.

Clearing the land, my uncle said. Then I'm going to have them dig for water.

Dig where? I said.

Straight down, my uncle said. After we get water, I'm going to have them plow the land and then I'm going to plant.

What are you going to plant? I said. Wheat?

Wheat? my uncle shouted. What do I want with wheat? Bread is five cents a loaf. I'm going to plant pomegranate trees.

How much are pomegranates? I said.

Pomegranates, my uncle said, are practically unknown in this country.

Is that all you're going to plant? I said.

I have in mind, my uncle said, planting several other kinds of trees.

Peach trees? I said.

About ten acres, my uncle said.

How about apricots? I said.

By all means, my uncle said. The apricot is a lovely fruit. Lovely in shape, with a glorious flavor and a most delightful pit. I shall plant about twenty acres of apricot trees.

I hope the Mexicans don't have any trouble finding water, I said. Is there water under this land?

Of course, my uncle said. The important thing is to get started. I shall instruct the men to watch out for rattlesnakes. Pomegranates, he said. Peaches. Apricots. What else?

Figs? I said.

Thirty acres of figs, my uncle said.

How about mulberries? I said. The mulberry tree is a very nice-looking tree.

Mulberries, my uncle said. He moved his tongue around in his mouth. A nice tree, he said. A tree I knew well in the old country. How many acres would you suggest?

About ten, I said.

All right, he said. What else?

Olive trees are nice, I said.

Yes, they are, my uncle said. One of the nicest. About ten acres of olive trees. What else?

Well, I said, I don't suppose apple trees would grow on this kind of land.

I suppose not, my uncle said. I don't like apples anyway.

He started the car and we drove off the dry land on to the dry road. The car bounced about slowly until we reached the road and then we began to travel at a higher rate of speed.

One thing, my uncle said. When we get home I would rather you didn't mention this *farm* to the folks.

Yes, sir, I said. (*Farm?* I thought. *What farm?*)

I want to surprise them, my uncle said. You know how your grandmother is. I'll go ahead with my plans and when everything is in order I'll take the whole family out to the farm and surprise them.

Yes, sir, I said.

Not a word to a living soul, my uncle said.

Yes, sir, I said.

Well, the Mexicans went to work and cleared the land. They cleared about ten acres of it in about two months. There were seven of them. They worked with shovels and hoes. They didn't understand anything about anything. It all seemed very strange, but they never complained. They were being paid and that was the thing that counted. They were two brothers and their sons. One day the older brother, Diego, very politely asked my uncle what it was they were supposed to be doing.

Señor, he said, please forgive me. Why are we cutting down the cactus?

I'm going to farm this land, my uncle said.

The other Mexicans asked Diego in Mexican what my uncle had said and Diego told them.

They didn't believe it was worth the trouble to tell my uncle he couldn't do it. They just went on cutting down the cactus.

The cactus, however, stayed down only for a short while. The land which had been first cleared was already rich again with fresh cactus and brush. My uncle made this observation with considerable amazement.

It takes deep plowing to get rid of cactus, I said. You've got to plow it out.

My uncle talked the matter over with Ryan, who had a farm-implement business. Ryan told him not to fool with horses. The modern thing to do was to turn a good tractor loose on the land and do a year's work in a day.

So my uncle bought a John Deere tractor. It was beautiful. A mechanic from Ryan's taught Diego how to operate the tractor, and the next day when my uncle and I reached the land we could see the tractor away out in the desolation and we could hear it booming in the awful emptiness of the desert. It sounded pretty awful. It *was* awful. My uncle thought it was wonderful.

Progress, he said. There's the modern age for you. Ten thousand years ago, he said, it would have taken a hundred men a week to do what the tractor's done today.

Ten thousand years ago? I said. You mean yesterday.

Anyway, my uncle said, there's nothing like these modern conveniences.

The tractor isn't a convenience, I said.

What is it, then? my uncle said. Doesn't the driver sit?

He couldn't very well stand, I said.

Any time they let you sit, my uncle said, it's a convenience. Can you whistle?

Yes, sir, I said. What sort of a song would you like to hear?

Song? my uncle said. I don't want to hear any song. I want you to whistle at that Mexican on the tractor.

What for? I said.

Never mind what for, my uncle said. Just whistle. I want him to know we are here and that we are pleased with his work. He's probably plowed twenty acres.

Yes, sir, I said.

I put the second and third fingers of each hand into my mouth and blew with all my might. It was good and loud. Nevertheless, it didn't seem as if Diego had heard me. He was pretty far away. We were walking toward him anyway, so I couldn't figure out why my uncle wanted me to whistle at him.

Once again, he said.

I whistled once again, but Diego didn't hear.

Louder, my uncle said.

This next time I gave it all I had, and my uncle put his hands over his ears. My face got very red, too. The Mexican on the tractor heard the whistle this time. He slowed the tractor down, turned it around, and began plowing straight across the field toward us.

Do you want him to do that? I said.

It doesn't matter, my uncle said.

In less than a minute and a half the tractor and the Mexican arrived. The

Mexican seemed very delighted. He wiped dirt and perspiration off his face and got down from the tractor.

Señor, he said, this is wonderful.

I'm glad you like it, my uncle said.

Would you like a ride? the Mexican asked my uncle.

My uncle didn't know for sure. He looked at me.

Go ahead, he said. Hop on. Have a little ride.

Diego got on the tractor and helped me on. He sat on the metal seat and I stood behind him, holding him. The tractor began to shake, then jumped, and then began to move. It moved swiftly and made a good deal of noise. The Mexican drove around in a big circle and brought the tractor back to my uncle. I jumped off.

All right, my uncle said to the Mexican. Go back to your work.

The Mexican drove the tractor back to where he was plowing.

My uncle didn't get water out of the land until many months later. He had wells dug all over the place, but no water came out of the wells. Of course he had motor pumps too, but even then no water came out. A water specialist named Roy came out from Texas with his two younger brothers and they began investigating the land. They told my uncle they'd get water for him. It took them three months and the water was muddy and there wasn't much of it. There was a trickle of muddy water. The specialist told my uncle matters would improve with time and went back to Texas.

Now half the land was cleared and plowed and there was water, so the time had come to plant.

We planted pomegranate trees. They were of the finest quality and very expensive. We planted about seven hundred of them. I myself planted a hundred. My uncle planted quite a few. We had a twenty-acre orchard of pomegranate trees away over to hell and gone in the strangest desolation anybody ever saw. It was the loveliest-looking absurdity imaginable and my uncle was crazy about it. The only trouble was, his money was giving out. Instead of going ahead and trying to make a garden of the whole six hundred and eighty acres, he decided to devote all his time and energy and money to the pomegranate trees.

Only for the time being, he said. Until we begin to market the pomegranates and get our money back.

Yes, sir, I said.

I didn't know for sure, but I figured we wouldn't be getting any pomegranates to speak of off those little trees for two or three years at least, but I didn't say anything. My uncle got rid of the Mexican workers and he and I took over the farm. We had the tractor and a lot of land, so every now and then we drove out to the farm and drove the tractor around, plowing up cactus and turning over the soil between the pomegranate trees. This went on for three years.

One of these days, my uncle said, you'll see the loveliest garden in the world in this desert.

The water situation didn't improve with time, either. Every once in a while there would be a sudden generous spurt of water containing only a few pebbles and my uncle would be greatly pleased, but the next day it would be muddy again and there would be only a little trickle. The pomegranate trees fought bravely for life, but they never did get enough water to come out with any fruit.

There were blossoms after the fourth year. This was a great triumph for my uncle. He went out of his head with joy when he saw them.

Nothing much ever came of the blossoms, though. They were very beautiful, but that was about all. Purple and lonely.

That year my uncle harvested three small pomegranates.

I ate one, he ate one, and we kept the other one up in his office.

The following year I was fifteen. A lot of wonderful things had happened to me. I mean, I had read a number of good writers and I'd grown as tall as my uncle. The farm was still our secret. It had cost my uncle a lot of money, but he was always under the impression that very soon he was going to start marketing his pomegranates and get his money back and go on with his plan to make a garden in the desert.

The trees didn't fare very well. They grew a little, but it was hardly noticeable. Quite a few of them withered and died.

That's average, my uncle said. Twenty trees to an acre is only average. We won't plant new trees just now. We'll do that later.

He was still paying for the land, too.

The following year he harvested about two hundred pomegranates. He and I did the harvesting. They were pretty sad-looking pomegranates. We packed them in nice-looking boxes and my uncle shipped them to a wholesale produce house in Chicago. There were eleven boxes.

We didn't hear from the wholesale produce house for a month, so one night my uncle made a long-distance phone call. The produce man, D'Agostino, told my uncle nobody wanted pomegranates.

How much are you asking per box? my uncle shouted over the phone.

One dollar, D'Agostino shouted back.

That's not enough, my uncle shouted. I won't take a nickel less than five dollars a box.

They don't want them at one dollar a box, D'Agostino shouted.

Why not? my uncle shouted.

They don't know what they are, D'Agostino shouted.

What kind of business man are you anyway? my uncle shouted. They're pomegranates. I want five dollars a box.

I can't sell them, the produce man shouted. I ate one myself and I don't see anything so wonderful about them.

You're crazy, my uncle shouted. There is no other fruit in the world like the pomegranate. Five dollars a box isn't half enough.

What shall I do with them? D'Agostino shouted. I can't sell them. I don't want them.

I see, my uncle whispered. Ship them back. Ship them back express collect.

The phone call cost my uncle about seventeen dollars.

So the eleven boxes came back.

My uncle and I ate most of the pomegranates.

The following year my uncle couldn't make any more payments on the land. He gave the papers back to the man who had sold him the land. I was in the office at the time.

Mr. Griffith, my uncle said, I've got to give you back your property, but I would like to ask a little favor. I've planted twenty acres of pomegranate trees out there on that land and I'd appreciate it very much if you'd let me take care of those trees.

Take care of them? Mr. Griffith said. What in the world for?

My uncle tried to explain, but couldn't. It was too much to try to explain to a man who wasn't sympathetic.

So my uncle lost the land, and the trees, too.

About three years later he and I drove out to the land and walked out to the pomegranate orchard. The trees were all dead. The soil was heavy again with cactus and desert brush. Except for the small dead pomegranate trees the place was exactly the way it had been all the years of the world.

We walked around in the orchard for a while and then went back to the car.

We got into the car and drove back to town.

We didn't say anything because there was such an awful lot to say, and no language to say it in.

JUMPING A CLAIM

FROM *Silverado Squatters*

ROBERT LOUIS STEVENSON

If you say Robert Louis Stevenson, the associative response is most likely to be *Treasure Island*. Not too surprising since the book is by far the best boy's adventure story in our literature, but not altogether an unmixed blessing for the reputation of a man who wrote pre-eminently for adults. Stevenson was a writer with a many-faceted talent and his essays, which stand with the very best in the language, deserve a more numerous reading public than they have today.

This selection from his *Silverado Squatters*, a narrative of a ghost mining town, is an episode from the period he spent in the United States.

NO ONE COULD LIVE AT SILVERADO AND NOT BE CURIOUS ABOUT THE STORY OF the mine. We were surrounded by so many evidences of expense and toil, we lived so entirely in the wreck of that great enterprise, like mites in the ruins of a cheese, that the idea of the old din and bustle haunted our repose. Our own house, the forge, the dump, the chutes, the rails, the windlass, the mass of broken plant; the two tunnels, one far below in the green dell, the other on the platform where we kept our wine; the deep shaft, with the sun-glints and the water-drops; above all, the ledge, that great gaping slice out of the mountain shoulder, propped apart by wooden wedges, on whose immediate margin, high above our heads, the one tall pine precariously nodded—these stood for its greatness; while, the dog-hutch, bootjacks, old boots, old tavern bills, and the very beds that we inherited from bygone miners, put in human touches and realised for us the story of the past.

I have sat on an old sleeper, under the thick madronas near the forge, with just a look over the dump on the green world below, and seen the sun lying broad among the wreck, and heard the silence broken only by the tinkling water in the shaft, or a stir of the royal family about the battered palace, and my mind has gone back to the epoch of the Stanleys and the Chapmans, with a grand *tutti* of pick and drill, hammer and anvil, echoing about the cañon; the assayer hard at it in our dining-room; the carts below on the road, and their cargo of red mineral bounding and thundering down the iron chute. And now all gone—all fallen away into this sunny silence and desertion: a family of squatters dining in the assayer's office, making their beds in the big sleeping room erstwhile so crowded, keeping their wine in the tunnel that once rang with picks.

But Silverado itself, although now fallen in its turn into decay, was once but a mushroom, and had succeeded to other mines and other flitting cities. Twenty years ago, away down the glen on the Lake County side there was a place, Jonestown by name, with two thousand inhabitants dwelling under canvas, and one roofed house for the sale of whiskey. Round on the western side of Mount Saint Helena, there was at the same date, a second large encampment, its name, if it ever had one, lost for me. Both of these have perished, leaving not a stick and scarce a memory behind them. Tide after tide of hopeful miners have thus flowed and ebbed about the mountain, coming and going, now by lone prospectors, now with a rush. Last, in order of time came Silverado, reared the big mill, in the valley, founded the town which is now represented, monumentally, by Hanson's, pierced all these slaps and shafts and tunnels, and in turn declined and died away.

> Our noisy years seem moments in the wake
> Of the eternal silence.

As to the success of Silverado in its time of being, two reports were current. According to the first, six hundred thousand dollars were taken out of that great upright seam, that still hung open above us on crazy wedges. Then the ledge pinched out, and there followed, in quest of the remainder, a great drifting and tunneling in all directions, and a great consequent effusion of dollars, until, all parties being sick of the expense, the mine was deserted, and the town decamped. According to the second version, told me with much secrecy of manner, the whole affair, mine, mill, and town, were parts of one majestic swindle. There had never come any silver out of any portion of the mine; there was no silver to come. At midnight trains of packhorses might have been observed winding by devious tracks about the shoulder of the mountain. They came from far away, from Amador or Placer, laden with silver in "old cigar boxes." They discharged their load at Silverado, in the hour of sleep; and before the morning they were gone again with their mysterious drivers to their unknown source. In this way, twenty thousand pounds' worth of silver was smuggled in under cover of night, in these old cigar boxes; mixed with Silverado mineral; carted down to the mill; crushed, amalgamated, and refined, and despatched to the city as the proper product of the mine. Stock-jobbing, if it can cover such expenses, must be a profitable business in San Francisco.

I give these two versions as I got them. But I place little reliance on either, my belief in history having been greatly shaken. For it chanced that I had come to dwell in Silverado at a critical hour; great events in its history were about to happen—did happen, as I am led to believe; nay, and it will be seen that I played a part in that revolution myself. And yet from first to last I never had a glimmer of an idea what was going on; and even now, after full reflection, profess myself at sea. That there was some obscure intrigue of the cigar-box order, and that I, in the character of a wooden puppet, set pen to paper in the interest of somebody, so much, and no more, is certain.

Silverado, then under my immediate sway, belonged to one whom I will call a Mr. Ronalds. I only knew him through the extraordinarily distorting medium of local gossip, now as a momentous jobber; now as a dupe to point an adage; and again, and much more probably, as an ordinary Christian gentleman like you or me, who had opened a mine and worked it for a while with better and worse fortune. So, through a defective windowpane, you may see the passer-by shoot up into a hunchbacked giant, or dwindle into a pot-bellied dwarf.

To Ronalds, at least, the mine belonged; but the notice by which he held it would run out upon the 30th of June—or rather, as I suppose, it had run out already, and the month of grace would expire upon that day, after which any American citizen might post a notice of his own, and make Silverado his. This, with a sort of quiet slyness, Rufe told me at an early period of our acquaintance. There was no silver, of course; the mine "wasn't worth nothing, Mr. Stevens," but there was a deal of old iron and wood around, and to gain possession of this old wood and iron, and get a right to the water, Rufe proposed, if I had no objections, to "jump the claim."

Of course, I had no objection. But I was filled with wonder. If all he wanted was the wood and iron, what, in the name of fortune, was to prevent him taking them? "His right there was none to dispute." He might lay hands on all tomorrow, as the wild cats had laid hands upon our knives and hatchet. Besides, was this mass of heavy mining plant worth transportation? If it was, why had not the rightful owners carted it away? If it was, would they not preserve their title to these movables, even after they had lost their title to the mine? And if it were not, what the better was Rufe? Nothing would grow at Silverado; there was even no wood to cut; beyond a sense of property, there was nothing to be gained. Lastly, was it at all credible that Ronalds would forget what Rufe remembered? The days of grace were not yet over: any fine morning he might appear, paper in hand, and enter for another year on his inheritance. However, it was none of my business; all seemed legal; Rufe or Ronalds, all was one to me.

On the morning of the 27th, Mrs. Hanson appeared with the milk as usual, in her sun-bonnet. The time would be out on Tuesday, she reminded us, and bade me be in readiness to play my part, though I had no idea what it was to be. And suppose Ronalds came? we asked. She received the idea with derision, laughing aloud with all her fine teeth. He could not find the mine to save his life, it appeared, without Rufe to guide him. Last year, when he came, they heard him "up and down the road a hollerin' and a raisin' Cain." And at last he had to come to the Hansons in despair, and bid Rufe, "Jump into your pants and shoes, and show me where this old mine is, anyway!" Seeing that Ronalds had laid out so much money in the spot, and that a beaten road led right up to the bottom of the dump, I thought this a remarkable example. The sense of locality must be singularly in abeyance in the case of Ronalds.

That same evening, supper comfortably over, Joe Strong busy at work on a drawing of the dump and the opposite hills, we were all out on the platform together, sitting there, under the tented heavens, with the same sense of privacy as if we had been cabined in a parlour, when the sound of brisk footsteps came mounting up the path. We pricked our ears at this, for the tread seemed lighter and firmer than was usual with our country neighbours. And presently, sure enough, two town gentlemen, with cigars and kid gloves, came debouching past the house. They looked in that place like a blasphemy.

"Good evening," they said. For none of us had stirred; we all sat stiff with wonder.

"Good evening," I returned; and then, to put them at their ease, "A stiff climb," I added.

"Yes," replied the leader; "but we have to thank you for this path."

I did not like the man's tone. None of us liked it. He did not seem embarrassed by the meeting, but threw us his remarks like favours, and strode magisterially by us towards the shaft and tunnel.

Presently we heard his voice raised to his companion. "We drifted every sort of way, but couldn't strike the ledge." Then again: "It pinched out here." And once more: "Every miner that ever worked upon it says there's bound to be a ledge somewhere."

These were the snatches of his talk that reached us, and they had a damning significance. We, the lords of Silverado, had come face to face with our superior. It is the worst of all quaint and of all cheap ways of life that they bring us at last to the pinch of some humiliation. I liked well enough to be a squatter when there was none but Hanson by; before Ronalds, I will own, I somewhat quailed. I hastened to do him fealty, said I gathered he was the

Squattee, and apologised. He threatened me with ejection, in a manner grimly pleasant—more pleasant to him, I fancy, than to me; and then he passed off into praises of the former state of Silverado. "It was the busiest little mining town you ever saw": a population of between a thousand and fifteen hundred souls, the engine in full blast, the mill newly erected; nothing going but champagne, and hope the order of the day. Ninety thousand dollars came out; a hundred and forty thousand were put in, making a net loss of fifty thousand. The last days, I gathered, the days of John Stanley, were not so bright; the champagne had ceased to flow, the population was already moving elsewhere, and Silverado had begun to wither in the branch before it was cut at the root. The last shot that was fired knocked over the stove chimney, and made that hole in the roof of our barrack, through which the sun was wont to visit slug-a-beds towards afternoon. A noisy last shot, to inaugurate the days of silence.

Throughout this interview, my conscience was a good deal exercised; and I was moved to throw myself on my knees and own the intended treachery. But then I had Hanson to consider. I was in much the same position as Old Rowley, that royal humourist, whom "the rogue had taken into his confidence." And again, here was Ronalds on the spot. He must know the day of the month as well as Hanson and I. If a broad hint were necessary, he had the broadest in the world. For a large board had been nailed by the crown prince on the very front of our house, between the door and window, painted in cinnabar—the pigment of the country—with doggrel rhymes and contumelious pictures, and announcing, in terms unnecessarily figurative, that the trick was already played, the claim already jumped, and Master Sam the legitimate successor of Mr. Ronalds. But no, nothing could save that man; *quem deus vult perdere, prius dementat.* As he came so he went, and left his rights depending.

Late at night, by Silverado reckoning, and after we were all abed, Mrs. Hanson returned to give us the newest of her news. It was like a scene in a ship's steerage: all of us abed in our different tiers, the single candle struggling with the darkness, and this plump, handsome woman, seated on an upturned valise beside the bunks, talking and showing her fine teeth, and laughing till the rafters rang. Any ship, to be sure, with a hundredth part as many holes in it as our barrack, must long ago have gone to her last port. Up to that time I had always imagined Mrs. Hanson's loquacity to be mere incontinence, that she said what was uppermost for the pleasure of speaking, and laughed and laughed again as a kind of musical accompaniment. But I now found there was an art in it. I found it less communicative than silence itself. I wished to know why Ronalds had come; how he had found his way without Rufe; and why, being on the spot, he had not refreshed his title. She talked interminably on, but her replies were never answers. She fled under a cloud of words; and when I had made sure that she was purposely eluding me, I dropped the subject in my turn, and let her rattle where she would.

She had come to tell us that, instead of waiting for Tuesday, the claim was to be jumped on the morrow. How? If the time were not out, it was impossible. Why? If Ronalds had come and gone, and done nothing, there was the less cause for hurry. But again I could reach no satisfaction. The claim was to be jumped next morning, that was all that she would condescend upon.

And yet it was not jumped the next morning, nor yet the next, and a whole week had come and gone before we heard more of this exploit. That day week, however, a day of great heat, Hanson, with a little roll of paper in his hand, and the eternal pipe alight; Breedlove, his large, dull friend, to act, I suppose, as witness; Mrs. Hanson, in her Sunday best; and all the children, from the oldest to the youngest;—arrived in a procession, tailing one behind another up the path. Caliban was absent, but he had been chary of his friendly visits since the row; and with that exception, the whole family was gathered together as for a marriage or a christening. Strong was sitting at work, in the shade of the dwarf madronas near the forge; and they planted themselves about him in a circle, one on a stone, another on the waggon rails, a third on a piece of plank. Gradually the children stole away up the cañon to where there was another chute, somewhat smaller than the one across the dump; and down this chute, for the rest of the afternoon, they poured one avalanche of stones after another, waking the echoes of the glen. Meantime we elders sat together on the platform, Hanson and his friend smoking in silence like Indian sachems, Mrs. Hanson rattling on as usual with an adroit volubility, saying nothing, but keeping the party at their ease like a courtly hostess.

Not a word occurred about the business of the day. Once, twice, and thrice I tried to slide the subject in, but was discouraged by the stoic apathy of Rufe, and beaten down before the pouring verbiage of his wife. There is nothing of the Indian brave about me, and I began to grill with impatience. At last, like a highway robber, I cornered Hanson, and bade him stand and deliver his business. Thereupon he gravely rose, as though to hint that this was not a proper place, nor the subject one suitable for squaws, and I, following his example, led him up the plank into our barrack. There he bestowed himself on a box, and unrolled his papers with fastidious deliberation. There were two sheets of note-paper, and an old mining notice, dated May 30th, 1879, part print, part manuscript, and the latter much obliterated by the rains. It was by this identical piece of paper that the mine had been held last year. For thirteen months it had endured the weather and the change of seasons on a cairn behind the shoulder of the cañon; and it was now my business, spreading it before me on the table, and sitting on a valise, to copy its terms, with some necessary changes, twice over on the two sheets of note-paper. One was then to be placed on the same cairn—a "mound of rocks" the notice put it; and the other to be lodged for registration.

Rufe watched me, silently smoking, till I came to the place for the locator's name at the end of the first copy; and when I proposed that he should sign, I thought I saw a scare in his eye. "I don't think that'll be necessary," he said slowly; "just you write it down." Perhaps this mighty hunter, who was the most active member of the local school board, could not write. There would be nothing strange in that. The constable of Calistoga is, and has been for years, a bed-ridden man, and, if I remember rightly, blind. He had more need of the emoluments than another, it was explained; and it was easy for him to "depytize," with a strong accent on the last. So friendly and so free are popular institutions.

When I had done my scrivening, Hanson strolled out, and addressed Breedlove, "Will you step up here a bit?" and after they had disappeared a little while into the chaparral and madrona thicket, they came back again, minus a notice, and the deed was done. The claim was jumped; a tract of mountain-side, fifteen hundred feet long by six hundred wide, with all the earth's precious bowels, had passed from Ronalds to Hanson, and, in the passage, changed its name from the "Mammoth" to the "Calistoga." I had tried to get Rufe to call it after his wife, after himself, and after Garfield, the Republican Presidential candidate of the hour—since then elected, and, alas! dead—but all was in vain. The claim had once been called the Calistoga before, and he seemed to feel safety in returning to that.

And so the history of that mine became once more plunged in darkness, lit only by some monster pyrotechnical displays of gossip. And perhaps the most curious feature of the whole matter is this: that we should have dwelt in this quiet corner of the mountains, with not a dozen neighbours, and yet struggled all the while, like desperate swimmers, in this sea of falsities and contradictions. Wherever a man is, there will be a lie.

THE JOBBING GARDENER

FROM *The Country Heart*

H. E. BATES

It will be no surprise to the reader that the author of this essay on the travails of garden owners is a gardener himself—beset with the usual afflictions and blessed with the usual incorrigible optimism of the breed.

The Country Heart, from which this selection comes, could be an apt title for any of H. E. Bates' books. The characters in his novels are rural workers, or those displaced into the towns from the country. He understands both their background and motivations and transmits their inarticulate feelings with great sensitivity and uncommon skill.

IF YOUR GARDEN IS JUST TOO SMALL FOR A FULL-TIME GARDENER AND JUST TOO large to be kept clean by your own hands, then you will fall victim, sooner or later, to the jobbing gardener. You first find him in the advertisement columns of the local newspaper, and it appears from the wording of the advertisement that he is practically in distress. "Two or three days a week urgently wanted. Any time. Anywhere." So you rush off to him at the first opportunity, knowing how difficult gardeners are to get, and find yourself confronted at the cottage door by his wife, who puts her nose round the door and says, "Well?" and who when you explain says he's had practically the whole neighbourhood round that morning bothering him to go here and go there, "and he don't for the life of him know what to do, he's got too much on hand already, but, anyway, what name is it?—he'll very like come round when he's had his tea."

You forget to point out the odd state of things by which a man who already has too much work is forced to waste money advertising for more, and you go home and wait for him to come. You wait there all evening, with the depressing feeling that he is conferring an immense favour on you by even considering your name, and in the end, of course, he does not come. He does not come, in fact, within the next ten days, and you begin to get desperate. Spring is coming on; the onions are not in; the borders are not forked; the rambler roses have not been tied. Finally you can wait no longer and you decide in desperation on an advertisement of your own. You draft this with great care and take it into the offices of the local newspaper. It will appear the following day. That evening, in the middle of supper (it is always in the middle of a meal), the maid comes in and says excuse her, please, but it's Mr. Pimpkins. You cannot for the life of you remember anyone named Pimpkins, but you leave your mutton chop to get cold and go to the kitchen door, and there, looking as pleasant as if he came straight from the undertaker's, is Mr. Pimpkins.

You say good-evening, not having the slightest idea who he is, and he says: "I couldn't come afore. I ent bin well."

He does in fact look rather cadaverous and is obviously, in the language of the films, a sour puss. He is about sixty-three, with legs like scythe handles. He seems to be wearing three suits, of which he has the brown trousers of one, the blue waistcoat of another and the black jacket of the third. He wears a stiff collar without a tie and his Adam's apple lodges on it like the butt of a pump handle.

As he offers no further explanation of his presence, you say you are very sorry he ent bin well, and he says:

"Yis, it gives me such gee-up every few weeks. I've 'ad it this twelvemonth or more. Course I were in there nigh on a twelvemonth."

"You were?" you say, and he says "Yis! Twelvemonth all but three weeks," as if he is rather pained that you are unfamiliar with this private and mysterious phase of his history.

You keep silence, sympathetically, and then he warms up. You ought of course to have been prepared, but you are not:

" 'Ad over three hundred injections."

"Did you indeed?"

"Ah. Course I were in there a twelvemonth."

"Really," you say, and then, because after all it would be nice to touch at least the fringe of the subject in hand, you remark that you expect he is getting about a bit now.

"Yis, but I hadn't ought to!" he says. "I ent right, y'know. I ent right."

"It's been a tough winter for everybody," you say.

"Ah?" he says. He puts into his voice a hint of vindictiveness. "Some 'ave bin all right. Some ent done bad. Some as I know. I tell you."

By this time the grease has grown white and cold on your mutton chop or the remains of it have been burnt to a cinder under the grill, and the situation needs a piece of desperate brutality.

"Well, Mr. Pimpkins," you say, "I've got an appointment in ten minutes. How many days a week do you think you can come?"

"Well," he says with absolutely funereal fatalism, "I hadn't ought to come at all be rights."

"Oh?"

"Be rights," he says, "I hadn't ought."

"Oh?"

"I've had so many arter me."

"Well, do you think you could come two days? Two and a half days?"

"Well," he says, "I shall etta see. I shall etta see what I can do for you. I shall etta see if I can fit y'in Thursdays an' Saturdays."

All right, you tell him, you'll leave it like that an he'll etta see. The notion that he is conferring an immense favour on you has by this time increased enormously and you yourself do not care any longer whether he comes or not. But you are a civil person, and it has been a charming spring day, and you politely mention this fact as you say good-evening and he goes down the garden path.

"Ah!" he says, "too nice! We shall etta suffer for it! You see. It ent seasonable. We shall etta suffer!"

Finally he goes and you go back to a mutton chop that has lost its identity. You have given up caring now whether he comes or not, and you console yourself that you have after all put in an advertisement of your own.

Unfortunately there are no replies from your own advertisement, and you are forced back on the hope that Mr. Pimpkins will come. And finally, all in his own good time, at leisure, at the curious hour of twenty minutes past nine on Thursday morning, he comes.

It is a very nice morning: larks are singing over the ploughed land; sparrows are pecking the sweet polyanthus buds. You can smell spring in the air and it is time to sow onions.

You have a well-prepared bed under a south wall and it is there, by early sowing, that you raise early vegetables. You point out to Mr. Pimpkins that you think it would be an excellent thing to sow a few rows of early carrots, onions and peas in this bed, and you give him the seeds.

He ignores them utterly.

"I ent got mine in," he says.

"I'm all for early sowing," you say.

"You don't want to be in 'urry," he says.

"I'm all for early sowing," you say. "This is an early garden. We're always early."

"That rose oughta bin tied up," he says.

You agree that the rose oughta bin tied up and perhaps he will do it during the day? You also want the peas, carrots and onions sowing, and will he clear the next piece of ground of brussels sprouts, which have gone over?

"You don't wanta git them up," he says.

"They're finished," you say. "They're simply using good ground."

"I ent got mine up," he says.

This being final, you walk away. Mr. Pimpkins ent got his up, so you don't get yours up. The sooner you realize that the better.

Forty minutes later you come out into the garden to see if Mr. Pimpkins is finding everything to his satisfaction. Mr. Pimpkins is nowhere to be seen. No seeds have been sown, no rows drawn. There are signs that the rose has been pruned, but Mr. Pimpkins himself has vanished. You walk up and down the garden several times and then finally, by chance, you see Mr. Pimpkins.

He is sitting in the greenhouse. It is very warm and sunny in the greenhouse and Mr. Pimpkins is sitting on a box. The *Daily Mail* is spread on his knees, and on the *Daily Mail* is spread a mountainous sandwich of bread and cheese, a couple of slices of bacon and a large thermos flask of tea. Mr. Pimpkins is slowly masticating his way through both the news and the food. You go into the greenhouse, struck instantly by its soft and genial warmth, to remark to Mr. Pimpkins, hullo, this is where he is.

"Jist evvin me breakfast," he says.

You are wondering why Mr. Pimpkins cannot have his breakfast, as other people do, in his own home and in his own time, when the problem is solved for you.

"Ent bin able to git nothing down fust thing since I were bad."

"Oh?"

"I ent arf th' eater I were," he says. "Missus used to say she wondered wheer I put it all."

As he is about to overload his stomach with a hunk of bread and cheese weighing about a quarter of a pound, which at any moment he will wash down with a pint of tea, you, too, are inclined to wonder where he puts it all.

"Ent you got no heat in your greenhouse?" he finally says.

You apologize for the lack of heating in the greenhouse, which is only eight by fifteen, although you cannot help noticing at the same time that Mr. Pimpkins looks as warm as toast. You point out that it is really only a little place for raising seeds, at which Mr. Pimpkins, who appears already to have spent twenty minutes or more on his breakfast, begins an expansive reminiscence on the wonderful greenhouses of Lord Blather of Shotover, for whom he worked, man and boy, for thirty years. This reminiscence is like a river with countless tributaries. At each tributary Mr. Pimpkins branches off to tell either the story of the under-butler who carried on a long and foul intrigue about the chicken kept by him for Lord Blather in 1902, or the story of Lord Blather's son, who misled a parlourmaid in 1906 and two housemaids in 1907, and against whom, for some dark reason, Mr. Pimpkins still nurses an indissoluble hatred. These tributaries in turn have backwaters, and Mr. Pimpkins, exploring them all, does so on the supposition that you are as familiar with Lord Blather's lineage and property, his servants and their intrigues, their families and antecedents, as Mr. Pimpkins himself. These explorations take half an hour, by which time Mr. Pimpkins condescends to return to the main theme, the whole point of which is that Lord Blather suffered with his kidneys and did not like cucumbers. Having presented you with this tremendous information he screws down his thermos flask and says: "Well, I suppose we'd better git on afore we ev dinner-time on top of us."

Dinner-time is in fact on top on us before you know anything at all. Mr. Pimpkins again sits in the greenhouse to have his dinner, and at one-thirty, when you go in there to look at the petunia seedlings, you discover that the place has been fumigated by Mr. Pimpkins' pipe, in which he smoked a species of shag that smells like a combination of burning horse-hooves and dung. Outside, Mr. Pimpkins is calmly clipping the lonicera hedge.

You suppress your annoyance and ask why the hedge takes preference over the onions, still not sown.

"Oughta bin done afore," he says.

This is final. Nothing can get past it. As the weeks go past you are to discover painfully that the garden is full of jobs that oughta bin done afore and that Mr. Pimpkins will, regardless of whatever you say, do them.

After this, having been caught in the morning by the private history of Lord Blather, you retire as far from Mr. Pimpkins as possible in the belief that he works better in solitude. At three o'clock you come back to the lonicera hedge, which divides the garden from the field beyond, only to discover Mr. Pimpkins sharing a pipeful of shag with Charley, the horse-keeper from the farm, who is supposed to be chain-harrowing the pasture. You hear Charley say it feels like rain, and Mr. Pimpkins earnestly agrees he is right. You get the impression that Mr. Pimpkins would be extremely glad if it did rain, and you seize a hoe and begin to make loud and angry noises on the plot by the wall. Ten minutes later he condescends to exchange heavy farewells with Charley, as if both were going to the ends of the earth. "Well, mind ow you goo on," he says. And Charley says "Ah!" and "Gee-up!" to the horses. Mr. Pimpkins then strikes practically a dozen matches, gives as many spits, and finally proceeds to clip the hedge in a cloud of evil fog.

You yourself work hard on the seed drills for the rest of the afternoon, and at four-thirty you go to the house for a hasty cup of tea. At a quarter to five you go to find Mr. Pimpkins again to ask him for the seeds, only to find he has gone home, taking the seeds in his pocket.

Mr. Pimpkins continues to come all summer. Your first real shock is when you pay him at the end of the first week. The local rate used to be a shilling an hour, but it has risen to one and a penny. When you ask Mr. Pimpkins how much, he says, "I got it down somewheres," and forages in his pocket for a dirty scrap of paper from which falls a shower of shag. "Semteen hours at one an' four I mek it," he says, "an' you goo arves wi' Miss Ratcliffe on insurance." You are about to protest at this monstrous statement when you remember that one of your pet hopes about the countryside is higher wages for country workers, and who are you not to set an example? Of Miss Ratcliffe you have never heard, and you can only wonder how it is you should have halved the burden of insurance with her when she employs Mr. Pimpkins for four days and you for two.

Mr. Pimpkins continues to confer the favour of his presence on you, weather and health permitting, every Thursday and Saturday. Sometimes it rains; sometimes "it's me back giving me gee-up again"; sometimes "Miss Ratcliffe dint gie me no peace till I went and done that cesspool job." Miss Ratcliffe emerges as a tyrant. If Mr. Pimpkins dominates you, Miss Ratcliffe dominates Mr. Pimpkins. Though he leaves you promptly at four forty-five, he apparently works without protest for Miss Ratcliffe until seven-thirty. He protests that March is too early for planting potatoes, but in April, when you finally plant them, it appears that Miss Ratcliffe ad ern in three weeks agoo. Your onions, which you eventually sow yourself, germinate magnificently; but you ought to see Miss Ratcliffe's. Miss Ratcliffe is always referred to as She. You suggest that Mr. Pimpkins should sow French beans in boxes, but Mr. Pimpkins is against it: She never does. You suggest planting out the celery, but, Good God, no, She ain't got ern out yet. Doesn't Mr. Pimpkins think the tulips are good? He does; but She's got a bed of tulips Mr. Pimpkins planted and you never see nothing like it. Shouldn't we grow summer cabbage? "Well," Mr. Pimpkins says, "you do what you like, but She never does." In the end, oppressed either by what Miss Ratcliffe does so excellently or what she doesn't do at all, you have a violent desire to wring Miss Ratcliffe's neck.

All through the summer Miss Ratcliffe, Lord Blather, the butler who intrigued against Mr. Pimpkins and, above all, the hospital, are Mr. Pimpkin's dominating themes. If you ask him if he thinks it advisable to thin the peaches he goes back to the year 1903, when, it appears, the peaches at Lord

Blather's were as large as pumpkins. If you complain of a cold in the head he will instantly draw your attention to the acute sufferings of stone in the kidney and layin' on me back for a twelvemonth. In short, nothing you do is so good, so bad, so successful or so painful as the things done by Miss Ratcliffe, Lord Blather, and Mr. Pimpkins.

Apart from the fact that he never does as he is told, always clipping the hedge when you want seeds sown, always tying roses when you want the lawn cut, Mr. Pimpkins has certain favourite horticultural pastimes. One of these is the process of settin' back. Most of your cherished shrubs, roses and perennials, it seems, want settin' back. The art of settin' back is to seize secateurs and shears and cut the most flourishing species of the garden to the ground. Anything growing with unusually healthy vigour wants settin' back. Mr. Pimpkins adores this pastime, and whenever your back is turned he tries it out on the forsythia, the ceanothus, the philadelphus, the flowering currant, the buddleia, the southernwood and the rest. You come into the garden to regard with horror some treasured shrub cut to the ground. "Ah! but you wun arf see a difference," Mr. Pimpkins says: than which, of course, there is no truer word. You certainly do see a difference. Unfortunately, the forsythia and the philadelphus have been cut at the wrong season and will not, now, flower for two years. The buddleia is the summer variety and not the autumn variety, and will not flower for two years either. The flowering currant is indestructible, anyway, but the ceanothus and the southernwood die in the winter. Certainly you don't arf see a difference in things!

All this time Mr. Pimpkins succeeds in making you feel that he is continually conferring an immense favour on you; that you are a horticultural ignoramus; that your garden and all it contains are quite beneath comparison with those of the best people; and that at any moment he will have to withdraw his patronage. "I ev a job to fit in everybody now," he says, "and She keeps a-bothering me to goo full time." All this appears to come rather strangely for a man who, only a month or two ago, was begging by advertisement for extra work, but you let it pass.

From this time onward Mr. Pimpkins' hours become increasingly erratic. He arrives at ten past nine and leaves at five to twelve; he arrives at one twenty and knocks off at five. He comes for only a day and a half, then a day, and finally half a day a week. By the time he has lit his pipe thirty times, 'ad me mite o' breakfast, and set back the *Rosa Moyseii,* which in consequence is reduced to nothing, it is time to goo 'ome an' av me bit o' dinner.

Finally there arrives a week when Mr. Pimpkins does not come at all. You can hardly believe this, and you wait another week for confirmation. He still does not come, and the next day you hear, by means of the village Gestapo, that Mr. Pimpkins is working for Miss Ratcliffe full time.

On the day you hear that announcement you go out into the garden. You walk up and down. The air is free of shag, and in the greenhouse Mr. Pimpkins, who ent arf th' eater he were, is no longer trying to get down enough food for a cart horse. There is no Lord Blather, no butler, no Miss Ratcliffe. But this is not all. There is another difference. It is more subtle; it seems to be part of yourself and you cannot define it.

For a long time you cannot understand what it is or why it affects you as it does. Then suddenly you do understand. You realize that the garden is your own: it belongs not to Mr. Pimpkins any longer, but to you; you can do what you like with it and not as Mr. Pimpkins says you must do.

And for the first time for several months you are happy.

GERMAN SOWER

THE LONESOME PLACE IN THE WOODS

FROM *The Fields*

CONRAD RICHTER

Conrad Richter, in his trilogy of pioneer life, *The Trees, The Fields,* and *The Town,* has looked more deeply into the minds and hearts of our forebears than any other American writer. They were complex people, these pioneers, drawn by more than the simple securities to migrate to lands that no white foot before theirs had walked. Of all the challenges they had to meet, the greatest was loneliness. But when the towns came and the people, they found that the lonely land had left its mark too deep on them. They were the people of the trees and the fields and not of the town. Richter drew his characters from diaries, handed-down tales, and early writings. His prose is extraordinarily simple and extraordinarily beautiful.

MORE THAN ONCE IN HER LIFE SAYWARD RECKONED SHE WAS WORE OUT, BUT never had she felt like this spring and early summer. She reckoned it was the hard winter she put in, clearing more land, chopping down the big butts closest to the barn, niggering them off, plowing up the new ground. Resolve and Guerdon were in school all winter. Most of the work she had done herself. And her, thirty-four, the mother of a whole grist of young Wheelers! She wasn't as young as she used to be. But that wasn't what made her down in the mouth. No, it was something else done it. When she got through all that back-breaking work this spring, hardly could she see she had done away with any of the woods. There the woods still stood, close as before, it seemed, hanging over them like always, big, thick, deep, monstrous, good for nothing and no end to them, a swallowing up her lonesome improvement of log barn, cabin, meeting house and school.

All that spring she was mopey and out of sorts. From the Pawwawing days on, she just dragged around. It must be the woods-sickness, she reckoned, for she pined for some other place to be, she did not know where.

Just so she could step from her door and her eye range free across a stretch of God's earth unhindered by trees. Then something inside of her would slacken, she felt, and she could mend.

With Resolve and the other boys helping, she bobbled around enough to put her crops in the ground. But how would she get through harvest, she wondered, with her hay, wheat and flax all coming this year in a pile and ready to spoil if you got behind? Sometimes she puzzled if that handbill had anything to do with it. There it hung, red as calico, above Portius's table so all who came on business could read. More than once when she was alone in the house save for the littlest ones, she had spelled it out.

NOTICE

The public is informed of the laying out of a Town at the Confluence of the River and its Squaw Branch. Near Vrain's Store and Tavern. To be called Tateville. Lots will be numbered and Buyers may have first and second Choice.

Public Auction Independence Monday on the Premises.

TATE AND VRAIN, *Proprietors*

It took her back to Lancaster town in Pennsylvany her mam knew as a girl, with a center square and brick houses standing tight against each other, some on one side of the road, some on the other. It minded her of the town at the point of the Ohio, too, the one Genny had come back from her wedding trip with Louie and told them about, with smith and hatter shops and a doctor you could call day or night from his chemist shop to pull you through a bad spell. It even had a dominie, Genny said, who didn't just visit like a circuit rider. No, he lived there and could bury you any day it pleased God you should die.

Oh, Sayward thought, how easy and sinful it would be to live a pampered life in town with no more land to work than a garden, with no more outside chores than splitting firewood, tending a cow and a few geese, and pushing the town pump handle. Why, some town bodies even traded for their bake stuff with a cake woman! Sayward told herself she must be getting weak and wicked, a milksop and pigeon-hearted, God help her, but this spring and summer she envied them who would live in that town.

Saturday she and the boys were out making hay. She had the scythe, and Resolve and Guerdon were cutting around the stumps with the reap hooks. Guerdon said, "Mam!" and she looked up to see a gentleman riding in from the trace on his fine, short-haired horse. He sat heavy on the saddle with a light blue cloak hanging down against the wetness of the woods. Oh, they knew that horse and the man riding him. Folks said Major Tate started out in life driving stakes for a surveyor in Maryland, and now he could drive his own coach out here if it had good enough roads to drive it on. He bowed to Sayward, asking for Portius like he had before. She bade Kinzie go along and tie up his horse while he went in the cabin.

He wasn't in very long before Portius came out. He looked mighty sober and dignified standing there calling her. Now what could this be, Sayward asked herself. She gave her scythe to Resolve who threw his reap hook to Kinzie. When she opened the door, the visitor sat on Portius's hickory chair, and her four little girls in a row on a bench staring at him. Never said they a word.

"Come in, Mrs. Wheeler, come in!" the major said, standing up and bidding her in her own house like it was his. "I was just telling your husband and he said you should hear. The Indian they call Tom Lyons was murdered on the Shawaneetown trace last night. And another with him."

It was mighty quiet for a little in the cabin.

"Do they know who done it?" Sayward asked.

"No," the major said emphatically. He seated himself again. "They say Tom Lyons was at George Roebuck's yesterday and brought along this friend of his from the Auglaize River. I understand he was a full-blooded, ugly-looking savage. By evening he got drunk and boasted he had killed a white man from this settlement up in the Western Reserve."

"It might a been Linus Greer," Sayward said. "This was a long time ago."

"I think Greer's the name. The savage told how he killed him. You know the way they pantomime! He showed how he sneaked after him, shooting off his rifle, taking out his tomahawk and making as though he scalped him. All the time he uttered such fearful yells, they said, and made such horrible grimaces that some of the settlers got uneasy and went home. But Tom Lyons and his friend didn't get home. Just a little while ago the Shawanees found them about halfway to Shawaneetown. Tom Lyons was shot and his ugly friend shot and scalped. Some of Greer's old friends may have done it, I don't know, but it was a very foolish thing to do. The Shawanees are bitter against us whites now. I hear they murdered a Coldwell woman and boy just before I came."

Sayward did not say anything. Her four little girls, one of them not much more than a baby, listened with big eyes from their bench.

The major went on.

"Have you ever thought of living in the safety and comfort of a town, ma'am?"

"Oh, I thought about it," Sayward told him.

A look passed between the two men.

"This is a surprise to me," Portius said in his deep voice.

"What did you think about it, Mrs. Wheeler?" the major asked kindly.

"How easy it would be to live 'ar," Sayward answered.

"Mrs. Wheeler," the major said thoughtfully, "I'm sure you know I'd like to give your husband more legal work to do. But before you came in, I told him he lived too far down here. It would be better to have him in town. Also he would build up a more extensive practise."

"I kin see he'd like it up 'ar," Sayward agreed, meek as could be, a little too meek if anything.

"Your children would like it, ma'am. Town has advantages, develops their wit and speech. Makes them quicker in mind and civil in manners. They amount to more—go farther in the world. Yours are especially worth improving."

"Oh, I reckon nobody would want to change his young 'uns for anybody else's," Sayward said.

"If you'd like, I could help you sell your place here," the town builder offered. "I might even take it in trade. After all, your husband and I would be associated together, and I have had a great deal of experience in handling property. Meantime you can come up and pick out the lot of your choice. You might prefer one of the brick houses we're building. We expect to get a great deal of brick up the river."

Sayward's eyes were far away. She saw the dark, impenetrable forest, that always stood in the back of her mind, dissolve, and red brick walls rise in its place. So it was true, then, she told herself, the red handbill town of her thoughts.

"Thankee, but I never could go up 'ar to live," she said in a low voice.

"Why, ma'am, you just informed me you would like it!" the major protested.

"Oh, I'd like nothin' better," she agreed. "Many's the time I wished I could live in your town. The childer would have it easier 'ar. Likely they would get brighter like you said. Portius would have it a pile handier. But I never could give up and go. I'd feel ashamed to run off and be licked by the trees."

"Gross nonsense!" the major said energetically. "Now I must leave. But I'm coming back for these papers in the morning. When I do, I shall make you an offer. Your husband can make out a contract and we can all sign it. I move with dispatch. My last town, I bought the land Monday, laid it out Tuesday, sold the lots Wednesday and raised the first dwelling Thursday."

He rose to go. When Sayward opened the door for him, she saw her hayfield simmering in the sun. It lay bare and empty of humans. For a lick her heart nigh stopped beating. Then she heard her boys scatter around the corner like turkeys in the brush. They must have been up against the cabin logs listening.

The major hadn't ridden off ten poles till the three of them were at her. It was plain they had heard all that was said and reckoned their mammy foolish and stubborn as General Wayne's one-eyed ox for saying she wouldn't leave this lonesome place in the woods for town. Wasn't their pappy Major Tate's lawyer? That made the town as good as theirs already, and they wouldn't give up. They hadn't a thought to go back to the hayfield now. No, the hay, flax, wheat and corn could all go to the Diel. There they stood with their hearts pumping and their tow shirts a quiver. They couldn't wait. They'd have given the clothes off their backs to hear they were moving today to a place called Tateville they never saw and that wasn't even built yet. A hundred reasons they told why they had to go. Sayward didn't need to hear. She knew by heart how it would be once they found out. Didn't she mind plain as yesterday how her brother and sisters and even her pappy back in the old state wanted to go up West? Pennsylvany wasn't good enough for them any more. They could hardly wait till they'd up and start. Only her mother didn't want to go. She had her heart set on living her life back among friends and relations. But she had to give in and tramp all the way out here to die in the wilderness. Always Sayward had the notion her mam hadn't enough spunk, and that's why she let them have their way. More than once Sayward told herself that when she had young ones she wouldn't let them twist her around their finger. But now she had a better idea of what her mam went through. You had to be pigheaded to set yourself against all the rest of your family and mighty calloused to say no when your own flesh and blood were pulling at your skirt, a begging with their mouths, and their eyes looking like they'd give up and die if you didn't say yes. And right beside them stood your man watching grave-faced what you'd make up your mind to do.

"We kain't fool now. We got work to do," she told them and led the way back to the hayfield.

But in her heart never did she see how she'd get through the work this summer. Wheat was coloring up fast. It would have to be reaped, bound, shocked, flailed and the chaff fanned out. Then her flax had to be taken care of, pulled, spread, turned, ripped for the seeds, and that was only a start of the long "tejus" work before it could be spun. All the time corn and potatoes would have to be hoed and sprouts and weeds fought. And meanwhile the hay had to be made and put away. It was all coming in a pile. You couldn't put off a crop once it was ready.

And yet she felt sad to think of selling her place. Her pap had picked it. Of all the land around here, this was her choice, for they had come first. These woods hadn't even a tomahawk-right when they came, save for Louie

Scurrah's cabin. Her pap had the pick of the whole country, and now she was a giving it up.

She wished she could see it again before she signed any papers. She hankered to walk the bounds, for that was the dearest walk to anybody who owned land, tramping around your own ground, seeing how far it went. All the way out here it ran, you'd tell yourself. Now that over there was somebody else's.

She watched Resolve. He could handle the scythe good as she could. Guerdon and Kinzie had the two reap hooks. They hadn't any more.

"It has somethin' I want to do," she told the boys. "You work here till I get back."

Then she went off, a slow, heavy figure in the old, faded dove-gray, homespun short gown, moving along the run, past the beech stump spring and toward the timber. She could feel her boys look up to watch her. They were wondering, what was she after. Was she going in there just a short piece to do her business, or where was she heading for?

"I wouldn't go in the woods far, Mam!" Resolve called to her.

"I'll git you the rifle if you want!" Guerdon offered.

"You'll do no such thing," Sayward reproved them both. She knew what they were thinking. "I'll carry no gun, and I'm afeard of no Injuns." Then she went on into the timber.

Back in the open fields, a small summer air had been stirring, but in the woods it felt still and close as death. She minded the first time her pap had fetched them to this spot and how her mam had to open her mouth to swoop in what air she could in this thatched-in, choked-up place. Raising her eyes she could see a mote of sunlight breaking through the roof of leaves a hundred feet up. That up there, she had thought, must be God's earth, while this down here was a deep well, and they stood on the bottom. Oh, the woods looked open and bright enough when leaves first came out in the spring. But those leaves didn't hold tiny and baby-green long. Every week they got bigger and thicker till they shut off the sky. By July they were heavy and dark-colored and they would stay like that till frost nipped them.

That's the way the leaves hung overhead now as she tramped her bottom land and the ground began to rise under foot. She tramped through the oaks and hickories with never a squirrel's bark to break the solitude. God, but it was like the grave in here, and all the way to where Buckman Tull's compass had told him to flitch the trees. Wyitt had held the rod. You couldn't see any difference in the ground, but this was where her line ran. It was her ground up to here and Mageel MacMahon's over there. Wasn't it curious the way the Irish picked the hills for their places? They claimed it was for the lay of the land and the clear running springs, but Portius thought the smaller timber they had to fell on the hills had something to do with it.

She had the strangest feeling here standing plumb on her line. Now she turned to follow that line north, past the old wolves' crossing, past the fallen timbers with the "yaller" oyster shells growing out of the dead wood, past the briers and brambles to the stony point. Right in these rocks somewheres was her first corner. Buckman and Wyitt had piled rocks high as a boy's head to mark it. Must be over there or back here, some place close around anyway. Yonder it set with some of the rocks down. If you stood on that rock pile in the spring, Wyitt claimed, you could see something, for this rocky point was where snakes holed up for the winter deep in the old earth, lying in knots, one wound harmlessly around the other. It couldn't be they lay together on account of warmth, for they were down where it never froze, being neither hot nor cold.

She better watch, she told herself, she didn't step on some other kind of "spotted sarpent" sneaking up to her on his belly as one likely had to the Coldwell woman and boy. Why, that showed how low in her mind she was lately! Many a Shawanee, Delaware or Wyandot had she met alone in the woods in her time, and never a fret, only a look, as she passed them the time, that they better not make a wrong move or they'd wish they hadn't. But now she began to wonder had she done right leaving her three young boys alone back there in the hayfield. She hurried down her east line that ran through a "holler" dark as a pot, where water rose in the earth and her own ground oozed and boiled black under foot. This was ground once she reckoned would make corn and potato land some day. She crossed the trace that ran to George Roebuck's and came out after while at the big buttonwood on the river. This was her witness tree, and it needed no flitching, for its hollow shell could hold nigh as many folks as the meeting house.

Well, those were two of her corners. Now she needed no line to guide her, for the river was her boundary. Down here was a place to get gourds in the late summer. You sliced off the tops for lids, pulled out the guts and had all the piggins and pipkins for your shelfboards you wanted. Her cabin must lay yonder, but in all the tangled wilderness of leaves and vines, she couldn't see it. And she couldn't see her third corner either, when she got there. This was at the riffles where you thought you heard voices calling of people long since dead and gone. The June flood must have washed her scabby, red-birch witness tree out. Well, the floods would never wash out the rocky bed of the riffles, and that could be her corner, with all the watery voices as her witnesses.

She hated to turn west again to the melancholy gloom of the swamps.

She passed the old beaver gats where on a summer night you could hear raccoons making funny noises chewing and swallowing the frogs they caught. These were the dim, sunken places, where the butts leaned this way and that, finding it hard to hold themselves up straight in the soft mud. Their roots stood out like bull spiders. She tramped on through a herd of great ash trees stretching up and up. Oh, the ash was the finest of all butts, clean and straight, and not so coarse as the oak. Some were smooth as a board on one side and nobody knew why. But they were a God's own trial to cut down and burn. Yonder at that old Indian mound was her last corner. Here she turned north to where she had first met her bounds.

She had tramped clean around her place now. She had come back to the line where she started. She had made a square circle and all that lay inside was "her'n" and Portius's. She turned down the path slowly now, and when she came from the woods she stopped. It was something to tramp all that way in the dark forest and then come out in the brightness of your own fields. On this rise she could see the whole improvement, her log cabin and barn, the log school and meeting house, but the mortal best were her fields laying cleared, green and golden in the sun.

She stood there a while for she knew every patch of ground she had opened to daylight. That strip of potatoes was the first piece she ever planted. She could still mind herself walking barefoot in the soft, worked ground that day and how the corn grains she dropped in the rows had seemed drops of gold and rubystone to a woodsy. Yonder beyond the potatoes stretched her field of flax, high as her breasts and level as standing water. The sky-blue flowers had faded now and seeds were forming in the boll. Her own hand had sown it this last late April and her little girls had weeded it in May. No heavy boot dare tramp those tender stalks down. Her girls had to walk barefoot and face the wind so the plants they trod would be helped by the blowing air to rise again. Across from the flax she could see her meadow pasture running down in the woods, a long narrow piece a little too wet to plow, curving with the run so that your eye couldn't find the sheep at the far end, for the forest turned round it like a ram's horn and shut them in. And yonder was the hayfield she left a little while ago, with mowed red top, sweet grass, clover, wild teas and thorny dewberry vines all curing together in the sun. She could hear her boys a fighting and quarreling. It was good to know all was well with them while she was off.

But her favorite patch was the one standing closest to her now. Only last week the stalks were still green and supple. Most every day she had come here to feel the heads and watch the wind run through the field like water. Sometimes the waves minded her of silver fire weaving this way and that. The shadows were the smoke following after. Sometimes they minded her of ghostly forms passing through, strange shapes turning this way and that. You couldn't see them, but you could the paths they made in the green. One day last week the wind came from the east. The waves that time rose from the bottom, and then it looked like a waterfall running up hill. Oh, ever since those stalks had stayed so fresh and green through the cold winter she had the feeling that something in that wheat was alive and everlasting.

Now those scabby heads had filled and hardened, and the whole patch lay "yaller" as a sovereign in the sun. She sat down on a stump just inside it. Her head was as high as the stalks. Her eyes could watch the furry, bent-down heads. They turned so easy this way and that, making a soft, gentle, brushing noise in the wind. That was the scaly beards rubbing against each other. The soft, musky smell that wheat had getting ripe came around her like a cloud. It was like a fine dust of flour with the beards ground up. Those licks of beard on the air were so small you couldn't see them, but they stuck in your throat. You would hardly believe that field had barrels of flour in it a hanging on the stalk. It was the field of life, that's what it was. When they reaped it, she would bind up a sheaf special and keep it for harvest home in the meeting house this fall. Afterwards she would hang it up in the cabin like the Covenhovens had one in their best room. It would look like a picture on the wall.

Oh, if she wanted to sell this place, never should she have walked the boundaries today. Going through the deep woods like that and coming out in the cleared fields just made her see how much she had done here. Her fields lay around her house like a bright star with its points running into the dark woods here and yonder, following the richest and easiest-cleared land. She hated to disappoint the boys and Portius. But never did she see how she could sign any paper giving up this place she had made with her own sweat and hands. Come to think of it, the work didn't seem quite so hard any more. With her boys a helping, she reckoned she could get through.

3

Men Against the Earth

The earth's yield has never been cheaply gathered. Its bounteous fruits have been torn from a hard, unwilling soil. Man has paid dearly for his tenancy of the planet. He holds it only by sufferance.

He has seen earthquake swallow towns, landslides tear the face of a mountain, a volcano shower a city with burning death. Against a choleric, omnipotent nature, he has stood opposed only with hands and wit and the tools he has fashioned with them both. This is the great and recurring theme of much of the finest and most impassioned writing in our literature, this struggle of man to harness the explosive energies of his earth.

LANDSLIDE

AND OVERHEAD WAS THE GREAT RIVER

FROM *St. Columba and the River*

THEODORE DREISER

The most perceptive judgment that has been made of Theodore Dreiser in the decade since he died—the argument invariably revolves around his style—is that he had little talent but much genius. There is no question of his place as the most significant realistic novelist America has produced. His characters grow as people do, developing out of the accumulation of the detail of their lives. But by very virtue of this detail added to detail, the characters emerge as startlingly familiar—ourselves, a sister, a cousin, the man next door. His comparatively few short stories, of which this selection is a notable example, follow this same meticulously pieced pattern.

KNOW, O READER, THAT THE BUSINESS OF TUNNELING IS ONE OF THE MOST hazardous and dramatic, albeit interesting, of all known fields of labor. It consists, in these latter days at least, in so far as under-water tunneling is concerned, of sinking huge shafts at either end or side of a river, lake or channel (one hundred feet, perhaps, within the shore line) to a depth of, say, thirty feet below the water level, and from these two points tunneling outward under the bottom of the river until the two ends meet somewhere near the middle. The exact contact and precise joining of these outer ends is considered one of the true tests of skilful engineering. McGlathery personally understood all this but dimly. And even so it could not cheer him any.

And it should be said here that the safety of the men who did the work, and the possibility of it, depended first on the introduction at either end, just at the base of the shafts and then at about every hundred or so feet, as the tunnel progressed outward, of huge cylindrical chambers, or locks, of heavy iron—air locks, no less—fifteen feet in diameter, and closed at each end by massive doors swinging inward toward the shore line, so that the amazing and powerful pressure of air constantly forced outward from the shore by huge engines could not force them open. It was only by the same delicate system which causes water locks to open and close that they could be opened at all. That is, workingmen coming down into the shaft and desiring to pass into the head of the tunnel beyond the lock, would have to first enter one of these locks, which would then gradually be filled with air compressed up to the same pressure as that maintained in the main portion of the tunnel farther in. When this pressure had been reached they could easily open the inward swinging door and pass into the tunnel proper. Here, provided that so much had been completed, they might walk, say, so much as a hundred or more feet, when they would encounter another lock. The pressure in the lock, according to who had last used it, would be either that of the section of the tunnel toward the shore, or of the section beyond, toward the centre of the river. At first, bell cords, later telephones, and then electric signals controlled this—that is, the lowering or raising of the pressure of air in the locks so that one door or the other might be opened. If the pressure in the lock was different from that in your section, and you could not open the door (which you could not), you pulled the cord or pushed the button so many times, according to your position, and the air in the lock was adjusted to the section of the tunnel in which you stood. Then you could open the door. Once in, as in a water lock, the air was raised or lowered, according to your signal, and you could enter the next section outward or inward. All these things had been adjusted to a nicety even in those days, which was years ago.

The digging of this particular tunnel seemed safe enough—for McGlathery at least, once he began working here. It moved at the rate of two and even three feet a day, when things were going well, only there were days and days when, owing to the need of shoring and timbering and plate setting, to say nothing of the accidental encountering of rock in front which had to be drilled away, the men with picks and shovels had to be given a rest, or better yet, set to helping the joiners in erecting those cross beams and supports which made the walls safe. It was so that Dennis learned much about joining and even drilling.

Nevertheless, in spite of the increased pay, this matter of working under the river was a constant source of fear to him. The earth in which he worked was so uncertain. One day it would be hard black mud, another soft, another silt, another sand, according as the tunnel sloped further and further under the bed. In addition, at times great masses of it fell, not enough to make a hole in the roof above, but enough, had it chanced to fall on one of the workers, to break his back or half bury him in mud. Usually it was broken by the beams overhead. Only one day, some seven months after he had begun and when he was becoming fairly accustomed to the idea of working here, and when his skill had increased to such an extent that he was considered one of the most competent workers in his limited field, the unexpected happened.

He had come down one morning at eight with the rest of his gang and was working about the base of two new supports which had just been put in place, when he noticed, or thought he did, that the earth seemed wetter than usual, sticky, watery, and hard to manage. It could not have been much worse had a subterranean spring been encountered. Besides, one of the gasoline lamps having been brought forward and hung close by, he noticed by its light that the ceiling seemed to look silvery gray and beady. He spoke of it to Cavanaugh, who stood by.

"Yis," said his foreman dubiously, staring upward, " 'tis wet. Maybe the air pumps is not workin' right. I'll just make sure," and he sent word to the engineer.

The shaft superintendent himself appeared.

"Everything's all right up above," he said. "Two thousand pounds to the square inch. I'll just put on a little more, if you say so."

"Ye'd better," replied Cavanaugh. "The roof's not actin' right. And if ye see Mr. Henderson, send him down. I'd like to talk to him."

"All right," and off he went.

McGlathery and the others, at first nervous, but now slightly reassured, worked on. But the ground under their feet became sloppy, and some of the silvery frosting on the roof began to drop and even trickle as water. Then a mass of sloppy mud fell.

"Back, men!"

It was the voice of Cavanaugh, but not quicker than the scampering of the men who, always keenly alive to the danger of a situation, had taken note of the dripping water and the first flop of earth. At the same time, an ominous creak from one of the beams overhead gave warning of the imminence of a catastrophe. A pell-mell rush for the lock some sixty feet away ensued. Tools were dropped, precedence disregarded. They fell and stumbled over the beams and between, pushing each other out of the way into the water and mud as they ran, McGlathery a fair second to none.

"Open the door! Open the door!" was the cry as they reached the lock, for some one had just entered from the other side—the engineer. "For Christ's sake, open the door!" But that could not be done so quickly. A few moments at least had to elapse.

"It's breakin' in!" cried some one in a panicky voice, an ironworker.

"Great God, it's coming down!" this from one of the masons, as three lamps in the distance were put out by the mud.

McGlathery was almost dying of fear. He was sweating a cold sweat. Five dollars a day indeed! He should stay away from water, once and for all. Didn't he know that? It was always bad luck to him.

"What's the trouble? What's the trouble?" called the amazed engineer as, unconscious of what was happening outside, he pushed open the door.

"Git out of the way!"

"Fer God's sake, let us in!"

"Shut the door!" this from a half dozen who had already reached safety assuming that the door could be instantly closed.

"Wait! Cavanaugh's outside!" This from some one—not McGlathery, you may be sure, who was cowering in a corner. He was so fearful that he was entirely unconscious of his superior's fate.

"To hell with Cavanaugh! Shut the door!" screamed another, a great ironworker, savage with fear.

"Let Cavanaugh in, I say!" this from the engineer.

At this point McGlathery, for the first time on this or any other job, awoke to a sense of duty, but not much at that. He was too fearful. This was what he got for coming down here at all. He knew Cavanaugh—Cavanaugh was his friend, indeed. Had he not secured him this and other jobs? Surely. But then Cavanaugh had persuaded him to come down here, which was wrong. He ought not to have done it. Still, even in his fear he had manhood enough to feel that it was not quite right to shut Cavanaugh out. Still, what could he do—he was but one. But even as he thought, and others were springing forward to shut Cavanaugh out, so eager were they to save themselves, they faced a gleaming revolver in the steady hand of the big foreman.

"I'll shoot down the first damned man that tries to shut the door before me and Kelly are in," the big foreman was calling, the while he was pulling this same Kelly from the mud and slime outside. Then fairly throwing him into the lock, and leaping after him, he turned and quietly helped close the door.

McGlathery was amazed at this show of courage. To stop and help another man like that in the face of so much danger! Cavanaugh was even a better and kinder man than he had thought—really a great man—no coward like himself. But why had Cavanaugh persuaded him to come down here when he knew that he was afraid of water! And now this had happened. Inside as they cowered—all but Cavanaugh—they could hear the sound of crushing timber and grinding brick outside, which made it quite plain that where a few moments before had been beams and steel and a prospective passageway for men, was now darkness and water and the might of the river, as it had been since the beginning.

McGlathery, seeing this, awoke to the conviction that in the first place he was a great coward, and in the second that the tunnel digging was no job for him. He was by no means fitted for it, he told himself. " 'Tis the last," he commented, as he climbed safely out with the others after a distressing wait of ten minutes at the inward lock. "Begob, I thought we was all lost. 'Twas a close shave. But I'll go no more below. I've had enough." He was thinking of a small bank account—six hundred dollars in all—which he had saved, and of a girl in Brooklyn who was about to marry him. "No more!"

But, at that, as it stood, there was no immediate danger of work being offered. The cave-in had cost the contractors thousands and in addition had taught them that mere air pressure and bracing as heretofore followed were not sufficient for successful tunneling. Some new system would have to be devised. Work on both halves of the tunnel was suspended for over a year and a half, during which time McGlathery married, a baby was born to him, and his six hundred had long since diminished to nothing. The difference between two and five dollars a day is considerable. Incidentally, he had not gone near his old foreman in all this time, being somehow ashamed of himself, and in consequence he had not fared so well. Previously Cavanaugh had kept him almost constantly employed, finding him faithful and hard-working, but now owing to stranger associates there were weeks when he had no work at all and others when he had to work for as little as one-fifty a day. It was not so pleasant. Besides, he had a sneaking feeling that if he had behaved a little more courageously at that time, gone and talked to his old foreman afterwards or at the time, he might now be working for good pay. Alas, he had not done so, and if he went now Cavanaugh would be sure to want to know why he had disappeared so utterly. Then, in spite of his marital happiness, poverty began to press him so. A second and a third child were born—only they were twins.

In the meantime, Henderson, the engineer whom Cavanaugh had wanted to consult with at the time, had devised a new system of tunneling, namely, what subsequently came to be known as the pilot tunnel. This was an iron tube ten feet in length and fifteen feet in diameter—the width of the tunnel, which was carried forward on a line with the axis of the tunnel into the ground ahead. When it was driven in far enough to be completely concealed by the earth about, then the earth within was removed. The space so cleared was then used exactly as a hub is used on a wagon wheel. Beams like spokes were radiated from its sides to its centre, and the surrounding earth sustained by heavy iron plates. On this plan the old company had decided to undertake the work again.

One evening, sitting in his doorway thumbing his way through an evening paper which he could barely read, McGlathery had made all this out.

Mr. Henderson was to be in charge as before. Incidentally it was stated that Thomas Cavanaugh was going to return as one of the two chief foremen. Work was to be started at once. In spite of himself, McGlathery was impressed. If Cavanaugh would only take him back! To be sure, he had come very near losing his life, as he thought, but then he had not. No one had, not a soul. Why should *he* be so fearful if Cavanaugh could take such chances as he had? Where else could he make five dollars a day? Still, there was this haunting sensation that the sea and all of its arms and branches, wherever situated, were inimical to him and that one day one of them would surely do him a great injury—kill him, perhaps. He had a recurring sensation of being drawn up into water or down, he could not tell which, and of being submerged in ooze and choking slowly. It was horrible.

But five dollars a day as against one-fifty or two or none at all (seven, once he became very proficient) and an assured future as a tunnel worker, a "sand-hog," as he had now learned such men as himself were called, was a luring as well as a disturbing thought. After all, he had no trade other than this he had begun to learn under Cavanaugh. Worse he was not a union man, and the money he had once saved was gone, and he had a wife and three children. With the former he had various and sundry talks. To be sure, tunneling was dangerous, but still! She agreed with him that he had better not, but—after all, the difference that five, maybe seven, instead of two a day would make in their living expenses was in both their minds. McGlathery saw it. He decided after a long period of hesitation that perhaps he had best return. After all, nothing had happened to him that other time, and might it ever again, really? He meditated.

As has been indicated, a prominent element in McGlathery's nature was superstition. While he believed in the inimical nature of water to him, he also believed in the power of various saints, male and female, to help or hinder. In the Catholic Church of St. Columba of South Brooklyn, at which McGlathery and his young wife were faithful attendants, there was a plaster statue of a saint of this same name, a co-worker with St. Patrick in Ireland, it appears, who in McGlathery's native town of Kilrush, County of Clare, on the water's edge of Shannon, had been worshipped for centuries past, or at least highly esteemed, as having some merit in protecting people at sea, or in adventures connected with water. This was due, perhaps, to the fact that Kilrush was directly on the water and had to have a saint of that kind. At any rate, among other things, he had occasionally been implored for protection in that realm when McGlathery was a boy. On his setting out for America, for instance, some few years before at the suggestion of his mother, he had made a novena before this very saint, craving of him a safe conduct in crossing the sea, as well as prosperity once he had arrived in America. Well, he had crossed in safety, and prospered well enough, he thought. At least he had not been killed in any tunnel. In consequence, on bended knees, two blessed candles burning before him in the rack, a half dollar deposited in the box labeled "St. Columba's Orphans," he finally asked of this saint whether, in case he returned to this underground tunnel work, seeing that necessity was driving him, would he be so kind as to protect him? He felt sure that Cavanaugh, once he applied to him, and seeing that he had been a favorite worker, would not begrudge him a place if he had one. In fact he knew that Cavanaugh had always favored him as a good useful helper.

After seven "Our Fathers" and seven "Hail Marys," said on his knees, and a litany of the Blessed Virgin for good measure, he crossed himself and arose greatly refreshed. There was a pleasant conviction in his mind now, newly come there before this image, that he would never come to real harm by any power of water. It was a revelation—a direct communication, perhaps. At any rate, something told him to go and see Cavanaugh at once, before the work was well under way, and not be afraid, as no harm would come to him, and besides, he might not get anything even though he desired it so much if he delayed. He bustled out of the church and over to the waterfront where the deserted shaft was still standing, and sure enough, there was Cavanaugh, conversing with Mr. Henderson.

"Yis—an' what arr ye here fer?" he now demanded to know of McGlathery rather amusedly, for he had sensed the cause of his desertion.

"I was readin' that ye was about to start work on the tunnel again."

"An' so we arr. What av it?"

"I was thinkin' maybe ye'd have a place fer me. I'm married now an' have three children."

"An' ye're thinkin' that's a reason fer givin' ye something, is it?" demanded the big foreman rather cynically, with a trace of amusement. "I thought ye said ye was shut av the sea—that ye was through now, once an' fer all?"

"So I did, but I've changed me mind. It's needin' the work I am."

"Very well, then," said Cavanaugh. "We're beginnin' in the mornin'. See that ye're here at seven sharp. An' mind ye, no worryin' or lookin' around. We've a safe way now. It's different. There's no danger."

McGlathery gratefully eyed his old superior, then departed, only to return the next morning a little dubious but willing. St. Columba had certainly indicated that all would be well with him—but still— A man is entitled to a few doubts even when under the protection of the best of saints. He went down with the rest of the men and began cleaning out that nearest section of the tunnel where first water and then earth had finally oozed and caked. That done he helped install the new pilot tunnel which was obviously a great improvement over the old system. It seemed decidedly safe. McGlathery attempted to explain its merits to his wife, who was greatly concerned for him, and incidentally each morning and evening on his way to and from his task he dropped in at St. Columba's to offer up a short silent prayer. In spite of his novena and understanding with the saint he was still suspicious of this dread river above him, and of what might happen to him in spite of St. Columba. The good saint, due to some error on the part of McGlathery, might change his mind.

Nothing happened, of course, for days and weeks and months. Under Cavanaugh's direction the work progressed swiftly, and McGlathery and he, in due time, became once more good friends, and the former an expert bracer or timberer, one of the best, and worth seven a day really, which he did not get. Incidentally, they were all shifted from day to night work, which somehow was considered more important. There were long conversations now and again between Cavanaugh and Henderson, and Cavanaugh and other officials of the company who came down to see, which enlightened McGlathery considerably as to the nature and danger of the work. Just the same, overhead was still the heavy river—he could feel it pushing at him at times, pushing at the thick layer of mud and silt above him and below which with the aid of this new pilot shield they were burrowing.

Yet nothing happened for months and months. They cleared a thousand feet without a hitch. McGlathery began to feel rather comfortable about it all. It certainly seemed reasonably safe under the new system. Every night he went down and every morning came up, as hale and healthy as ever, and every second week, on a Tuesday, a pay envelope containing the handsome sum of seventy-two dollars was handed him. Think of it! Seventy-two dollars! Naturally, as a token of gratitude to St. Columba, he contributed liberally to his Orphan's Home, a dollar a month, say, lit a fresh candle before his shrine every Sunday morning after high mass, and bought two lots out on the Goose Creek waterfront—on time—on which some day, God willing, he proposed to build a model summer and winter cottage. And then—! Well, perhaps, as he thought afterward, it might have been due to the fact that his prosperity had made him a little more lax than he should have been, or proud, or not quite as thoughtful of the saint as was his due. At any rate, one night, in spite of St. Columba—or could it have been with his aid and consent in order to show McGlathery his power?—the wretched sneaky river did him another bad turn, a terrible turn, really.

It was this way. While they were working at midnight under the new form of bracing, based on the pilot tunnel, and with an air pressure of two thousand pounds to the square inch which had so far sufficed to support the iron roof plates which were being put in place behind the pilot tunnel day after day, as fast as space permitted, and with the concrete men following to put in a form of arch which no river weight could break, the very worst happened. For it was just at this point where the iron roof and the mud of the river bottom came in contact behind the pilot tunnel that there was a danger spot ever since the new work began. Cavanaugh had always been hovering about that, watching it, urging others to be careful—"taking no chances with it," as he said.

"Don't be long, men!" was his constant urge. "Up with it now! Up with it! In with the bolts! Quick, now, with yer riveter—quick! quick!"

And the men! How they worked there under the river whenever there was sufficient space to allow a new steel band to be segmentally set! For at that point it was, of course, that the river might break through. How they tugged, sweated, grunted, cursed, in this dark muddy hole, lit by a few glittering electric arcs—the latest thing in tunnel work! Stripped to the waist, in mud-soaked trousers and boots, their arms and backs and breasts mud-smeared and wet, their hair tousled, their eyes bleary—an artist's dream of bedlam, a heavenly inferno of toil—so they labored. And overhead was the great river, Atlantic liners resting upon it, thirty or fifteen or ten feet of soil only, sometimes, between them and this thin strip of mud sustained, supposedly, by two thousand pounds of air pressure to the square inch—all they had to keep the river from bleeding water down on them and drowning them like rats!

"Up with it! Up with it! Up with it! Now the bolts! Now the riveter! That's it! In with it, Johnny! Once more now!"

Cavanaugh's voice urging them so was like music to them, their gift of energy, their labor song, their power to do, their Ei Uchnam.

But there were times also, hours really, when the slow forward movement of the pilot tunnel, encountering difficult earth before it, left this small danger section unduly exposed to the rotary action of the water overhead which was constantly operating in the bed of the river. Leaks had been discovered from time to time, small tricklings and droppings of earth, which brought Cavanaugh and Henderson to the spot and caused the greatest tension until they had been done away with. The air had a tendency to bore holes upward through the mud. But these were invariably stanched with clay, or, if growing serious, bags of shavings or waste, the air pressure blowing outward from below being sufficient to hold these in place, provided the breach was not too wide. Even when "all hands" were working directly under a segment wide enough for a ring of plates, one man was told off to "kape an eye on it."

On the evening in question, however, after twenty-eight men, including Cavanaugh and McGlathery, had entered at six and worked until midnight, pushing the work as vigorously as usual, seven of the men (they were told off in lots of seven to do this) were allowed to go up to the mouth of the tunnel to a nearby all-night saloon for a drink and a bite of food. A half hour to each lot was allowed, when another group would depart. There was always a disturbing transition period every half hour between twelve and two, during which one group was going and another coming, which resulted at times in a dangerous indifference which Cavanaugh had come to expect at just about this time and in consequence he was usually watching for it.

On the other hand, John Dowd, ditcher, told off to keep an eye on the breach at this time, was replaced on this particular night by Patrick Murtha, fresh from the corner saloon, a glass of beer and the free lunch counter still in his mind. He was supposed to watch closely, but having had four glasses in rapid succession and meditating on their excellence as well as that of the hot frankfurters, the while he was jesting with the men who were making ready to leave, he forgot about it. What now—was a man always to keep his eye on the blanked thing! What was going to happen anyway? What could happen? Nothing, of course. What had ever happened in the last eight months?

"Sssst!"

What was that? A sound like the blowing off of steam. All at once Cavanaugh, who was just outside the pilot tunnel indicating to McGlathery and another just where certain braces were to be put, in order that the pilot tunnel might be pushed forward a few inches for the purpose of inserting a new ring of plates, heard it. At a bound he was back through the pilot hub, his face aflame with fear and rage. Who had neglected the narrow breach?

"Come now! What the hell is this?" he was about to exclaim, but seeing a wide breach suddenly open and water pour down in a swift volume, his spirit sank and fear overcame him.

"Back men! Stop the leak!"

It was the cry of a frightened and yet courageous man at bay. There was not only fear, but disappointment, in it. He had certainly hoped to obviate anything like this this time. But where a moment before had been a hole that might have been stopped with a bag of sawdust (and Patrick Murtha was there attempting to do it) was now a rapidly widening gap through which was pouring a small niagara of foul river water, ooze and slime. As Cavanaugh reached it and seized a bag to stay it, another mass of muddy earth fell, striking both him and Murtha, and half blinding them both. Murtha scrambled away for his life. McGlathery, who had been out in the front of the fatal tunnel with others, now came staggering back horribly frightened, scarcely knowing what to do.

"Quick, Dennis! Into the lock!" Cavanaugh called to him, while he himself held his ground. "Hurry!" and realizing the hopelessness of it and his own danger, Dennis thought to run past, but was stopped by the downpour of water and mud.

"Quick! Quick! Into the lock! For Christ's sake, can't ye see what's happenin'? Through with ye!"

McGlathery, hesitating by his chief's side, fearful to move lest he be killed, uncertain this time whether to leave his chief or not, was seized by Cavanaugh and literally thrown through, as were others after him, the blinding ooze and water choking them, but placing them within range of safety. When the last man was through Cavanaugh himself plunged after, wading knee-deep in mud and water.

"Quick! Quick! Into the lock!" he called, and then seeing McGlathery, who was now near it but waiting for him, added, "In, in!" There was a mad scramble about the door, floating timbers and bags interfering with many, and then, just as it seemed as if all would reach safety, an iron roof plate overhead, loosened by the breaking of plates beyond, gave way, felling one man in the half-open doorway of the lock and blocking and pinning it in such a way that it could be neither opened nor closed. Cavanaugh and others who came up after were shut out. McGlathery, who had just entered and saw it, could do nothing. But in this emergency, and unlike his previous attitude, he and several others on the inside seized upon the dead man and tried to draw him in, at the same time calling to Cavanaugh to know what to do. The latter, dumbfounded, was helpless. He saw very clearly and sadly that very little if anything could be done. The plate across the dead man was too heavy, and besides, the ooze was already pouring over him into the lock. At the same time the men in the lock, conscious that although they were partially on the road to safety they were still in danger of losing their lives, were frantic with fear.

Actually there were animal roars of terror. At the same time McGlathery, once more realizing that his Nemesis, water, had overtaken him and was likely to slay him at last, was completely paralyzed with fear. St. Columba had promised him, to be sure, but was not this that same vision that he had had in his dreams, that awful sense of encroaching ooze and mud? Was he not now to die this way, after all? Was not his patron saint truly deserting him? It certainly appeared so.

"Holy Mary! Holy St. Columba!" he began to pray, "what shall I do now? Mother of God! Our Father, who art in Heaven! Bejasus, it's a tight place I'm in now! I'll never get out of this! Tower of Ivory! House of Gold! Can't we git him in, boys? Ark of the Covenant! Gate of Heaven!"

As he gibbered and chattered, the others screaming about him, some pulling at the dead man, others pulling at the other door, the still eye of

Cavanaugh outside the lock waist-deep in mud and water was surveying it all.

"Listen to me, men!" came his voice in rich, heavy, guttural tones. "You, McGlathery! Dennis! Arr ye all crazy! Take aaf your clothes and stop up the doorway! It's yer only chance! Aaf with yer clothes, quick! And those planks there—stand them up! Never mind us. Save yerselves first. Maybe ye can do something for us afterwards."

As he argued, if only the gap in the door could be closed and the compressed air pushing from the tunnel outward toward the river allowed to fill the chamber, it would be possible to open the other door which gave into the next section shoreward, and so they could all run to safety.

His voice, commanding, never quavering, even in the face of death, subsided. About and behind him were a dozen men huddled like sheep, waist-deep in mud and water, praying and crying. They had got as close to him as might be, still trying to draw upon the sustaining force of his courage, but moaning and praying just the same and looking at the lock.

"Yis! Yis!" exclaimed McGlathery of a sudden, awakening at last to a sense of duty and that something better in conduct and thought which he had repeatedly promised himself and his saint that he would achieve. He had been forgetting. But now it seemed to him once more that he had been guilty of that same great wrong to his foreman which had marked his attitude on the previous occasion—that is, he had not helped him or any one but himself. He was a horrible coward. But what could he do? he asked himself. What could he do? Tearing off his coat and vest and shirt as commanded, he began pushing them into the opening, calling to the others to do the same. In a twinkling, bundles were made of all as well as of the sticks and beams afloat in the lock, and with these the gap in the door was stuffed, sufficiently to prevent the air from escaping, but shutting out the foreman and his men completely.

"It's awful. I don't like to do it," McGlathery kept crying to his foreman but the latter was not so easily shaken.

"It's all right, boys," he kept saying. "Have ye no courage at aal?" And then to the others outside with him, "Can't ye stand still and wait? They may be comin' back in time. Kape still. Say yer prayers if ye know any, and don't be afraid."

But, although the air pressing outward toward Cavanaugh held the bundles in place, still was not sufficient to keep all the air in or all the water out. It poured about the dead man and between the chinks, rising inside to their waists also. Once more it threatened their lives and now their one hope was to pull open the shoreward door and so release themselves into the chamber beyond, but this was not to be done unless the escaping air was completely blocked or some other method devised.

Cavanaugh, on the outside, his whole mind still riveted on the men whom he was thus aiding to escape, was the only one who realized what was to be done. In the panel of the door which confronted him, and the other, which they were trying to break open, were thick glass plates, or what were known as bull's eyes, through which one could see, and it was through the one at his end that Cavanaugh was peering. When it became apparent to him that the men were not going to be able to open the farthest door, a new thought occurred to him. Then it was that his voice was heard above the tumult, shouting:

"Break open the outside bull's eye! Listen to me, Dennis! Listen to me! Break open the outside bull's eye!"

Why did he call to Dennis, the latter often asked himself afterwards. And why did Dennis hear him so clearly? Through a bedlam of cries within, he heard, but also realized that if he or they knocked out the bull's eye in the other door, and the air escaped through it inward, the chances of their opening it would be improved, but the life of Cavanaugh and his helpless companions would certainly be destroyed. The water would rush inward from the river filling up this chamber and the space in which stood Cavanaugh. Should he? So he hesitated.

"Knock it out!" came the muffled voice of his foreman from within where he was eyeing him calmly. "Knock it out, Dennis! It's yer only chance! Knock it out!" And then, for the first time in all the years he had been working for him, McGlathery heard the voice of his superior waver slightly: "If ye're saved," it said, "try and do what ye can fer the rest av us."

In that moment McGlathery was reborn spiritually. Although he could have wept, something broke in him—fear. He was not afraid now for himself. He ceased to tremble, almost to hurry and awoke to a new idea, one of undying, unfaltering courage. What! There was Cavanaugh outside there, unafraid, and here was he, Dennis McGlathery, scrambling about like a hare for his life! He wanted to go back, to do something, but what could he? It was useless. Instead, he assumed partial command in here. The spirit of Cavanaugh seemed to come over to him and possess him. He looked about, saw a great stave, and seized it.

"Here, men!" he called with an air of command. "Help knock it out!" and with a will born of terror and death a dozen brawny hands were laid on it. With a mighty burst of energy they assaulted the thick plate and burst it through. Air rushed in, and at the same time the door gave way before them, causing them to be swept outward by the accumulated water like straws. Then, scrambling to their feet, they tumbled into the next lock, closing the door behind them. Once in, they heaved a tremendous sigh of relief, for here they were safe enough—for the time being anyhow. McGlathery, the new spirit of Cavanaugh in him, even turned and looked back through the bull's eye into the chamber they had just left. Even as they waited for the pressure here to lower sufficiently to permit them to open the inner door he saw this last chamber they had left his foreman and a dozen fellow workers buried beyond. But what could he do? Only God, only St. Columba, could tell him, perhaps, and St. Columba had saved him—or had he?—him and fifteen other men, the while he had chosen to allow Cavanaugh and twelve men to perish! Had St. Columba done that—or God—or who?

" 'Tis the will av God," he murmured humbly—but why had God done that?

But somehow, the river was not done with him yet, and that, seemingly, in spite of himself. Although he prayed constantly for the repose of the soul of Thomas Cavanaugh and his men, and avoided the water, until five years later, still there was a sequel. By now McGlathery was the father of eight children and as poor as any average laborer. With the death of Cavanaugh and this accident, as has been said, he had forsworn the sea—or water—and all its works. Ordinary house shoring and timbering were good enough for him, only—only—it was so hard to get enough of this at good pay. He was never faring as well as he should. And then one day when he was about as hard up as ever and as earnest, from somewhere was wafted a new scheme in connection with this same old tunnel.

A celebrated engineer of another country—England, no less—had appeared on the scene with a new device, according to the papers. Greathead was his name, and he had invented what was known as "The Greathead Shield," which finally, with a few changes and adaptations, was to rid tunnel work of all its dangers. McGlathery, sitting outside the door of his cottage overlooking Bergen Bay, read it all in the Evening *Clarion,* and wondered whether it could be true. He did not understand very much about this new shield idea even now, but even so, and in spite of himself, some of the old zest for tunneling came back to him. What times he had had, to be sure! What a life it had been, if a dog's one—and Cavanaugh—what a foreman! And his body was still down there entombed—erect, no doubt, as he was left. He wondered. It would be only fair to dig him out and honor his memory with a decent grave if it could be done. His wife and children were still living in Flatbush. It stirred up all the memories, old fears, old enthusiasms, but no particular desire to return. Still, here he was now, a man with a wife and eight children, earning three a day, no less—mostly less—whereas tunneling paid seven and eight to such as himself, and he kept thinking that if this should start up again and men were advertised for, why shouldn't he go? His life had been almost miraculously saved these two times—but would it be again?—that was the great question. Almost unceasingly he referred the matter to his saint on Sundays in his church, but receiving no definite advice as yet and there being no work doing on the tunnel, he did nothing.

But then one day the following spring the papers were full of the fact that work would soon actually be resumed, and shortly thereafter, to his utter amazement, McGlathery received a note from that same Mr. Henderson under whom Cavanaugh had worked, asking him to call and see him. Feeling sure that it was the river that was calling him, he went over to St. Columba's and prayed before his saint, putting a dollar in his Orphan's box and a candle on his shrine, and then arising greatly refreshed and reassured, and after consulting with his wife, journeyed over to the river, where he found the old supervisor as before in a shed outside, considering one important matter and another.

What he wanted to know was this—did McGlathery want to take an assistant-foremanship under a new foreman who was going to be in charge of the day work here, one Michael Laverty by name, an excellent man, at seven dollars a day, seeing that he had worked here before and understood the difficulties, etc.? McGlathery stared in amazement. He an assistant-foreman in charge of timbering! And at seven dollars a day! He!

Mr. Henderson neglected to say that because there had been so much trouble with the tunnel and the difficulties so widely advertised, it was rather difficult to get just the right sort of men at first, although McGlathery was good enough any time. But the new shield made everything safe, he said. There could be no calamity this time. The work would be pushed right through. Mr. Henderson even went so far as to explain the new shield to him, its excellent points.

But McGlathery, listening, was dubious, and yet he was not thinking of the shield exactly now, nor of the extra pay he would receive, although that played a big enough part in his calculations, but of one Thomas Cavanaugh, mason foreman, and his twelve men, buried down below there in the ooze, and how he had left him, and how it would only be fair to take his bones out, his and the others', if they could be found, and give them a decent Christian burial. For by now he was a better Catholic than ever, and he owed that much to Cavanaugh, for certainly Cavanaugh had been very good to him—and anyhow, had not St. Columba protected him so far? And might he not in the future, seeing the position he was in? Wasn't this a call, really? He felt that it was.

Just the same, he was nervous and troubled, and went home and consulted with his wife again, and thought of the river and went over and prayed in front of the shrine of St. Columba. Then, once more spiritualized and strengthened, he returned and told Mr. Henderson that he would come back. Yes, he would come.

He felt actually free of fear, as though he had a mission, and the next day began by assisting Michael Laverty to get out the solid mass of earth which filled the tunnel from the second lock outward. It was slow work, well into the middle of the summer before the old or completed portion was cleared and the bones of Cavanaugh and his men reached. That was a great if solemn occasion—the finding of Cavanaugh and his men. They could recognize him by his big boots, his revolver, his watch, and a bunch of keys, all in position near his bones. These same bones and boots were then reverently lifted and transferred to a cemetery in Brooklyn, McGlathery and a dozen workers accompanying them, after which everything went smoothly. The new shield worked like a charm. It made eight feet a day in soft mud, and, although McGlathery, despite his revived courage, was intensely suspicious of the river, he was really no longer afraid of it in the old way. Something kept telling him that from now on he would be all right—not to fear. The river could never hurt him any more, really.

But just the same, a few months later—eight, to be exact—the river did take one last slap at him, but not so fatally as might have appeared on the surface, although in a very peculiar way, and whether with or without St. Columba's aid or consent, he never could make out. The circumstances were so very odd. This new cutting shield, as it turned out, was a cylinder thirteen feet long, twenty feet in diameter, and with a hardened steel cutting edge out on front, an apron, fifteen inches in length and three inches thick at the cutting edge. Behind this came what was known as an "outside diaphragm," which had several openings to let in the mud displaced by the shield's advance.

Back of these openings were chambers four feet in length, one chamber for each opening, through which the mud was passed. These chambers in turn had hinged doors, which regulated the quantity of mud admitted, and were water tight and easily closed. It was all very shipshape.

Behind these little chambers, again, were many steel jacks, fifteen to thirty, according to the size of the shield, driven by an air pressure of five thousand pounds to the square inch, which were used to push the shield forward. Back of them came what was known as the tail end of the shield, which reached back into the completed tunnel and was designed to protect the men who were at work putting in the new plates (at that danger point which had killed Cavanaugh) whenever the shield had been driven sufficiently forward to permit of a new ring of them.

The only danger involved in this part of the work lay in the fact that between this lining and the tail end of the shield was always a space of an inch to an inch and a half which was left unprotected. This small opening would, under ordinary circumstances, be insignificant, but in some instances where the mud covering at the top was very soft and not very thick, there was danger of the compressed air from within, pushing at the rate of several thousand pounds to the square inch, blowing it away and leaving the aperture open to the direct action of the water above. This was not anticipated, of course, not even thought of. The shield was going rapidly forward and it was predicted by Henderson and Laverty at intervals that the tunnel would surely go through within the year.

Some time the following winter, however, when the shield was doing such excellent work, it encountered a rock which turned its cutting edge and, in addition, necessitated the drilling out of the rock in front. A bulkhead had to be built, once sufficient stone had been cut away, to permit the repairing of the edge. This took exactly fifteen days. In the meantime, at the back of the shield, at the little crevice described, compressed air, two thousand pounds to the square inch, was pushing away at the mud outside, gradually hollowing out a cup-like depression eighty-five feet long (Mr. Henderson had soundings taken afterwards), which extended backward along the top of the completed tunnel toward the shore. There was then nothing but water overhead.

It was at this time that the engineers, listening to the river, which, raked by the outpouring of air from below, was rolling gravel and stones above the tunnel top and pounding on it like a drum, learned that such was the case. It was easy enough to fix it temporarily by stuffing the crevice with bags, but one of these days when the shield was repaired it would have to be moved forward to permit the insertion of a new ring of plates, and then, what?

At once McGlathery scented trouble. It was the wretched river again (water), up to its old tricks with him. He was seriously disturbed, and went to pray before St. Columba, but incidentally, when he was on duty, he hovered about this particular opening like a wasp. He wanted to know what was doing there every three minutes in the day, and he talked to the night foreman about it, as well as Laverty and Mr. Henderson. Mr. Henderson, at Laverty's and McGlathery's request, came down and surveyed it and meditated upon it.

"When the time comes to move the shield," he said, "you'll just have to keep plenty of bags stuffed around that opening, everywhere, except where the men are putting in the plates. We'll have extra air pressure that day, all we can stand, and I think that'll fix everything all right. Have plenty of men here to keep those bags in position, but don't let 'em know there's anything wrong, and we'll be all right. Let me know when you're ready to start, and I'll come down."

When the shield was eventually repaired and the order given to drive it just twenty-five inches ahead in order to permit the insertion of a new ring of plates, Mr. Henderson was there, as well as Laverty and McGlathery. Indeed, McGlathery was in charge of the men who were to stuff the bags and keep out the water. If you have ever seen a medium-sized red-headed Irishman when he is excited and determined, you have a good picture of McGlathery. He was seemingly in fifteen places at once, commanding, exhorting, persuading, rarely ever soothing—and worried. Yes, he was worried, in spite of St. Columba.

The shield started. The extra air pressure was put on, the water began to pour through the crevice, and then the bags were put in place and stopped most of it, only where the ironworkers were riveting on the plates it poured, poured so heavily at times that the workers became frightened.

"Come now! What's the matter wid ye! What arr ye standin' there fer? What arr ye afraid av? Give me that bag! Up with it! That's the idea! Do ye think ye're goin' to be runnin' away now?"

It was McGlathery's voice, if you please, commanding!—McGlathery, after his two previous experiences! Yet in his vitals he was really afraid of the river at this very moment.

What was it that happened? For weeks after, he himself, writhing with "bends" in a hospital, was unable to get it straight. For four of the bags of sawdust burst and blew through, he remembered that—it was a mistake to have sawdust bags at all. And then (he remembered that well enough), in stuffing others in, they found that they were a bag short, and until something was secured to put in its place, for the water was streaming in like a waterfall and causing a flood about their ankles, he, McGlathery, defiant to the core, not to be outdone by the river this time, commanded the great thing to be done.

"Here!" he shouted, "the three av ye," to three gaping men near at hand, "up with me! Put me there! I'm as good as a bag of sawdust any day. Up with me!"

Astonished, admiring, heartened, the three of them jumped forward and lifted him. Against the small breach, through which the water was pouring, they held him, while others ran off for more bags. Henderson and Laverty and the ironworkers, amazed and amused and made braver themselves because of this very thing—filled with admiration, indeed, by the sheer resourcefulness of it, stood by to help. But then, if you will believe it, while they were holding him there, and because now there was nothing but water above it, one end of the shield itself—yes, that great iron invention—was lifted by the tremendous air pressure below—eleven or thirteen or fourteen inches, whatever space you can imagine a medium sized man being forced through—and out he went, McGlathery, and all the bags, up into the river above, the while the water poured down, and the men fled for their lives.

A terrific moment, as you can well imagine, not long in duration, but just long enough to swallow up McGlathery, and then the shield, having responded at first to too much air pressure, now responding to too little (the air pressure having been lessened by the escape), shut down like a safety valve, shutting off most of the water and leaving the tunnel as it was before.

But McGlathery!

Yes, what of him?

Reader—a miracle!

A passing tug captain, steaming down the Hudson at three one bright December afternoon was suddenly astonished to see a small geyser of water lift its head some thirty feet from his boat, and at the top of it, as it were lying on it, a black object which at first he took to be a bag or a log. Later he made it out well enough, for it plunged and bellowed.

"Fer the love av God! Will no one take me out av this? Git me out av this! Oh! Oh! Oh!"

It was McGlathery right enough, alive and howling lustily and no worse for his blow-out save that he was suffering from a fair case of the "bends" and suffering mightily. He was able to scream, though, and was trying to swim. That old haunting sensation!—he had had it this time, sure enough. For some thirty or forty seconds or more he had been eddied swiftly along the top of the tunnel at the bottom of the river, and then coming to where the air ricocheted upward had been hustled upward like a cork and literally blown through the air at the top of the great volume of water, out into space. The sudden shift from two thousand pounds of air pressure to none at all, or nearly none, had brought him down again, and in addition induced the severe case of "bends" from which he was now suffering. But St. Columba had not forgotten him entirely. Although he was suffering horribly, and was convinced that he was a dead man, still the good saint must have placed the tug conveniently near, and into this he was now speedily lifted.

"Well, of all things!" exclaimed Captain Hiram Knox, seeing him thoroughly alive, if not well, and eyeing him in astonishment. "Where do you come from?"

"Oh! Oh! Oh!" bawled McGlathery. "Me arms! Me ribs! Oh! Oh! Oh! The tunnel! The tunnel below, av course! Quick! Quick! It's dyin' av the bends I am! Git me to a hospital, quick!"

The captain, truly moved and frightened by his groans, did as requested. He made for the nearest dock. It took him but a few moments to call an ambulance, and but a few more before McGlathery was carried into the nearest hospital.

The house physician, having seen a case of this same disease two years before, and having meditated on it, had decided that the hair of the dog must be good for the bite. In consequence of this McGlathery was once more speedily carted off to one of the locks of this very tunnel, to the amazement of all who had known of him (his disappearance having aroused general excitement), and he was stared at as one who had risen from the grave. But, what was better yet, under the pressure of two thousand pounds now applied he recovered himself sufficiently to be host here and tell his story —another trick of his guardian saint, no doubt—and one rather flattering to his vanity, for he was now in no least danger of dying.

The whole city, if not the whole country, indeed, was astounded by the accident, and he was a true nine days' wonder, for the papers were full of the strange adventure. And with large pictures of McGlathery ascending heavenward, at the top of a geyser of water. And long and intelligent explanations as to the way and why of it all.

But, better yet, four of the happiest weeks of his life were subsequently spent in that same hospital to which he had first been taken relating to all and sundry his amazing adventure, he being interviewed by no less than five representatives of Sunday editors and eleven reporters for city dailies, all anxious to discover just how it was that he had been blown through water and air up through so great a thing as a river, and how he felt while en route. A triumph.

Rivers may be smart, but saints are smarter, thanks be.

A PILGRIM BY HOLBEIN

NO MORE WOODEN TOWERS FOR SAN FRANCISCO, 1906

FROM *The Temblor*

MARY AUSTIN

Mary Austin, in this eyewitness account of the California earthquake of 1906, writes of "the broken bits of human tragedy, curiously unrelated," which she saw all round her, the individual detail of a great natural disaster.

Mary Austin all her life was concerned with the singularity of the individual. She herself was uncompromisingly out of tune with the close-packed life of our time, and escaped from it into the desert areas of Arizona and into Indian life and legend.

THERE ARE SOME FORTUNES HARDER TO BEAR ONCE THEY ARE DONE WITH THAN while they are doing, and there are three things that I shall never be able to abide in quietness again—the smell of burning, the creaking of house-beams in the night, and the roar of a great city going past me in the street.

Ours was a quiet neighborhood in the best times; undisturbed except by the hawker's cry or the seldom whistling hum of the wire, and in the two days following April eighteenth, it became a little lane out of Destruction. The first thing I was aware of was being wakened sharply to see my bureau lunging solemnly at me across the width of the room. It got up first on one castor and then on another, like the table at a séance, and wagged its top portentously. It was an antique pattern, tall and marble-topped, and quite heavy enough to seem for the moment sufficient cause for all the uproar. Then I remember standing in the doorway to see the great barred leaves of the entrance on the second floor part quietly as under an unseen hand, and beyond them, in the morning grayness, the rose tree and the palms replacing one another, as in a moving picture, and suddenly an eruption of night-gowned figures crying out that it was only an earthquake, but I had already made this discovery for myself as I recall trying to explain. Nobody having suffered much in our immediate vicinity, we were left free to perceive that the very instant after the quake was tempered by the half-humorous, wholly

American appreciation of a thoroughly good job. Half an hour after the temblor people sitting on their doorsteps, in bathrobes and kimonos, were admitting to each other with a half twist of laughter between tremblings that it was a really creditable shake.

The appreciation of calamity widened slowly as water rays on a mantling pond. Mercifully the temblor came at an hour when families had not divided for the day, but live wires sagging across housetops were to outdo the damage of falling walls. Almost before the dust of ruined walls had ceased rising, smoke began to go up against the sun, which, by nine of the clock, showed bloodshot through it as the eye of Disaster.

It is perfectly safe to believe anything any one tells you of personal adventure; the inventive faculty does not exist which could outdo the actuality; little things prick themselves on the attention as the index of the greater horror.

I remember distinctly that in the first considered interval after the temblor, I went about and took all the flowers out of the vases to save the water that was left; and that I went longer without washing my face than I ever expect to again.

I recall the red flare of a potted geranium undisturbed on a window ledge in a wall of which the brickwork dropped outward, while the roof had gone through the flooring; and the cross-section of a lodging house parted cleanly with all the little rooms unaltered, and the halls like burrows, as if it were the home of some superior sort of insect laid open to the microscope.

South of Market, in the district known as the Mission, there were cheap man-traps folded in like pasteboard, and from these, before the rip of the flames blotted out the sound, arose the thin, long scream of mortal agony.

Down on Market Street Wednesday morning, when the smoke from the burning blocks behind began to pour through the windows we saw an Italian woman kneeling on the street corner praying quietly. Her cheap belongings were scattered beside her on the ground and the crowd trampled them; a child lay on a heap of clothes and bedding beside her, covered and very quiet. The woman opened her eyes now and then, looked at the reddening smoke and addressed herself to prayer as one sure of the stroke of fate. It was not until several days later that it occurred to me why the baby lay so quiet, and why the woman prayed instead of flying.

Not far from there, a day-old bride waited while her husband went back to the ruined hotel for some papers he had left, and the cornice fell on him; then a man who had known him, but not that he was married, came by and carried away the body and shipped it out of the city, so that for four days the bride knew not what had become of him.

There was a young man who, seeing a broken and dismantled grocery, meant no more than to save some food, for already the certainty of famine was upon the city—and was shot for looting. Then his women came and carried the body away, mother and betrothed, and laid it on the grass until space could be found for burial. They drew a handkerchief over its face, and sat quietly beside it without bitterness or weeping. It was all like this, broken bits of human tragedy, curiously unrelated, inconsequential, disrupted by the temblor, impossible to this day to gather up and compose into a proper picture.

The largeness of the event had the effect of reducing private sorrow to a mere pin prick and a point of time. Everybody tells you tales like this with more or less detail. It was reported that two blocks from us a man lay all day with a placard on his breast that he was shot for looting, and no one denied the aptness of the warning. The will of the people was toward authority, and everywhere the tread of soldiery brought a relieved sense of things orderly and secure. It was not as if the city had waited for martial law to be declared, but as if it precipitated itself into that state by instinct as its best refuge.

In the parks were the refugees huddled on the damp sod with insufficient bedding and less food and no water. They laughed. They had come out of their homes with scant possessions, often the least serviceable. They had lost business and clientage and tools, and they did not know if their friends had fared worse. Hot, stifling smoke billowed down upon them, cinders pattered like hail—and they laughed—not hysteria, but the laughter of unbroken courage.

That exodus to the park did not begin in our neighborhood until the second day; all the first day was spent in seeing such things as I relate, while confidently expecting the wind to blow the fire another way. Safe to say one-half the loss of household goods might have been averted, had not the residents been too sure of such exemption. It happened not infrequently that when a man had seen his women safe he went out to relief work and returning found smoking ashes—and the family had left no address. We were told of those who had dead in their households who took them up and fled with them to the likeliest place in the hope of burial, but before it had been accomplished were pushed forward by the flames. Yet to have taken part in that agonized race for the open was worth all it cost in goods.

Before the red night paled into murky dawn thousands of people were vomited out of the angry throat of the street far down toward Market. Even the smallest child carried something, or pushed it before him on a rocking chair, or dragged it behind him in a trunk, and the thing he carried was the index of the refugee's strongest bent. All the women saved their best hats and their babies, and, if there were no babies, some of them pushed pianos up the cement pavements.

All the faces were smutched and pallid, all the figures sloped steadily forward toward the cleared places. Behind them the expelling fire bent out over the lines of flight, the writhing smoke stooped and waved, a fine rain of cinders pattered and rustled over all the folks, and charred bits of the burning fled in the heated air and dropped among the goods. There was a strange, hot, sickish smell in the street as if it had become the hollow slot of some fiery breathing snake. I came out and stood in the pale pinkish glow and saw a man I knew hurrying down toward the gutted district, the badge of a relief committee fluttering on his coat. "Bob," I said, "it looks like the day of judgment!" He cast back at me over his shoulder unveiled disgust at the inadequacy of my terms. "Aw!" he said, "it looks like hell!"

It was a well-bred community that poured itself out into Jefferson Square, where I lay with my friend's goods, and we were packed too close for most of the minor decencies, but nobody forgot his manners. "Beg pardon!" said a man hovering over me with a 200-pound trunk. "Not at all!" I answered making myself thin for him to step over. With an "Excuse me, madam!" another fleeing from the too-heated border of the park to its packed center, deftly up-ended a roll of bedding, turned it across the woman who lay next to me—and the woman smiled.

Right here, if you had time for it, you gripped the large, essential spirit of the West, the ability to dramatize its own activity, and, while continuing in it, to stand off and be vastly entertained by it. In spite of individual heart-sinkings, the San Franciscans during the week never lost the spirited sense of being audience to their own performance. Large figures of adventure moved through the murk of these days—Denman going out with his gun and holding up express wagons with expensively saved goods, which were dumped out on sidewalks that food might be carried to unfed hundreds; Father Ramm cutting away the timbers of St. Mary's tower, while the red glow crept across the charred cross out of reach of the hose; and the humble sacrifices—the woman who shared her full breast with the child of another whose fountain had failed from weariness and fright—would that I had her name to hold in remembrance! She had stopped in the middle of a long residence hill and rested on a forsaken stoop, nourishing her child quietly, when the other woman came by panting, fainting and afraid, not of her class, nor her race, but the hungry baby yearned toward the uncovered breast—and they both of them understood that speech well enough.

Everybody tells you tales like this, more, and better. All along the fire line of Van Ness Avenue, heroic episodes transpired like groups in a frieze against the writhing background of furnace-heated flame; and, for a pediment to the frieze, rows of houseless, possessionless people wrapped in a large, impersonal appreciation of the spectacle.

From Gough Street, looking down, we saw the great tide of fire roaring in the hollow toward Russian Hill; burning so steadily for all it burned so fast that it had the effect of immense deliberation; roaring on toward miles of uninhabited dwellings so lately emptied of life that they appeared consciously to await their immolation; beyond the line of roofs, the hill, standing up darkly against the glow of other incalculable fires, the uplift of flames from viewless intricacies of destruction, sparks belching furiously intermittent like the spray of bursting seas. Low down in front ran besmirched Lilliputians training inadequate hose and creating tiny explosions of a block or so of expensive dwellings by which the rest of us were ultimately saved; and high against the tip of flames where it ran out in broken sparks, the figure of the priest chopping steadily at the tower with the constrained small movement of a mechanical toy.

Observe that a moment since I said houseless people, not homeless; for it comes to this with the bulk of San Franciscans, that they discovered the place and the spirit to be home rather than the walls and the furnishings. No matter how the insurance totals foot up, what landmarks, what treasures of art are evanished, San Francisco, *our* San Francisco is all there yet. Fast as the tall banners of smoke rose up and the flames reddened them, rose up with it something impalpable, like an exhalation. We saw it breaking up in the movements of the refugees, heard it in the tones of their voices, felt it as they wrestled in the teeth of destruction. The sharp sentences by which men called to each other to note the behavior of brick and stone dwellings contained a hint of a warning already accepted for the new building before the old had crumbled. When the heat of conflagration outran the flames and reaching over wide avenues caught high gables and crosses of church steeples, men watching them smoke and blister and crackle into flame, said shortly, "No more wooden towers for San Francisco!" and saved their breath to run with the hose.

What distinguishes the personal experience of the destruction of the gray city from all like disasters of record, is the keen appreciation of the deathlessness of the spirit of living. For the greater part of this disaster—the irreclaimable loss of goods and houses, the violent deaths—was due chiefly to man-contrivances, to the sinking of made ground, to huddled buildings cheapened by greed, to insensate clinging to the outer shells of life; the strong tug of nature was always toward the renewal of it. Births near their time came on hurriedly; children were delivered in the streets or the midst of burnings, and none the worse for the absence of conventional circumstance; marriages were made amazingly, as the disorder of the social world threw all men back severely upon its primal institutions.

After a great lapse of time, when earthquake stories had become matter of humorous reminiscence, burning blocks topics of daily news, and standing in the bread line a fixed habit—by the morning of the third day, to be exact—there arose a threat of peril greater than the thirst or famine, which all the world rose up swiftly to relieve.

Thousands of families had camped in parks not meant to be lived in, but to be looked at; lacking the most elementary means of sanitation. With the rising of the sun, a stench arose from these places and increased perceptibly; spreading with it like an exhalation, went the fear of pestilence. But this at least was a dread that every man could fight at his own camp, and the fight was the modern conviction of the relativity of sanitation to health. By mid-morning the condition of Jefferson Square was such that I should not have trusted myself to it for three hours more, but in three hours it was made safe by no more organized effort than came of the intelligent recognition of the peril. They cleaned the camp first, and organized committees of sanitation afterward.

There have been some unconsidered references of the earthquake disaster to the judgment of God; happily not much of it, but enough to make pertinent some conclusions that shaped themselves swiftly as the city fought and ran. Not to quarrel with the intelligence that reads God behind seismic disturbance, one must still note that the actual damage done by God to the city was small beside the possibilities for damage that reside in man-contrivances; for most man-made things do inherently carry the elements of their own destruction.

How much of all that happened of distress and inestimable loss could have been averted if men would live along the line of the Original Intention, with wide, clean breathing spaces and room for green growing things to push up between?

I have an indistinct impression that the calendar time spent in the city after the temblor was about ten days. I remember the night of rain, and seeing a grown man sitting on a curbstone the morning after, sobbing in the final break-down of bodily endurance. I remember too the sigh of the wind through windows of desolate walls, and the screech and clack of ruined cornices in the red noisy night, and the cheerful banging of pianos in the camps; the burials in trenches and the little, bluish, grave-long heaps of burning among the ruins of Chinatown, and the laughter that shook us as in the midst of the ashy desert we poured in dogged stream to the ferry, at a placard that in a half-burned building where activity had begun again, swung about in the wind and displayed this legend:

DON'T TALK EARTHQUAKE
TALK BUSINESS

All these things seem to have occurred within a short space of days, but when I came out at last at Berkeley—too blossomy, too full-leafed, too radiant—by this token I knew that a great hiatus had taken place. It had been long enough to forget that the smell of sun-steeped roses could be sweet.

ERUPTION OF MOUNT VESUVIUS

THE RETURN OF THE FOREST

FROM *Cream Hill*

LEWIS GANNETT

Cream Hill, from which we have taken this selection, is a native's return, but an unwitting native some generations removed. Lewis Gannett visited Connecticut, liked the countryside, bought a farm, and then discovered that it lay between two farm sites that had belonged to his great-great-grandfather.

Gannett, a city dweller, was for many years daily book reviewer for the New York *Herald Tribune.* He escapes to Cream Hill weekends and summers and is firmly convinced that indigenous Americans—plants, animals and people—were meant to be forest dwellers.

A LITTLE MAN WITH A BIG BEAKED NOSE, A PARSON YET A SPECULATOR IN IDEAS as well as in lands, on October 12 and 13, 1762, planted grape and apple seeds on what he called his "farms" in the hills of Northwestern Connecticut. Some he planted high up on the back of Mount Tarrydiddle, and some deep in the woods toward the north township line. But when I bought an old farmhouse and a bit of land on Cream Hill a hundred and sixty-two years later, I did not know that this great-great-grandfather of mine had once owned two "farms" in that town, one across the brook to the east, the other two miles to the west.

I stumbled, a few years later, on a map he had drawn in his diary, and since then I have made many pilgrimages in search of Ezra Stiles' farm sites. I can step into the woods a few yards from my house and walk through unbroken wilderness toward either of them. An overgrown town road abandoned more than a century ago, charcoal-burners' traces unused for fifty years, or the fire road cut by the CCC boys in the early 1930's can hardly be described as "breaks" in the forest.

Almost everywhere, deep in the woods, you come on massive lichen-grown stone walls, mute evidence of the pioneers' backbreaking effort to tame this wilderness. Even the steepest of these hillsides was once cleared, and many of them were plowed and planted. But long ago the painful clearings quietly grew up again to trees.

Sometimes one finds, close to a stone wall, one of those curiously leveled and trench-girt circles of ground known hereabouts as "charcoal pits." They indicate a second archaeological period in the brief history of white men in these hills. After the ground had been plowed and abandoned it grew up to brush, and then to birch and chestnut forest, tall and thick enough to be worth cutting and processing into charcoal to stoke the furnaces that worked the iron ore from the Mount Riga iron mines, fifteen miles northwest of us. And when the iron mines were abandoned, early in this century, a third period began, in which, for the first time, the forests are cherished, by the state or by private owners who are not farmers but sentimental city folk like myself.

Clearing began with the first settlements in this region, and continued for about a century. Our town's first settlers came in 1739, each of them contracting to clear six acres (and build an eighteen-foot-square house) within two years, but many of them were speculators interested only in proving their claims and selling. So poorly did they build that my great-great-grandfather Ezra, surveying his land in 1762, found on it what he called a "ruin"—a house that could not have been built more than twenty-three years before, but already was falling apart. Men who built as poorly as that doubtless "cleared" as casually.

Ezra, who had a curious taste for exact details, set down in his diary that our town counted sixty families in 1755 and one hundred and ten in 1762. I take it, therefore, that most of the land was then still primeval forest. The great hill clearings came later. Our town boomed for almost a century. In 1776 it had a larger population than it supports today; it reached its peak, more than double its present figure, in 1850. Since then the woods have been coming back. The stone walls we clamber across in the forests today are at least a century old; the charcoal pits date back, roughly, half a century. Today summer residents, handier with golf clubs or tennis rackets than with ax or scythe, are assisting the forests in their slow effort to return to their pristine state. Every year more fields grow up to brush.

It doesn't take long for a field to grow up when farmers cease to work it. I have watched what twenty years can do in my own hill pasture. In 1924 I took a snapshot, looking down across an open fern-and-boulder-strewn pasture slope to the house and barns. Today, from the spot where I stood with my Kodak in 1924, you cannot even see a roof. The pasture has become the kind of dense, poor forest known hereabouts as "sprout land."

First came the "hardhack," yellow-tarred shrubby cinquefoil; then the lush sumachs. Under the sumachs "popples" (aspens) and birches and elms found footing. Now ashes, hickories, and maples are taking over, with here and there an occasional young pine, visible only in winter when the hardwoods are bare.

Sometimes in winter, in the woods about us, I can trace cart tracks which cannot have been used for half a century; the slight depressions are invisible when leaf-covered. Cellar holes last longer—we have found seven abandoned cellar holes within a mile of our house—but even a cellar hole fills up and all but vanishes under the ever-forming soil in a century and a half. Despite Ezra's careful maps, I have never been able to locate with precision the spots on his "farms" where he planted grape and apple seeds in 1762, or to discover the site of his "ruin." It is all unbroken woods now, and I like it better so.

In Ezra's day, I think, it was mostly oak forest hereabouts, with a sprinkling of chestnut that turned it into a candlelit woodland garden in spring, and an occasional patch of pine. The chestnut succumbed to the blight before my day here. Occasionally a tree growing from what must be very tired roots survives long enough to set a few flowers and ripen a bur or two, and then withers. People who have grown up since 1910 have no conception of the glory of these woods in May in the days when chestnut sprays illuminated the whole forest.

Cream Hill has changed since Ezra saw it. About the only trees in our town which can have been Ezra's contemporaries are the 175-foot "virgin pines" near the Plains, great trees which are today glorified in the guidebooks as unique in New England. The land across the highway from me reaches up to a white oak on Rugg Mountain which has been used as a boundary marker for a century and a half, but that oak will not long bound or mark in any discernible fashion at all. It is only a shell today. No one can reckon its age by its rings; its hollow heart must have served as a home for squirrels and coons since long before I was born.

A tree three feet through looks big to city folk, or even to country folk, today. But on a three-foot ash, cut when the town rebuilt the Cream Hill Road in 1946, I could count only ninety rings. A three-foot hickory, which we cut after lightning struck it in the 1930's, was barely a century old. Even the tall pines at the Plains were young in Ezra's day. Some of them fell in the hurricane of 1938 and, when cut, proved to be almost exactly two hundred and fifty years old.

Yet in Ezra's diary he makes note of a pine tree three feet through with four hundred rings, and of an oak five feet through with two hundred and thirty-two rings. Such trees must have grown in dense forest, aspiring toward the light—in such forests as no living man has seen north of the Great Smokies, or east, in this latitude, of the Cascade Mountains. There must have been majestic woods hereabouts—beautiful to our imagining eyes, but a terrific chore to the farmer who yearned for clear fields.

They burned the trees off in those days, cutting only what they needed for lumber, and, obviously, they burned much of the soil with the trees, thereby changing the face of our countryside for generations to come. Decades later, the land was relogged several times; even today there is always a little commercial timber cutting going on in our woods. When the forest close to the old Salisbury and Mount Riga iron mines northwest of us was exhausted the charcoal-burners drifted down into our region. Old-timers say that the chestnut grew fast enough to make a fresh harvest of charcoal every forty years. But though the shafts of some of the old chestnuts still stand like corpses in our woods, the native chestnut as a race is almost as extinct as the mammoth. . . .

There were more lady's slippers, pink and yellow both, in the woods in Ezra's day, more wintergreen and partridgeberry, because there were more pine woods, and the pine-woods flowers fade away when the hardwood second growth comes in. You find different flowers under ash and maple from those under oak and pine. There were, I am sure, fewer of the little bluets that my Quaker grandmother used to call "quaker-ladies"; they dust the cow pastures with their snow-like blossom in May. But there were fewer cow pastures in Ezra's day, and today again, as the cow pastures grow up to brush, the quaker-ladies fade away.

Drive along any New England road today, and note the "wild" flowers that give it character: most of them are immigrants from Europe, strangers who arrived and made themselves at home with the white man. We recognize the pale pink bouncing Bet and the abundant banks of tawny day lilies as "escapes" from vanished gardens—partly because they tend to linger in the neighborhood of betraying lilac bushes and apple trees. But even deep into the woods along the old cart roads, other plant immigrants have wandered.

The yellow rocket and wild mustard that gleam in May; most of the clovers—the red, the pink alsike, the yellow hop, and the tall sweet white and sweet yellow clover—are immigrants. So are the feathery white wild carrot ("Queen Anne's lace") and the familiar yellow wild parsnip, the daisies and the starry yarrow, the sky-blue chicory and the coarse blueweed that looks so lovely at a distance (I brought some of it into my garden once and had a time getting rid of it). So too are a golden army: the roadside buttercups, dandelions, butter-and-eggs, St.-John's-wort, the delicate celandine poppy, tansy, the velvety-leaved mulleins, and the great coarse elecampane that some call "wild sunflower."

Ezra probably never saw a black-eyed Susan; it came from our own West, years later, with clover seed. Our commoner thistles are from Europe, even that which we miscall Canada thistle. So is teasel. The handsome orange hawkweed, often called "devil's paintbrush," and the brilliant spiked loosestrife that paints the marshes purple in August, both invaded this countryside within the memory of living man; the pestiferous shrubby cinquefoil (which our farmers call "hardhack," the name I give to steeplebush) is another European invader. Our "wild" roadsides are not native American at all.

Weeding in our gardens today, we are mostly rescuing European flowers and vegetables from European weeds. Not merely the useful timothy and redtop but the pernicious crab, quack, bent, foxtail, and wire grasses are importations; so is that pesky tiny daisy-like weed that my neighbors dub "German-weed" and the more poetic call "gallant soldiers." So are the wiry-rooted sheep sorrel and the tough-rooted big docks, including the clinging burdock, most of our stinging nettles, the woolly catnip and the smoother peppermint, the ugly common plantain and the pretty little thyme-leaved speedwell that nestles in the lawn, shepherd's purse, purple self-heal and the creeping gill-over-the-ground, the nightshade that is not really so deadly as its name indicates, and the little cheese mallow whose fruits the children munch, almost all the various pigweeds, both the common chickweed that blooms, in a year of thaws, during every month of the calendar, and the coarser mouse-ear chickweed.

A historical botanist could prolong that list almost infinitely. It is long enough to make this clear: the Cream Hill roadsides do not look today at all as they did in anyone's great-great-grandfather's time—not, at least, until mid-August, when the goldenrods flame. Our goldenrods and asters are native American. Ezra too must have admired them, when he rode his horse up from New Haven to inspect his tenant farms, his saddlebags prudently packed with sermons. Possibly he dismounted now and then to pick a native bottle gentian in the August woods, or, in September, to look closer at the reflection of the sky in a swampy patch of fringed gentian. His diary does not say. It details the salaries of Connecticut parsons; it comments on local industries and even reflects on the deplorable sexual customs of Indians, but it never mentions a wild flower.

As he rode northward, Ezra probably rode through cut-over lands already growing up to bush, and these at least were certainly going native. For, though European wild flowers have taken over our roadsides and entered our woods, it is a striking fact that the only European tree you will find in Cream Hill woods is the apple. Those apple-seeds Ezra planted in 1762 may have produced puny fruit, but the tree was tenacious. Its descendants are still reseeding themselves in competition with the maples and oaks, beside the imperishable stone walls. They prefer a little sunshine, but survive considerable shade. If the state forest program continues, however, and the overgrown pasture lands are given time to grow up into deep forests, it is probable that even the apples will die out of the shady woodlands, and that the forests will again be, as they were in Ezra's day, one hundred per cent native American. Our forests change; they go through a cycle—sumach, popple, birch, elm and ash, maple, oak and pine—but, unlike the cycle of the roadsides, it is an all-American cycle.

Now this is a curious fact, worth meditating. Native American trees do not survive in the cities. Pines die in sooty air. The native sycamore struggles in the world of pavements, where its cousin the Oriental plane tree does well. English elms do better than American in New York City, though neither really likes the dirt of the metropolis. All the trees that really adapt themselves to solid-block city life come from Asia—the ginkgo or maidenhair tree, which thrives around Gramercy Park, on Central Park South, and West Eleventh and East Nineteenth Streets; the ailanthus or tree of heaven (the tree that grew in Brooklyn, which, before Betty Smith wrote her book, was better known as the Manhattan back-yard tree); the paper mulberry that is a weed in Brooklyn Heights back yards; and the horse chestnut.

So, too, the house or "English" sparrows, the pigeons, and the starlings—the three birds most at home the year round in New York City—are all Eurasian immigrants, as are the alley cats and rats and mice, the city's only self-perpetuating quadrupeds.

It would seem that Americans—trees, flowers, and, perhaps, humans—were meant to be forest dwellers. Perhaps that is why so many of us who live most of our lives in cities feel that we shrink and shrivel, physically and spiritually, unless we sometimes get back to the country. We boast of our skyscrapers, but we are not at home in them. Something of the red man's psychology has entered into us. It may be sheer mysticism, but it is a solacing thought that real Americans—windflowers, sugar maples, hermit thrushes, chipmunks, or humans–cannot stand the dust; while only authentic American trees and wild flowers and birds and mammals can survive in the forest. In the forests the world that Ezra saw is slowly returning; and in the forests we, too, feel an atavistic at-homeness.

A PASSION FOR THE GOLD

FROM *The Fortunes of Richard Mahoney*

HENRY HANDEL RICHARDSON

There are few descriptions of gold digging, its mirages, hazards, illusory rewards, that are so restrainedly and so unerringly real as Henry Handel Richardson's in this selection from her *Fortunes of Richard Mahoney*. Her writing is so quiet, one critic said of her, "that its merits and . . . the essential imaginativeness of her work may be missed by those eager for display." Richardson stands with the great English writers of the last generation. Her Mahoney trilogy of Australian life has often been compared with Romain Rolland's *Jean Christophe* and Thomas Mann's *Buddenbrooks*.

UNDER A SKY SO PURE AND LUMINOUS THAT IT SEEMED LIKE A THINLY DRAWN veil of blueness, which ought to have been transparent, stretched what, from a short way off, resembled a desert of pale clay. No patch of green offered rest to the eye; not a tree, hardly a stunted bush, had been left standing, either on the bottom of the vast shallow basin itself, or on the several hillocks that dotted it, and formed its sides. Even the most prominent of these, the Black Hill, which jutted out on the Flat like a gigantic tumulus, had been stripped of its dense timber, feverishly disemboweled, and was now become a bald protuberance, strewn with gravel and clay. The whole scene had that strange, repellent ugliness that goes with the breaking-up, and throwing into disorder, of what has been sanctified as final: it belongs, in particular, to the wanton disturbing of earth's gracious, green-spread crust. In the pre-golden era, this wide valley, lying open to sun and wind, had been a lovely grassland, ringed by a circlet of wooded hills; beyond these, by a belt of virgin forest. A limpid river, and more than one creek, had meandered across its face; water was to be found there, even in the driest summer. She-oaks and peppermints had given shade to the flocks of the early settlers; wattles had bloomed their brief delirious yellow passion against the gray-green foliage of the gums. Now, all that was lift of the original "pleasant resting-place," and its pristine beauty, were the ancient volcanic cones of Warrenheip and Buninyong. These, too far off to supply wood for firing or slabbing, still stood green and timbered, and looked down upon the havoc that had been made of the fair, pastoral lands.

Seen nearer at hand, the dun-colored desert resolved itself into uncountable pimpling clay- and mud-heaps, of divers shades and varying sizes: some consisted of but a few bucketfuls of mullock, others were taller than the tallest man. There were also hundreds of rain-soaked, mud-bespattered tents, sheds and awnings; wind-sails, which fell, funnel-like from a kind of gallows, into the shafts they ventilated; flags fluttering on high posts in front of stores. The many human figures that went to and fro were hardly to be distinguished from the ground they trod. They were coated with earth, clay-clad in ochre and gamboge. Their faces were daubed with clauber; it matted great beards, and entangled the coarse hairs on chests and brawny arms. Where, here and there, a blue jumper had kept a tinge of its blueness, it was so besmeared with yellow that it might have been expected to turn green. The gauze neck-veils that hung from the brims of wide-awakes or cabbage-trees, were become stiff little lattices of caked clay.

There was water everywhere. From the spurs and gullies round about, the autumn rains had poured freely down on the Flat; river and creeks had been over their banks; and such narrow ground-space as remained between the thick-sown tents, the myriads of holes that abutted one on another, jealous of every inch of space, had become a trough of mud. Water meandered over this mud, or carved its soft way in channels; it lay about in puddles, thick and dark as coffee-grounds; it filled abandoned shallow holes to the brim. The humps of clay and gravel had been worked into a state of glutinous filth, by the thousands of jackbooted feet that crossed and recrossed them, that slipped on them, and squelched in them, and stuck fast.

From this scene rose a blurred hum of sound; rose, and, as it were, remained stationary above it—like a smoke-cloud, which no wind comes to drive away. Gradually, though, the ear made out, in the conglomerate of noise, a host of separate noises, infinitely multiplied: the sharp tick-tick of surface-picks, the dull thud of shovels, their muffled echoes from the depths below. There was also the continuous squeak and groan of windlasses; the bump of the mullock emptied from the bucket; the trundle of wheelbarrows, pushed along a plank from the shaft's mouth to the nearest pool; the dump of the dart on the heap for washing; the crunching of cart-wheels, and a horse's smacking efforts to get a footing on the slippery ground. Along the banks of a creek, hundreds of cradles rattled and grated; the noise of the spades chopping the gravel in the puddling-tubs, or the Long Toms, was like the scrunch of shingle under waves. The drip and plash of falling water was all-pervading: it was poured from buckets, where wet holes were baling out; from long-handled dippers into buddles and cradles; while here and there it fell, with a splash, from the tall pole of a weegee.—The fierce yelping of the dogs chained to the flag-posts of stores, mongrels, which yapped at friend and foe alike, supplied a note of ear-splitting discord.

But, except for this, it was a wholly mechanical din. Human brains directed operations, human hands carried them out, but the sound of the human voice was, for the most part, lacking. The diggers were a somber, preoccupied race, little given to lip-work. Even the "shepherds," who, in waiting to see if their neighbors struck the lead, beguiled the time with euchre and "lambskinnet," played moodily, their mouths glued to their pipe-stems; they were tail-on-end to fling down the cards for pick and shovel. The great majority, ant-like in their indefatigable business, neither turned a head nor looked up: backs were bent, eyes fixed, in a hard scrutiny of cradle or tin-dish: it was the earth that held them, the familiar, homely earth, whose common fate it is to be trodden heedlessly underfoot. Here, it was a lodestone that drew all men's thoughts. And it took toll of their bodies in odd, exhausting forms of labor, which were swift to weed out the unfit.

The men at the windlasses spat into their horny palms and bent to the crank: they paused only to pass the back of a hand over a sweaty forehead, or to drain a nose between two fingers. The barrow-drivers shoved their loads, the bones of their forearm standing out like ribs. Beside the pools, the puddlers chopped with their shovels; some even stood in the tubs, and worked the earth with their feet, as wine-pressers trample grapes. The cradlers, eternally rocking with one hand, held a long stick in the other, with which to break up any clods a careless puddler might have deposited in the hopper. Behind these came the great army of fossickers, washers of surface-dirt, equipped with knives and tin-dishes, and content if they could wash out half-a-pennyweight to the dish. At their heels, still others, who treated the tailings they threw away. And, among these last, was a sprinkling of women, more than one with an infant sucking at her breast. Withdrawn into a group for themselves worked a body of Chinese, in loose blue blouses, flappy blue leg-bags, and huge conical straw hats. They, too, fossicked and re-washed, using, in the process, extravagant quantities of water.

Thus the pale-eyed multitude worried the surface, and, at the risk and cost of their lives, probed the depths. Now that deep sinking was in vogue, gold-digging no longer served as a play-game for the gentleman and the amateur; the greater number of those who toiled at it were work-tried, seasoned men. And yet, although it had now sunk to the level of any other arduous and uncertain occupation, and the magic prizes of the early days were seldom found, something of the old, romantic glamour still clung to this most famous gold-field, dazzling the eyes and confounding the judgment. Elsewhere, the horse was in use at the pudding-trough, and machines for crushing quartz were under discussion. But the Ballarat digger resisted the introduction of machinery, for fear of the capitalist machinery would bring in its train. He remained the dreamer, the jealous individualist; he hovered for ever on the brink of a stupendous discovery.

This dream it was, of vast wealth, got without exertion, which had decoyed the strange, motley crowd, in which peers and churchmen rubbed shoulders with the scum of Norfolk Island, to exile in this outlandish region. And the intention of all alike had been: to snatch a golden fortune from the earth; and then, hey, presto! for the old world again. But they were reckoning without their host; only too many of those who entered the country went out no more. They became prisoners to the soil. The fabulous riches of which they had heard tell, amounted, at best, to a few thousands of pounds: what folly to depart with so little, when mother earth still teemed! Those who drew blanks nursed an unquenchable hope, and labored all their days like navvies, for a navvy's wage. Others again, broken in health, or disheartened, could only turn to an easier handiwork. There were also those who, as soon as fortune smiled on them, dropped their tools and ran to squander the work of months in a wild debauch; and these invariably returned, tail down, to prove their luck anew. And, yet again, there were those who, having once seen the metal in the raw: in dust, fine as that brushed from a butterfly's wing; in heavy, chubby nuggets; or, more beautiful still, as the daffodil-yellow veining of bluish-white quartz: these were gripped in the subtlest way of all. A passion for the gold itself awoke in them, an almost sensual craving to touch and possess; and, to these, the glitter of a few specks at the bottom of pan or cradle came, in time, to mean more than "home," or wife, or child.

Such were the fates of those who succumbed to the "unholy hunger."—It was like a form of revenge taken on them, for their loveless schemes of robbing and fleeing; a revenge contrived by the ancient, barbaric country they had so lightly invaded. Now, she held them captive—without chains; ensorcelled—without witchcraft; and, lying stretched in the sun like some primeval monster, her breasts freely bared, she watched, with a malignant eye, the efforts made by these puny mortals to tear their lips away.

A STRONG EARTHQUAKE

FROM *Letter to Sir Horace Mann, March 11, 1750*

HORACE WALPOLE

A first earthquake was a rarity for sophisticated eighteenth-century London, a second was a casual conversation piece. Or so Horace Walpole intimates, and there were few writers of the time who held a more sensitive finger to the fashionable pulse. Walpole is best known as the author of *The Castle of Otranto,* the earliest of the Gothic novels that tried to combine equal parts of horror and romance. As novelist, Walpole has only historical interest; as letter writer he is unsurpassed in the English language and, many think, even outshines his French model, Mme. de Sévigné. This letter is from his forty-year correspondence with Sir Horace Mann.

March 11, 1750.

"Portents and prodigies have grown so frequent,
That they have lost their names."—*Dryden.*

MY TEXT IS NOT LITERALLY TRUE; BUT AS FAR AS EARTHQUAKES GO TOWARDS lowering the price of wonderful commodities, to be sure we are overstocked. We have had a second, much more violent than the first; and you must not be surprised if, by next post, you hear of a burning mountain sprung up in Smithfield. In the night between Wednesday and Thursday last—exactly a month since the first shock—the earth had a shivering fit between one and two, but so slight, that if no more had followed, I don't believe it would have been noticed. I had been awake, and had scarce dosed again—on a sudden I felt my bolster lift up my head; I thought somebody was getting from under my bed, but soon found it was a strong earthquake, that lasted near half a minute, with a violent vibration and great roaring. I rang my bell; my servant came in, frightened out of his senses: in an instant we heard all the windows in the neighbourhood flung up. I got up and found people running into the streets, but saw no mischief done: there has been some; two old houses flung down, several chimneys, and much china-ware. The bells rung in several houses. Admiral Knowles, who has lived long in Jamaica, and felt seven there, says this was more violent than any of them: Francesco prefers it to the dreadful one at Leghorn. The wise say, that if we have not rain soon, we certainly will have more. Several people are going out of town, for it has nowhere reached above ten miles from London: they say they are not frightened, but that it is such fine weather, "Lord! one can't help going into the country!" The only visible effect it has had was on the Ridotto, at which, being the following night, there were but four hundred people. A parson, who came into White's the morning of earthquake the first, and heard bets laid on whether it was an earthquake or the blowing up of powder-mills, went away exceedingly scandalised, and said: "I protest they are such an impious set of people, that I believe if the last trumpet was to sound they would bet puppet-show against Judgment."

THEIR FINAL RESTING PLACES

FROM *The Proper Bostonians*

CLEVELAND AMORY

Cleveland Amory knows the foibles and oddities of the vanishing four hundred. He himself is a scion, a somewhat irreverent one, of a first family.

In this selection he discusses proper Bostonian funeral customs and "the affair Higginson," "the post-mortem adventure," as he calls it, of one of Boston's very first families.

THE PROPER BOSTONIAN FUNERAL CUSTOM DOES NOT END WITH THE CLOSING OF the funeral service. Great attention is also paid to the final resting place of the deceased. In Boston's early days Old Granary, across from the ancient Park Street Church, was a sort of Proper Bostonian Westminster Abbey. Here First Family dead lie buried four-deep, with tablets commemorating such luminaries as Benjamin Franklin's father and mother, Paul Revere, John Hancock and Samuel Adams. In more recent times Forest Hills, located on the high road to Milton, and Mount Auburn, the so-called "Gateway to Heaven" in Cambridge, have risen to positions of high favor. The latter has a special niche in Boston legend from its commemoration in a three-part poem written many years ago by a First Family lady with the assistance of her seamstress. Unfortunately never completed in publishable form, the poem was conceived to tell the story of the cemetery in its three phases: Mount Auburn As It Was on the Day of Creation, Mount Auburn As It Is, and Mount Auburn As It Shall Be on the Day of Resurrection.

The crowding of these graveyards in latter years has proved no small impediment to the correct carrying-on of the custom of ancestor worship. Many notable First Family remains have had to be moved several times, the outstanding example being the post-mortem adventures of General Joseph Warren of Bunker Hill fame. Originally buried on the battlefield where he fell, he was moved in 1825 to Old Granary, space having been generously donated by the Boston Minot Family, close friends of the Warrens. But

Minots soon needed more room themselves and Warren was forced to move a third time, on this occasion travelling to a branch Warren Family tomb in St. Paul's churchyard. As time went on, however, more immediate Warrens began to look on the General, for all his distinction, as somewhat of an intruder, and still another move was necessitated. This was to Forest Hills, General Warren's fourth, and so far final, resting place.

The moving of General Warren was comparatively easy in view of the fact that he could always be accurately identified by a bullet hole behind the left ear of his skull and by two false teeth that had been wired in place by Paul Revere. But in the moving of other remains mistakes have been made. When England wished the body of their war hero, Major Pitcairn, brought back from Boston for burial in Westminster Abbey, Boston was glad to comply and with Proper Bostonian efficiency sent along a body right on schedule—not, however, the body of the Major which was many years later found to be still in the city. The body of Gilbert Stuart, the painter, in transit from Old Granary to another graveyard, disappeared altogether. More recently social Boston was shocked by what remains today undoubtedly the greatest case of mass grave-juggling in its history—the affair Higginson.

Suspicion had somehow grown up that all was not well with the Higginson Family lot at Old Granary. After some legal complications a Higginson relative finally received permission to have the Granary caretaker dig up the lot and check the matter. The suspicion proved to be well founded when the caretaker, after diligently digging for two days under the lot carefully marked with the names of eleven Higginsons, was unable to find a single body. Other Higginsons now became interested and a thorough investigation was undertaken. After some time it was learned that old George Higginson, a man going on ninety and mindful of his future, had been frightened over a proposed extension of Tremont Street—which he felt might obliterate the Family lot entirely—and had taken it upon himself to order all Higginson occupants of Old Granary moved. He had done this through a third party, however, and an absent-minded man himself had never checked the carrying-out of his orders. He knew only that they had been moved, all eleven of them.

Relatives immediately checked Mount Auburn. But there were no recent Higginson arrivals at the Gateway to Heaven. Forest Hills was combed with equal lack of success. By this time all Proper Boston was interested. Finally, at the little Walnut Hills Cemetery in Brookline, a caretaker solved the riddle. He announced he had recently received a shipment of Higginsons and what was all the fuss about anyway?

The caretaker was as good as his word. He did indeed have the bodies. There was only one trouble. Somewhere along the way there had been two additions in the Higginson Family. The Walnut Hills caretaker had received

—and buried—not eleven bodies, but thirteen. Furthermore he was proud of the new lot on his grounds, and as far as he and other authorities of Walnut Hills were concerned there would be no more digging and checking of bodies.

In a way the affair Higginson may be said to be concluded. In another way, however, it is not. It may take a sympathetic understanding of the Proper Bostonian, as well as of the power of First Family customs, to appreciate the fact, but the affair still causes uneasiness of mind among certain present-day Higginsons. Aspiring to their final resting places, they cannot help knowing that the time is coming when they must enter such retirement in the company of, as they or any other Proper Bostonian would put it, two "total strangers."

COVERED WAGONS PUSHING WEST

THE VILLAGE OF CALAMITY

FROM *Old Junk*

H. M. TOMLINSON

At the pit mouth we stand with H. M. Tomlinson watching the rescue parties go down the mine shaft and come up with the dead. That interval of waiting which the writer describes in this selection is perhaps the longest and most despairing any man can know.

H. M. Tomlinson is the venerable man of English letters. He celebrated his eightieth birthday some years ago with a volume of autobiographical essays he called *On Being Out of Date*. He prefers the temper of older times; his childhood memories are of Queen Victoria and Carlyle. His novels have won a large audience on both sides of the Atlantic, his finely wrought essays a smaller and probably more discriminating one.

THERE WAS GREAT BARR, IDLE, STILL, AND QUIET. THROUGH THE BIRMINGHAM suburbs, out into the raw, bleak winter roads between the hedges, quite beyond the big town smoking with its enterprising labours, one approached the village of calamity in diffidence. You felt you were intruding; that you were an interloper, coming through curiosity that was not excused by the compunction you felt, to see the appearance of a place that had tragedy in nearly all its homes. Young men streamed by on bicycles in the same direction, groups were hurrying there on foot.

The road rose in a mound to let the railway under, and beyond the far dip was the village, an almost amorphous group of mean red dwellings stuck on ragged fields about the dominant colliery buildings. Three high, slim chimneys were leisurely pouring smoke from the grotesque black skeleton structures above the pits. The road ran by the boundary, and was packed with people, all gazing absorbed and quiet into the grounds of the colliery; they were stacked up the hedge banks, and the walls and trees were loaded with boys.

A few empty motor cars of the colliery directors stood about. A carriage-horse champed its bit, and the still watchers turned at once to that intrusive sound. Around us, a clear winter landscape (for it had been raining) ran to the distant encompassing hills which lifted like low ramparts of cobalt and amethyst to a sky of luminous saffron and ice-green, across which leaden clouds were moving. The country had that hard, coldly radiant appearance which always impresses a sad man as this world's frank expression of its alien disregard; this world not his, on which he has happened, and must endure with his trouble for a brief time.

As I went through the press of people to the colliery gates, the women in shawls turned to me, first with annoyance that their watching should be disturbed, and then with some dull interest. My assured claim to admittance probably made them think I was the bearer of new help outside their knowledge; and they willingly made room for me to pass. I felt exactly like the interfering fraud I was. What would I not have given then to be made, for a brief hour, a nameless miracle-worker.

In the colliery itself was the same seeming apathy. There was nothing to show in that yard, black with soddened cinders and ash muck, where the new red-brick engine-houses stood, that somewhere half a mile beneath our feet were thirty men, their only exit to the outer world barred by a subterranean fire. Nothing showed of the fire but a whitish smoke from a ventilating shaft; and a stranger would not know what that signified. But the women did. Wet with rain they had been standing watching that smoke all night, and were watching it still, for its unceasing pour to diminish. Constant and unrelenting, it streamed steadily upward, as though it drew its volume from central fires that would never cease.

The doors of the office were thrown open, and three figures emerged. They broke into the listlessness of that dreary place, where nothing seemed to be going on, with a sudden real purpose, fast but unhurried, and moved towards the shaft; three Yorkshire rescue experts—one of them to die later—with the colliery manager explaining the path they should follow below with eager seriousness. "Figures of fun!" They had muzzles on their mouths and noses, goggles on their eyes, fantastic helms, and queer cylinders and bags slung about them. As they went up the slope of wet ash, quick and full of purpose, the crowd broke silence and cheered emotionally that little party of forlorn hope.

They entered the cage, and down they went. Still it was difficult for me to think that we were fronting tragedy, for no danger showed. An hour and more passed in nervous and dismal waiting. There was a signal. Some men ran to the pithead carrying hot bricks and blankets. The doctors took off their coats, and arranged bottles and tinkling apparatus on chairs stuck in the mud. The air smelt of iodoform. A cloth was laid on the ground from the shaft to the engine-house, and stretchers were placed near. The women, some carrying infants, broke rank. That quickly up-running rope was bringing the first news. The rope stopped running and the cage appeared. Only the rescue party came out, one carrying a moribund cat. They knew nothing; and the white-faced women, with hardly repressed hysteria, took again their places by the engine-house.

So we passed that day, watching the place from which came nothing but disappointment. Occasionally a child, too young to know it was adding to its mother's grief, would wail querulously. There came a time when I and all there knew that to go down that shaft was to meet with death. The increasing exhaustion and pouring sweat of the returning rescue parties showed that. Yet the miners who were not selected to go down were angry; they violently abused the favouritism of the officials who would not let all risk their lives.

I have a new regard for my fellows since Great Barr. About you and me there are men like that. There is nothing to distinguish them. They show no signs of greatness. They have common talk. They have crude ways. They walk with a lurch. Their eyes are not eager. They are not polite. Their clothes are dirty. They live in cheap houses on cheap food. They call you "sir." They are the great unwashed, the mutable many, the common people. The common people! Greatness is as common as that. There are not enough honours and decorations to go round. Talk of the soldier! *Vale* to Welsby of Normanton! He was a common miner. He is dead. His fellows were in danger, their wives were white-faced and their children were crying, and he buckled on his harness and went to the assault with no more thought for self than great men have in a great cause; and he is dead. I saw him go to his death. I wish I could tell you of Welsby of Normanton.

I left that place where the star-shine was showing the grim skeleton of the shaft-work overhead in the night, and where men moved about below in the indeterminate dark like dismal gnomes. There was a woman whose cry, when Welsby died, was like a challenge.

Next morning, in Great Barr, some blinds were down, the street was empty. Children, who could see no reason about them why their fathers should not return as usual, were playing football by the tiny church. A group of women were still gazing at the grotesque ribs and legs of the pithead staging as though it were a monster without ruth.

THE BREATH OF THE EARTH

FROM *The Well*

AUGUSTO CESPEDES

In this selection, Augusto Cespedes, noted Bolivian writer, tells of an incident in the Chaco War fought between Paraguay and Bolivia. What began as a dispute over boundary lines, developed into a bitter and brutal full-scale war which lasted for the three years from 1932 to 1935 and harrowed both countries.

Harriet de Onis, critic and translator of Latin-American literature, writes that "the nature of the struggle in the Chaco desert, where the soldiers fought harder for a drink of water than for a thousand acres of land, is more vividly revealed in the episode of 'The Well' . . . than in any history."

I AM MIGUEL NAJAYA, SERGEANT IN THE BOLIVIAN ARMY, AND I HAVE BEEN IN *this hospital of Tarairi for fifty days with an attack of beriberi due to vitamin deficiency, which is sufficient grounds, according to the doctors, for me to be evacuated to La Paz, my native city and my fond dream. I have been serving for two and a half years, and neither the bullet-wound I got in the ribs last year nor this fine case of beriberi have got me my discharge.*

In the meantime I get bored, wandering about among the specters in underdrawers who are the patients in this hospital, and as I have nothing to read in the sultry hours of this hell, I read myself, I re-read my diary. By stringing together the separate pages of this diary, I have managed to piece out of it the story of a well which is now in the hands of Paraguayans.

To me this well will always be ours, perhaps because of the agony it made us go through. Around it and within it a terrible drama in two acts was presented: the first, getting it started, and the second, digging it out.

This is what those pages say:

January 15, 1933. A summer without water. In this zone of the Chaco, north of Platanillos, it almost never rains, and the little it has rained has evaporated. To the north, to the south, to right or to left, whichever way you look or walk through the almost incorporeal transparence of the forest of ashen tree-trunks, unburied skeletons condemned to remain standing in the lifeless sand, there is not a drop of water, which, however, does not prevent men at war from living here. We live, wasted, unhappy, aged before our time, the trees with more branches than leaves, the men with more thirst than hate.

I am in charge of twenty soldiers, whose faces are splattered with freckles, with scabs like disks of leather on their cheek-bones, and eyes always bright with fever. Many of them had been sent to the defense of Aguarrica and Kilometer Seven of the Saavedra Alihuata Road, from which their wounds or sicknesses took them to the hospital of Muñoz and afterwards to that of Ballivián. When they recovered they were brought back, by way of Platanillos, to form part of the Second Army. They were attached to the Engineers' Corps, where I was sent, too; we have been here for a week now, close to Fort Loa, building a road. The country is covered with thorny brush, labyrinth-like and colorless. There is no water.

Ahead of us is a regiment which holds the hill that protects this zone.

January 17. In the afternoon, amidst clouds of dust that perforate the curving aerial paths that stretch to the pulp of the orange sun, gilding the edges of the anemic foliage, the water-truck arrived.

It is an old truck, its fenders all dented and twisted, the windshield gone, one headlight held together by strips of tape, looking as though it had been through a cyclone, and loaded with black barrels. The cropped head of the driver looks like a gourd. He shines with sweat and his shirt, open to the navel, reveals his wet breast.

"The creek is drying up," he announced today. "The water ration for the regiment is smaller now."

"This hauling water for the soldiers is going to turn me to water," added the helper who came with him.

He was as dirty as the driver; the latter was distinguished by reason of his shirt, whereas the former owed his personality to his greasy pants. He's tight, and he tries to beat me down on the ration of coca for my men. But once in a while he gives me a pack of cigarettes.

The driver tells me that at Platanillos they are thinking of moving our division farther up. This gives the soldiers food for talk. There's one from Potosí, Chacón, small, hard, and dark as a hammer, who voices the baleful question:

"Will there be water?"

"Less than here," is the answer.

"Less than here? Are we to live on air, like the caraguatas?"

The suffering of the soldiers, which increases with the growing heat, is related in their minds to the relief the water, become an obsession, might give but does not.

Unscrewing the stopper of one of the barrels, they pour out our water in two gasoline cans, one for cooking, the other for drinking, and the truck drives on. A little water always spills out on the ground, wetting it, and swarms of white butterflies gather thirstily around the dampness. Sometimes I decide to be extravagant with a handful of water, and I pour it on the back of my neck, and some little bees, who live on God knows what, come and get entangled in my hair.

January 21. Last night it rained. During the day the heat was like a rubber suit. The reflection of the sun on the sand stabbed at us with its white darts. But at six o'clock it rained. We stripped and bathed in the downpour. Under our feet the warm mud slipped between our toes.

January 25. Again the heat. Again that dry, invisible flame which sticks to the body. It seems to me someone should open a window somewhere to let in a little air. The sky is a huge stone in which the sun is set.

We live with axe and shovel under our arms. The rifles are half-buried under the dust in the tents, and we are nothing but road-builders cutting a straight line over the hill, opening a road, for what purpose we do not know, through the tangled brush, which shrivels with the heat, too. The sun burns everything. A field of hay which yesterday morning was yellow is white today, and dry, flattened out, because the sun has walked over it. From eleven in the morning until three in the afternoon it is impossible to work, for the hillside is like a furnace. During those hours, after searching in vain for a compact mass of shade, I stretch out under any tree, in the illusive shelter of branches which look like a diagram of twisted nerves.

The earth, without moisture to give it cohesion, rises like a white death, enveloping the tree-trunks in its dusty embrace, beclouding the network of shade, which is torn to tatters by the rushing torrent of sun. The gleam of the sun produces a magnetic vibration upon the profile of the near-by hayfield, which is rigid and pale as a corpse.

Prostrate, limp, we lie in the grip of the lethargy of the daily fever, sunk in a warm stupor against which the whir of the locusts, endless as time, saws back and forth. The heat, a transparent specter stretched face-down over the wasteland, snores in the shrilling of the locusts. They fill the woods, where they have their invisible, mysterious workshop with its millions of little wheels, trip-hammers, and whistles at work, which deafen the air for miles and miles around.

We, at the center of this exasperating polyphony, live a bare life of words without thoughts, hour after hour, watching in the colorless sky the rocking flight of the buzzards, which give my eyes the impression of decorative bird figures on an infinite stretch of papered wall.

In the distance, from time to time, come sporadic sounds of gunfire.

February 10. The heat has taken possession of our bodies, making them one with the inorganic laziness of the earth, turning them to dust, jointless, soft, feverish. They exist for us only by reason of the torment it causes us to transmit from the skin the sweaty awareness of the oven-hot kiss of the heat. We only come to ourselves at night. The day gives itself up in the great blaze of the sun's last crimson glow, and night comes determined to sleep, but it is beset on all sides by the pricks of endless animal cries: whistles, shrilling, cawing, a gamut of voices strange to us, to our upland, mountain ears.

Night and day. By day we are silent, but the words of my men awaken at night. There are some who are veterans, like Nicolás Pedraza, of Valle Grande, who has been in the Chaco since 1930, who helped build the road to Loa, Bolívar, and Camacho. He has malaria, and is as yellow and dry as a hollow reed.

"The *pilas* have come up the trail from Camacho, they say," says Chacón, from Potosí.

"There's no water there, all right," speaks up Pedraza, in the manner of one who knows.

"But the *pilas* can always find some. They know these hills better than anybody else," interposes Irusta, a dour fellow from La Paz, with jutting cheek-bones and slanting eyes, who was in the battles of Yujra and Cabo Castillo.

At this a fellow from Cochabamba, nicknamed Cosñi, speaks up:

"Yeah, that's what they say. . . . What about that *pila* we found at Siete dead of thirst when the creek was just a little way off, sarge?"

"That's right," I answer. "And there was that other one we found, by Campos, who got poisoned eating wild prickly pears."

"You don't die of hunger. But you do die of thirst. There in that field by Siete I saw our men sucking up mud the afternoon of the 10th of November."

Facts and words pile up and disappear. They pass like the breeze over the grass, without even moving it.

I have nothing else to put down.

February 6. It has rained. The trees look new. We've had water in our cisterns, but we haven't had bread or sugar. The provision trucks got bogged down in the mud.

February 10. They are moving us up twelve miles. The road we've cleared is not going to be used, but we'll cut another.

February 18. The driver with the torn shirt has brought us bad news. "The creek has dried up. Now we have to bring water from 'La China.' "

February 26. We didn't have any water yesterday. It is harder to bring it up because of the distance the truck has to travel. Yesterday, after chopping trees all day in the woods, we went down to the road to wait for the truck, and the last rays of the sun—rose-colored this time—tinted the earth-hued faces of my men, but they waited in vain for the usual noise to come down the dust of the road.

The water-carrier got here this morning, and a tumult of hands, jugs, and canteens, clashing loudly and angrily, sprang up about the water-barrel. A fight broke out that I had to settle.

March 1. A fair little lieutenant, with a full beard, has arrived at this post. He talked to me, asking me how many men I had in my squad.

"There's no water at the front," he said. "Two days ago two men got sunstrokes. We'll have to try to dig for water."

"At 'La China' they say they've dug wells."

"And they got water."

"They did."

"It's a matter of luck."

"Over this way, too, near Loa, they tried to dig some wells."

Whereupon Pedraza, who was listening to us, said that it was a fact, about three miles from here there was a hole that had been there as long as anyone could remember. It was just a few yards deep. Those who had dug for water there must have given up the idea. Pedraza thought it would be worth "digging a little more."

March 2. We've looked over the place Pedraza was talking about. There is a big hole there, almost grown over with brush, near a big *palobobo* tree. The blond lieutenant said that he would inform headquarters, and this afternoon we received orders to go on excavating the hole until we found water. I have assigned eight sappers to the work: Pedraza, Irusta, Chacón, Cosñi, and four other Indians.

March 3. The hole is about sixteen feet across and about sixteen deep. The ground is like cement. We have cleared a path right up to the spot and have made camp close by. We'll be able to work all day, for the heat is not so bad.

The soldiers, naked to the waist, shine like fish. Snakes of sweat with little heads of dirt run down their torsos. They throw down the pick, which sinks into the loose sand, and then let themselves down by a leather belt. The earth that comes out is dark, soft. Its optimistic color is a pleasant novelty along the edge of the cavity.

March 10. Forty feet. It looks as though we were going to find water. The dirt we bring up gets damper all the time. We have laid a floor over part of the well, and I had the men build a ladder and trestle horses of *mataco* wood so we can bring up the dirt by a pulley. The soldiers keep spelling one another, and Pedraza assures us that in another week he'll have the pleasure of inviting General X to "cool his arse in the water of the well."

March 22. I've been down in the well. On entering it, a sensation of almost solid contact runs up the body. Where the line of the sun stops, one has the feeling of a different kind of air, the air of the earth. As I go down in the shadow and touch the soft earth with my bare feet, I am bathed in coolness. I am about sixty feet down. I raise my head, and the black tube of the hole rises above me until it ends at the mouth, through which gushes the overflow of light from the surface. The bottom is muddy and the wall crumbles away easily at the touch. I have come out all muddy, and the mosquitoes have swarmed over me, making my feet swell.

March 30. It is a strange thing that is happening. Up to ten days ago we got almost liquid mud out of the well, and now it's dry dirt again. I've been down in the well again. The breath of the earth makes the lungs contract. The wall is damp to the touch, but on reaching the bottom I see that we have been digging through a layer of moist clay. I tell them to stop digging to see if in a few days water will begin to filter in.

April 12. A week went by and the bottom of the well was still dry. Then the digging began again, and today I went down. It is seventy-eight feet deep; everything is dark there, and only by the touch, like a person afflicted with night-blindness, can one make out the form of this subterranean womb. Earth, earth, thick earth which clenches its fists in the dark throes of asphyxiation. The earth which has been dug out has left in the hollow the specter of its presence, and when I strike the wall with the pick, it answers me with an echoless "toc-toc" which seems to hit against my breast.

While I was plunged in that darkness an old sensation of loneliness that had possessed me when I was a child, filling me with a strange fear as I crossed through the tunnel that perforated a hill near Capinota, where my mother lived, welled up in me again. I used to go into it cautiously, awed by the almost sexual presence of its terrestrial secret, watching the wings of the insects, crystalline insects, moving over the cracks in the earth against the light. It frightened me when I reached the middle of the tunnel, where the darkness became denser, but when I had passed it and found myself advancing faster and faster toward the brightness opening at the other end, a great joy came over me. This joy never reached to my hands, whose skin always recoiled at the touch of the walls of the tunnel.

Now I do not see the light ahead of me, but above me, high and out of reach, like a star. Oh, the flesh of my hands has grown used to everything, it is almost one with the earth's substance and no longer knows repugnance.

April 28. I am afraid our search for water has failed. Yesterday we reached ninety-eight feet without finding anything but dust. We ought to stop this useless work, and I have sent a request for an interview to the captain of the battalion, who has given me an appointment for tomorrow.

April 29. "Captain," I said, "we've dug ninety-eight feet without striking water."

"But we must have water," he answered.

"Then let them try somewhere else, captain."

"No, no. Go on digging. Two wells ninety-eight feet deep won't give water. One a hundred and thirty feet deep may."

"Yes, captain."

"Besides, you may be going to strike it soon."

"Yes, captain."

"All right, then, another little effort. Our men are dying of thirst."

They are not dying, but they are agonizing every day. It is an unending torture, kept up from day to day with one jug of water to a soldier. My men, down in the well, suffer more from thirst than those outside, with the dust and work, but they have to go on digging.

I transmitted the order to them, and they voiced their useless protest. I managed to quiet them by offering them, in the captain's name, increased rations of coca and water.

May 9. The work goes on. The well is gradually acquiring a fearsome personality, real, voracious; it has become the boss, the unknown master of the sappers. As time goes by, the earth sinks deeper into them as they go deeper into it, becoming a part of them as by the force of gravity of a passive element, compact and endless. They advance along that road of night, through that vertical cavern, as in obedience to some sinister attraction, some inexorable law that condemns them to recede from the light, reversing the sense of their existence as human beings. Every time I look at them they give me the impression of not being made up of cells, but of molecules of dust, dirt in their ears, on their eyelids, in their eyebrows, in their nostrils, in their hair, their eyes, their souls filled with the dirt of the Chaco.

May 24. They have advanced several yards farther. The work is slow. One soldier inside digs, another one outside works the pulley, and pulls up the dirt in a bucket improvised from a gasoline can. The soldiers complain of asphyxia. When they work the air presses in on their bodies. Under their feet and around them and above them the earth becomes like the night. Somber, gloomy, taciturn, impregnated with a heavy silence, motionless and suffocating, a leaden mass piles up above the worker, burying him in darkness like a worm hidden in some geologic age, many centuries distant from the surface of the earth.

They drink the warm, heavy water of the canteen, which goes quickly, for although the "well-workers" get a double ration of water, it evaporates on their lips with that *black thirst.* With their bare feet they feel through the hot dust for the old coolness of the furrows they used to dig in the watered earth of the fields of their distant valleys, the memory of which still lives in their epidermis.

Then they dig, dig with their picks, while the earth slides down, burying their feet, but the water never appears. The water that we crave with the obsession of madmen may gush up in this voiceless, soundless hole.

June 5. We have gone down almost a hundred and thirty feet. To encourage my men I have gone down in the well to work, too. It seemed to me that I was falling endlessly, as in a dream. Down there I am forever separated from other men, far from the war, transported by the loneliness to a destiny of annihilation which strangles me with the impalpable hands of nothingness. No light can be seen, and the weight of the atmosphere presses in on all the planes of the body. The column of darkness falls vertically upon me and buries me, far from the ears of men.

I have tried to work, striking furious blows with the pick, in the hope of hurrying the passage of time with swift activity. But time is fixed and unchanging in this spot. If the light did not mark the change of the hours, time would stand still in this underground with the black uniformity of a dark room. This is the death of light, this is the root of that great tree that grows in the night and blots out the sky, covering the earth with mourning.

June 16. Strange things happen. This dark room enclosed in the bottom of the well reveals images of water through the reagent of dreams. The obsession of water is creating a peculiar, fantastic world which exists at a depth of a hundred and thirty-five feet and which reveals itself in a curious event that took place at this level.

Cosñi Herboso told me about it. Yesterday he had fallen asleep at the bottom of the cistern when he saw a serpent of silver begin to shine. He caught hold of it and it came to pieces in his hands, but others appeared and began to move about in the bottom of the well until they formed a spring of white, whispering bubbles which grew, lighting up the gloomy cylinder, like a magic serpent, which lost its stiffness to take on the flexibility of a column of water, on which Cosñi felt himself raised through the air until he came up to the surface of the earth.

And there, what a surprise! All the countryside had been changed by the touch of the water. Each tree had become a fountain. The hayfield was gone and in its place was a green lake where the soldiers were bathing in the shade of the willows. It caused him no surprise to see the enemy firing machine-guns from the opposite bank, and our men diving in the water after the bullets amidst shouting and laughter. All he wanted to do was drink. He drank from the fountains, he drank from the lake, submerging himself through countless liquid planes which lapped against his body, while the spray of the fountains wet his head. He drank, drank, but his thirst was not quenched by this water, so light and abundant, like a dream.

That night Cosñi had fever. I sent him up to the regiment's first-aid station.

June 24. The divisional commander stopped his car as he went by here. He talked to me, hardly able to believe that we have dug down almost a hundred and forty-eight feet, taking out the dirt pailful by pailful with a belt.

"You have to shout to the soldiers to make them hear when their turn is over, colonel," I said to him.

The colonel later sent back several packages of coca and cigarettes, and a bugle.

So we are tied to this well. We go ahead, or rather we go back to the bottom of the planet, to a geological era inhabited by darkness. It is the pursuit of water through an impenetrable mass. More withdrawn, more gloomy, dark as their thoughts and their destiny, my men dig on and on, digging air, earth, and life with the slow, spiritless activity of gnomes.

July 4. Can it be that there really is water? Ever since Cosñi's dream they all find it. Pedraza says he was almost drowned in a sudden gush of water that rose higher than his head. Irusta says his pick hit against some chunks of ice, and yesterday Chacón came out talking about a cave that was lighted up by the pallid reflection of the waves of an underground lake.

Do all this suffering, this seeking, this desire, all these thirsty souls gathered together in this deep hole, give rise to this florescence of springs?

July 16. The men are getting sick. They refuse to go down into the well. I have to make them do it. They have asked me to let them join the troops at the front. I have gone down again, and I have come up amazed and frightened. We are down almost a hundred and sixty-four feet. The air, which has grown blacker and blacker, closes in on the body, producing such a feeling of discomfort and uneasiness on every plane that it almost breaks the imperceptible thread that, like a memory, links the dwarfed being with the surface of the earth through that deep darkness which hangs over him like a leaden weight. No lowering tower of stone ever weighed with the somber gravitation of that cylinder of foul, hot air which slowly sinks downward. The men are the foundation. The arms of the underground earth smother the men; they cannot stay longer than an hour in that abyss. It is a nightmare. This earth of the Chaco is a strange thing, accursed.

July 25. The bugle—the gift of the division—is blown down the mouth of the cistern every hour to call the worker up. Its call must be like a gleam of light in the depths. But this afternoon, in spite of the bugle, nobody came up.

"Who's down there?" I asked.

"Pedraza."

They called him with shouts and the bugle. "*Tarariii!* . . . Pedrazaaaa!"

"Maybe he's gone to sleep."

"Or died," I added, and ordered them down to see what had happened.

A soldier descended, and after a long time, in the midst of the circle we formed around the mouth of the well, the body of Pedraza, half-asphyxiated, rose, fastened to the leather belt, hauled up by the pulley and pushed by the soldier.

July 29. Today Chacón fainted, and was lugubriously hoisted up like a hanged man.

September 4. Will there ever be an end to this? We no longer dig to find water, but in obedience to some fatal plan, some inscrutable design. The days of my soldiers are sucked into the maelstrom of this tragic hollow which swallows them blindly in its strange, silent growth, screwing them into the earth.

Up here above, the well has taken on the outlines of something inevitable, eternal and powerful as war. The earth which has been removed from it has piled up in thick lips, on which lizards and redbirds gather. When the digger appears at the well's mouth, a mixture of sweat and dirt, eyelids and hair white with dust, he seems to emerge from some remote Plutonian realm, like a prehistoric monster arising from primeval slime. Sometimes, just to say something, I ask:

"How about it?"

"Just the same, sarge, nothing."

Always nothing, just like the war. This nothing will never end.

October 1. We've been ordered to stop digging. After seven months' work we have not found water.

The appearance of the outpost has changed a lot. Log cabins have been built, and a battalion headquarters. We're going to start clearing a road toward the east, but our camp is to remain here.

The well, too, will stay here, abandoned, with its mute, terrible mouth and its sterile depth. This hole in our midst is always an intruder, a stupid enemy, but one that must be taken into account, as indifferent to our hatred as a scar. It is utterly useless.

December 7 (*Platanillos Hospital*). The damned well was good for something after all!

My impressions are still clear, for the attack took place on the 4th, and on the 5th I came down with malaria and they brought me here.

Some prisoner captured at the front, where a legend had sprung up about the well, must have told the Paraguayans that behind the Bolivian positions there was a well. Spurred on by thirst, the Guaranys decided to attack.

At six in the morning the machine-guns began to gash the woods. We only realized that the forward trenches had been taken when we heard the fire of the Paraguayans less than seven hundred feet from where we were. Two Stokes grenades fell behind our tents.

I armed my sappers with their dirty rifles and deployed them for attack. Just then one of our officers came rushing up with a squad of soldiers and a machine-gun and ordered them to hold the line to the left of the well while we took over the sector to the right. Some of the men parapeted themselves behind the piles of earth that had been dug out. The bullets cut the branches with a noise like the slash of a machete. Two bursts of fire split the *palobobo* tree like an axe. The firing of the *pilas* grew heavier, and through the reports their savage shouts could be heard as they concentrated the fury of their attack on the well. But we did not yield an inch, *defending it as though there were really water there.*

The cannon balls plowed up the earth, the bursts of machine-gun fire split skulls and breasts, but we did not give up the well in five hours of combat.

By twelve o'clock everything had become vibrant silence. The *pilas* had withdrawn. Then we gathered up our dead. The *pilas* had left five, and among our eight were Cosñi, Pedraza, Irusta and Chacón, their breasts bare, their teeth showing, forever covered with dirt.

The heat, a transparent specter lying face-down over the hillside, was calcinating body and brain and making the ground crackle. To save the trouble of digging graves, I thought of the well.

We dragged the thirteen corpses to the edge and slowly pushed them into the opening, where, complying with the law of gravity, they tumbled over and disappeared, swallowed up by the darkness.

"Is that all there are?"

Then we shoveled in dirt, lots of dirt. But even so that dry well is still the deepest in all the Chaco.

THE CLIMATE OF MESSINA

FROM *Old Calabria*

NORMAN DOUGLAS

Critics have remarked the terrifyingly intelligent gleam in Norman Douglas' eyes. They regret, some of them, that he worked in small things. And it is true that besides *South Wind* and *Old Calabria* he is much taken with small things—cookery, street cries, unorthodox limericks, the archaeology of the island of Capri, the birds and beasts of the Greek Anthology. But the consequence of each of his varied enthusiasms was a finished miniature, painted in subtle colors and reflecting his sophisticated but always understanding judgments of things and people. This selection on the Messina earthquake is from his *Old Calabria,* which may be classified as a travel book; it is very much more than that.

THE CHRONICLES OF MESSINA RECORD THE SCARCELY HUMAN FEATS OF THE DIVER Cola Pesce (Nicholas the Fish). The dim submarine landscapes of the Straits with their caves and tangled forests held no secrets from him; his eyes were as familiar with sea-mysteries as those of any fish. . . .

Many are the fables connected with his name, but the most portentous is this: One day, during his subaqueous wanderings, he discovered the foundations of Messina. They were insecure! The city rested upon three columns, one of them intact, another quite decayed away, the third partially corroded and soon to crumble into ruin. He peered up from his blue depths, and in a fateful couplet of verses warned the townsmen of their impending doom. In this prophetic utterance ascribed to the fabulous Cola Pesce is echoed a popular apprehension that was only too justified.

F. Münter—one of a band of travellers who explored these regions after the earthquake of 1783—also gave voice to his fears that Messina had not yet experienced the full measure of her calamities. . . .

I remember a night in September of 1908, a Sunday night, fragrant with the odours of withered rosemary and cistus and fennel that streamed in aromatic showers from the scorched heights overhead—a starlit night, tranquil and calm. Never had Messina appeared so attractive to me. Arriving there generally in the daytime and from larger and sprightlier centres of civilization, one is prone to notice only its defects. But night, especially a southern night, has a wizard touch. It transforms into objects of mysterious beauty all unsightly things, or hides them clean away; while the nobler works of man, those façades and cornices and full-bellied balconies of cunningly wrought iron rise up, under its enchantment, ethereal as the palace of fairies. And coming, as I then did, from the sun-baked river-beds of Calabria, this place, with its broad and well-paved streets, its glittering cafés and demure throng of evening idlers, seemed a veritable metropolis, a world-city.

With deliberate slowness, *ritardando con molto sentimento,* I worked my way to the familiar restaurant.

At last! At last, after an interminable diet of hard bread, onions and goat's cheese, I was to enjoy the complicated menu mapped out weeks beforehand, after elaborate consideration and balancing of merits; so complicated, that its details have long ago lapsed from my memory. I recollect only the sword-fish, a local specialty, and (as crowning glory) the *cassata alla siciliana,* a glacial symphony, a multicoloured ice of commingling flavours, which requires far more time to describe than to devour. Under the influence of this Sybaritic fare, helped down with a crusted bottle of Calabrian wine—your Sicilian stuff is too strong for me, too straightforward, uncompromising; I prefer to be wheedled out of my faculties by inches, like a gentleman—under this genial stimulus my extenuated frame was definitely restored; I became mellow and companionable; the traveller's lot, I finally concluded, is not the worst on earth. Everything was as it should be. As for Messina—Messina was unquestionably a pleasant city. But why were all the shops shut so early in the evening?

"These Sicilians," said the waiter, an old Neapolitan acquaintance, in reply to my enquiries, "are always playing some game. They are pretending to be Englishmen at this moment; they have the Sunday-closing obsession on the brain. Their attacks generally last a fortnight; it's like the measles. Poor people."

Playing at being Englishmen!

They have invented a new game now, those that are left of them. They are living in dolls' houses, and the fit is likely to last for some little time.

An engineer remarked to me, not long ago, among the ruins:

"This *baracca,* this wooden shelter, has an interior surface area of less than thirty square metres. Thirty-three persons—men, women, and children—have been living and sleeping in it for the last five months."

"A little overcrowded?" I suggested.

"Yes. Some of them are beginning to talk of overcrowding. It was all very well in the winter months, but when August comes. . . . Well, we shall see."

No prophetic visions of the Messina of today, with its minute sheds perched among a wilderness of ruins and haunted by scared shadows in sable vestments of mourning, arose in my mind that evening as I sat at the little marble table, sipping my coffee—overroasted, like all Italian coffee, by exactly two minutes—and puffing contentedly at my cigar, while the sober crowd floated hither and thither before my eyes. Yes, everything was as it should be. And yet, what a chance!

What a chance for some God, in this age of unbelief, to establish his rule over mankind on the firm foundations of faith! We are always complaining, nowadays, of an abatement of religious feeling. How easy for such a one to send down an Isaiah to foretell the hour of the coming catastrophe, and thus save those of its victims who were disposed to hearken to the warning voice; to reanimate the flagging zeal of worshippers, to straighten doubts and segregate the sheep from the goats! Truly, He moves in a mysterious way, for no divine message came; the just were entombed with the unjust amid a considerable deal of telegraphing and heart-breaking.

A few days after the disaster the Catholic papers explained matters by saying that the people of Messina had not loved their Madonna sufficiently well. But she loved them none the less, and sent the earthquake as an admonishment. Rather a robust method of conciliating their affection; not exactly the *suaviter in modo*. . . .

But if genuine prophets can only flourish among the malarious willow swamps of old Babylon and such-like improbable spots, we might at least have expected better things of our modern spiritualists. Why should their apparitions content themselves with announcing the decease, at the Antipodes, of profoundly uninteresting relatives? Alas! I begin to perceive that spirits of the right kind, of the useful kind, have yet to be discovered. Our present-day ghosts are like seismographs; they chronicle the event after it has happened. Now, what we want is—

"The Signore smokes, and smokes, and smokes. Why not take the tram and listen to the municipal music in the gardens?"

"Music? Gardens? An excellent suggestion, Gennarino." . . .

It struck me that the sufferings of the survivors would be alleviated if all the sheds in which they are living could be painted white or pearl-grey in order to protect them, as far as possible, from the burning rays of the sun. I mentioned the idea to an overseer.

"We are painting as fast as we can," he replied. "An expensive matter, however. The Villagio Elena alone has cost us, in this respect, twenty thousand francs—with the greatest economy."

This will give some notion of the scale on which things have to be done.

The settlement in question contains some two hundred sheds—two hundred out of over ten thousand.

But I was alluding not to these groups of hygienic bungalows erected by public munificence and supplied with schools, laboratories, orphanages, hospitals, and all that can make life endurable, but to the others—those which the refugees built for themselves—ill-contrived hovels, patched together with ropes, potato-sacks, petroleum cans and miscellaneous odds and ends. A coat of whitewash, at least, inside and out. . . . I was thinking, too, of those still stranger dwellings, the disused railway trucks which the government has placed at the disposal of homeless families. At many stations along the line may be seen strings of these picturesque wigwams crowded with poor folk who have installed themselves within, apparently for ever. They are cultivating their favourite flowers and herbs in gaudy rows along the wooden platforms of the carriages; the little children, all dressed in black, play about in the shade underneath. The people will suffer in these narrow tenements under the fierce southern sun, after their cool courtyards and high-vaulted chambers! There will be diseases, too; typhoids from the disturbed drainage and insufficient water-supply; eye troubles, caused by the swarms of flies and tons of accumulated dust. The ruins are also overrun with hordes of mangy cats and dogs which ought to be exterminated without delay.

If, as seems likely, those rudely improvised sheds are to be inhabited indefinitely, we may look forward to an interesting phenomenon, a reversion to a corresponding type of man. The lack of the most ordinary appliances of civilization, such as linen, washing-basins and cooking utensils, will reduce them to the condition of savages who view these things with indifference or simple curiosity; they will forget that they ever had any use for them. And life in these huts where human beings are herded together after the manner of beasts—one might almost say *fitted in,* like the fragments of a mosaic pavement—cannot but be harmful to the development of growing children.

The Calabrians, I was told, distinguished themselves by unearthly ferocity; Reggio was given over to a legion of fiends that descended from the heights during the week of confusion. "They tore the rings and brooches off the dead," said a young official to me. "They strangled the wounded and dying, in order to despoil them more comfortably. Here, and at Messina, the mutilated corpses were past computation; but the Calabrians were the worst."

Vampires, offspring of Night and Chaos.

So Dolomieu, speaking of the *dépravation incroyable des mœurs* which accompanied the earthquake of 1783, recounts the case of a householder of Polistena who was pinned down under some masonry, his legs emerging out of the ruins; his servant came and took the silver buckles off his shoes and then fled, without attempting to free him. We have seen something of this kind more recently at San Francisco.

"After despoiling the corpses, they ransacked the dwellings. Five thousand beds, sir, were carried up from Reggio into the mountains."

"Five thousand beds! *Per Dio!* It seems a considerable number."

A young fellow, one of the survivors, attached himself to me in the capacity of guide through the ruins of Reggio. He wore the characteristic earthquake look, a dazed and bewildered expression of countenance; he spoke in a singularly deliberate manner. Knowing the country, I was soon bending my steps in the direction of the cemetery, chiefly for the sake of the exquisite view from those windswept heights, and to breathe more freely after the dust and desolation of the lower parts. This burial-ground is in the same state as that of Messina, once the pride of its citizens; the insane frolic of nature has not respected the slumber of the dead or their commemorative shrines; it has made a mockery of the place, twisting the solemn monuments into repulsive and irreverential shapes.

But who can recount the freaks of stone and iron during those moments —the hair-breadth escapes? My companion's case was miraculous enough. Awakened from sleep with the first shock, he saw, by the dim light of the lamp which burns in all their bedrooms, the wall at his bedside weirdly gaping asunder. He darted to reach the opening, but it closed again and caught his arm in a stony grip. Hours seemed to pass—the pain was past enduring; then the kindly cleft yawned once more, allowing him to jump into the garden below. Simultaneously he heard a crash as the inner rooms of the house fell; then climbed aloft, and for four days wandered among the bleak, wet hills. Thousands were in the same plight.

I asked what he found to eat.

"*Erba, Signore.* We all did. You could not touch property; a single orange, and they would have killed you."

Grass!

He bore a name renowned in the past, but his home being turned into a dust-heap under which his money, papers and furniture, his two parents and brothers, are still lying, he now gains a livelihood by carrying vegetables and fruit from the harbour to the collection of sheds honoured by the name of market. Later in the day we happened to walk past the very mansion, which lies near the quay. "Here is my house and my family," he remarked, indicating, with a gesture of antique resignation, a pile of wreckage.

Hard by, among the ruins, there sat a young woman with dishevelled hair, singing rapturously. "Her husband was crushed to death," he said, "and it unhinged her wits. Strange, is it not, sir? They used to fight like fiends, and now—she sings to him night and day to come back."

Love—so the Greeks fabled—was the child of Chaos.

In this part of the town stands the civic museum, which all readers of Gissing's "Ionian Sea" will remember as the closing note of those harmonious pages. It is shattered, like everything else that he visited in Reggio; like the hotel where he lodged; like the cathedral whose proud superscription *Circumlegentes devenimus Rhegium* impressed him so deeply; like that "singular bit of advanced civilization, which gave me an odd sense of having strayed into the world of those romancers who forecast the future—a public slaughter-house of tasteful architecture, set in a grove of lemon trees and palms, suggesting the dreamy ideal of some reformer whose palate shrinks from vegetarianism." We went the round of all these places, not forgetting the house which bears the tablet commemorating the death of a young soldier who fell fighting against the Bourbons. From its contorted iron balcony there hangs a rope by which the inmates may have tried to let themselves down.

A friend of mine, Baron C—— of Stilo, is a member of that same patriotic family, and gave me the following strange account. He was absent from Reggio at the time of the catastrophe, but three others of them were staying there. On the first shock they rushed together, panic-stricken, into one room; the floor gave way, and they suddenly found themselves sitting in their motor-car which happened to be placed exactly below them. They escaped with a few cuts and bruises.

An inscription on a neighbouring ruin runs to the effect that the *mansion having been severely damaged in the earthquake of* 1783, *its owner had rebuilt it on lines calculated to defy future shatterings.* Whether he would rebuild it yet again?

Nevertheless, there seems to be some chance for the revival of Reggio; its prognosis is not utterly hopeless.

But Messina is in desperate case.

That haughty sea-front, with its long line of imposing edifices—imagine a painted theatre decoration of cardboard through which some sportive behemoth has been jumping with frantic glee; there you have it. And within, all is desolation; the wreckage reaches to the windows; you must clamber over it as best you can. What an all-absorbing post-tertiary deposit for future generations, for the crafty antiquarian who deciphers the history of mankind out of kitchen-middens and deformed heaps of forgotten trash! The whole social life of the citizens, their arts, domestic economy, and pastimes, lies embedded in that rubbish. "A musical race," he will conclude, observing the number of decayed pianofortes, guitars, and mandolines. The climate of Messina, he will further argue, must have been a wet one, inasmuch as there are umbrellas everywhere, standing upright among the debris, leaning all

Weber: Black Star

DIAMOND DIGGERS IN AFRICA AWAIT THE SIGNAL TO STAKE THEIR CLAIMS

Underwood and Underwood

BAILING SEEPAGE FROM A PIT IN A BRAZILIAN BLACK DIAMOND MINE

Constance Stuart: Black Star

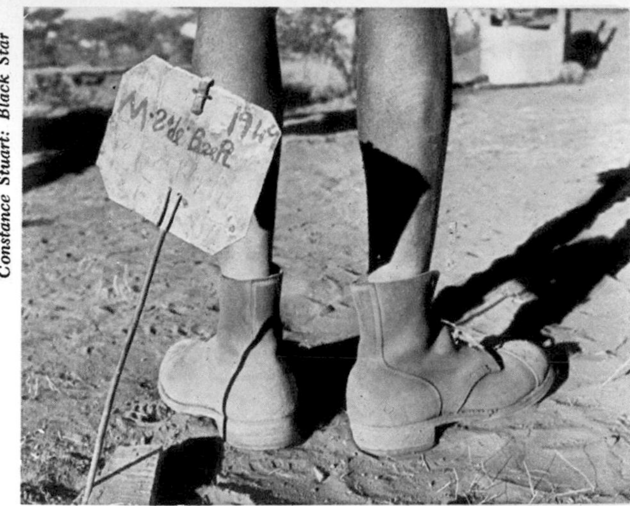

right: A PRIMITIVE DIGGER'S STAKE TO HIS CLAIM

below: PROFILE OF AN AFRICAN DIAMOND MINE

Constance Stuart: Black Star

right: OPEN COPPER MINE NEAR SALT LAKE CITY

below: THE PREMIER DIAMOND MINE IN SOUTH AFRICA WHERE THE LARGEST WHITE DIAMOND YET DISCOVERED WAS FOUND IN 1905

Speiser: Monkmeyer

Underwood and Underwood

Underwood and Underwood

Underwood and Underwood

above: WET CUTTING IN A BRITISH COAL MINE. WATER IS PROJECTED ONTO THE TEETH OF THE PICKS TO DAMPEN THE DUST

left: BRITISH COAL MINES

SHASTA DAM IN CALIFORNIA AS IT NEARED COMPLETION

Underwood and Underwood

Underwood and Underwood

right: OIL STRIKE

below: A FOREST OF DERRICKS IN TEXAS

[Un]derwood and Underwood

Mrs. James Davis: FPG

MARTIN EDWARDS PANS A SAMPLE OF ORE FOR GOLD

forlorn against the ruins, or peering dismally from under them. It rained much during those awful days, and umbrellas were at a premium. Yet fifty of them would not have purchased a loaf of bread.

It was Goethe who, speaking of Pompeii, said that of the many catastrophes which have afflicted mankind few have given greater pleasure to posterity. The same will never be said of Messina, whose relics, for the most part, are squalid and mean. The German poet, by the way, visited this town shortly after the disaster of 1783, and describes its *zackige Ruinenwüste*—words whose very sound is suggestive of shatterings and dislocations. Nevertheless, the place revived again.

But what was 1783?

A mere rehearsal, an amateur performance.

Wandering about in this world of ghosts, I passed the old restaurant where the sword-fish had once tasted so good—an accumulation of stones and mortar—and reached the cathedral. It is laid low, all save the Gargantuan mosaic figures that stare down from behind the altar in futile benediction of Chaos; inane, terrific. This, then, is the house of that feudal lady of the *fortiter in re,* who sent an earthquake and called it love. Womanlike, she doted on gold and precious stones, and they recovered her fabulous hoard, together with a copy of a Latin letter she sent to the Christians of Messina by the hand of Saint Paul.

And not long afterwards—how came it to pass?—my steps were guided amid that wilderness towards a narrow street containing the ruins of a *palazzo*. . . .

A rope of bed-sheets knotted together dangled from one of the upper windows, its end swaying in mid-air at the height of the second floor. Many of them do, at Messina: a desperate expedient of escape. Some pots of geranium and cactus, sadly flowering, adorned the other windows, whose glass panes were unbroken. But for the ominous sunlight pouring through them from *within,* the building looked fairly intact on this outer side. Its ponderous gateway, however, through which I had hoped to enter, was choked up by internal debris, and I was obliged to climb, with some little trouble, to the rear of the house.

If a titanic blade had sheared through the *palazzo* lengthwise, the thing could not have been done more neatly. The whole interior had gone down, save a portion of the rooms abutting on the street-front; these were literally cut in half, so as to display an ideal section of domestic architecture. The house with its inmates and all it contained was lying among the high-piled wreckage within under my feet; masonry mostly—entire fragments of wall interspersed with crumbling mortar and convulsed iron girders that writhed over the surface or plunged sullenly into the depths; fetid rents and gullies in between, their flanks affording glimpses of broken vases, candelabras, hats, bottles, birdcages, writing-books, brass pipes, sofas, picture-frames, table-cloths, and all the paltry paraphernalia of everyday life. No attempt at stratification, horizontal, vertical, or inclined; it was as if the objects had been thrown up by some playful volcano and allowed to settle where they pleased. Two immense chiselled blocks of stone—one lying prone at the bottom of a miniature ravine, the other proudly erect, like a Druidical monument, in the upper regions—reminded me of the existence of a staircase, a *diabolical* staircase.

Looking upwards, I endeavoured to reconstruct the habits of the inmates, but found it impossible, the section that remained being too shallow. Sky-blue seems to have been their favourite colour. The kitchen was easily discernible, the hearth with its store of charcoal underneath, copper vessels hanging in a neat row overhead, and an open cupboard full of household goods; a neighbouring room (the communicating doors were all gone), with lace window-curtains, a table, lamp, and book, and a bedstead toppling over the abyss; another one, carpeted and hung with pictures and a large faded mirror, below which ran a row of shelves that groaned under a multitudinous collection of phials and bottles.

The old man's embrocations. . . .

MEDIEVAL GERMAN NOBLEMAN BIDDING FAREWELL TO HIS WIFE

"THAT LITTLE BLOW WASN'T A REAL DUST STORM"

FROM *The Night the Old Nostalgia Burned Down*

FRANK SULLIVAN

Historians continue to ponder learnedly over the economic, social, and political reasons for the Westward Migration. Frank Sullivan's Aunt Martha Gallup has her own interpretation. Since Aunt Martha was on the spot, her first-hand observations cannot be dismissed lightly. She was twenty-six in 1754 and although she's getting on now, she still retains all her unusual faculties.

Frank Sullivan was one of the very bright stars in the constellation of columnists that made the New York *World* of the twenties the most brightly written newspaper of the period. Aunt Martha delivered her sage, if somewhat unexpected comments on events and people in Sullivan's column daily. Irwin Edman said that she had "far more serious commentaries to make on contemporary life and morals than many of our most pontifical moral analysts."

AUNT SARAH GALLUP, THE GRAND OLD LADY OF THE ADIRONDACKS, IS DOWN FROM her home in Holcomb Landing, N. Y., to celebrate the 180th anniversary of her third marriage, which took place in 1754, when she was twenty-six.

"Who was your third husband, Aunt Sarah?" I asked her.

"I never knew his name," she said, gently. "I met him in a battle in the French and Indian War. I was a fool for a uniform in those days. But I never got to know his name."

"Did that dust storm of two weeks ago hit you, Aunt Sarah?" I said.

"He did, with the butt end of his musket, but I didn't mind because it was in a battle, after all. Besides, I gave him tit for tat."

"I didn't say did he hit you. I said did that dust storm that blew in from the Middle West two weeks ago, hit you people in the Adirondacks hard? Scientists say it lifted a half billion tons of dust from the Middle West and deposited it in the East."

"Oh, that. Yes, that hit us, if you want to call it 'hit.' That little blow wasn't a real dust storm."

"You mean to sit there and deny that a half billion tons of dust isn't a real dust storm? Fie, Aunt Sarah!"

"Fie, my eye. I mean it wasn't a patch on the dust storms we used to get from the Middle West when I was a girl. And when I mean it, I mean it. When I was a girl, most of our dust storms used to come from Ohio, which was very rich in dust at that time.

"We used to think it was practically a dustless summer if we didn't get at least ten or twelve good bang-up dust storms from Ohio between April and October. And they weren't any paltry half-billion-ton dust storms either. When a dust storm came along in my day, pretty much all of Ohio would come sailing through the air and land on us. It used to be a nuisance, too, because it meant that you had to drop everything and carry Ohio back to Ohio."

"Why didn't you just leave it lay, Aunt Sarah?"

"Because Ohio was a buffer state between Indiana and Pennsylvania, and they were at loggerheads. With Ohio over in New York, that would mean that Indiana and Pennsylvania might slide together. The dust storms usually blew up from the West, but one time a real smart one came up the seaboard from Virginia, and that day instead of having Ohio on our hands, and clothes, we found ourselves covered with Virginia. So we had to set to work and carry Virginia back to ole Virginia. A fellow wrote a song about it later.

"Those dust storms really started what you people call the pioneer movement. A dust storm would come along and plunk Ohio down in New York or New England. Then the farmers would have to stop haying and tote Ohio back. When they got Ohio back in Ohio lots of 'em decided they liked it there, and allowed they'd stay. That's where you got your pioneers. People carrying dust back to the Middle West from the thirteen original colonies. Of course, sometimes a dust storm would blow the pioneers back East where they started from. My Uncle Melancthon tried for years to settle in Ohio but every time he'd trek for there, no sooner would we think we finally had got rid of Uncle Melancthon than up would come a dust storm, and fust thing we know the door would blow open and, whisk! in would blow Uncle Melancthon from Ohio. 'Hello, folks,' he'd say—shaking a couple of acres of what would now be Toledo from his clothes—'here I am back, like a bad penny.' "

"Didn't all that travel make him dizzy, Aunt Sarah?"

"He already was."

"What became of him? How did he make out finally?"

"Well, it was very simple. He made a few simple calculations, as a result of which he pioneered to Nebraska, so that when the next dust storm came up, instead of being blow from Ohio back to Holcomb Landing, he was blown from Nebraska back to Ohio, where he wanted to be."

EARLY COSMOLOGICAL CHART

"AS IF I WAS BURIED ALIVE"

FROM *When the Mountain Fell*

C. F. RAMUZ

Most American readers are unfamiliar with the novels of Charles Ferdinand Ramuz, largely because his very individual style—Ramuz has been characterized as an author who uses words like a painter—is so difficult to translate. His work has long been esteemed on the continent and, shortly before he died in 1947, he was considered for the Nobel Prize.

He spent most of his life among the people he portrays in this selection from his novel *When the Mountain Fell,* the peasants and winegrowers of his native Swiss canton. The earth is their livelihood and the unchanging seasonal round of plowing, cultivating, harvesting their living. When the mountain falls, it is a momentary unreality, to become legend almost as it happens, abstracted from the cycle of their lives.

WHEN THE MEN FROM ANZEINDAZ WERE TELLING ABOUT IT, THEY SAID,

"It began like a salvo of cannon—all six guns in the battery firing at once.

"And then," they said, "there was a blast of wind.

"After that more cannons, shots and explosions, Bang! Crash! Bang! Crash! as if the mountain were shooting at us from all sides.

"The wind flung the door wide open, as if somebody had burst in, and the ashes from the fireplace began falling on us as if it were snowing in the cabin.

"As for us, well, you know, there on the pass we aren't far below the place where the landslide broke off. We're just a little bit more on one side and in back, and the first noise we heard was the crash of the overhang when it hit bottom; after that it was just war between one range and another, one ridge and the other, one peak and the other. It was like thunder around each of the mountains which stand in a half circle there—from the Argentine to the Morcles, from the Rocks of the Wind to Saint Martin."

They were already on their feet. There were three of them. They couldn't find their tinder.

The cows, which had been brought in for the night but not tied up, were making a terrible racket in the stable and threatening to knock everything down.

First of all the men had to go and straighten that out.

They had a horn lantern with them, although it seemed foolish at first to take it in such brilliant moonlight. But soon they were astonished to see a gray shadow coming over the moon, which began to look faded and bleak as it does when there is an eclipse, while on the other hand the light from the lantern shone brighter and brighter, casting a circle of light on the short grass before their feet.

It was then that they saw the great pale cloud rising before them. The silence was coming back little by little, and in the quiet the cloud towered higher and higher behind the ridge which still hid the depths of Derborence; it was like a wall rising above another wall. It was like a great pillar of smoke, but flat, with no billows or curves; it was like a bank of mist, but slower, heavier; and the whole mass grew from within toward the top, like bread rising when the dough is mixed and put in the bread trough, and it swells in the trough, and overflows the edges.

The men said to each other, "My God, what's that?"

They said, "It's dust."

They said, "The mountain has fallen."

They coughed, they sneezed, they bowed their heads, trying to shelter behind their hat brims.

But it was a fine powder, an impalpable dust and, since it floated everywhere in the air, it penetrated everything. In any case they had to plunge into it, for it was now coming toward them. They went forward a few steps, then a few more. They stopped. One of them even said, "Do you think it's safe to go any further?"

He said, "Is it solid underfoot, ahead there? Anyhow, it doesn't look as if we could see much."

But they were pushed ahead by pride; they were pushed ahead by curiosity.

Besides, the noises were becoming rarer and rarer, with longer intervals between them. They were duller and more internal, like intestinal rumblings inside the earth; so that the three men could move forward with more confidence to the edge of the abyss.

They could see nothing, nothing but this white moving mass. At times they saw nothing at all; at times there came a break or tear in the swirling clouds and they could see still more mist beyond, but the clouds themselves hid everything else. They hid not only the bottom of the valley, but the walls around it, so that the men could neither see where the avalanche had broken off, nor where it had landed—there was nothing but swirling fumes, as if they were looking into a steaming wash boiler, nothing but a vast confusion of vapors faintly lit and reddened by the moonlight. The moon was all red up there in the sky. First it disappeared in the streaming mist, then reappeared again.

The lantern on the ground beside the men paled, shone out strongly, paled again; they themselves were lying flat on the ground, their heads barely far enough over the edge to let them see.

And one of them said, "How many do you suppose they were?"

"Lord Jesus!"

The third said, "Have to know whether they'd all come up yet or not. . . . Fifteen, maybe. Twenty. . . ."

Although they still coughed from time to time, they were growing used by now to the lack of air, so they stayed there and began to talk in low tones. From underneath them came muffled grumblings from deep in the earth; and since they were stretched out flat on the ground, each one could hear with his whole body the noises of the mountain, rising inside him to his ears. . . .

Two months, or nearly two months, had passed. People had come to the mountain. They clambered over the great pile of rock. They had all the time they needed to hunt from one end to the other through the tumbled stones of its surface. They found nothing. Nothing anywhere, not a single person, living or dead. Cabins, animals and men had disappeared completely under the stones.

Then came the Federal engineers, taking their turn after the doctor, the coroner, and the throngs of curious spectators. They were there to estimate the volume of the landslide: a hundred and fifty million cubic feet.

They, too, had all the time they needed while they took their measurements. They unrolled their long tapes, with the little black division marks, laying them flat against the rocks, first across the valley, then down its length. Then one of the men climbed to the top of what seemed to be the highest boulder in the mass, trying to estimate its depth.

They calculated the size of the avalanche so that the necessary changes could be made in the maps; so that what was indicated on the records as pastures and fertile fields could be replaced by the notation: "waste land."

The survey took a long time, but they had all the time in the world to complete it. No one interfered with them as they worked. The people who came out of curiosity grew fewer and fewer as the days went by, and the world of nature was peaceful and acquiescent, having returned to rest, to immobility, to indifference. Finally, last of all, came scientists from the city, who climbed up as far as the glacier and went carefully all over it, looking for any fresh crevasses that might spell a new danger, either imminent or in the distant future. But everything seemed to be securely in its proper place. The beautiful white sheet of snow was untorn and swept smoothly from edge to edge of the icefield which lay almost flat behind the crest.

Little by little the clouds of dust had risen above the surrounding walls, and then blown away. The valley of Derborence was now completely visible. The air which had been opaque and swirling with dust was now clear and transparent, and the sightseers who came as far as the valley had only to tip their heads back to see, high up at the extreme frontier between earth and sky, the place where the landslide had broken off. Before the catastrophe the rock had jutted out at this point and hung over empty space, surmounted with a heavy load of bristling ice pinnacles. Now what had once stood out in relief against the sky was hollow, what had been convex was concave. The bulge of the rock had been replaced with a vast and steeply inclined gully. Its contents had been emptied, all at once, on the pasture, which then had ceased to be a pasture, on those who lived there, who lived there no longer, on everything alive, which had been instantly deprived of life. The immobility and the stillness of death reigned over the valley. There was only one moving object: high up in the gully a muddy mass, a kind of sluggish river of sand and earth and water, still oozed downhill. Confined and channelled by its high borders, it moved gradually down until it spread itself noiselessly on the cone of debris below. It was silent, slowly advancing; its flow so imperceptible that you had to look carefully a long time to make sure it was moving at all. . . .

The mountain began to laugh again.

Then, suddenly, there was this head. But the rocks stood so thickly around the spot where it emerged that nobody could see it.

He got his head out.

It was nearly two months after the landslide. He crawled out of a hole. First his head squeezed between two stones—out into daylight. Nobody saw him.

Only the eagle could have seen him, the mountain eagle, soaring overhead on his strong wings and turning on the earth below that piercing scrutiny which can distinguish instantly moving objects from still ones, living from lifeless matter. The eagle is above everything, and no matter how high he soars, his little gray eyes notice the slightest change in the pattern of the world below. They see the hare gambolling on the slope, the baby marmot just coming out of his hole.

As for the head, nobody saw it. It was too little, too lost in the great waste of stone.

Only the eagle might have noticed it, because the head moved and the stones around it did not move. The eagle circles slowly on his great wings, tipping them only enough to catch the wind, like the sails of a ship. He veers and turns, sailing far off on his great circle of air, sweeping back again, and dominating from his great height that immense hollow below where the boulders seem no bigger than scattered gravel.

It was down there that something was moving. In the last hour or two the sun had risen above the mountains. Now it shone full on the hollow, and something moved and moved again in a little patch of shadow there like a drop of ink on a gray blotter.

You could have seen him from high up in the air, but only from there, when he first got his head out. At first his head was the only thing to show above the rocks.

You would have to have been high enough to say to the eagle, "Lower yourself a little, come down and look! Leave the heights and drop closer."

But then, pausing in his descent, he would have hesitated, for man is not his prey, and he is afraid of man.

Though it was only a poor sort of a man who came out from under the ground, a miserable remnant of a man, appearing in a crack between the haphazard tumble of rocks; come out of the shadow, out of unimaginable depths, out of the night; and now struggling toward the day.

He was lighter than the shadow which still surrounded him; his skin was pale and his shoulders gleamed whitely under his rags. He got his head out, he lifted his head.

From where he was he could see nothing.

When he looked up there was nothing to see but the blue of the sky. The sky was smooth and flat, cut out in a circle and stretched tightly overhead like the paper cover on a jam pot.

Inside his crack, a fault in the rock which widened as it came to the surface, he raised himself on his hands and knees. He was still partly hidden, then he moved forward and his head came to the edge of the shadow.

The sun struck his head.

He stopped again.

His hair was long and fell raggedly down the nape of his neck.

Finally he flung his hands away from his eyes. His hands clung to each side of his head above his ears, as limp as wet rags.

His eyelids fluttered. He shut his eyes, opened them, shut them again.

There he was, with his head in the sun, and he was no longer accustomed to it. He had to get used to the sun again—the sunlight was beautiful, but it hurt; it felt good, but it burned too.

He felt like a small child who has been made to drink a wine tonic. The blood rang in his ears, and he couldn't tell if the humming was inside or outside him, for he had lost the faculty of hearing and the power of sight, lost the happy gift of telling the colors, lost his taste, his smell, and the ability to recognize shapes and distinguish distances.

He shut his eyes, he opened them. Then he put his fingers in his ears and shook his head like a dog coming out of the water. And little by little the sweetness of life began to steal over him, murmuring to him with its sun, its colors, and all its good things, and wrapping him in comfort like a warm suit of clothes all over his body.

He breathed deeply as if he were drinking.

The air came into his body, it had a taste and a perfume, it flowed softly through his lungs and his belly, bringing strength back with it. After a little he began to climb again. He clambered up between two big boulders that stood high above the tumbled stones until he reached the top of one of them and could see out widely over the valley.

There he stretched out on a slab of rock.

Now his body was all bathed in sunlight, he was surrounded by it, completely under the dominion of the sun, and now at last he had room enough. There was even more room than he needed.

He stretched his legs out comfortably and yawned. He raised his arms above his head and swept them down in a wide arc to his sides. They didn't touch anything, they touched nothing but the air, which was soft and elastic, giving way at a touch and then flowing gently back again.

It felt good. "It feels good," he said aloud and yawned again. He scratched his head, his neck, his back and legs. He was out of the shadow now, he was all visible. He was a grayish-white color like a turnip, and his toes stuck out of the broken ends of his shoes. One trouser leg was torn off at the knee, the other split up at the side. He lay sprawled out at his ease. Then he yawned again and leaned on his other elbow. He had on what was left of a coat, torn right up to his shoulders in back and wide open in front, showing his hollow chest. His chin was covered with a stubby tough beard.

He was the same color all over, from head to foot, clothes and all, a color which grew lighter and lighter as the sunlight touched it. Everything—leather, cloth, canvas, his own skin and hair—was the same dirty gray now turning to white. . . .

"Pont! It's you. Honest to God! Where have you been?"

They kept asking him, "How on earth did you manage to get out from underneath?"

The whole village was buzzing like an overturned beehive.

"Wait a bit!" he told them. "I haven't got things straight in my head yet. Where am I? Oh yes, I've come out from under the ground, and there you are, and here am I. All right!"

"Your health!"

"It's funny. . . . Now I can't remember. . . . Everything comes and goes."

"Your health, Antoine!"

"And if you're finishing the harvest now, you'll have to explain things to me, because you hadn't even started haying when . . . wait a minute. Yes, that's right, you hadn't started yet. I remember. . . . What day is it? and the date? I already asked my wife that. Yes? What? The seventeenth of August, is it? The seventeenth of August, what year? You see I've lived so long away from years, from weeks, from days and nights. . . ."

They told him.

"Well, then," he said, "now we need to count up. I know I can't. You do it," he told Nendaz. "How many does it make?"

"Seven weeks, and even a bit more. It'll be eight weeks in a day or two."

"Lord!"

There he sat at the table, his glass before him, and everybody clustered around.

"You see, you get so you aren't used to daylight any more. You only see it once in a long while, a little bit, way up above. First it's there, then it isn't. Very far up there, between the stones. . . . The mountain fell down."

Through the open window the air flowed into the room. Wasps came in, too, and bees, and flies. All kinds of flies came in at the window. Some were blue and green; other little black ones made a cloud around people's heads. They looked like one of the black muslin veils that the beekeepers wear when they get honey from the hives. Antoine had one too; he sat there in it looking out at the others with his pale sunken eyes whose look seemed to meet theirs without really taking it in.

People came in, went out. The others shushed them, "Hey you, be quiet!" He paid no attention to anybody. He sat there, his look turned inward, as if he were following something going on there behind his eyes, first one picture, then suddenly another one taking its place.

"Wait a bit, it's coming back . . . the mountain fell down."

He asked, "Could you hear the noise down here, when it fell?"

"Lord! I should think we did!" said Nendaz. "But we didn't know what it was. We would have thought it was a storm if it hadn't been such a fine night."

"A fine night, was it?"

"Lord yes! Stars all over, and not a cloud in the sky. So finally everybody went back to bed. Not me, though, ask Justin if I did. Because I said to myself, 'Maybe it's something else.' And I had my own idea what."

"I didn't hear a thing," said Antoine. "For me it wasn't the noise—too loud to hear, maybe. It was like a heavy knee pressing on my chest, and I fell right down from the wall, with the bed and the straw mattress. The bed, the mattress and me, there we were all three of us on the floor."

"Ssshh! Listen!" everybody said. "Shut up, you!"

This was to the man with the broken arm who was just coming in.

"For me," he said, "it was a beam coming down on my shoulder. They fixed it up for me with splints. . . ."

But Antoine was going right on talking, "The point was the mountain had fallen—the mountain fell on me. And I lay there on the ground without moving, for I didn't know whether I could or not, you see, and anyway I didn't feel like moving just then. How long? Who could tell? And then, there was somebody. . . ."

It was as if he had just seen somebody, unexpectedly, there inside his head.

"And he called to me. . . . Yes."

But already he seemed to forget what he was talking about. Who was it? They didn't know. Antoine was already speaking of something else.

"That's the way you are, at a time like that," he was saying. "I was all taken up with the business of not moving. I didn't have the time to go take a look, lying there wondering whether I still had my arms and legs. For all I knew my back was broken. Somebody said, 'Where are you?' I said, 'Here.' And that was all. I lay there, and then, little by little, I began to move my right hand. First just the tips of my fingers, then the hand, then the arm up to the elbow, and finally my whole arm. . . ."

"Hello Antoine!" somebody said.

Two more men from Premier had just come in. Antoine didn't hear them.

"I thought to myself, 'Well, that makes one arm, anyway. Fine! Now let's take a look at the other one.' And with my right arm I went over to pay a visit to the left. . . ."

"Aren't you drinking?" they asked.

"Yes, I'm drinking. It's all right. And at the same time I lifted my left arm right up in the air. See? That was all right too!"

He laughed, and everybody laughed with him.

"Only now there were my two legs to find out about, and all the time I kept asking myself, 'Didn't somebody call me a while ago?' but anyway there was nothing any more. And I saw that I had one knee left, that made one. And another knee. Two! And both of them in good working order. I tried them out, lying there working my legs up and down like a little baby kicking on a bed when you take his clothes off."

People spoke to him, they asked him questions; he didn't hear them.

He was not governed by the outside world but from within, by the memories that came back to him, returning without order or sequence, so that at times he went ahead of himself, then suddenly was brought back to an earlier place in the story.

"Finally I was sitting up. Nothing was missing anywhere about me. I had two arms, two legs and a body—not to mention my head of course . . . only do you know what? When I lifted my arm—I could lift it, you know. It was all right. Well, say, I lifted my arm up, and right there over my head, not three inches above it, there was a sort of ceiling: it was the mountain that had fallen down, it was a big slab of the mountain tilting up there right over my head. And I was caught in the angle underneath, just as if I was buried alive. . . . The twenty-third of June, you said it was? Yes, well, the twenty-third of June, near two o'clock in the morning maybe. Just about then. And I began yelling just as loud as I could, as if somebody could hear me. . . ."

He picked up his glass, and now it was he who said, "Your health! Your health too, Placide. You here too? Oh yes, you had your arm broken. And the others?"

There was a silence. But he forgot his question immediately.

"Oh! you certainly can be stupid at a time like that, can't you! At first I shouted just as hard as I could, but then I thought all of a sudden, 'I'd better not use too much air.' And I shut up. It struck me that there might not be much air left, and I started trying to breathe just as little as I could. I shut my mouth, tightened my lips, and just breathed through my nose, a little at a time, like this. . . ."

He sketched the gesture of pinching his nostrils together.

"Because you can just imagine, if I didn't have air. . . . To have to do without not only space and light, but air. . . ."

"How about food?" someone asked.

He said, "Wait."

"And water?"

"You're going too fast," he told them. "It's air that people need first of all, isn't it? It's much more important even than food or water. Right then I felt fine, because I could see pretty soon that there would be plenty of air, because of all the cracks there were between the stones. They were piled up to an enormous thickness overhead, but the whole heap was all full of cracks and holes that the air could get through. I could get along on all fours—there wasn't room to stand up—and I saw I had a chance, because the back wall of the cabin was still standing, there where it backed up against the solid rock.

"We'd already made two cheeses," he went on, "and we'd brought up enough bread to last us six weeks. And you can just imagine the luck, they'd landed on the right side for me, I mean right up against my rock, still on their shelf, so that when I felt along the rock with my hand . . ."

Everybody said, "Ah!" and Antoine nodded. "You understand? And I even had the mattress. . . ."

They understood. He went on.

They had to imagine, he told them, that the whole mass of the landslide was honeycombed, just like a sponge, with holes leading in all directions, only unfortunately the tunnels didn't always run into each other. One would suddenly come to a dead end, and although there might be another tunnel just a few inches away, there was nothing to be done, the way was blocked. For there might not be much distance between the end of one passage and the beginning of another, but what lay between was far stronger than any wall, being made of the same stuff all through, of solid stone, and all the same stone too. He would have needed gunpowder to budge it. They could just imagine the time he wasted on that sort of thing. They could count it up for themselves. Seven weeks!

He would follow up one crack, flat on his stomach, as far as he could, then, still lying flat, he would edge his way into another one, then perhaps he might be on his hands and knees, and the rock over his head would be slanting upward. . . . He was still talking. "I'd be all encouraged when it started going up, for the daylight was overhead. But then, the next minute it would start sloping down, and I'd get discouraged again.

"It took time," he went on. "A day, two days—maybe three or even four, how could I tell how many? But do you begin to guess the trouble? Because I didn't have anything to drink. . . . My mouth was drying out as hard as horn, my lips were cracking, my tongue felt like a piece of leather and had swelled up so it wouldn't fit inside my mouth any more. Finally I came back and lay down on the mattress, telling myself, 'You'd better lie still.' You just don't know how lucky you are, up here, with your clocks on the wall, the whole sky overhead, and I kept saying to myself, "What luck they have, with their fountains—their beautiful fountains—and their springs flowing right out on top of the ground. And here I am, if I could only have just one little drop of water, oozing out from time to time at the end of a bit of moss!'

"Plop."

What was that sound?

They were at Rebord's, the room was full of people; Antoine lifted his finger, "Plop. . . ."

It was like a slowly swinging pendulum at first. Then faster, faster. . . . "Plop . . . plop . . . plop!"

He got up from his mattress and crawled forward, holding his hands out in front of him. And all of a sudden he raised his head and the water came running down over his face.

"It was the runoff from the glacier. It had been all dammed up by the landslide, and now it was finding its way out between the rocks; one trickle had come over as far as my crack. It was just like a little hanging string and I could feel it moving and alive between my hands when I raised them up straight. There it was, it was alive, and I was going to live too, because of it, and quick quick I went to get a bucket to catch it in, because I thought, 'If it should ever stop, now. . . .' And there I was—saved! Because now I had everything, you understand, everything a man needs to live. Something to eat, to drink, to breathe, to sleep on. . . . All I had to do now was use the time I had—and plenty of that too, wasn't there? I was certainly going to have all the time I needed, we can see that now, can't we? Seven weeks, and even more than seven weeks. . . ."

All the afternoon it went on like that, at Rebord's.

New arrivals kept coming in and interrupting him. People asked him questions or proposed his health, and he would have to stop to answer them, or drink another glass.

But each time he would go back to his story.

"The cracks were just like the drains they have under the roads. Mostly they were so narrow I'd rub against them on both sides when I crawled through. Where I could see the walls I'd made marks on them so I could find my way back, but where there wasn't any light at all I'd just have to go back and forth, over and over, until I learned the way by heart. Sometimes I'd go a long way in one direction, then the passage would come to a dead end, blocked up solid, and I'd have to go back on my tracks. Sometimes it would be right over my head that I could see a faint gleam of light. I'd try to climb straight up to it, like a chimney sweeper. Up . . . and up. . . . Then suddenly I'd see a slab of rock sticking right out across the crack. No good, I'd have to climb down again. Then I'd see some light over to the left and I'd start off again toward it, just like a plant growing toward the light: that first shoot from the seed that's as delicate and thin as thread, and as strong as a bar of iron. But I didn't have the equipment a plant has, nor its power either, for I kept going first in one direction and then in another, on the track of ideas that would turn out to be no good. Seven weeks of that! Sticking to it was what it took. And caution too, because sometimes the crack I was in would be all choked up with small stones and rubble, and I'd have to clear it out very carefully, working with just the tips of my fingers, very slowly, and stopping to test the ceiling every few minutes—you can imagine the time it took."

And he went on, "Seven weeks!"

Twilight was beginning to fall.

"Well, anyway," they said, "here you are, finally."

THE AWFUL MOVING TIDE OF EARTH

FROM *City of Illusion*

VARDIS FISHER

Perhaps it is a vestigial thing, sunken deep in the ancestral consciousness, that makes death underground so horrifying. In this selection by Vardis Fisher, miners stand helpless watching a man buried alive.

Fisher is a historical novelist, author of the much-praised *Children of God,* a fictional history of Mormonism. Critical concensus is that he tells a grand story in a grand manner.

IN THE FOUL AND POISONOUS GLOOM MEN LABORED, NAKED TO THEIR WAISTS, with sweat like melting lard on their bodies. Their faces were blackened from the smoke of blasting, their hair was matted, the leather of their boots was wet from the water running down their legs. They were only the beasts of labor, bent over pick and shovel, toiling in deadly heat, breathing impure air, and living from day to day in dread of a deluge of water or an avalanche of stone. They were only a part of the machinery, one with the wheelbarrows and cables, cages and lifts.

One day when Fred Grebe, the sly and brutal superintendent, came underground, Luff spoke to him. Why, he asked, didn't the owners get behind Sutro and help him dig a tunnel? The sumps had scum on them a foot deep; even the rats died in the poisonous air. A tunnel would ventilate the mines and let the water flow out; and the men would not be drowned or blown to pieces or buried alive.

"This is a good mine," said Grebe. "Twice as many men is killed in the Potosi or Gould and Curry or the Kentuck."

"But we need a tunnel—a tunnel to carry the water, a railroad to haul the ore, and fresh air coming in to blow the gases up the shafts."

"To hell with a tunnel. We're doing all right. We're taking out five thousand dollars a day."

"Five thousand a day!" cried an angry miner. "Five thousand a day to send to them Bowers people while . . . we work for four dollars a day and get killed!"

"If you don't like it down here," said Grebe, "you'n get you a job somewhere else. It's my job to get the ore to the mills."

It was not the labor that irked Luff McCoy, or the miser's wage; it was the vision of death in horrible ways. Twice within the first week . . . he had seen death strike. . . .

The first blow came in an afternoon. Powder monkeys were sinking a shaft while Luff and others assisted. They drilled and charged four holes to fire at once, and then pulled the bell-rope for the cage. When it came down, they lit the fuses and yanked the rope once as a signal to ascend. The cage did not move. They signaled again and again, and watched the sputtering fuses.

"Something is wrong up there!" a man yelled, and yanked the rope.

Realizing that soon they would be trapped, a man dashed to the fuses to snuff them out. Two of them he tore away but the other two had burned into stone beyond his reach.

"Look out!" he cried.

One of the men was still desperately yanking at the signal rope. Other men leapt to the farthest wall and threw themselves flat on the stone floor. Two men started to climb the cables and timbers, going hand over hand like desperate monkeys; and Luff called to them to come down. The man who had snuffed the fuses sat as if paralyzed. "God!" he said, but he did not move. Like a man chained to the spot and fascinated by the horror of his predicament, he looked at the two fuses burning deep into stone. The two men were still climbing. Luff among a dozen others hugged the floor with arms over his head.

And then the explosion came—a deafening belch of sound and thousands of flying stone bullets. The rock erupted in one mighty blast of thunder; then there was a chamber filled with smoke and silence. Luff remained still, wondering if there was a delayed fuse; but at last he rose and peered into the gloom. Others joined him but one who had hugged the floor did not move. The men went over and looked up the smokefilled shaft. One of the two climbing men had fallen, riddled by bullets of stone; the other hung there in the shaft, impaled on a stout splinter that had been ripped half the length of a log. Of the man who had sat paralyzed by the fuses there was not a trace anywhere, nor did they ever find any.

"Well," said Luff, "that got at least four of us."

Another man was invoking the wrath of God upon the one who tended the hoist. He yanked at the rope. And now the signal was answered. The men entered the cage and ascended, and the cage made mincemeat of the man impaled in the shaft. When they reached the surface, a dozen furious men strode over to the engineer. It was obvious that he had been asleep.

"You dog of a man!" one of them roared. "You scurvy sleepy-headed bastard! Why didn't you raise that cage when we signaled?"

"Huh?" said the engineer, rubbing at his eyes. "Why, I just done it."

"You just murdered four men!"

Another spoke. "Let's throw the son-of-a-bitch down the shaft!"

"What do you mean going to sleep when we're blasting?"

"Asleep?" said the engineer, unable to make sense of all this. "Why, you signaled and I brung her up."

"Let's throw him in!"

"No," said Luff. "That will do no good now. They're dead."

"Who's dead?" asked the hoistman.

At this moment Fred Grebe came along. "What's all the racket here?"

"Go down and see for yourself! Four men blowed to pieces because your lazy cage-boss went to sleep."

"Is that true?" asked Grebe of his engineer.

"Honest," said the man, looking foolish and bewildered, "I don't know what it's all about. They yanked the rope and I upped her right quick."

"You'll have to fire this man," said Luff.

"You giving me orders?" asked Fred.

"We're giving you orders."

"And if I don't?"

"Then we'll throw you both down the shaft."

Fred Grebe could change face with astonishing ease. In awful fury he swung to his engineer. "Skin the hell out!" he roared. "You're fired!"

"Me? Why, they yanked the rope and I brung her up."

"Skin out!" . . .

A few days later, death struck again. They were blasting a crosscut. After a charge had spit in a horrible darkness of thunder and stone, one man, in advance of the others, climbed over tons of shattered rock on the floor and was descending to a floor beyond when suddenly, without any warning at all, the earth ceiling above him gave way. The man was buried to his shoulders. He bawled with mad and inhuman terror; and when the others hastened forward they could see only his head. Luff looked up at the ceiling: it was raining earth and fragments like huge dirty flakes of snow.

"We can't go in," he said.

"No," said another. "The whole damn thing will fall any minute."

Nine men stood there, forty feet away, and looked at the one imprisoned. His arms were captured. Soon he was buried to his neck as if he were vanishing in quicksand. Only his face, turned toward them, was visible; the falling earth was two inches deep on his hair. They could see his bulging eyes and his bawling mouth that pleaded, cursed, and wept. For a long moment he was silent, and when he spoke again he called them by name.

"Luff, good God, you ain't reckonun to let me die like this! . . . Lars, please come and dig me out! . . . Bill. . . ." His eyes rolled from face to face as he spoke. "Bill, I been your friend, ain't I? I'd help you, Bill. . . ." And all the while he was slowly sinking. The earth beneath him was working convulsively in its bowels, rolling deep under, moving like guts in a strong physic, as if the entire Bowers mine were getting ready to let go and plunge. Even the earth and stones around his shoulders were quiveringly astir in a slow tide.

"Let's joke," said Luff. "We can't do a thing, but jokes might make it easier."

There was nothing else they could do. The man was as inexorably doomed as if he were sinking in the ocean with a ton of iron tied to his feet.

Luff ran back to a stope. He returned with an armful of oakum and a gallon of kerosene. Soaking up the oakum in the oil, he tossed it out halfway to the man and threw a lighted match on it. It blazed up, devouring the gloom of the cavern, showing the face of the man; and in a voice maddened by fear and agony he thanked them, he blessed them. He said they were brave; they were his friends. The light, he said, would guide them while they dug him out; and when they did not move toward him, he cried like an animal out of terrible desolation. He was smothering, he told them; his heart and guts were being pushed in upon him, driven to his bones.

His wild cries and sobbing pleas were almost more than they could endure.

"Have you," Luff called to him, "heard the latest story about me? I was going down the street with a sack of flour on my back. Sam Brown saw me when I passed the Crystal saloon. He laughed like hell. 'Look at that crazy fool!' he said. 'There he goes with a sack of flour and I'll bet he ain't got a quart of whisky in the house!' "

But the man was sobbing in frenzy. The oakum was a bonfire of light. Then suddenly the great heap of earth and stone rolled in its bowels and the man sank two inches. Earth closed over his mouth. He tried to blow it away and they saw a tiny cloud of dust when once his breath burst through. They could see only his eyes now. Luff began to tell another story but stopped, sickened and choked. The oakum was burning low. Instead of looking at them, the man's eyes, bursting from his skull, stared at the friendly light burning itself out.

Luff turned to the other men. They were weeping. Then he realized that he was weeping too. Unable to endure the scene they turned away; and when, after a little while, they looked back again, the man was gone. There was only the awful moving tide of earth and stone, and the glow of oakum that had burned itself out.

THE GREAT LANDSLIDE CASE

FROM *Roughing It*

SAMUEL CLEMENS

Mark Twain's *Roughing It* from which this selection is taken has all the gaudy and ample vitality of the frontier spirit—its horseplay, its swaggering exaggeration, its love of the practical joke. It was a product of the Mark Twain of the buoyant earlier years. It is burlesque, but of an easy, comfortable sort, different both in quality and kind from the still-gay but sharper satire of the later *Gilded Age,* the savage attack against church and property of *The Connecticut Yankee* and *Joan of Arc,* and the chill and frozen irony of the disillusioned *Mysterious Stranger.*

THE MOUNTAINS ARE VERY HIGH AND STEEP ABOUT CARSON, EAGLE, AND WASHOE Valleys—very high and very steep, and so when the snow gets to melting off fast in the spring and the warm surface-earth begins to moisten and soften, the disastrous landslides commence. The reader cannot know what a landslide is, unless he has lived in that country and seen the whole side of a mountain taken off some fine morning and deposited down in the valley, leaving a vast, treeless, unsightly scar upon the mountain's front to keep the circumstance fresh in his memory all the years that he may go on living within seventy miles of that place.

General Buncombe was shipped out to Nevada in the invoice of territorial officers, to be United States Attorney. He considered himself a lawyer of parts, and he very much wanted an opportunity to manifest it—partly for the pure gratification of it and partly because his salary was territorially meager (which is a strong expression). Now the older citizens of a new territory look down upon the rest of the world with a calm, benevolent compassion, as long as it keeps out of the way—when it gets in the way they snub it. Sometimes this latter takes the shape of a practical joke.

One morning Dick Hyde rode furiously up to General Buncombe's door in Carson City and rushed into his presence without stopping to tie his horse. He seemed much excited. He told the General that he wanted him to conduct a suit for him and would pay him five hundred dollars if he achieved a victory. And then, with violent gestures and a world of profanity, he poured out his griefs. He said it was pretty well known that for some years he had been farming (or ranching, as the more customary term is) in Washoe District, and making a successful thing of it, and furthermore it was known that his ranch was situated just in the edge of the valley, and that Tom Morgan owned a ranch immediately above it on the mountainside. And now the trouble was, that one of those hated and dreaded landslides had come and slid Morgan's ranch, fences, cabins, cattle, barns, and everything down on top of *his* ranch and exactly covered up every single vestige of his property, to a depth of about thirty-eight feet. Morgan was in possession and refused to vacate the premises—said he was occupying his own cabin and not interfering with anybody else's—and said the cabin was standing on the same dirt and same ranch it had always stood on, and he would like to see anybody make him vacate.

"And when I reminded him," said Hyde, weeping, "that it was on top of my ranch and that he was trespassing, he had the infernal meanness to ask me why didn't I *stay* on my ranch and hold possession when I see him a-coming! Why didn't I *stay* on it, the blathering lunatic—by George, when I heard that racket and looked up that hill it was just like the whole world was a-ripping and a-tearing down that mountainside—splinters and cord-wood, thunder and lightning, hail and snow, odds and ends of haystacks, and awful clouds of dust!—trees going end over end in the air, rocks as big as a house jumping 'bout a thousand feet high and busting into ten million pieces, cattle turned inside out and a-coming head on with their tails hanging out between their teeth!—and in the midst of all that wrack and destruction sot that cussed Morgan on his gatepost, a-wondering why I didn't *stay and hold possession!* Laws bless me, I just took one glimpse, General, and lit out'n the county in three jumps exactly.

"But what grinds me is that that Morgan hangs on there and won't move off'n that ranch—says it's his'n and he's going to keep it—likes it better'n he did when it was higher up the hill. Mad! Well, I've been so mad for two days I couldn't find my way to town—been wandering around in the brush is a starving condition—got anything here to drink, General? But I'm here *now,* and I'm a-going to law. You hear *me!*"

Never in all the world, perhaps, were a man's feelings so outraged as were the General's. He said he had never heard of such high-handed conduct in all his life as this Morgan's. And he said there was no use in going to law—Morgan had no shadow of right to remain where he was—nobody in the wide world would uphold him in it, and no lawyer would take his case and no judge listen to it. Hyde said that right there was where he was mistaken—everybody in town sustained Morgan; Hal Brayton, a very smart lawyer, had taken his case; the courts being in vacation, it was to be tried before a referee, and ex-Governor Roop had already been appointed to that office, and would open his court in a large public hall near the hotel at two that afternoon.

The General was amazed. He said he had suspected before that the people of that territory were fools, and now he knew it. But he said rest easy, rest easy and collect the witnesses, for the victory was just as certain as if the conflict were already over. Hyde wiped away his tears and left.

At two in the afternoon referee Roop's Court opened, and Roop appeared throned among his sheriffs, the witnesses, and spectators, and wearing upon his face a solemnity so awe-inspiring that some of his fellow-conspirators had misgivings that maybe he had not comprehended, after all, that this was merely a joke. An unearthly stillness prevailed, for at the slightest noise the judge uttered sternly the command:

"Order in the Court!"

And the sheriffs promptly echoed it. Presently the General elbowed his way through the crowd of spectators, with his arms full of law-books, and on his ears fell an order from the judge which was the first respectful recognition of his high official dignity that had ever saluted them, and it trickled pleasantly through his whole system:

"Way for the United States Attorney!"

The witnesses were called—legislators, high government officers, ranchmen, miners, Indians, Chinamen, negroes. Three-fourths of them were called by the defendant Morgan, but no matter, their testimony invariably went in favor of the plaintiff Hyde. Each new witness only added new testimony to the absurdity of a man's claiming to own another man's property because his farm had slid down on top of it. Then the Morgan lawyers made their speeches, and seemed to make singularly weak ones—they did really nothing to help the Morgan cause. And now the General, with exultation in his face, got up and made an impassioned effort; he pounded the table, he banged the law-books, he shouted, and roared, and howled, he quoted from everything and everybody, poetry, sarcasm, statistics, history, pathos, bathos, blasphemy, and wound up with a grand war-whoop for free speech, freedom of the press, free schools, the Glorious Bird of America and the principles of eternal justice! [Applause.]

When the General sat down, he did it with the conviction that if there was anything in good strong testimony, a great speech and believing and admiring countenances all around, Mr. Morgan's case was killed. Ex-Governor

Roop leaned his head upon his hand for some minutes, thinking, and the still audience waited for his decision. And then he got up and stood erect, with bended head, and thought again. Then he walked the floor with long, deliberate strides, his chin in his hand, and still the audience waited. At last he returned to his throne, seated himself, and began, impressively:

"Gentlemen, I feel the great responsibility that rests upon me this day. This is no ordinary case. On the contrary, it is plain that it is the most solemn and awful that ever man was called upon to decide. Gentlemen, I have listened attentively to the evidence, and have perceived that the weight of it, the overwhelming weight of it, is in favor of the plaintiff Hyde. I have listened also to the remark of counsel, with high interest—and especially will I commend the masterly and irrefutable logic of the distinguished gentleman who represents the plaintiff. But, gentlemen, let us beware how we allow mere human testimony, human ingenuity in argument and human ideas of equity, to influence us at a moment so solemn as this. Gentlemen, it ill becomes us, worms as we are, to meddle with the decrees of Heaven. It is plain to me that Heaven, in its inscrutable wisdom, has seen fit to move this defendant's ranch for a purpose. We are but creatures, and we must submit. If Heaven has chosen to favor the defendant Morgan in this marked and wonderful manner; and if Heaven, dissatisfied with the position of the Morgan ranch upon the mountainside, has chosen to remove it to a position more eligible and more advantageous for its owner, it ill becomes us, insects as we are, to question the legality of the act or inquire into the reasons that prompted it. No—Heaven created the ranches, and it is Heaven's prerogative to rearrange them, to experiment with them, to shift them around at its pleasure. It is for us to submit, without repining. I warn you that this thing which has happened is a thing with which the sacrilegious hands and brains and tongues of men must not meddle. Gentlemen, it is the verdict of this court that the plaintiff, Richard Hyde, has been deprived of his ranch by the visitation of God! And from this decision there is no appeal."

Buncombe seized his cargo of law-books and plunged out of the courtroom frantic with indignation. He pronounced Roop to be a miraculous fool, an inspired idiot. In all good faith he returned at night and remonstrated with Roop upon his extravagant decision, and implored him to walk the floor and think for half an hour, and see if he could not figure out some sort of modification of the verdict. Roop yielded at last and got up to walk. He walked two hours and a half, and at last his face lit up happily and he told Buncombe it had occurred to him that the ranch underneath the new Morgan ranch still belonged to Hyde, that his title to the ground was just as good as it had ever been, and therefore he was of opinion that Hyde had a right to dig it out from under there and—

The General never waited to hear the end of it. He was always an impatient and irascible man, that way. At the end of two months the fact that he had been played upon with a joke had managed to bore itself, like another Hoosac Tunnel, through the solid adamant of his understanding.

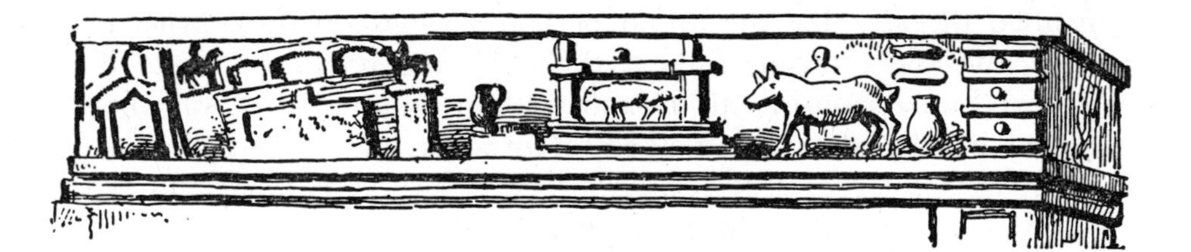

THE EARTHQUAKE OF 63 AT POMPEII IN BAS RELIEF

THE HORIZON WAS CRUMBLING

FROM *The Skin*

CURZIO MALAPARTE

We are too far distant in time to feel the death of Pompeii when Vesuvius erupted. Time has leached out the horror. But here is Naples in 1947 with Vesuvius again active and showering the city with death. Curzio Malaparte, in this selection from his autobiographical memoir, *The Skin,* takes the reader to the slums of Naples and shows the scene with all its terror and animality.

There is great power in Malaparte's writing, but little sympathy. He prefers to relate the inhuman, the macabre. His choice is not inconsistent with Malaparte's earlier politics. He was one of the first members of the Italian Fascist party and under Mussolini was editor of Turin's *La Stampa.* He shifted his political loyalties with Mussolini's defeat.

THE SKY TO THE EAST WAS SCARRED BY A HUGE, CRIMSON GASH, WHICH TINGED the sea blood-red. The horizon was crumbling away, plunging headlong into an abyss of fire. Shaken by subterranean convulsions, the earth trembled; the houses rocked on their foundations; and already one could hear the dull thud of tiles and lumps of plaster as they came apart from the roofs and the cornices of the verandahs, and hurtled down on to the pavements below, like harbingers of universal destruction. A dreadful grinding noise filled the air, like the sound of bones when they are broken and crushed. And above the din, above the wails and terrified shrieks of the people, who were running hither and thither, groping their way through the streets like blind creatures, there arose a terrible cry, which rent the heavens.

Vesuvius was screaming in the night, spitting blood and fire. Never since the day that saw the final destruction of Herculaneum and Pompeii, buried alive in their tomb of ashes and lava, had so dread a voice been heard in the heavens. A gigantic pillar of fire rose sky-high from the mouth of the volcano—a vast, stupendous column of smoke and flames, which penetrated deep into the firmament, so that it touched the pale stars. Down the slopes of Vesuvius flowed rivers of lava, sweeping toward the villages which lay scattered amid the green of the vineyards. The blood-red glare of the glowing lava was so vivid that for miles around the mountains and the plain were lit up with unbelievable brilliance. Woods, rivers, houses, meadows, fields and paths could be seen far more clearly and distinctly than by day; and already the sun was a remote and faded memory.

The mountains of Agerola and the ridges of Avellino were suddenly seen to fall apart, uncovering the secrets of their green valleys and woods. A distance of many miles lay between Vesuvius and the Monte di Dio, from the summit of which, dumb with horror, we contemplated that marvelous spectacle; yet our eyes, as they searched and explored the Vesuvian countryside, which but a little while before had been sleeping peacefully in the moonlight, picked out men, women and animals as though they had been magnified and brought closer by a powerful lens. We saw them fleeing to the vineyards, the fields and the woods, or wandering among the houses of the villages, which the flames were already lapping on every side. And not only could we make out their gestures and demeanor, but we could even distinguish their tousled hair, their unkempt beards, their staring eyes and wide-open mouths. We even seemed to hear the hoarse whistling sound with which they expelled the breath from their lungs.

The sea presented, perhaps, an even more horrifying picture than the land. As far as the eye could reach there was nothing but a hard, livid crust, pitted everywhere with holes that resembled the pockmarks of some frightful disease; and beneath that motionless crust one sensed the explosive presence of a prodigious force, of a fury scarce repressed, as though the sea were threatening to rise from its bed, to break its hard, scaly back, that it might make war on the land and vent its dreadful fury. Outside Portici, Torre del Greco, Torre Annunziata and Castellammare boats could be seen retreating in great haste from the perilous shore, propelled in desperation by oars alone, since out at sea the wind had dropped like a dead bird, though it was blowing violently to landward. Other boats were to be seen hurrying from Sorrento, Meta and Capri to bring help to the luckless inhabitants of the seaside villages, trapped by the fury of the flames. Torrents of mud flowed sluggishly down the sides of Mount Somma, forming twisted, coiled heaps like black snakes; and where the torrents of mud met the rivers of lava clouds of purple vapor rose aloft, and a dreadful hissing sound reached our ears, like the sizzling of red-hot iron when it is immersed in water.

A huge black cloud, in shape resembling the ink sac of a cuttlefish, swollen with ashes and fragments of glowing lava, was struggling to break away from the crest of Vesuvius. Propelled by the wind, which, fortunately for Naples, was by some miracle blowing from the northwest, it trailed slowly across the sky in the direction of Castellammare di Stabia. The roar emitted by that black, lava-filled cloud as it rolled through the heavens was like the rumbling of a truck laden with stones when it enters a bumpy street. Every so often, from some gap in the cloud, a deluge of lava rained down upon earth and sea, landing on the fields and the hard sea-crust with a crash like that which is heard when the same truck tips up its load; and as the lava touched the ground and the hard surface of the sea it raised clouds of reddish dust, which spread into the sky, blotting out the stars. Vesuvius screamed horribly in the red darkness of that awful night, and a despairing lament arose from the unhappy city.

I pressed Jack's arm, and felt him tremble. His face was pale as he contemplated that vision of hell, and horror, dread and wonder mingled in his wide eyes. "Let us go," I said to him, tugging him by the arm. We moved away, and set off along the Vicolo di Santa Maria Egiziaca in the direction of the Piazza Reale. The walls of that narrow alley reflected such a blaze of crimson light that we walked like blind men, groping our way. Naked people were leaning out of all the windows, waving their arms and calling to one another with shrill cries and piercing wails. Others who were rushing panic-stricken through the streets raised their eyes, crying out themselves and weeping, without pausing or slowing down in their headlong flight. There were people everywhere, some looking miserable, others fierce, clad in rags or naked; some were hurrying to the chapels with wax candles and torches for the Madonnas and the Saints; others, kneeling on the pavement, were calling aloud upon the Virgin and St. Januarius to help them, beating their breasts, while frenzied tears poured down their ravaged cheeks. . . .

In the maze of alleys that leads down to Toledo and Chiaia the mob grew thicker and more frenzied at every step; for popular disorders develop in the same way as disorders of the blood in the human body: in such cases the blood tends to collect in one place and to cause disturbances now in the heart, now in the brain, now in one or other of the intestines. People were coming down from the remotest quarters of the city and collecting in what from time immemorial have been regarded as the holy places of Naples—in the Piazza Reale, around the Tribunali, the Maschio Angioino and the Cathedral, where the miraculous blood of St. Januarius is preserved. There the uproar was terrific, sometimes assuming the proportions of a riot. Lost in that fearsome crowd, which swept them now this way, now that, as it surged to and fro, turning them round and buffeting them like the gale in Dante's Hill, the American soldiers looked as if they too were possessed by a primeval terror and fury. Their faces were begrimed with sweat and ashes, their uniforms were in rags. Now they too were humbled. No longer were they free men, no longer were they proud conquerors. They were conquered wretches, victims of the blind fury of nature. They too were seared to the depths of their souls by the fire that was consuming the sky and the earth.

From time to time a hollow, muffled rumbling, which spread through the secret recesses of the earth, shook the pavement beneath our feet and made the houses rock. A hoarse, deep, gurgling voice rose from the wells and from the mouths of the sewers. The fountains exhaled sulphurous vapors or threw up jets of boiling mud. That subterranean rumbling, that deep voice, that boiling mud caused a sudden efflux of people from their lairs in the bowels of the earth. For during those melancholy years the wretched populace, in order to escape the merciless air raids, had made their homes in the winding tunnels of the ancient Angevin aqueduct which runs beneath the streets of Naples. This aqueduct, say the archaeologists, was excavated by the first inhabitants of the city, who were Greeks or Phoenicians, or by the Pelasgians, those mysterious men who came from the sea. There is an allusion to the Angevin aqueduct and to its strange population in Boccaccio's tale of Andreuccio da Perugia. These unhappy creatures were emerging from their filthy hell-holes, from the dark caves, the underground passages, the wells and the mouths of the sewers. Each one carried on his shoulders his wretched chattels, or, like a modern Aeneas, his aged father, or his young children, or the pecuriello, the paschal lamb, which at Eastertide (it was actually Holy Week) brings joy to even the meanest Neapolitan home, and is sacred, because it is the image of Christ.

This "resurrection," to which the coincidence of Easter gave a dread significance, the resurgence from the tomb of these ragged hordes, was a sure sign of the existence of a danger both grave and imminent. For what hunger, and cholera, and earthquakes—which, according to an ancient belief, destroy palaces and hovels but respect the caverns and the underground passages beneath the city's foundations—cannot accomplish was possible to the rivers of boiling mud with which Vesuvius in its spite was gleefully driving those poor wretches like rats from the sewers.

Those crowds of mud-stained, spectral beings who were everywhere emerging from beneath the ground, that seething mob which was rushing like a river in flood toward the low-lying parts of the city, and the brawls, the yells, the tears, the oaths, the songs, the panic, the sudden stampedes, and the ferocious struggles that would break out in the vicinity of a chapel, a fountain, a cross, or a baker's shop, created a frightful, stupendous chaos of sound, which filled the city and was overflowing on to the seafront, into Via Partenope, Via Caracciolo, the Riviera di Chiaia, and the streets and squares that front the sea between the Granili and Mergellina. It was as if the people in their despair looked to the sea alone for salvation, as if they expected that the waves would quench the flames which were devouring the land, or that the marvelous compassion of the Virgin or St. Januarius would enable them to walk on the waters and escape.

But when they reached the sea front, where they were greeted by the fearsome spectacle of Vesuvius, red-hot, with streams of lava winding their way down its slopes, and the blazing villages (the blast from the prodigious conflagration spread as far as the island of Capri, which could be seen drifting on the horizon, and the snow-covered mountains of Cilento), the crowd dropped to their knees; and at the sight of the sea, which was covered with a horrible green and yellow film like the mottled hide of some loathsome reptile, they called upon heaven to help them, uttering loud wails, bestial yells and savage oaths. Many, spurred on by the curses and the frightful abuse of the infuriated, envious populace, plunged into the waves, hoping that they would provide a foothold and were ignominiously drowned.

After wandering round for a long time we finally emerged into the vast square, dominated by the Maschio Angioino, that opens on to the harbor. And there before us, swathed from head to foot in its purple mantle, we saw Vesuvius. That ghostly Caesar with his doglike head, sitting on his throne of lava and ashes, cleft the sky with his flame-crowned head, and barked horribly. The pillar of fire that rose from his throat penetrated deep into the celestial vault and vanished into the abyss of heaven. Rivers of blood streamed from his gaping red jaws, and earth, sky and sea trembled.

The faces of the crowd that filled the square were shiny and flat-looking; they were seamed with shadowy black and white lines, as in a flash-bulb photograph. There was something of the harshness and frozen immobility of a photograph in those wide, staring eyes and intent faces, in the façades of the houses and the other impersonal features of the scene, and almost, one felt, in the people's gestures. The fierce light of the flames beat down upon the walls and illuminated the gutters and cornices of the balconies; and the contrast between the bloodshot sky, which had a sombre, purplish tint, and the red-rimmed roofs was illusory in its effect. Crowds of people were hurrying down to the sea, pouring into the square from the hundred alleys that converge upon it from all sides. As they walked they gazed up at the black clouds, swollen with glowing lava, that rolled across the sky immediately above the sea, and at the red-hot stones that ploughed their way noisily through the murky air like comets. A terrible clamor arose from the square; and every so often a deep silence would fall upon the crowd, broken at intervals by a groan, a wail, or a sudden cry—a solitary cry that died away instantly without leaving behind it a trace of an echo, like a cry that goes up from a bare mountaintop.

Over on the far side of the square hordes of American soldiers were making a violent assault on the railings that block the entrance to the

FIGHTING THE DREAD LOCUSTS IN KENYA

nderwood and Underwood

right: A CRATER, SURROUNDED BY OLIVE TREES, OCCUPIED BY THE NORTH AFRICAN CAVE PEOPLE

below: TIMMOUDI, AN AFRICAN VILLAGE OF 200 PEOPLE WHO LIVE IN HOUSES OF CLAY

Dharmya: Black Star

Mauritus: Black Star

A CARAVAN RESTS

Underwood and Underwood

A FARMER IN PALESTINE

Underwood and Underwood

TREADING A WATERWHEEL IN CHINA

Herbert Lanks: Black Star

Underwood and Underwood

FARMERS IN LAPLAND

HARVESTING WHEAT BY HAND IN INDIA

Underwood and Underwood

FPG

left: EARTHQUAKE IN LA POMA, ARGENTINA

below: RESULT OF AN EARTHQUAKE IN TURKEY

Ulus: Black Star

derwood and Underwood

AFTER A TORNADO

Underwood and Underwood

left: DREDGE BOAT STRANDED THREE MILES INLAND, AFTER THE GALVESTON FLOOD OF 1900

below: AFTER A SOUTH DAKOTA SAND-STORM

Monkmeyer

harbor, trying to break the great iron bars. Hoarse, plaintive cries for help came from the ships' sirens. Pickets of armed sailors were rushing to take up their positions on the decks and along the sides of their vessels. Fierce scuffles were breaking out on the moles and gangways between the sailors and the hordes of fear-crazed soldiers who were rushing the ships that they might escape the wrath of Vesuvius. Here and there, lost in the crowd, were American, British, Polish, and French soldiers, wandering about in bewilderment and terror. Some tried to force their way through the press, clutching the arms of weeping women, whom they appeared to have kidnaped; others allowed themselves to be swept along on the tide, dazed by the ferocity and novelty of the awful scourge. They were surrounded by swarms of prostitutes, half-naked, or wrapped in the ceremonial cloaks of yellow, green and scarlet silk worn by the women in the brothels. And some chanted their own private litanies; others uttered mysterious phrases in loud, piercing voices; others in rhythmic tones invoked the name of God—"O God! O God!"—frantically waving their arms above the sea of heads and distorted faces, and keeping their eyes fixed on the sky as if, through the rain of ashes and fire, they were watching the slow flight of an Angel armed with a flaming sword.

By now the night was waning, and a delicate pallor was suffusing the sky over toward Capri and above the wooded slopes of the mountains of Sorrento. Even the fires of Vesuvius were losing something of their terrible brilliance and were beginning to appear green and transparent; the flames were turning pink, and looked like huge rose petals scattered by the wind. As the nocturnal mists gave way to the uncertain light of dawn the rivers of lava ceased to glow; they grew dim, and were transformed into black snakes, just as red-hot iron, when it is left on the anvil, gradually becomes covered with black scales, which emit dying blue and green sparks.

Slowly the dawn was lifting that infernal panorama, still dripping with red darkness, out of the deep bowl of the flaming night, as a fisherman raises a clump of coral from the bed of the sea. The virgin light of day was washing the pale green of the vineyards, the antique silver of the olive trees, the deep blue of the cypresses and pines, the voluptuous gold of the brooms. In such a setting the black rivers of lava shone with a funereal radiance, glowing darkly as some crustaceans do when they lie on the seashore in the sun, or like certain kinds of dark stones when the rain has restored their lustre. In the distance, beyond Sorrento, a patch of red was gradually climbing above the horizon. Slowly it dissolved into the air, and the sky, which was full of yellow, sulphurous clouds, was suffused with a transparent blood-red glow, until unexpectedly the sun, white as the eyelid of a dying bird, broke through the turbulent mists.

A tremendous clamor arose from the square. The crowd stretched out their arms toward the rising sun, shouting "The sun! The sun!" as if this were the first time the sun had ever risen over Naples. And perhaps the sun was indeed rising now for the first time on Naples from the abyss of chaos, amid the turmoil of creation, climbing from the bed of a sea whose creation was not yet complete. And as always happens in Naples after a time of terror, grief and tears, the return of the sun, following a night of such endless agony, changed horror and weeping into joy and jubilation. Here and there arose the sound of the first applause, the first glad voices, the first songs, and those sharp guttural cries, attuned to the age-old melodic themes of elemental fear, pleasure and love, with which the people of Naples, in the manner of animals, that is to say in a wonderfully naïve and innocent way, express joy, amazement, and that happy fear which men and animals always feel when they have rediscovered the meaning of joy and are astonished to be alive.

Gangs of boys were running among the crowd, chasing from end to end of the square and crying "E fornuta! è fornuta!" Those words—"It's over! It's over!"—announcing the ending not only of the scourge but of the war. "E fornuta! è fornuta!" answered the crowd, for always the sun's appearance deludes the people of Naples, inspiring them with the false hope that their misfortunes and sufferings are about to end. A cart drawn by a horse entered the square from Via Medina, and the sight of that horse filled the crowd with joyous amazement, as though it was the first horse ever created. One and all shouted: "See that? See that? A horse! A horse!" And as if by magic there arose on all sides the voices of the itinerant vendors, offering for sale sacred images, rosaries, amulets, dead men's bones, postcards representing scenes from former eruptions of Vesuvius, and statuettes of St. Januarius, who with a gesture had halted the stream of lava at the gates of Naples.

4

Men Study the Earth

In the rocks, the geologist reads the story of a continuous creation. They are pages in the earth's autobiography, a two-billion-year-old record that began with the Proterozoic lifeless world. Our species, *homo sapiens,* is only fifty thousand years old. The earth's age, as the universe measures time, is the briefest present in an incalculably ancient past. It is being changed second by passing second, by wind and sun and rain, by flood and earthquake, by man's powerful creative tools and even more powerful instruments of destruction. What shape will our earth take in a million years? And man, how will he have been altered by the endless process of evolution?

Our scientists see in the record of the rocks not the past alone, but the shape of the future. From their writings we have chosen those which have best transformed the daring formulae of science into the stuff of literature.

WHAT IS A WEED?

FROM *Flowering Earth*

DONALD CULROSS PEATTIE

This selection by Donald Culross Peattie on the rise of our modern flora is as close to a prose poem on evolution and adaptation as any naturalist is likely to come.

Peattie is both scientist and poet. His first writings, a book of poetry and a study of the botany of North Carolina and Indiana, were published almost simultaneously. He says that in order to avoid a split personality, he combined his dual activities and took to nature writing. He has been rightly termed "America's most lyric naturalist."

FOR EVERY MAN THERE IS SOME SPOT ON EARTH, I THINK, WHICH HE HAS PLEDGED himself to return to, some day, because he was so happy there once. Even to long for it is holiday of a sort. These visits of revery may be all that he can pay it, for years, perhaps until his shade is free to haunt where it pleases. But some are lucky; some get back, and find it, to every trembling leaf and stanch old tree trunk, untouched by any alteration but the seasons'.

My place, my chosen bailiwick in the hereafter, is in the Appalachian country, field of my earliest forays when I turned plantsman at twenty. Those mountains, the oldest on the face of the continent, are the kindest. They are blue with the haze of southern warmth, covered with a rustling mantle of shade, abloom in spring, full of falls and brooks where the white quartz gleams, as good as diamonds to any child. And I was a child there. So when I go back, it seems like home, all over again each time.

But the home core of it lies under no roof but the Carolina sky. It has walls, yes, high rocky ones that pocket fern and orchis, saxifrage and trillium, and it is inhabited, not only by the cardinal and thrush, but by a minor deity of its own. She is a waterfall, white, radiant, immortal if not living, and she is always there for me when I go back.

I was away from her for many years, but I had the place by heart. During that long absence there came to me a request for a report of my Carolina glen, and there on the other side of the ocean, amid the hot dust of Mediterranean hills, I was able to compose from memory a list—a florula, as botanists call it —of all that grew beside the falls. Verifying it years later, on an exile's return, I found I had omitted only two species.

For there is a particularity about the flora of that ancient mountain chain. It has no parallel, as I have said, save in high places in China and Japan. But it is esoteric in more than range; it is the last stand of what I have called the Renaissance of plant life. After the pillared glooms of the Mesozoic forests, after the day of conifer might and cycad ascendancy, the first great flowering of the world began. Through the Tertiary, the last age of antiquity, the eon before modernity dawned, this experiment of blossoming went on. And what grew then, all over a world that was warmer than ours and spared our harsh extremes, was very much the same flora that nods and glistens in the spray of my laughing falls.

Never in time before had the forests bloomed or spread broad, filmy and deciduous leaves. And neither in all storied Europe nor in our own magnificent West is there today a living grace like that of the Appalachian woods in spring. My glen is a temple of it, the waterfall niched in the far heart. To reach it, I used to take the nine o'clock local from the Piedmont village; with the help of two engines to drag us up the steepest grade east of the Rockies, the train would attain the water tank in fifteen minutes, and stop there, panting, to drop the extra engine. I dropped off there, too. And when the train, wagging its dragon tail, had vanished, I was alone with April. In the morning freshness there was no sound but the music of leaves, and the rushing of many confluent brooks. Cross a meadow, and there was the entrance to the glen, screened in sunny greenery. At once the smell of lichen and loam and fern blew out to me, sharpened with the honeyed odor of azaleas, and I always stopped a minute just to listen with closed eyes, and to draw a deep breath of happiness.

Then the glen once more received me.

Hours like those make no saga. Eventless in their perfection, they cannot be communicated like a tale. There is nothing to tell but how the sunlight is green-filtered and cool with the breadth of falling water, how the trail follows the stream up and up, over fallen logs, with the summons of the hidden cascade rushing ever louder in your ears, and the sense of green, lighthearted sacrosanct deepening as the rock walls rise. How when you thirst there, you drink from cupped hands at that spring that gushes from the brow of a rock to drum in a perpetual shower upon the Euclidian beauty of trillium. The trilliums there have different odors that are in my nostrils now as I remember —one smelled of roses, one of honey, one of bay rum, one of crushed strawberries, one had no scent, and the last perfume I can neither describe nor forget, for it was loveliest of all.

This is not science; this is trifling with the great plant story I have set out to tell. But, I tell you, just to remember that place is holiday for me. There was no time there, except, far and lonely through the leaves, the whistle of the noon train coming down, when I would know I could let myself eat lunch at last, on the broad rock table at the foot of the falls. After all, there was not much science then for me in the glen, in those boyhood visits that I remember best. But I carried into it, along with my vasculum for collecting, just enough knowledge to set all I saw alight with realization. I knew I stood amid the purest example of the plant life of another age left in the world today. I was learning to name everything I touched or smelled or saw abloom high overhead, like the white fragrant bells of the sourwood swinging seventy-five feet above me, loud with the eagerness of bees. I knew the redbud by its rose-magenta flowers like small butterflies, the buckeye lifting its turrets of pale yellow blossoms, the silver-bell tree hanging drooping clusters. Dogwood of course I knew, and azalea, rhododendron, mountain laurel; some species of all these are tall as trees in my glen. Taller trees stand protector, soft magnolias and hard maples with scarlet flowers, black gums and sweet gums, tulip trees, hickories, and butternuts of the indelible dye, that stains the fingers still as once it dyed the shirts of Jackson's fighting hosts.

The glen was my book, that April I was twenty. I idled over it, watching the rhododendron snow its petals on the dark pools that spun them round in a swirl of brown foam and beached them on a tiny coast glittering with mica and fool's gold. But I got it by heart, the dripping rocks, the ferny grottos, the eternal freshness, the sense of loam, of deep sweet decay, of a chain of life continuous and rich with the ages. The walking fern I gathered there, that walks across its little forest world by striking root with its long tips, tip to root and root to tip walking away from the localities that knew it once, has its oriental counterpart; of that I was aware. And I knew that Shortia, the flower that was lost for a century after Michaux found it "dans les hautes montagnes de Carolinie," has its next of kin upon the mountains of Japan. Sometimes I met mountain people hunting ginseng for the Chinese market; long ago the Chinese all but exterminated that herbalistic panacea of theirs, and now they turn for it to the only other source, the Appalachians.

Later I came to understand what mighty upheavals of the earth, what changes in the world's weather had scattered this once wide-spread flora and locked it away in mountains an ocean and a continent apart. Once the Appalachian-Oriental forests overspread the whole of the north temperate world. Witness of that has been found in amber cast up from the Baltic, blossoms of the Tertiary lying imprisoned there in a waxen perfection. Again at the village of Florissant, in Colorado, a fossil flora rich in Appalachian and tropical types tells how different then was the lie of the land and the very air that blew over it.

For in that pre-Adamite day the earth was a more equable sort of place, and the pattern of its lands was more solid and more even. Tropic and arctic both were tempered. It was a genial and cosmopolitan world; tree fern and laurel reached to Greenland, and the elephant and the camel and the tiger lived in the United States. For millions of years a lush and sprightly plant life labored untroubled in the sun, laying down the soft Tertiary coals that today are found so widely in western America.

But it was a young world still, and not a settled one. One by one the land bridges of the continents began to break, isolating Madagascar from India, cutting off Australia from Asia. The Antarctic bridges sank beneath the sea, and the great North Atlantic bridge went too.

And as the land sank, elsewhere it rose, in impassable mountain barriers. The Rockies rose, tilting up the trans-Mississippi plains with them, giving us the prairies and Pike's Peak. In time, in many millennia, the Sierra Nevada was in its turn thrust up; it caught the Great Basin between its snows and the Rockies, and turned it into a desert. In South America the Andes shouldered high through the old tropical rain forest. The Himalayas were lifted from the hot Gangetic jungles. In Europe the Alps came into being.

All over the world the temperature must have begun to go down, as the glaciers gathered. Winters lasted longer, frost came earlier. The banner of autumn colors, perhaps, was hung for the first time in those earliest deciduous woods. And now, when England was covered with mountains of ice, and woolly mammoths and mastodons, bison and reindeer and the fierce dire wolves were roaming France, a creature called *Pithecanthropus erectus* made his low-browed appearance.

In that uneasy world, the glaciers came and went perhaps four times. Tundras and bogs full of peat moss and reindeer lichen bordered those ice fields. Dust bowls of wind-blown loess filled central Europe and our West and Middle West. Rockies and Alps and Sierra wore immense ice caps almost to their bases. All that was soft and fair and genial in the old Tertiary flora was killed, or driven into refuges like far China or my Blue Ridge hills. And man, who is always at his best in hard times, lighted his first camp fires against the great winter of the Pleistocene glacial period.

Fire, the fire of life, leaps to its every chance. Quench it here, its seed springs there, and races in conquering flame on every lucky wind. None more indomitable than the green fire of plant life. Adjusting to drought and cold, to sopping bog and bleak desert, it caught hold, seized its chances, and evolved into that triumphant conflagration we may call the Great Northern Flora.

It covers Europe today, Iceland and what little of Greenland is not still wrapped in its particular ice age; it ranges across Siberia, Alaska and Canada, and has found its way deep into the United States; it is, in the temperate zone, the modern flora. Like much else in modern life, it is strong, dominant, aggressive, not built to last but to catch as catch can. It is for a short life and a flowery one; it runs to annuals and low soft perennials, to high fertility and modest living standards. At its best it is beautiful, with the brave beauty of Canterbury bells of Transylvania, lupines of California, foxgloves of England, golden daisies of the prairies. It can be ugly, with the pushing coarseness of pigweed and tumbleweed and burdock. It can overrun the territory it claims by mob rule, a rabble of dandelions crowding in the lawn, blue devil deviling the farmer, arrogant thistles of Europe taking the pampas over, mile by mile, and gorse, thorn-armed and bannered with showy blossoms, driving the almost Mesozoic timid flora of New Zealand back into a last stand in the mountains.

When the glaciers caught the Tertiary vegetation between their ice and the impassable barriers represented by Alps, Mediterranean and Sahara, they crushed out its delicate life. Let the patricians fall, and the plebeians rise up, vigorous with those hardier virtues that are bred in a long cruel competition. They must have lain potential in the older, more primitive Tertiary families, but suppressed, throughout the days of its pride, like the fertile lowly in some ancient oligarchic civilization.

The plants that repopulated Europe came out of the Russian steppes, out of the Caucasus, that cradle of races, out of what are today the many-peopled, many-tongued Balkans, and the Siberian forests and high Asiatic plateaux. They filled Europe with a colorful polyarchy of innumerable tribes, each forced to excel the others in fertility and armament, defense and aggression. They invaded all environments, called to aid ancient wind and modern insects, even birds to pollinate them. Some are so vital that they will do without pollination and yet set seed. There is no end to the cunning of their devices of penetration: winged seeds and barbed seeds, and creeping roots throwing up endless suckers. With thorny stems and poisonous alkaloids they defend themselves. They store their strength in corms, taproots, bulbs. In blazing desert reaches their leaves grow narrow as needles, as if squinting against the glare; in forests, they lay out their broad leaves with an intricate care to catch every ray of the light. They are life as we know it today, ingenious, indomitable, all a struggle for a place in the sun.

Now plants had entered into intense competition with *Homo sapiens,* a creature determined to clear his lands for a few species like wheat and barley, rice and maize. Those plant that did not enter his good graces fought him as weeds, or betook themselves to bogs and moors, strands and alpine meadows where he would not molest them. So we have not only nettles and cockles and tares, but the flora of the herbalists, of Grimm's fairy-tales, of the Scotch heather and the Irish bogs, of the plain of Marathon, with poet's narcissus blooming from the blood of heroes. This is the rich plant civilization that gives us scarlet anemones of Provence, the alpine blossoms that the poet-botanist Haller gathered, and wide-eyed arctic wildflowers named by Linnaeus upon his Lapland faring.

It has inherited the earth, this Great Northern Flora, like man himself. And it has followed him wherever he has gone, wherever, with his plough and axe, his petted cereals and his close-cropping cattle, he comes to lord it over native peoples and native vegetations unequipped to repel him. English sheep brought English burs in their wool to New Zealand. At man's heels Russian thistle invaded North America like a Tartar host, spreading from west to east on the wind of conquest; man settled our western cactus in Australia, and there it has become a bristling horde harrying all that grows in its way.

So a sinless world altered, and with gardens came the weeds in them. What is a weed? I have heard it said that there are sixty definitions. For me, a weed is a plant out of place. Or, less tolerantly, call it a foreign aggressor, which is a thing not so mild as a mere escape from cultivation, a visitor that sows itself innocently in a garden bed where you would not choose to plant it. Most weeds have natal countries, whence they have sortied. So Japanese honeysuckle, English plantain, Russian thistle came from lands we recognize, but others, like gypsies, have lost all record of their geographic origin. Some of them turn up in all countries, and are listed in no flora as natives. Some knock about the seaports of the world, springing up wherever ballast used to be dumped from the old sailing ships. Others prefer cities; they have lost contact with sweet soil, and lead a guttersnipe existence. A little group occurs only where wool waste is dumped, others are dooryard and pavement weeds, seeming to thrive the more as they are trod by the feet of man's generations. Some prized in an age of simpler tastes have become garden *declassés* and street urchins; thus it comes about that the pleasant but plebeian scent of Bouncing Bet, that somewhat blowsy pink of old English gardens, is now one of the characteristic odors of American sidewalk ends, where the pavement peters out and the shacks and junked cars begin.

Of such are the plant immigrants come steerage to our shores. They have a sociology of their own, their own ecology and folkways—weed-ways, rather. There are more laws on our statute books governing the responsibility of the landowner toward weeds than toward any other group of plants. And more will yet be enacted, for there are more weeds to come. Agricultural journals, if you follow them, contain constant references to invasions of newcomers, fresh outbreaks by old offenders, new instances of some economically hard-pressed native that has suddenly taken to vagrancy. In the last year California spent almost half a million dollars on weed control, fighting camel-thorn of Arabia that has become naturalized in the desert counties, St. John's-wort of Europe that is ruining the ranges in the cool Klamath country.

So man has put his hand upon the green body of life. He is both friend and enemy to it; he fights it and encourages it, he conserves and destroys it, does little consistently, and much with sporadic brilliance. What, then, of the flora of the future?

As long as man keeps the upper hand with Nature, he is going to strive to bring about a flora once more cosmopolitan. His commerce and exchange of crops and weeds, of garden materials and attendant pests, will break down insularity and provincialism just as technical civilization drives out local customs and costumes, and smooths away dialects in favor of a uniform speech. Like the rest of our future, this promises mixed blessings. On the Mojave it is grateful to rest under the shade of tamarix trees brought in from the Sahara, giving respite where even the native mesquite will not cast its thin umbrage. Upon the prairie, where once the virgin sod was proud with tall native grasses and blazing composites, it is lamentable to feel the foreign weeds crowd harsh about the ankles. To the coming of such changes there is no simple answer.

But there are dreams, there are plans. Already with plant breeding and hybridization man has accomplished miracles beyond Nature's own power. Greater things could yet be done, in afforestation of the tree-starved lands, in cereals that would be clean, once more, of the rusts and smuts that civilization has broadcasted.

But it might be that man himself will run to weed. If he returns to unthinking brute savagery, if he departs, like the armored tyrannosaurs, then Nature will go her own serene way again. Then all will be left to her selective processes, and to the geologic future of the earth. Today we live in an age of composites, in the temperate zone, of orchids in the tropics. When their great day is done, the next to dominate the earth will once more rise from the sturdy and humble. From the grasses, perhaps, or out of the very brambles that now lurk outcast and unwanted on the fringe of our sufferance, and there, unchallenged, are experimenting with countless new species.

But sufficient to our own long day is this modern flora of ours. If I have left no simple impression of what it is like, then I have left the correct impression. There are some hundred thousand species of flowering plants on earth today, and they are scattered through some two hundred and fifty families. Add to these all the mosses and ferns, the Gymnosperms and fungi, seaweeds and algas, and you have some three hundred thousand races of plant life populating the Green Kingdom. All this, out of the first bacteria that colonized the planet. All this brilliant land flora, after naked Psylophyton tentatively trying the new environment of the old Devonian continent.

Never in past geologic time can there have been so complex a vegetation as today, for never were there so many climates, such mountains, such deserts, such seas, such arctics, such island archipelagoes, such insularity everywhere. You could have written a florula of Cambrian times upon a very few pages. Today there breathes no man who can master more than a little portion of the plant world, or a selected group of families. Sir Joseph Dalton Hooker, in his prime, could recognize on sight ten thousand species, because he had collected and identified everywhere, from the Indian jungles to lonely Kerguelen Island in the Pacific, and he knew the diatomaceous flora of the arctic ocean as well as the sweet rustic wildflowers of England. After the age of ninety his prodigious memory fell off a bit. But he was one of the rare titans of classification, like Linnaeus and De Candolle. A fair-to-middling student is glad to recognize on sight two thousand kinds of plants, and he easily goes rusty without constant practice. I remember best, I find, not the plants I learned most recently, but, like poetry, those I memorized when the tablets of my brain were fresh. It follows therefore that I recall still, with a morning clarity, the inhabitants of my distant glen, those old Tertiary Appalachian aristocrats blooming where no weed ever sets root, where there is neither the gaudy splendor of these Californian poppies, nor the urban squalor of quitch grass and pigweed and goosefoot. The last plant I shall forget, surely, will be the first I ever taught myself to know—the windflower of those Blue Ridge woods.

A WANDERER AMONG ROCKS

FROM *The Old Red Sandstone*

HUGH MILLER

Hugh Miller was controversialist for Genesis in the middle nineteenth century. He was a Scottish geologist, self-taught, who learned the elements of the science by working as apprentice and journeyman stonemason, a schooling which he describes with great charm in this selection from *The Old Red Sandstone.*

His scientific findings have suffered the erosion of time, but he is still read with delight by both geologists and the sapient reader. In many of his works he fought valiantly to reconcile the findings of his science with the Scriptures. The geologic periods he interpreted as the days of Creation and the description of Creation itself as a prophetic vision.

IT WAS TWENTY YEARS, LAST FEBRUARY, SINCE I SET OUT A LITTLE BEFORE SUNrise to make my first acquaintance with a life of labor and restraint, and I have rarely had a heavier heart than on that morning. I was but a slim, loose-jointed boy at the time—fond of the pretty intangibilities of romance, and of dreaming when broad awake; and, woful change! I was now going to work at what Burns has instanced in his "Twa Dogs" as one of the most disagreeable of all employments—to work in a quarry. Bating the passing uneasiness occasioned by a few gloomy anticipations, the portion of my life which had already gone by had been happy beyond the common lot. I had been a wanderer among rocks and woods—a reader of curious books when I could get them—a gleaner of old traditionary stories; and now I was going to exchange all my day-dreams, and all my amusements, for the kind of life in which men toil every day that they may be enabled to eat, and eat every day that they may be enabled to toil!

The quarry in which I wrought lay on the southern shore of a noble inland bay, or frith, rather, with a little clear stream on the one side, and a thick fir wood on the other. It had been opened in the Old Red Sandstone of the district, and was overtopped by a huge bank of diluvial clay, which rose over it in some places to the height of nearly thirty feet, and which at this time was rent and shivered, wherever it presented an open front to the weather, by a recent frost. A heap of loose fragments, which had fallen from above, blocked up the face of the quarry, and my first employment was to clear them away. The friction of the shovel soon blistered my hands; but the pain was by no means very severe, and I wrought hard and willingly, that I might see how the huge strata below, which presented so firm and unbroken a frontage, were to be torn up and removed. Picks, and wedges, and levers were applied by my brother-workmen; and simple and rude as I had been accustomed to regard these implements, I found I had much to learn in the way of using them. They all proved inefficient, however; and the workmen had to bore into one of the inferior strata, and employ gunpowder. The process was new to me, and I deemed it a highly amusing one: it had the merit, too, of being attended with some such degree of danger as a boating or rock excursion, and had thus an interest independent of its novelty. We had a few capital shots: the fragments flew in every direction; and an immense mass of the diluvium came toppling down, bearing with it two dead birds, that in a recent storm had crept into one of the deeper fissures, to die in the shelter. I felt a new interest in examining them. The one was a pretty cock goldfinch, with its hood of vermilion, and its wings inlaid with the gold to which it owes its name, as unsoiled and smooth as if it had been preserved for a museum. The other, a somewhat rarer bird, of the woodpecker tribe, was variegated with light blue and a grayish yellow. I was engaged in admiring the poor little things, more disposed to be sentimental, perhaps, than if I had been ten years older, and thinking of the contrast between the warmth and jollity of their green summer haunts, and the cold and darkness of their last retreat, when I heard our employer bidding the workmen lay by their tools. I looked up, and saw the sun sinking behind the thick fir wood beside us, and the long, dark shadows of the trees stretching downwards towards the shore.

This was no very formidable beginning of the course of life I had so much dreaded. To be sure, my hands were a little sore, and I felt nearly as much fatigued as if I had been climbing among the rocks; but I had wrought and been useful, and had yet enjoyed the day fully as much as usual. It was no small matter, too, that the evening, converted, by a rare transmutation, into the delicious "blink of rest" which Burns so truthfully describes, was all my own. I was as light of heart next morning as any of my brother-workmen. There had been a smart frost during the night, and the rime lay white on the grass as we passed onwards through the fields; but the sun rose in a clear atmosphere, and the day mellowed, as it advanced, into one of those delightful days of early spring, which give so pleasing an earnest of whatever is mild and genial in the better half of the year. All the workmen rested at midday, and I went to enjoy my half-hour alone on a mossy knoll in the neighboring wood, which commands through the trees a wide prospect of the bay and the opposite shore. There was not a wrinkle on the water, nor a cloud in the sky, and the branches were as moveless in the calm as if they had been traced on canvas. From a wooded promontory that stretched half way across the frith, there ascended a thin column of smoke. It rose straight as the line of a plummet for more than a thousand yards, and then, on reaching a thinner stratum of air, spread out equally on every side, like the foliage of a stately tree. Ben Wevis rose to the west, white with the yet unwasted snows of winter, and as sharply defined in the clear atmosphere, as if all its sunny slopes and blue retiring hollows had been chiselled in marble. A line of snow ran along the opposite hills; all above was white, and all below was purple. They reminded me of the pretty French story, in which an old artist is described as tasking the ingenuity of his future son-in-law, by giving him, as a subject for his pencil, a flower-piece composed of only white flowers, of which the one half were to bear their proper color, the other half a deep purple hue, and yet all be perfectly natural; and how the young man resolved the riddle, and gained his mistress, by introducing a transparent purple vase into the picture, and making the light pass through it on the flowers that were drooping over the edge. I returned to the quarry, convinced that a very exquisite pleasure may be a very cheap one, and that the busiest employments may afford leisure enough to enjoy it.

The gunpowder had loosened a large mass in one of the inferior strata, and our first employment, on resuming our labors, was to raise it from its bed. I assisted the other workmen in placing it on edge, and was much struck by the appearance of the platform on which it had rested. The entire surface was ridged and furrowed like a bank of sand that had been left by the tide an hour before. I could trace every bend and curvature, every cross hollow and counter ridge of the corresponding phenomena; for the resemblance was no half resemblance—it was the thing itself; and I had observed it a hundred and a hundred times, when sailing my little schooner in the shallows left by the ebb. But what had become of the waves that had thus fretted the solid rock, or of what element had they been composed? I felt as completely at fault as Robinson Crusoe did on his discovering the print of the man's foot on the sand. The evening furnished me with still further cause of wonder. We raised another block in a different part of the quarry, and found that the area of a circular depression in the stratum below was broken and flawed in every direction, as if it had been the bottom of a pool recently dried up, which had shrunk and split in the hardening. Several large stones came rolling down from the diluvium in the course of the afternoon. They were of different qualities from the Sandstone below, and from one another; and, what was more wonderful still, they were all rounded and water-worn, as if they had been tossed about in the sea, or the bed of a river, for hundreds of years. There could not, surely, be a more conclusive proof that the bank which had enclosed them so long could not have been created on the rock on which it rested. No workman ever manufactures a half-worn article, and the stones were all half-worn! And if not the bank, why then the sandstone underneath? I was lost in conjecture, and found I had food enough for thought that evening, without once thinking of the unhappiness of a life of labor.

The immense masses of diluvium which we had to clear away rendered the working of the quarry laborious and expensive, and all the party quitted it in a few days, to make trial of another that seemed to promise better. The one we left is situated, as I have said, on the southern shore of an inland bay—the Bay of Cromarty; the one to which we removed has been opened in a lofty wall of cliffs that overhangs the northern shore of the Moray Frith. I soon found I was to be no loser by the change. Not the united labors of a thousand men for more than a thousand years could have furnished a better section of the geology of the district than this range of cliffs. It may be regarded as a sort of chance dissection on the earth's crust. We see in one place the primary rock, with its veins of granite and quartz, its dizzy precipices of gneiss, and its huge masses of hornblende; we find the secondary rock in another, with its beds of sandstone and shale, its spars, its clays, and its nodular limetones. We discover the still little known but highly interesting fossils of the Old Red Sandstone in one deposition; we find the beautifully preserved shells and lignites of the Lias in another. There are the remains of two several creations at once before us. The shore, too, is heaped with rolled fragments of almost every variety of rock—basalts, ironstones, hypersthenes, porphyries, bituminous shales, and micaceous schists. In short, the young geologist, had he all Europe before him, could hardly choose for himself a better field. I had, however, no one to tell me so at the time, for geology had not yet travelled so far north; and so, without guide or vocabulary, I had to grope my way as I best might, and find out all its wonders for myself. But so slow was the process, and so much was I a seeker in the dark, that the facts contained in these few sentences were the patient gatherings of years.

In the course of the first day's employment, I picked up a nodular mass of blue limestone, and laid it open by a stroke of the hammer. Wonderful to relate, it contained inside a beautifully finished piece of sculpture—one of the volutes apparently of an Ionic capital; and not the far-famed walnut of the fairy tale, had I broken the shell and found the little dog lying within, could have surprised me more. Was there another such curiosity in the whole world? I broke open a few other nodules of similar appearance—for they lay pretty thickly on the shore—and found that there might. In one of these there were what seemed to be the scales of fishes, and the impressions of a few minute bivalves, prettily striated; in the centre of another there was actually a piece of decayed wood. Of all Nature's riddles these seemed to me to be at once the most interesting, and the most difficult to expound. I treasured them carefully up, and was told by one of the workmen to whom I showed them, that there was a part of the shore about two miles farther to the west, where curiously shaped stones, somewhat like the heads of boarding-pikes, were occasionally picked up; and that in his father's days the country people called them thunderbolts, and deemed them of sovereign efficacy in curing bewitched cattle. Our employer, on quitting the quarry for the building on which we were to be engaged, gave all the workmen a half-holiday. I employed it in visiting the place where the thunderbolts had fallen so thickly, and found it a richer scene of wonder than I could have fancied in even my dreams.

What first attracted my notice was a detached group of low lying skerries, wholly different in form and color from the sandstone cliffs above, or the primary rocks a little farther to the west. I found them composed of thin strata of limestone, alternating with thicker beds of a black slaty substance, which, as I ascertained in the course of the evening, burns with a powerful flame, and emits a strong bituminous odor. The layers into which the beds readily separate are hardly an eighth part of an inch in thickness, and yet on every layer there are the impressions of thousands and tens of thousands of the various fossils peculiar to the Lias. We may turn over these wonderful leaves one after one, like the leaves of a herbarium, and find the pictorial records of a former creation in every page. Scallops, and gryphites, and ammonites, of almost every variety peculiar to the formation, and at least some eight or ten varieties of belemnite; twigs of wood, leaves of plants, cones of an extinct species of pine, bits of charcoal, and the scales of fishes; and, as if to render their pictorial appearance more striking, though the leaves of this interesting volume are of a deep black, most of the impressions are of a chalky whiteness. I was lost in admiration and astonishment, and found my very imagination paralyzed by an assemblage of wonders, that seemed to outrival, in the fantastic and the extravagant, even its wildest conceptions. I passed on from ledge to ledge, like the traveller of the tale through the city of statues, and at length found one of the supposed aerolites I had come in quest of, firmly imbedded in a mass of shale. But I had skill enough to determine that it was other than what it had been deemed. A very near relative, who had been a sailor in his time on almost every ocean, and had visited almost every quarter of the globe, had brought home one of these meteoric stones with him from the coast of Java. It was of a cylindrical shape and vitreous texture, and it seemed to have parted in the middle when in a half-molten state, and to have united again, somewhat awry, ere it had cooled enough to have lost the adhesive quality. But there was nothing organic in its structure, whereas the stone I had now found was organized very curiously indeed. It was of a conical form and filamentary texture, the filaments radiating in straight lines from the centre to the circumference. Finely-marked veins like white threads ran transversely through these in its upper half to the point, while the space below was occupied by an internal cone, formed of plates that lay parallel to the base, and which, like watch-glasses, were concave on the under side, and convex on the upper. I learned in time to call this stone a belemnite, and became acquainted with enough of its history to know that it once formed part of a variety of cuttle-fish, long since extinct.

My first year of labor came to a close, and I found that the amount of my happiness had not been less than in the last of my boyhood. My knowledge, too, had increased in more than the ratio of former seasons; and as I had acquired the skill of at least the common mechanic, I had fitted myself for independence. The additional experience of twenty years has not shown me that there is any necessary connection between a life of toil and a life of wretchedness; and when I have found good men anticipating a better and a happier time than either the present or the past, the conviction that in every period of the world's history the great bulk of mankind must pass their days in labor, has not in the least inclined me to scepticism.

My curiosity, once fully awakened, remained awake, and my opportunities of gratifying it have been tolerably ample. I have been an explorer of caves and ravines—a loiterer along sea-shores—a climber among rocks—a laborer in quarries.

FORTY MILES OF OUR PLANET'S CRUST

FROM *Adventures of a Biologist*

J. B. S. HALDANE

With J. B. S. Haldane we explore forty miles down toward the center of the earth equipped with little more than science's imaginative projection. Our actual knowledge of the inside of the earth, says the writer in this selection, is "tantalizingly scrappy." We are fortunate in our guide. He is a distinguished British scientist and educator who thinks "that a scientist, if he can do so, should help to render science intelligible to ordinary people." Dr. Haldane most eminently can do so.

ANYONE EXCEPT A PRISONER CAN GO AND SEE WHAT THINGS ARE LIKE TEN MILES north, east, south, or west. If he is rich enough he can hire a balloon and go ten miles up. But no one has ever been even two, let alone ten, miles below the earth's surface.

At the present moment our imagination is turned upwards. For every hundred men who could tell me the height record of the human race, hardly one could tell me its depth records either under the earth or under the sea. And yet this upward record-breaking contributes neither to wealth, power, nor knowledge. There are no minerals in the air, and man's wealth comes mainly from underground. There is no value even for war purposes in flying above six miles. There is no knowledge to be gained which could not be gained by sending up apparatus in unmanned balloons. . . .

We know a little about the inside of the earth, but our knowledge is tantalizingly scrappy. First of all it is very hot. As we go down the rocks get progressively hotter. In English mines a mile or so deep the men work in bathing-trunks, and I have seen them emptying the sweat out of their boots when they stopped work for lunch.

For every mile that we go down the rock temperature rises about 90° F. in Europe, though rather more slowly in South Africa; but of course ventilation keeps the air in mines cooler than the rocks. This means that two miles down, the rocks are at the boiling-point of water, while ten or fifteen miles down they are red-hot. The Lancashire coalminers explain the matter simply. They say they are getting near hell.

The pressure rises with the temperature. At a depth of a mile the rock above the miner weighs over thirty tons per square inch. And this pressure acts in all directions. If we go down a deep mine which has been abandoned for a month or two during a strike we find that not merely has the roof begun to cave in, but the floor has bulged up. So a shaft ten miles deep would have to be protected against the rock pressure by lining it with armour plate many feet in thickness. Otherwise the rocks would flow inwards like so much butter.

It is generally agreed that at a great enough depth the interior of the earth is liquid. Every solid substance when hot enough becomes a gas, and most of them pass through a liquid phase first. But both melting and boiling are usually checked by high pressure, so it is hard to be sure whether heat or pressure will predominate inside the earth.

As everyone knows, molten lava sometimes pours out of volcanoes. Can we take it as a fair sample of what we should meet if we went down deep enough? Underneath its thin skin is the earth solid or liquid? This problem is only partly solved. There are two answers which seem to be contradictory.

The first answer comes from the study of gravity. If a plumb-line is held near the foot of a cliff, the bob is pulled away from the vertical by the attraction of the cliff. It was expected that mountain ranges would act in the same way. But they do not. Often the bob seems to be pushed away from them. This is because they are made of lighter material than the rest of the earth's crust. Their density can also be measured in other ways, all of which give the same result.

Mountain ranges stick up because they are made of light rock. The ocean floor is low because it is made of heavy rock. In simple language, the earth's crust consists of slag floating on hell-fire. When a load is taken off, the surface rises. The Alps were originally a plateau only about four thousand feet high. When the rain and ice cut valleys in it, some of the weight was taken off the supporting liquid, and the crust bulged up to make the present peaks.

This bulging is sometimes a slow process. Scandinavia was still covered by a sheet of ice fourteen thousand years ago. It was almost all melted by 7000 B.C. The crust had sagged under the strain, and is still rising, in some places by half an inch per year. Unfortunately from time to time rocks may snap, and we get earthquakes. However, the quakes due to this cause are much milder than those due to folding.

The solid crust is about forty miles thick: more in some places, and much less in volcanic regions. But the underlying layer, though it yields to slow pressure, does not seem to be a genuine liquid. The evidence is as follows. When a great earthquake occurs anywhere, the shock is recorded by instruments all over the world. The first wave caused by an earthquake in New Zealand takes about twenty minutes to reach England.

Now when we can study waves which go through anything we learn a great deal about it. For example, we know that the upper air lets light waves through but reflects most radio waves back, and this allows us, among other things, to calculate its temperature, which is rather high. A solid will transmit two sorts of waves, namely, push waves, where the particles move along the line of travel, and shake waves, where they move sideways. A true liquid will only transmit push waves. If you raise the pressure at one end of a pipe full of water you can transmit the push to the other end, but if you turn the water round you cannot transmit the twist, as you could with a solid rod.

The radius of the earth is four thousand miles. The inner core for two thousand miles out from the centre is a true liquid and will not transmit shake waves. It probably consists of liquid iron, so hot that if the pressure above it were taken off, it would fly apart as gas. For two thousand miles between the iron and the solid crust is a layer of rock which is solid enough to carry shake waves, but not solid enough to bear the weight of mountain ranges, or even ice-fields, indefinitely.

Lava is liquid because the pressure has been taken off it, but under heavy pressure, even when very hot, it is so stiff as to have many of the properties of a solid. Our knowledge of these matters mostly comes from American workers. Some of them worked in Hawaii, pushing down steel tubes into the lakes of lava of its great volcanoes, taking temperatures and analysing the molten rock at different depths.

Others, in Washington, worked in the laboratory with what might be called artificial volcanoes. It is easy enough to subject any material to very high temperatures. You have only to put it into the arc of an ordinary arc-lamp. And in special presses, pressures of a hundred thousand atmospheres have been reached.

But the combination of the two was not so easy. Bombs were built of vanadium-containing steel such as is used for the armour of battleships. Inside the bomb an electric furnace heated up small fragments of rock enclosed in platinum capsules. Pressures corresponding to those found many miles below ground were meanwhile applied, the bombs being filled with liquid carbon dioxide.

These bombs occasionally burst, and the fact that their contents were white-hot did not make things any pleasanter. In fact, the real volcanoes of Hawaii were perhaps rather safer than the artificial ones at Washington. But the latter did serve to explain how the real ones worked. Among other things it was found that white-hot rock would dissolve a great deal of water at high pressure. When the pressure was taken off the water separated out, and finally became steam, thus accounting for volcanic explosions.

Other experiments showed how mineral ores were formed. When melted rock cools down, some parts solidify before others, just as the oily part of gravy congeals before the watery part. In some kinds of molten rock the valuable minerals separate first and sink to the bottom; in others they stay liquid for a long time, and rise to the top. By such experiments the actual distribution of ores in the earth is beginning to be understood. Laboratory experiments show why in Cornwall the quartz veins contain copper at the top and tin lower down.

But this whole branch of science is in its infancy. Experiments are costly and sometimes dangerous. They enable us to predict to a certain extent what we shall find underground, but not exactly. In the long run we shall have to go down and find out. Let us suppose that a state, or a really enterprising millionaire, has put down $100,000,000 or so to sink a shaft ten or twenty miles deep, what would be the first step?

Naturally we would not choose a country liable to earthquakes or natural volcanoes. There would not be much advantage in simply making another volcano. But the first step would be to make an artificial earthquake. The best artificial earthquake so far was at Oppau in Germany, where 4,500 tons of explosive accidentally went off in 1921. The earthquake was recorded, and gave information about the various kinds of rock under Germany.

The most usual finding is a mile or so of sedimentary rocks laid down in water, then six or eight miles of granite, which has solidified from the molten state, and below this several layers of denser rock of the general nature of basalt. Special laboratories would be built to test the behaviour of the rocks under high pressure and temperature, so that the miners would know what to expect.

After the first mile or two there would be little chance of striking coal or oil, but metals and precious stones might well be found if the shaft was sunk in a suitable area. We do not know how diamonds are formed, but we know that they can only be formed at enormous pressures and temperatures. The South African diamonds occur in "pipes" full of a peculiar blue volcanic rock which has come up from a great depth. A sufficiently deep mine might yield diamonds in enormous quantity. But it is just as likely that these stones may be made artificially as a by-product of an experiment in artificial vulcanism.

The one thing which will certainly be found is heat. Before the shaft is two miles deep special cooling arrangements will be needed. Probably liquid air will be sent down a pipe to cool the workings. Where the red-hot layer is reached the shaft will become a possible source of power. If two shafts fifteen miles deep were connected by a tunnel (armour-plated, of course), a river dropped down one of them would come up the other as steam, and would be a very considerable source of power. In a century or so, when the world's supply of oil has run out, and coal is getting a good deal scarcer, power may be worth a good deal more than it is today.

Whether it pays or not, we shall have to explore the first forty miles of our planet's crust, the truly solid part. And we shall do it if science goes on. The result may be of as little economic value as the exploration of Antarctica, or it may pay as well as the exploration of Canada. It may make gold as plentiful as copper, which would merely wreck our monetary systems, or diamonds as cheap as tin, in which case we should use them for a great variety of cutting tools, for the bearings of machinery, and for microscope lenses. It may merely clear up a few doubtful scientific points.

Human curiosity will not be satisfied until we have got to the earth's centre. I cannot imagine how this would even be attempted, but I certainly cannot say that it is impossible. It will not be easy or safe, but miners are as brave as airmen, and when we begin to run short of some essential minerals we shall turn our eyes downwards, and begin the exploration of the unknown depths below us.

WHEN THE MAP IS IN TUNE

FROM *The Right Place*

C. E. MONTAGUE

Robert Louis Stevenson once observed, "I am told there are people who do not care for maps, and I find it hard to believe." Stevenson dismisses these people as hopeless wanderers in a directionless world. C. E. Montague, in this beguiling essay on the pleasures of map reading, thinks them only misguided and holds out a warm and glowing prospect of an earth all mapped and contoured for the initiated. Reading Montague, one feels that here is a man one would have liked to walk with. It has been said that there is something of the clean air of the mountains he loved in his short stories, some of which may be classed with the finest in the language. His essays, too, have this Alpine fragrance.

IT HURTS TO THINK OF THE PLEASURES THAT PEOPLE TURN AWAY FROM THEIR doors. There are some who have not even learnt to read maps. "Read" is the word mostly used, but "tune" would be better. For, till you know the trick, a fine map is about the nearest thing there is to

> a cunning instrument cased up,
> Or, being open, put into his hands
> That knows no touch to tune the harmony.

Unless you are a mountaineer, an engineer, or a surveyor, the odds are that the great illumination will escape you, all your life; you may return to the grave without having ever known what it is like when the contour lines begin to sing together, like the Biblical stars.

Those contour lines are the crux. The beginner, the infant at this game, craves for a hill-coloured map, with its expressive coloured scale, from the lush green of alluvial meadows a few feet above the sea-level to sultry reddish-brown for Snowdon and Cumbrian hills. Quite good things are they, too, in their way, as pretty nursery rhymes are good till you grow up enough to like Shelley. They give you fine vivid notions about the general modelling of a country. In fact we might want nothing more if the part of the earth's crust which stands up into the air were modelled like the part which lies under the sea. Of course the ocean floor is not flat. It has uplands and lowlands. But these rise and fall gently, in long sweeping slopes. Their low and softly undulating relief has been preserved in the sheltered peace of deep waters. That of lands exposed to the air has been everywhere lacerated and trenched, split up with wedges of ice, eroded by streams and battered and eaten by waves. So the irregularities of its surface have grown intricate and fantastic to a degree which cannot be fully expressed, on a map of practicable scale, by any system of colours that vary with heights.

Almost the same may be said of those masterpieces of the map-engraver's art, the best of our old hill-shaded Ordnance maps. In these you all but saw the actual slopes—at any rate the general slopes—of your hills and the tracts of high light along the ridges that they held up to the sun. Their summary of the make of a mountain mass, as a whole, is so vivid that to this day some of us prefer to walk the Derbyshire hills with no other map than this old thing of beauty, on which no railway is yet to be found threading Edale.

But no true epicure of the map will remain long content with these elementary pleasures. Soon he finds that both hill-tinted maps and hill-shaded maps have to stop where the real finesse of delineation begins. No tinted or shaded map of the English Lakes will tell you the true shape of Gillercombe or of Combe Ghyll, or distinguish the warty crown of Glaramara from Great Gable's regular dome. Only a few years ago our one-inch Ordnance map of Scawfell and its buttresses made the craggy north face of Great End look as if you could march a division of troops up or down it, big guns and all. There comes a time when the epicure craves for something at once more difficult and more richly stimulating and rewarding. He wants something on which to put forth his strength. And this he gets in any contour-lined map that is perfectly done. He gets it in some sheets, though not by any means all, of our one-inch Ordnance Survey. He gets it in a few special maps like the 1/50,000 Barbey map of the chain of Mont Blanc. Above all he gets it in every sheet of the glorious Siegfried map of Switzerland, the most wonderful representation ever given of mountainous land.

The maturing map-reader, planning his holidays in the hills, will now be able to know much more besides the height at which he would stand at any point on a fell path or on an open mountain side. The map will also tell him what he would see in every direction if he were there. The sensitively winding contour curves will show him from just what point on the Watendlath-Rosthwaite track the top of Great End will come into sight. They will show him whether, from Seatoller Fell, Helvellyn will be within view, or whether the intervening Armboth Fell is just high enough to blot the greater mountain out. A glance at the condensing or spreading lines should tell him which side of Scawfell is a crag to be climbed and which is a turf slope to be walked. Before he has ever tramped up Borrowdale or Greenup Ghyll he will know how much of the valley in front will be hidden by each jutting promontory of high ground on either side.

As in the reading of printed words or a musical score, precision and speed in the reading of maps can pretty rapidly be carried further and further. Soon the map is read, as it were, not word by word, but phrase by phrase; the meaning of whole passages of it leaps out; you see, with something like the summary grasp your eye would get of the actual scene, the long façades of precipice and hanging glacier that there must be where the blue contour lines crowd up closely together right under a peak of twelve thousand feet, with a northern exposure, and also the vast, gently sloping expanses of snow-field below, where the lines flow out wider and wider apart, expressing broad shelves, and huge, shallow basins hoisted on upper floors of the mountain. A musician's mental ear, I suppose, can hear directly, when he reads a succession of notes on ruled paper, the rise and fall of an air, the jaunty lilt or triumphant rush or plaintive trail of its gait, its swelling loudness or shrunken whisper. So the reader of maps is freed, before long, from the need to go through a conscious act of interpretation when gazing at the mapped contours of a mountain that he has never seen. He no longer has to tell himself, as he cons the endless lines: "Where I see a succession of rising contour lines close together, and, just above them, a few lines further apart, and, above these, others close together again, it means that there is here a hollow in the mountain"; or "where the curvilinear contours change their course and all stab inwards pointedly towards the heart of the hill, roughly parallel to each other, make an acute angle, and then come out again to resume their old general direction, it means a deep, narrow glen or gully running up the hill-side." He has no more need to do that than you or I have to worry over the spelling and syntax of Keats in the "Ode to Autumn." The notation once learnt, the map conveys its own import with an immediateness and vivacity comparable with those of the score or the poem. Convexities and concavities of ground, the bluff, the defile, the long mounting bulge of a grassy ridge, the snuggling hollow within a mountain shaped like a horseshoe—all come directly into your presence and offer you the spectacle of their high or low relief with a vivid sensuous sharpness.

Much enjoyment of these delights can generate in the mind a new power of topographic portraiture, a knack of forming circumstantially correct visions of large patches of the earth's surface. You learn, like a portrait-painter, to penetrate by the help of intuitive inference; you get at one thing through another. You see on a good map the course of the Mersey—short, traversing a plain for more than the latter half of its length; but also, in its head streams the Etherow and the Goyt, crossing rapid successions of contour lines in the Pennine moorlands of Longdendale and the Peak. You guess at once what the temper of such a river must be. For it is a very down-comer pipe, as a builder might say, in its upper course, to drain the steeper side of the much-drenched roof of the Pennine, from Buxton northward to somewhere near Oldham. Clearly a stream to be vexed with extravagant spates, swiftly rising and swiftly subsiding, before at last its pace wears itself out in the fat Cheshire flats, as the rushing and tearing Rhine of Bâle slows down in level Holland. Then you examine the Mersey on your map, in the lowland reaches just after it works clear of the hills; and, with a happy inward crow of satisfaction you see, if your map is a thoroughly good one, how the stream is flanked throughout the many miles from Stockport to Sale with enormous flood banks raised to guard the riverain farms from just that termagant fury that you had looked out for.

Every educated person knows, in a sense, how the surface of England is modelled—how the formative ridge of the Pennine is dropped half-way down the country southwards like the firmer cartilage in the flesh of a widening nose; how the lateral bracket of the Lake hills is attached unsymmetrically to this central framework by the Shap bar, and so on. But few such persons conceive it with any imaginative energy or with the delight that such energy brings. The rest have the kind of knowledge that lies dead in the mind, as a classical education lies dead in the minds of most of those who have had it. It has to be raised from the dead by some evocatory miracle of appeal to the sensuous imagination—the kind of imagination that rejoices to take up and carry on the work of a bodily sense at a point where bodily sense can go no further. The work is carried on, at the best, with so much of the eager immediacy of actual sight, or hearing, and so little of the dusty cloudiness of common abstract thought, that on a peak of the Alps you may obtain a sensation almost indistinguishable from seeing with the bodily eye the whole structure of the Apennines, the Lombard plain and the silted Venetian lagoon, laid out under your eye. Or from a bulge of high ground in our Midlands, where the Nen, the Welland and the Bristol Avon rise almost together, you may suddenly feel that you see the whole complex of English rivers as sharply clear as you may see the rummaging roots of a bulb grown in a clear glass jar full of water.

> These delights if you would have,
> Come live with me and be my love.

Thus does the large-scale map woo the susceptible mind. Geography, in such a guise, is quite a different muse from the pedantic harridan who used to plague the spirit of youth with lists of chief towns, rivers and lakes, and statistics of leather, hardware and jute.

Conscience murmurs here that I may be muddling in somebody's mind the distinction between pictures and maps. So be it clearly set down that painters and map-makers do not, or should not, attempt to give you the same thing as each other. Least of all will they do so when each is working his best.

It is true that the early eighteenth-century fathers of the British art of water-colour—as much the one and only wholly British art, by birth, as the good moorland grouse is the one and only wholly British bird—were topographic draughtsmen rather than artists. They worked for land-owners and rich antiquarians and other great folk who wanted no fanciful visions but "plain records of facts." They learnt their job, in the main, from certain artisans who for two centuries past had got work, off and on, at tinting maps and engravings "with gummed colours, but tempered very thinne and bodilesse," as one old writer says. The early eighteenth-century men made pencil drawings which certainly verged on sketch maps. These they ventured to tint very faintly, going at first but little beyond the sober palette of the makers of modern auctioneers' plans of estates up for sale. No doubt they went in godly fear of losing their situations if they should launch out in heavenly colours like the oil-painters.

Again, it is true that some of the old hill-shaded Ordnance maps, engraved as with genius, verge upon the sphere of influence of art, if they do not trespass upon it. Some of their representations of mountains are almost temperamental; they awe or exhilarate you with the sombre darkness of their mountain sides and the brilliant high lights of the summit ridges where you come into the sun; here, you feel, is a measure of success, which can hardly be unconscious, in rendering the mountain glory and mountain gloom.

And yet neither of these compromises between art and science achieves, or could achieve, final success. The art of the old timidly tinting topographers, men like Dayes, Hearne and Paul Sandby, is now seen to be of moment mainly as the childhood of something else, something that could not attain its own completeness until it came into the freedom with which Cox and Turner were one day to make it free. So, too, the old hill-shaded Ordnance maps can only strike us now as wonderful and beautiful attempts to do what is not possible. Maps are maps and pictures are pictures and never the twain shall meet; for the better a map is, and the better a picture, the more deeply do they differ in intention and in effect.

A painter who is worth his salt will flatly refuse to give you just the precise physical facts of a landscape. It is not his business. His business is not to convey topographic information, but to express some emotion or other that he has felt in presence of that scene. Not fact, but his personal sense of fact; not the correct relative sizes of peaks that stand up round the head of a glacier, but some individual mood or quality of awe, perhaps, that possessed him and may perhaps have possessed nobody else that ever stood beneath that wall of wonder. To gain this end, he does, as a rule, bring into his picture something that may be made out to have some sort of likeness to what you or I might have seen from the point where he made his picture or sketch. In Turner's "Mer de Glace" you can undoubtedly discern a wild remote resemblance to certain physical features of the ice-fall leading up to the Col du Géant. At any rate, it is quite as like the Mer de Glace as it is like several other glaciers of the Alps. His St. Gotthard drawings, too, you might be rather more likely to identify with the St. Gotthard than with the St. Bernard or Simplon, if you know them all. But such resemblances are of little account. Turner clearly valued them little. He always threw them aside if they got in the way of his absorbing plan for expressing some grand excitement of his in terms which would win a way for it into the mind or heart of the right person looking at the picture. When one of his big emotions flooded him in presence of a black Alpine defile or a crumbling Border castle, the one thing for which he manifestly did not try was to make the public presently cry out, "How like it all is!" He treated crag and torrent, castle and forest and bridge, as so many freely transposable objects; he increased or diminished their comparative sizes as he thought fit; he moved them about and tried them in various relative positions, as poets shift their words about to make a line sound better; they and their sites and sizes, their make and texture, were no more to him than notes to be grouped at will into any chords that he might prefer for the working out of his tune.

So the most perfect of pictures may have no topographic value at all. As a guide to the traveller's feet it may delude and lead astray. Small blame to it. Guiding is not its business. So long as an artist is true to himself it matters little how false he may be to geography, geology or history. The Antony or the Macbeth of Shakespeare may well be completely unlike the original sinner bearing the name. Who cares? Perhaps both were dull men in the flesh; and, if so, what a mercy that Shakespeare has drawn them all wrong; their falsification was vastly worth while. If you know how to keep apart things that God has sundered, you do not go to Shakespeare or Turner for positive information about the lives or the measurements of the people and places that set their genius in action. You go to them for admittance into their personal confidence, not to find "the real Cæsar" or get tips for worrying out walking routes in the Alps, but to be taken up for the moment into the state of wise and beautiful passion in which these rare creatures do their work.

Still, it is into another's passion that you are admitted by art. Not what you ever felt for yourself when gazing out from Richmond Hill, but what the spirit of Turner felt at the instance of that expanse of champaign and river; not your own inarticulate tumult of joy in presence of Tuscan vistas of cypress and poplar, but the serene, clear-running ecstasy of John Bellini before the same prospect, is what your mind apprehends and enjoys for some propitious instants. Quite distinct from that choice and fugitive experience is that which we commonplace people achieve for ourselves when confronted with nature herself. Each in his own poor way, we have to play Turner as well as we can, and make our delight or our awe articulate to ourselves in some selecting and composing reverie over such bits of the world as are ours to behold.

In nature a great landscape is nearly always rather bewildering. Even more than other contents of experience, it seems to bury us under the multitude of separate objects that it offers for our perception. Each detail that we see cries out to be separately observed. Their relation to one another, their several shares in the make-up of the scene as a whole, are more shy. They keep themselves to themselves. From any central peak in a great mountain range you see all round you a host of white points like the tops of trees in a thin forest when seen from the top of a tree specially tall. You may see nothing at all of that which makes the whole mountain range, unlike the more fortuitous aggregation of trees, a single organism or cunningly sustained arrangement, so that no drop of snow that falls on the tip of any peak will have trouble in travelling down an unbroken sequence of inclined planes, diversified with a few sheer drops, all the way to the sea. The scene, it may well be, looks grand, in a way, but capricious and baffling; its pell-mell profusion of grandeur may rouse in you little more than a kind of baulked willingness to admire, if you could but see it, the chain of dependence which runs throughout the whole physical world. There, when confusion threatens, the map comes in to your aid.

Its service, like that of a field-glass, is quite unemotional. Unlike all the arts, cartography leaves you to work up for yourself what emotion you may in the presence of Himalayas or Alps. It only offers to extend your power of perceiving what the physical elements of that scene are, how they are related to one another as causes or effects, and how their several functions take their places within the larger general function of a mountain-range as a moderator of rivers and a sculptor of lands. No first-rate map-maker attempts to "come the poet" over you. None tries to compound any atmosphere of august melancholy to fill his large-scale map of Venice, or of majesty and mystery for his sheets of the Central and East Pennine Alps. His line is "Feel anything that you like, or that you can. Your feelings are your affair, and mine are mine. I offer merely to enlarge your power of sight and of comprehension. I give you, not emotion, but a reinforcement of that basis of bodily sense and intellectual penetration on which some kind of emotion may or may not afterwards rest."

So to its other fascinations a great map like the Siegfried adds the fascination of a lofty reserve. It goes, to all appearance unmoved, into the most moving of places. The men who drew its higher glacier contours lived for weeks at a time in remote huts, or passed their nights in sleeping-sacks on rocks or the snow, under frosty stars. Thence they would go out to work when the pomp of dawn was beginning. The work was sometimes stopped by storms that made the steel of their axes spit fire and sing; all the claps of thunder and their echoes would become one continuous, undulant roar. They carried their loads of instruments and marking-stakes up and down hundreds of steps slowly cut in steep slopes of hard blue ice. Sometimes one of them slipped. After a tour of duty up in the snows, where your eyes come to feel as if their lids were cut off, the map-men would descend some evening to where greenness begins like a balm to hurt minds and the streams make happy little sounds among Alpenrosen. But not a trace of anything that they may have felt has passed into these austere records of theirs. There is one glory of the sun and another of the moon: it is great that what Byron saw of the Alps should have stirred him to break out in glorious rant about his own personal sensations among them; it is great, too, that a different breed of men should be content, by way of their work, to sink utterly everything that is personal to them in its doing, so that when the work is done and its reticent tale is at every one's service,

no one asks
Who or what they have been
More than he asks what waves
In the moonlit solitudes mild
Of the midmost ocean have swelled,
Foamed for a moment, and gone.

Immense as our admiration must be for all who can talk to magnificent purpose about their own uncommon selves, one may admire, too, the magnificence of the unbroken silence of others.

Thus utterly different from the artist, the map-maker fastens upon you in quite a different state of yourself. There is a time for yielding your mind to the passionate mood into which some great artist has passed at the instance of something that he sees: you melt with a luxurious self-surrender into the golden pensiveness of Vergil as he gazes at a river laving immemorial walls; or you sink back and bask, with a will, in the visionary lustre of Turner's "Dido Building Carthage" or the sad sunshine of Thackeray's *Esmond*. But there are times, too, when you will take your emotions at nobody's hand. You want now not to borrow but to make. You are impelled to put forth directly upon what is around you whatever you have in yourself of the power of direct and independent feeling which everybody has in some degree, though it may only rise to momentous heights in a few people of genius. You wish to see, perhaps, the Alps or the English Lake hills through none of the beautiful kinds of stained glass that Byron and Ruskin, Turner and Wordsworth would interpose between your sight and these things "as they are," but through the glass, whatever its tint or its tintlessness may be, of your private temperament. And here the right map, explicit, exact and ungushing, seconds your effort.

"Things as they are"—the old phrase, no doubt is a trap. It implies some assumptions that seem to fade away into nonsense or nothing as soon as strict thought sets about its destructive work of analysis. Still, it may be used with due caution to signify those aspects of external things which fall under the jurisdiction of science rather than of art—all that can be measured, defined, referred to known causes and studied in its established effects. The phrase helps us to make clear to ourselves, so far as such clearness is not delusive, the distinction between our emotions and their objects, between our love and the beloved person, between fear and the enemy's attack or the storm's violence, between our own awe and the physical proportions of Westminster Abbey. Whatever philosophy may dissolve in the crucible minds of philosophers, we common people cling still to a working assumption that first there are things in existence outside our individual selves; that then we perceive them; and that, having perceived them, we then have, or may have, various feelings about them. The map is our friend at the second of these stages of approach to such emotion as we can muster.

It makes our perception go further, because it marshals into lucidity a mess of mixed, haphazard objects of perception. Into the inexpressive confusion which wide tracts of country present at first to the eye it brings an approach to simplicity and articulateness. It cannot be said that you are seeing as much from the summit of the Grand Combin, if you have no map, and can only see vague masses of black and white in the distance, as you see when you know that one high mass of white, about eighty miles off, is the

Dauphiné Meije, and that a low dark mass in the north is the Black Forest. Telescope, compass and map will all combine to extend your power of apprehending what you see. To love things you must know them, and these assistants will abridge for you the work of getting to know. By lightening that labour they leave your mind fresher and more full of spring, to put itself forth in the exercise of that curious mixed faculty which occupies a borderland between bodily sense and imagination, or between direct perception and creative thought. You may call it a trick of enhancing for the moment the subtlety and reach of a bodily sense. Or you may call it a knack of lending to imagined things an exceptional portion of the sharp and importunate reality of a piquant object of sense. It is that which brings all England into sight and stretches Europe itself out under your eyes like a map spread out on a floor.

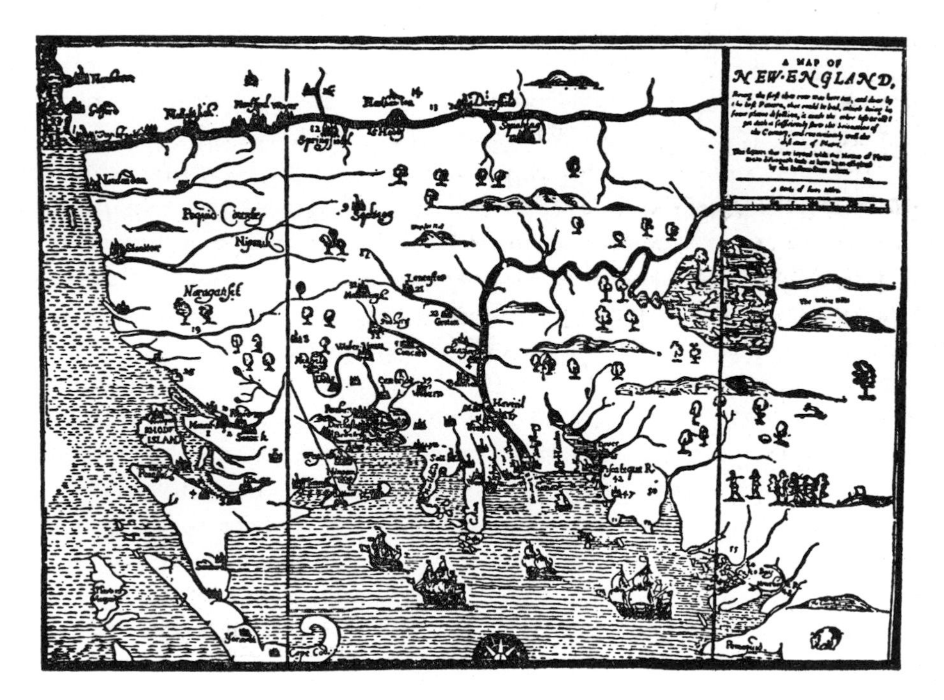

THE FIRST MAP TO BE DRAWN, ENGRAVED, PRINTED AND PUBLISHED IN THE AMERICAN COLONIES, 1677

UNDERGROUND RIVER

FROM *North with the Spring*

EDWIN WAY TEALE

One can make a case for the proposition that the naturalist is a man in the round, he lives in more than the one dimension that the rest of us inhabit. The scientist sees phenomena on the level of thought, the poet on the level of feeling, the naturalist on both.

Edwin Way Teale is one of these rounded men. He records not only shapes and colors, but the moods and tempers they evoke in the observer. In this selection from his *North with the Spring,* we walk with him through the twisting corridors of Nickajack Cave, float on an underground river, look at great stone icicles, tourists in a silent, timeless country.

THE YEAR STANDS STILL IN A CAVE. THERE IS NO SUMMER, NO WINTER THERE. Time is not divided into night and day, into four seasons of the year. The rising and setting of the sun is something remote and unreal. Calendars are meaningless in this moonless world of damp and darkness. Just outside the mouth of a cave wildflowers may bloom in May, their leaves may wither in August heat, they may be hidden beneath January snow. But within the cavern such extremes in weather are unknown. The year is one long unvarying season of even temperature. The position of the mercury hardly changes winter, summer, fall, and spring. It marks almost exactly the mean yearly temperature of the region.

Driving 500 miles—from Bull's Island south to Savannah and then angling northwest across Georgia to Chattanooga, Tennessee—we had traveled in brilliant, million-flowered spring all the way. Wisteria grew everywhere, even in the tops of lofty pines. It hung in lavender curtains or descended in pale-purple waterfalls from trees, from windmills, from fences. Blood-red thistles and sulphur-yellow thistles flowered beside the highway. Cherokee roses and zephyr lilies bloomed in yards. Redbud and dogwood bordered the road and ran up wooded hillsides. But we left all this behind, as we left spring behind, as we left even daylight behind, when we entered the cool darkness of Nickajack Cave, near Shellmound, Tennessee, 20 miles west of Chattanooga. Within this cavern the annual range in temperature is only a few degrees. The thermometer stands at between 54 and 56 degrees Fahrenheit virtually the year around.

Four hundred years ago, De Soto visited Nickajack Cave. Indians followed an ancient warpath for uncounted generations past its entrance. Soldiers of the Civil War fought for the cave and its saltpeter deposits. Dancers, in the 1890's, waltzed to orchestra music under its vaulted roof. Now, as we approached it, the cave was deserted. Its mouth, 175 feet wide and 60 feet high, yawned in the side of Raccoon Mountain. A thick stratum of blue-gray Warsaw limestone ran in a flat ceiling across the top, extending as far as we could see back into the cavern. Out of the darkness toward us flowed a river of cool air. We could feel it around us while we were still in sunshine. Also out of the darkness flowed a river of cool, green-tinted water, a subterranean stream issuing from the heart of the mountain. It emerged among great rocks at one side of the cave to wander away westward in the direction of the Nickajack Narrows of the Tennessee.

Just inside the cave we stopped to look around. Sixty feet above us the masonry globes of cliff swallow nests clung to the limestone ceiling. On the walls beside us, where, eighty years before, Civil War soldiers had cut their names in the rock, masonry tubes, each several inches long, were cemented side by side like the pipes of an organ. They were the nests of a dark mud-working wasp of the genus *Trypoxylon*. Below them, in the fine dust at the foot of the wall, ant lions had formed the inverted cones of their pits.

A hill within the cave lifted us nearer the ceiling, then let us down in a steep descent into galleries beyond. Light from the entrance decreased in a kind of sunset behind the hill. In semi-darkness we entered the largest corridor and switched on our flashlights. The beams slid along water-worn limestone, hopped across gaping side openings, revealed connecting galleries ahead. Like ants stealing along the branching corridors of a riddled tree trunk we moved deeper into the cavern.

The rock walls around us had once been, quite literally, alive. Three hundred million years before, in the Mississippian period of the Paleozoic Era, in a time of towering fern trees and giant club mosses, the calcareous remains of unnumbered small invertebrates had collected underwater to form a deep layer of limestone. Condensing the activity of aeons that followed into a swift succession of events, we imagined the limestone lifted in the making of mountains; imagined rain water falling through the air, collecting carbon dioxide, becoming weak carbonic acid as it fell; imagined it seeping into small openings, forming calcium bicarbonate, dissolving limestone, enlarging cracks, forming sinkholes, hollowing out galleries, spreading in branching corridors deeper and deeper into the mountain, finding an exit, forming a channel through which a flow of water made its way. Thus the cave and the subterranean river were born.

The corridors we followed are considerably above the level of the river now. Those of a still higher level are dry and dusty. Far back in Nickajack, we were told, a great room beyond a "crawl," 200 feet long and hardly eighteen inches in diameter, a room that once held a lake, is ankle deep in dust as fine as talcum powder. One cave explorer who stirred it up in passing reported that part of the dust still hung in the air when he returned four days later. What is supposed to be the biggest stalagmite in the world is said to rise from the floor of this room. It measures 174 feet around its base. Another Tennessee cavern, a cave at Elk Valley, contains a lethal passage so devoid of oxygen that the bodies of rats that have made their way into it and have been suffocated remain for years without decomposing.

The corridor we were following, winding and narrow, suddenly expanded into an immense room, a chamber roughly circular with the arch of its ceiling rising 60 feet above our heads. Sweeping across the curve of this ceiling, the beams of our flashlights picked out dark smudges on the limestone. They were formed by the close-packed bodies of hibernating bats. The lofty chamber was the main bat room of Nickajack.

A curious feature of the bat population of this cave is the fact that it changes winter and summer. Different species inhabit it at different seasons of the year. All the hibernating bats we saw that day belonged to the same species, *Myotis sodalis*. They arrive in October and leave before the middle of May. During the summer they are replaced by several species: the little brown bat, *Myotis l. lucifugus,* Trouessart's little brown bat, *Myotis keenii septentrionalis,* the pigmy bat, *Pipistrellus,* and the little gray bat, *Myotis grisescens.* This last species, described by A. H. Howell in 1909, was originally discovered at Nickajack Cave.

The winter bats were gone and the summer bats were back, a month later, on the 15th of May, when we swung south on our trail to pay a second visit to this remarkable cavern. As we followed the same narrow corridor on that later day it was filled with a faint sizzling sound, like grease in a frying pan. The air was heavy with a smell suggesting a poultry house. Each foot we advanced the sound grew in volume. It was joined, as we neared the end of the passage, by another sound, a sound like the rushing of wind in the cavern. Yet the air around us was stirred by only the faintest of breezes. We reached the doorway of the vaulted chamber once more and swung our flashlight beams upward. The air was filled with the wheeling forms of disturbed bats, their dim, indefinite shapes, like shadows of bats rather than bats themselves, becoming suddenly bright and sharp as they momentarily flicked across the beams of light. Their beating wings, a thousand tight-stretched membranes striking the air at once, produced the illusion of a great wind.

Above this wheeling multitude the dome of the cavern was decorated with continents and islands and archipelagos of black—masses of bats, bats beyond our counting or calculation. Around them the stone of the ceiling seemed studded with specks of shining silver or diamonds in the rock where drops of condensed moisture reflected back the rays of our flashlights. Continually, from the hanging clusters, fresh bats dropped to join the confused merry-go-round in the air. Immeasurably magnified, the sizzling sound we had heard in the corridor had risen into a metallic, grating, high-pitched climax—the sum total of an infinite number of squeaking calls given off by the flying mammals.

Besides the sounds we heard, we knew there were others, so high-pitched that our ears were unaware of their existence. These ultrasonic cries have a frequency of roughly 50,000 cycles per second, 30,000 cycles above the range of the human ear. Bats' ears, it has been shown, can hear up to 100,000 cycles. During flight the sensitive ears of these aerial mammals catch echoes of the high-frequency sound waves that warn them of obstacles ahead.

In a laboratory at Harvard University, where I visited Donald R. Griffin and Robert Galambos when they were making their pioneer researches in "bat radar" in 1940, I heard a Pierce apparatus catch and translate these ultrasonic cries into audible sounds. A bat flying about the room uttered a quick series of squeaks as it approached an object ahead. So rapid is this succession of "soundless sounds" that the records of the Harvard experimenters showed that as many as thirty, or even fifty, cries a second are sometime uttered by the flying bat.

Ever since the seventeenth century, when Spallanzani hung strings from a ceiling with a little bell at the end of each, and demonstrated to his own mystification that a bat flying in the dark could avoid striking the strings and ringing the bells, the navigational skill of these animals has been a source of amazement. The key to this ability is the short wave length of the ultrasonic sound. The bat's radar would be far less effective if it employed only the longer wave lengths of sounds we can hear. They would not echo back from small objects as do the short wave lengths of the high-pitched cries the bats use.

At a cave in Pennsylvania, Charles E. Mohr once observed a striking instance of the effectiveness of this system of sound navigation. In an attempt to capture bats for study, he stretched a tennis net across the mouth of a small cavern. It completely blocked the opening with the exception of a slight gap that a forefinger would have bridged, a gap less than three inches wide. Yet, every bat in the cave, flying at full speed in the dark, avoided the net and shot through this one small opening!

Several times, as we retraced our steps along the water-worn corridor, alarmed bats rushed by us down the passageway. They never touched us although, each time, they swept so close that we could feel on our faces the breeze that formed momentarily in their wake. On the wall of the corridor, within reach of my arm, a little brown bat hung upside down, wrapped in profound slumber, dead to all the excitement around it. I ran the tip of my forefinger gently along its back. It stirred in its sleep. Under my finger its fur was soft and velvety. It recalled the robe of bat skins worn by Atahualpa, the last of the Inca kings. Behind us the cries of the multitude of disturbed bats sank again to a mere sizzling noise. This sound, the sound of the active bats, was one of the few indications, in this seasonless world of the cavern, that spring had come.

Later that day, on the underground river in the cave, we observed another sign. We were riding in a small boat in which a farmer living nearby took us far back into the cavern on the subterranean stream. The only sounds on that silent, glassy flow were the startled exclamations of falling drops of water. Moisture collected on the rock overhead, swelled to a larger and larger drop, let go, struck the surface of the river with a liquid "plop!" that echoed in the stillness, magnified by the walls of stone. The sound of dripping water is the voice of the cavern. When spring replaces winter outside the cave, our companion told us, dripping increases in Nickajack.

Aristotle, who classified metals as "water in a sense and in a sense not," believed that winds rushing through subterranean caverns caused earthquakes. Around us, on this river in a cave, the air was unmoving. Here, even the smallest fluting of the wind is stilled. Twice we ran through "storms" along the way. But they were storms without wind and without violence. Each time, for a dozen yards or so, we passed through a kind of loose mist where innumerable droplets of water drifted in the air.

Where the stream that flows through Nickajack originates, nobody knows. After a heavy rain on the other side of the mountain, its flow increases. At such times its water becomes slightly milky. Normally it is so clear that in one of the lakes, where the stream spreads out in a wider cavern, an aluminum dipper can be seen distinctly, although it lies on the bottom under 30 feet of water.

Half a dozen times we floated across subterranean lakes surrounded by water-carved stone, fluted, rounded, sculptured into grotesque shapes in which an active imagination could see faces and cathedrals and animals, all immobile, all unchanged for centuries. Stalactites, those icicles of stone, all seemed icicles of ice here; all seemed melting, each with a large drop of water pendant at its tip. Wherever our electric searchlight turned, we saw the eerie scenery of the cave double, its inverted image below, mirrored on the unmarred surface of the water. But sometimes, as we looked, the image wavered, the mirror was shattered by the plunge of a large drop from the tip of a stalactite.

Both the carved stone and the stalactites around us were the product of unhasting change, of such vast stretches of time that they brought to mind the Oriental's definition of eternity: "When the Himalayas shall be ground to powder by a gauze veil floating against them once in a thousand years."

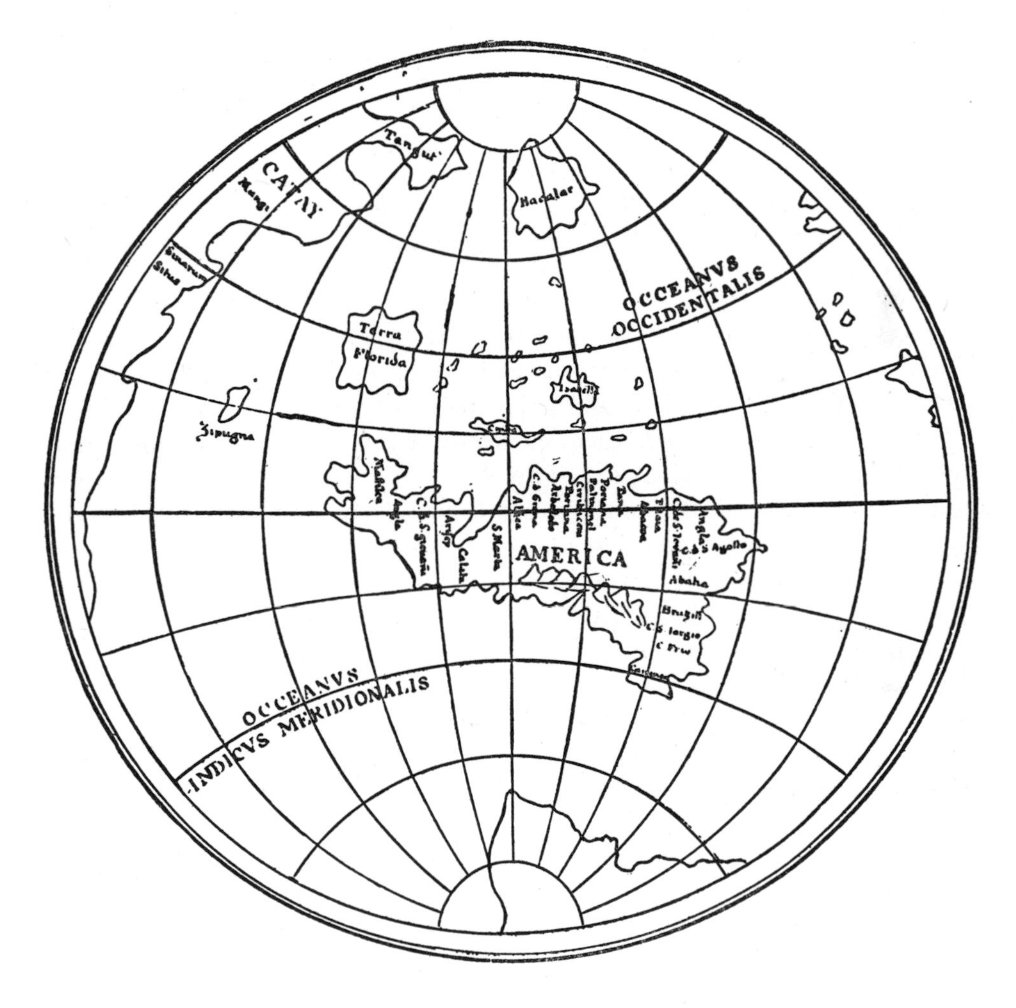

MAP DRAWN BY LEONARDO DA VINCI IN 1515

EXPERIMENT WITH ANTS

FROM *The Mason-Bees*

J. HENRI FABRE

When Jean Henri Fabre, the great French entomologist, decided to undertake for his life work the study of the habits, instincts, and life cycle of insects, he chose a happy method. Taking little account of books in the field or the conclusions of his predecessors, he based all his work on direct observation. The purity of his perception is apparent in this selection; and we are the wiser as his discriminating eye follows the ravaging Amazon ant on its singular journey home.

Among the treasures of my harmas-laboratory, I place in the first rank an Ant-hill of *Polyergus rufescens,* the celebrated Red Ant, the slave-hunting Amazon. Unable to rear her family, incapable of seeking her food, of taking it even when it is within her reach, she needs servants who feed her and undertake the duties of housekeeping. The Red Ants make a practice of stealing children to wait on the community. They ransack the neighbouring Ant-hills, the home of a different species; they carry away nymphs, which soon attain maturity in the strange house and become willing and industrious servants.

When the hot weather of June and July sets in, I often see the Amazons leave their barracks of an afternoon and start on an expedition. The column measures five or six yards in length. If nothing worthy of attention be met upon the road, the ranks are fairly well maintained; but, at the first suspicion of an Ant-hill, the vanguard halts and deploys in a swarming throng, which is increased by the others as they come up hurriedly. Scouts are sent out; the Amazons recognize that they are on a wrong track; and the column forms again. It resumes its march, crosses the garden-paths, disappears from sight in the grass, reappears farther on, threads its way through the heaps of dead leaves, comes out again and continues its search. At last, a nest of Black Ants is discovered. The Red Ants hasten down to the dormitories where the nymphs lie and soon emerge with their booty. Then we have, at the gates of the underground city, a bewildering scrimmage between the defending blacks and the attacking reds. The struggle is too unequal to remain indecisive. Victory falls to the reds, who race back to their abode, each with her prize, a swaddled nymph, dangling from her mandibles. The reader who is not acquainted with these slave-raiding habits would be greatly interested in the story of the Amazons. I relinquish it, with much regret: it would take us too far from our subject, namely, the return to the nest.

The distance covered by the nymph-stealing column varies: it all depends on whether Black Ants are plentiful in the neighbourhood. At times, ten or twenty yards suffice; at others, it requires fifty, a hundred or more. I once saw the expedition go beyond the garden. The Amazons scaled the surrounding wall, which was thirteen feet high at that point, climbed over it and went on a little farther, into a corn-field. As for the route taken, this is a matter of indifference to the marching column. Bare ground, thick grass, a heap of dead leaves or stones, brick-work, a clump of shrubs: all are crossed without any marked preference for one sort of road rather than another.

What is rigidly fixed is the path home, which follows the outward track in all its windings and all its crossings, however difficult. Laden with their plunder, the Red Ants return to the nest by the same road, often an exceedingly complicated one, which the exigencies of the chase compelled them to take originally. They repass each spot which they passed at first; and this is to them a matter of such imperative necessity that no additional fatigue nor even the gravest danger can make them alter the track.

Let us suppose that they have crossed a thick heap of dead leaves, representing to them a path beset with yawning gulfs, where every moment some one falls, where many are exhausted as they struggle out of the hollows and reach the heights by means of swaying bridges, emerging at last from the labyrinth of lanes. No matter: on their return, they will not fail, though weighed down with their burden, once more to struggle through that weary maze. To avoid all this fatigue, they would have but to swerve slightly from the original path, for the good, smooth road is there, hardly a step away. This little deviation never occurs to them.

I came upon them one day when they were on one of their raids. They were marching along the inner edge of the stone-work of the garden-pond, where I have replaced the old batrachians by a colony of Gold-fish. The wind was blowing very hard from the north and, taking the column in flank, sent whole rows of the Ants flying into the water. The fish hurried up; they watched the performance and gobbled up the drowning insects. It was a difficult bit; and the column was decimated before it had passed. I expected to see the return journey made by another road, which would wind round and avoid the fatal cliff. Not at all. The nymph-laden band resumed the parlous path and the Gold-fish received a double windfall: the Ants and their prizes. Rather than alter its track, the column was decimated a second time.

It is not easy to find the way home again after a distant expedition, during which there have been various sorties, nearly always by different paths; and this difficulty makes it absolutely necessary for the Amazons to return by the same road by which they went. The insect has no choice of route, if it would not be lost on the way: it must come back by the track which it knows and which it has lately travelled. The Processionary Caterpillars, when they leave their nest and go to another branch, on another tree, in search of a type of leaf more to their taste, carpet the course with silk and are able to return home by following the threads stretched along their road. This is the most elementary method open to the insect liable to stray on its excursions: a silken path brings it home again. The Processionaries, with their unsophisticated traffic-laws, are very different from the Mason-bees and others, who have a special sense to guide them.

The Amazon, though belonging to the Hymenopteron clan, herself possesses rather limited homing-faculties, as witness her compulsory return by her former trail. Can she imitate, to a certain extent, the Processionaries' method, that is to say, does she leave, along the road traversed, not a series of conducting threads, for she is not equipped for that work, but some odorous emanation, for instance, some formic scent, which would allow her to guide herself by means of the olfactory sense? This view is pretty generally accepted. The Ants, people say, are guided by the sense of smell; and this sense of smell appears to have its seat in the antennæ, which we see in continual palpitation. It is doubtless very reprehensible, but I must admit that the theory does not inspire me with overwhelming enthusiasm. In the first place, I have my suspicions about a sense of smell seated in the antennæ: I have given my reasons before; and, next, I hope to prove by experiment that the Red Ants are not guided by a scent of any kind.

To lie in wait for my Amazons, for whole afternoons on end, often unsuccessfully, meant taking up too much of my time. I engaged an assistant whose hours were not so much occupied as mine. It was my grand-daughter Lucie, a little rogue who liked to hear my stories of the Ants. She had been present at the great battle between the reds and blacks and was much impressed by the rape of the long-clothes babies. Well-coached in her exalted functions, very proud of already serving that august lady, Science, my little Lucie would wander about the garden, when the weather seemed propitious, and keep an eye on the Red Ants, having been commissioned to reconnoitre carefully the road to the pillaged Ant-hill. She had given proof of her zeal; I could rely upon it.

One day, while I was spining out my daily quota of prose, there came a banging at my study-door:

"It's I, Lucie! Come quick: the reds have gone into the blacks' house. Come quick!"

"And do you know the road they took?"

"Yes, I marked it."

"What! Marked it? And how?"

"I did what Hop-o'-My-Thumb did: I scattered little white stones along the road."

I hurried out. Things had happened as my six-year-old colleague said. Lucie had secured her provision of pebbles in advance and, on seeing the Amazon regiment leave barracks, had followed them step by step and placed her stones at intervals along the road covered. The Ants had made their raid and were beginning to return along the track of tell-tale pebbles. The distance to the nest was about a hundred paces, which gave me time to make preparations for an experiment previously contemplated.

I take a big broom and sweep the track for about a yard across. The dusty particles on the surface are thus removed and replaced by others. If they were tainted with any odorous effluvia, their absence will throw the Ants off the track. I divide the road, in this way, at four different points, a few feet apart.

The column arrives at the first section. The hesitation of the Ants is evident. Some recede and then return, only to recede once more; others wander along the edge of the cutting; others disperse sideways and seem to be trying to skirt the unknown country. The head of the column, at first closed up to a width of a foot or so, now scatters to three or four yards. But fresh arrivals gather in their numbers before the obstacle; they form a mighty array, an undecided horde. At last, a few Ants venture into the swept zone and others follow, while a few have meantime gone ahead and recovered the track by a circuitous route. At the other cuttings, there are the same halts, the same hesitations; nevertheless, they are crossed, either in a straight line or by going round. In spite of my snares, the Ants manage to return to the nest; and that by way of the little stones.

The result of the experiment seems to argue in favour of the sense of smell. Four times over, there are manifest hesitations wherever the road is swept. Though the return takes place, nevertheless, along the original track, this may be due to the uneven work of the broom, which has left certain particles of the scented dust in position. The Ants who went round the cleared portion may have been guided by the sweepings removed to either side. Before, therefore, pronouncing judgment for or against the sense of smell, it were well to renew the experiment under better conditions and to remove everything containing a vestige of scent.

A few days later, when I have definitely decided on my plan, Lucie resumes her watch and soon comes to tell me of a sortie. I was counting on it, for the Amazons rarely miss an expedition during the hot and sultry afternoons of June and July, especially when the weather threatens storm. Hop-o'-

My-Thumb's pebbles once more mark out the road, on which I choose the point best-suited to my schemes.

A garden-hose is fixed to one of the feeders of the pond; the sluice is opened; and the Ants' path is cut by a continuous torrent, two or three feet wide and of unlimited length. The sheet of water flows swiftly and plentifully at first, so as to wash the ground well and remove anything that may possess a scent. This thorough washing lasts for nearly a quarter of an hour. Then, when the Ants draw near, returning from the plunder, I let the water flow more slowly and reduce its depth, so as not to overtax the strength of the insects. Now we have an obstacle which the Amazons must surmount, if it is absolutely necessary for them to follow the first trail.

This time, the hesitation lasts long and the stragglers have time to come up with the head of the column. Nevertheless, an attempt is made to cross the torrent by means of a few bits of gravel projecting above the water; then, failing to find bottom, the more reckless of the Ants are swept off their feet and, without loosing hold of their prizes, drift away, land on some shoal, regain the bank and renew their search for a ford. A few straws borne on the waters stop and become so many shaky bridges, on which the Ants climb. Dry olive-leaves are converted into rafts, each with its load of passengers. The more venturesome, partly by their own efforts, partly by good luck, reach the opposite bank without adventitious aid. I see some who, dragged by the current to one or the other bank, two or three yards off, seem very much concerned as to what they shall do next. Amid this disorder, amid the dangers of drowning, not one lets go her booty. She would not dream of doing so: death sooner than that! In a word, the torrent is crossed somehow or other along the regular track.

The scent of the road cannot be the cause of this, it seems to me, for the torrent not only washed the ground some time beforehand, but also pours fresh water on it all the time that the crossing is taking place. Let us now see what will happen when the formic scent, if there really be one on the trail, is replaced by another, much stronger odour, one perceptible to our own sense of smell, which the first is not, at least not under present conditions.

I wait for a third sortie and, at one point in the road taken by the Ants, rub the ground with some handfuls of freshly-gathered mint. I cover the track, a little farther on, with the leaves of the same plant. The Ants, on their return, cross the section over which the mint was rubbed without apparently giving it a thought; they hesitate in front of the section heaped up with leaves and then go straight on.

After these two experiments, first with the torrent of water which washes away all trace of smell from the ground and then with the mint which changes the smell, I think that we are no longer at liberty to quote scent as the guide of the Ants that return to the nest by the road which they took at starting. Further tests will tell us more about it.

Without interfering with the soil, I now lay across the track some large sheets of paper, newspapers, keeping them in position with a few small stones. In front of this carpet, which completely alters the appearance of the road, without removing any sort of scent that it may possess, the Ants hesitate even longer than before any of my other snares, including the torrent. They are compelled to make manifold attempts, reconnaissances to right and left, forward movements and repeated retreats, before venturing altogether into the unknown zone. The paper straits are crossed at last and the march resumed as usual.

Another ambush awaits the Amazons some distance farther on. I have divided the track by a thin layer of yellow sand, the ground itself being grey. This change of colour alone is enough for a moment to disconcert the Ants, who again hesitate in the same way, though not for so long, as they did before the paper. Eventually, this obstacle is overcome like the others.

As neither the stretch of sand nor the stretch of paper got rid of any scented effluvia with which the trail may have been impregnated, it is patent that, as the Ants hesitated and stopped in the same way as before, they find their way not by sense of smell, but really and truly by sense of sight; for, every time that I alter the appearance of the track in any way whatever—whether by my destructive broom, my streaming water, my green mint, my paper carpet or my golden sand—the returning column calls a halt, hesitates and attempts to account for the changes that have taken place. Yes, it is sight, but a very dull sight, whose horizon is altered by the shifting of a few bits of gravel. To this short sight, a strip of paper, a bed of mint-leaves, a layer of yellow sand, a stream of water, a furrow made by the broom, or even lesser modifications are enough to transform the landscape; and the regiment, eager to reach home as fast as it can with its loot, halts uneasily on beholding this unfamiliar scenery. If the doubtful zones are at length passed, it is due to the fact that fresh attempts are constantly being made to cross the doctored strips and that at last a few Ants recognize well-known spots beyond them. The others, relying on their clearer-sighted sisters, follow.

Sight would not be enough, if the Amazon had not also at her service a correct memory for places. The memory of an Ant! What can that be? In what does it resemble ours? I have no answers to these questions; but a few words will enable me to prove that the insect has a very exact and persistent recollection of places which it has once visited. Here is something which I have often witnessed. It sometimes happens that the plundered Ant-hill offers the Amazons a richer spoil than the invading column is able to carry away. Or, again, the region visited is rich in Ant-hills. Another raid is necessary, to exploit the site thoroughly. In such cases, a second expedition takes place, sometimes on the next day, sometimes two or three days later. This time, the column does no reconnoitring on the way: it goes straight to the spot known to abound in nymphs and travels by the identical path which it followed before. It has sometimes happened that I have marked with small stones, for a distance of twenty yards, the road pursued a couple of days earlier and have then found the Amazons proceeding by the same route, stone by stone:

"They will go first here and then there," I said, according to the position of the guide-stones.

And they would, in fact, go first here and then there, skirting my line of pebbles, without any noticeable deviation.

Can one believe that odoriferous emanations diffused along the route are going to last for several days? No one would dare to suggest it. It must, therefore, be sight that directs the Amazons, sight assisted by its memory for places. And this memory is tenacious enough to retain the impression until the next day and later; it is scrupulously faithful, for it guides the column by the same path as on the day before, across the thousand irregularities of the ground.

THE ROCKS TREMBLED

FROM *Earthquake Storms*

JOHN MUIR

In this selection, John Muir, searching for the origin of avalanche taluses, those enormous heaps of boulders stacked at the base of cliffs, some of them five hundred feet high, sees his theory confirmed in the giant laboratory of the Sierras.

Muir was no cloistered investigator. He looked for his geologic answers on the high mountain tops of the Rockies and in the canyons of the Yosemite and phrased them in a language he had taken from Shakespeare and Milton rather than from the technical vocabulary of the sciences.

THE AVALANCHE TALUSES, LEANING AGAINST THE WALLS AT INTERVALS OF A mile or two, are among the most striking and interesting of the secondary features of the Valley. They are from about three to five hundred feet high, made up of huge, angular, well-preserved, unshifting boulders, and instead of being slowly weathered from the cliffs like ordinary taluses, they were all formed suddenly and simultaneously by a great earthquake that occurred at least three centuries ago. And though thus hurled into existence in a few seconds or minutes, they are the least changeable of all the Sierra soil-beds. Excepting those which were launched directly into the channels of swift rivers, scarcely one of their wedged and interlacing boulders has moved since the day of their creation; and though mostly made up of huge blocks of granite, many of them from ten to fifty feet cube, weighing thousands of tons with only a few small chips, trees and shrubs make out to live and thrive on them and even delicate herbaceous plants—draperia, collomia, zauschneria, etc., soothing and coloring their wild rugged slopes with gardens and groves.

I was long in doubt on some points concerning the origin of these taluses. Plainly enough they were derived from the cliffs above them, because they are of the size of scars on the wall, the rough angular surface of which contrasts with the rounded, glaciated, unfractured parts. It was plain, too, that instead of being made up of material slowly and gradually weathered from the cliffs like ordinary taluses, almost every one of them had been formed suddenly in a single avalanche, and had not been increased in size during the last three or four centuries, for trees three or four hundred years old are growing on them, some standing at the top close to the wall without a bruise or broken branch, showing that scarcely a single boulder had ever fallen among them. Furthermore, all these taluses throughout the Range seemed by the trees and lichens growing on them to be of the same age. All the phenomena thus pointed straight to a grand ancient earthquake. But for years I left the question open, and went on from cañon to cañon, observing again and again; measuring the heights of taluses throughout the Range on both flanks, and the variations in the angles of their surface slopes; studying the way their boulders had been assorted and related and brought to rest, and their correspondence in size with the cleavage joints of the cliffs from whence they were derived, cautious about making up my mind. But at last all doubt as to their formation vanished.

At half-past two o'clock of a moonlit morning in March, I was awakened by a tremendous earthquake, and though I had never before enjoyed a storm of this sort, the strange thrilling motion could not be mistaken, and I ran out of my cabin, both glad and frightened, shouting, "A noble earthquake! A noble earthquake!" feeling sure I was going to learn something. The shocks were so violent and varied, and succeeded one another so closely, that I had to balance myself carefully in walking as if on the deck of a ship among waves, and it seemed impossible that the high cliffs of the Valley could escape being shattered. In particular, I feared that the sheer-fronted Sentinel Rock, towering above my cabin, would be shaken down, and I took shelter back of a large yellow pine, hoping that it might protect me from at least the smaller outbounding boulders. For a minute or two the shocks became more and more violent—flashing horizontal thrusts mixed with a few twists and battering, explosive, upheaving jolts—as if Nature were wrecking her Yosemite temple, and getting ready to build a still better one.

I was now convinced before a single boulder had fallen that earthquakes were the talus-makers and positive proof soon came. It was a calm moonlight night, and no sound was heard for the first minute or so, save low, muffled, underground, bubbling rumblings, and the whispering and rustling of the agitated trees, as if Nature were holding her breath. Then, suddenly, out of the strange silence and strange motion there came a tremendous roar. The Eagle Rock on the south wall, about a half a mile up the Valley, gave way and I saw it falling in thousands of the great boulders I had so long been studying, pouring to the Valley floor in a free curve luminous from friction, making a terribly sublime spectacle—an arc of glowing, passionate fire, fifteen hundred feet span, as true in form and as serene in beauty as a rainbow in the midst of the stupendous, roaring rock-storm. The sound was so tremendously deep and broad and earnest, the whole earth like a living creature seemed to have at last found a voice and to be calling to her sister planets. In trying to tell something of the size of this awful sound it seems to me that if all the thunder of all the storms I had ever heard were condensed into one roar it would not equal this rock-roar at the birth of a mountain talus. Think, then, of the roar that arose to heaven at the simultaneous birth of all the thousands of ancient cañon-taluses throughout the length and breadth of the Range!

The first severe shocks were soon over, and eager to examine the new-born talus I ran up the Valley in the moonlight and climbed upon it before the huge blocks, after their fiery flight, had come to complete rest. They were slowly settling into their places, chafing, grating against one another, groaning, and whispering; but no motion was visible except in a stream of small fragments pattering down the face of the cliff. A cloud of dust particles, lighted by the moon, floated out across the whole breadth of the Valley, forming a ceiling that lasted until after sunrise, and the air was filled with the odor of crushed Douglas spruces from a grove that had been mowed down and mashed like weeds.

After the ground began to calm I ran across the meadow to the river to see in what direction it was flowing and was glad to find that *down* the Valley was still down. Its waters were muddy from portions of its banks having given way, but it was flowing around its curves and over its ripples and shallows with ordinary tones and gestures. The mud would soon be cleared away and the raw slips on the banks would be the only visible record of the shaking it suffered.

The Upper Yosemite Fall, glowing white in the moonlight, seemed to know nothing of the earthquake, manifesting no change in form or voice, as far as I could see or hear.

After a second startling shock, about half-past three o'clock, the ground continued to tremble gently, and smooth, hollow rumbling sounds, not always distinguishable from the rounded, bumping, explosive tones of the falls, came from deep in the mountains in a northern direction.

The few Indians fled from their huts to the middle of the Valley, fearing that angry spirits were trying to kill them; and, as I afterward learned, most of the Yosemite tribe, who were spending the winter at their village on Bull Creek forty miles away, were so terrified that they ran into the river and washed themselves—getting themselves clean enough to say their prayers, I suppose, or to die. I asked Dick, one of the Indians with whom I was acquainted, "What made the ground shake and jump so much?" He only shook his head and said, "No good. No good," and looked appealingly to me to give him hope that his life was to be spared.

In the morning I found the few white settlers assembled in front of the old Hutchings Hotel comparing notes and meditating flight to the lowlands, seemingly as sorely frightened as the Indians. Shortly after sunrise a low, blunt, muffled rumbling, like distant thunder, was followed by another series of shocks, which, though not nearly so severe as the first, made the cliffs and domes tremble like jelly, and the big pines and oaks thrill and swish and wave their branches with startling effect. Then the talkers were suddenly hushed, and the solemnity on their faces was sublime. One in particular of these winter neighbors, a somewhat speculative thinker with whom I had often conversed, was a firm believer in the cataclysmic origin of the Valley; and I now jokingly remarked that his wild tumble-down-and-engulfment hypothesis might soon be proved, since these underground rumblings and shakings might be the forerunners of another Yosemite-making cataclysm, which would perhaps double the depth of the Valley by swallowing the floor, leaving the ends of the roads and trails dangling three or four thousand feet in the air. Just then came the third series of shocks, and it was fine to see how awfully silent and solemn he became. His belief in the existence of a mysterious abyss, into which the suspended floor of the Valley and all the domes and battlements of the walls might at any moment go roaring down, mightily troubled him. To diminish his fears and laugh him into something like reasonable faith, I said, "Come, cheer up; smile a little and clap your hands, now that kind Mother Earth is trotting us on her knee to amuse us and make us good." But the well-meant joke seemed irreverent and utterly failed, as if only prayerful terror could rightly belong to the wild beauty-making business. Even after all the heavier shocks were over I could do nothing to reassure him. On the contrary, he handed me the keys of his little store to keep, saying that with a companion of like mind he was going to the lowlands to stay until the fate of poor, trembling Yosemite was settled. In vain I rallied them on their fears, calling attention to the strength of the granite walls of our Valley home, the very best and solidest masonry in the world, and less likely to collapse and sink than the sedimentary lowlands to which they were looking for safety; and saying that in any case they sometime would have to die, and so grand a burial was not to be slighted. But they were too seriously panic-stricken to get comfort from anything I could say.

During the third severe shock the trees were so violently shaken that the birds flew out with frightened cries. In particular, I noticed two robins flying in terror from a leafless oak, the branches of which swished and quivered as if struck by a heavy battering-ram. Exceedingly interesting were the flashing and quivering of the elastic needles of the pines in the sunlight and the waving up and down of the branches while the trunks stood rigid. There was no swaying, waving or swivelling as in wind-storms, but quick, quivering jerks, and at times the heavy tasseled branches moved as if they had all been pressed down against the trunk and suddenly let go, to spring up and vibrate until they came to rest again. Only the owls seemed to be undisturbed. Before the rumbling echoes had died away a hollow-voiced owl began to hoot in philosophical tranquillity from near the edge of the new talus as if nothing extraordinary had occurred, although, perhaps, he was curious to know what all the noise was about. His "hoot-too-hoot-too-whoo" might have meant, "what's a' the steer, kimmer?"

It was long before the Valley found perfect rest. The rocks trembled more or less every day for over two months, and I kept a bucket of water on my table to learn what I could of the movements. The blunt thunder in the depths of the mountains was usually followed by sudden jarring, horizontal thrusts from the northward, often succeeded by twisting, upjolting movements. More than a month after the first great shock, when I was standing on a fallen tree up the Valley near Lamon's winter cabin, I heard a distinct bubbling thunder from the direction of Tenaya Cañon. Carlo, a large intelligent St. Bernard dog standing beside me seemed greatly astonished, and looked intently in that direction with mouth open and uttered a low *Wouf!* as if saying, "What's that?" He must have known that it was not thunder, though like it. The air was perfectly still, not the faintest breath of wind perceptible, and a fine, mellow, sunny hush pervaded everything, in the midst of which came that subterranean thunder. Then, while we gazed and listened, came the corresponding shocks, distinct as if some mighty hand had shaken the ground. After the sharp horizontal jars died away, they were followed by a gentle rocking and undulating of the ground so distinct that Carlo looked at the log on which he was standing to see who was shaking it. It was the season of flooded meadows and the pools about me, calm as sheets of glass, were suddenly thrown into low ruffling waves.

Judging by its effects, this Yosemite, or Inyo earthquake, as it is sometimes called, was gentle as compared with the one that gave rise to the grand talus system of the Range and did so much for the cañon scenery. Nature, usually so deliberate in her operations, then created, as we have seen, a new set of features, simply by giving the mountains a shake—changing not only the high peaks and cliffs, but the streams. As soon as these rock avalanches fell, the streams began to sing new songs; for in many places thousands of boulders were hurled into their channels, roughening and half-damming them, compelling the waters to surge and roar in rapids where before they glided smoothly. Some of the streams were completely dammed; driftwood, leaves, etc., gradually filling the interstices between the boulders, thus giving rise to lakes and level reaches; and these again, after being gradually filled in, were changed to meadows, through which the streams are now silently meandering; while at the same time some of the taluses took the places of old meadows and groves. Thus rough places were made smooth, and smooth places rough. But, on the whole, by what at first sight seemed pure confounded confusion and ruin, the landscapes were enriched; for gradually every talus was covered with groves and gardens, and made a finely proportioned and ornamental base for the cliffs. In this work of beauty, every boulder is prepared and measured and put in its place more thoughtfully than are the stones of temples. If for a moment you are inclined to regard these taluses as mere draggled, chaotic dumps, climb to the top of one of them, and run down without any haggling, puttering hesitation, boldly jumping from boulder to boulder with even speed. You will then find your feet playing a tune, and quickly discover the music and poetry of these magnificent rock piles—a fine lesson; and all Nature's wildness tells the same story—the shocks and outbursts of earthquakes, volcanoes, geysers, roaring, thundering waves and floods, the silent uprush of sap in plants, storms of every sort—each and all are the orderly beauty-making love-beats of Nature's heart.

A PLEISTOCENE BANQUET

FROM *High Bonnet*

IDWAL JONES

Idwal Jones serves a dinner for the literary gourmet in this essay from his *High Bonnet,* adventures in *haute cuisine.* He is French in his cooking and his literary style, otherwise he is pure Californian. For wines, he favors the domestic brands—Californian, of course—and to support his choice, he has written the story of wineries and winegrowers in his native state with much partisanship, much unobtrusive erudition, and many pleasing historical side paths which he permits the reader to wander.

THE FAISAN D'OR WAS DEEP IN HER SEASONAL LULL, FOUR OF HER BANQUET halls shrouded; Urbain and Monsieur Paul, in an Anglophile mood, were poking about inns along the Thames, and for a month were to be lost in the Hebrides, looking for a certain wild Highlander whose pot still had never known the locks of the exciseman. I had been left with some vaguely denoted powers, and the occupancy of Monsieur Paul's sanctum. The staff was impressed, I think. The laundress brought in my linen so heavily starched that it was painful to wear; my bonnet was whiter, stiffer than before, a foot higher—a cloud atop a funnel.

I was having my breakfast of coffee and a brioche, with a copy of *Candide* propped against the cruet. Seeing an article closing with the signature "Lambert," I read it, as I did everything by that exquisite author of grocery catalogues, who nourished his spirit on the richness of the antique past. Some Russians, his story said, exploring a terminal moraine above the Arctic Circle, had dug deeper than usual in their hunt for rocks; they chipped out some bones, then a brace of musk oxen, perfectly preserved. More oxen were below, in that eternal icebox.

This was the peg on which our Academician had hung an essay remarkable for its learning and charm of expression. Pleistocene man had a thin time of it, by all accounts. The climate was not at its best, and when the earth shook under the mammoths that trotted past, he hid in his cave. There were also saber-tooth tigers, and lions twice the size of the breed at the zoo.

As often as not, he was the hunted and not the hunter; he dined on roots, for he had no other weapon than a chunk of flint. If luck favored him, he could knock over a leathery bird, or some kind of hare.

I was pondering over this when François lounged in.

"Old fellow," he shouted, "that's fatal—wearing a hat that high. You know what happens to a chef whose hat is too—too altitudinous! He gets flung out!"

"You ought to be wearing it, François. The second in command, you know."

He grinned. We both knew I had been put in as a stopgap in this dull season, and that Monsieur Paul, though secure in his tenure of office, and the *doyen* of his profession, regarded him as the only possible rival in the esteem of the patrons.

"It's quiet, Jean-Marie. Only half the staff here, and unless we get some excitement we'll have to go into the streets and whip up a riot." He poured himself a glass of brandy and sank heavily into a chair. "It's even stupider than it was last year. I should have gone fishing."

"Read this," I said. "It's Mayor Lambert in his best vein."

He read it, gulped his brandy down, then paced the room, agitatedly polishing his pince-nez. He tried to speak, but his will could bring forth only a deep breath and gesticulations. Another glass, and he stared, blinking, at the article; then he tore feebly at his neckcloth.

"Jean-Marie—think of it! A million years! That musk-ox beef has been pretty well hung! If we could only get a joint of it!"

"Melun-Perret ought to hear of this," I laughed.

"I have an idea!" the Creole broke in. "A Pleistocene banquet! That would be something. Think of what it would mean to the Faisan d'Or. Astounding *réclame,* for one thing, with the moral of a vast increase in business. How that would please Urbain!"

"It would be a novelty." I wrote on a pad. "Pleistocene banquet. Soup, a *potage* of musk-ox tail. Then a prime roast of musk ox, a double-rack, with King Edward the Seventh trimmings—garnish, sauce, and so forth. Vegetable, purée of fossil moss."

My Creole rubbed his hands. "And some fossils from the Sorbonne, tottering professors, very learned, with beards parted in the middle! A banquet for archaeologists. The very notion of it, my young friend, is staggering!"

"We must first catch our musk ox, of course," I said. "A mere detail. I shall discuss it with Melun-Perret. He will regard it as a most prodigious idea, such a dinner. Also," I warmed up, "it seems to me that our Mayor is deserving of the Legion of Honor ribbon, and this would bring his name into cosmic renown. Alas, that so great a scholar should have been doomed to obscurity through his brains!

"And by the way, François, it is his birthday on Thursday next. We shall have a little dinner at his place, and you will cook it."

And so we were agreed. I dispatched a telegram to Georges at his house in the Champs Élysées. He was so pleased at the notion that he postponed for a week the installation of a new and beautiful Grecian in an apartment that he maintained discreetly elsewhere.

We were eight in all. Mayor Lambert had brightened his flat, dusted his books, arranged flowers on the trestle-board table in an alcove, and brought in three Academicians. . . . Georges, his bland and candid eye rolling benevolently at us through the smoke, got out pencil and envelope, and planned the banquet for us.

"A month from tonight. Item: full haunch of musk ox. Item: fossil moss, if edible." He rolled his perfecto and scribbled. "Item: some Pleistocene sweetbreads for a *vol-au-vent*. How's that for a start?"

"But that will take months," said Lambert.

"Four days at the outside, I assure you. I'll send my plane and sky chauffeur up there. He'll take along some vodka and a case of Port, for our Russian friends will need some cheering in that gloom. Anything else we can get out of the Pleistocene?"

"Nothing," said the Mayor. "But I know where we can get some old rice. Four measures, at least. In sealed urns, dug up in the ruins of Palmyra. That's a quantity, you see. More than you'd get from a hundred mummies with rice in their clutch."

Georges murmured with approbation.

"We're getting somewhere. Now, the wine."

"We'll find none so old," said the Academician. "Lucky for us. My Bulgar colleague, Professor Vuletich, gave me a taste of that Opimian, bottled in the year Caius Gracchus was slain in the revolt of the plebs. It has a lump of purple enamel. We made a tincture in alcohol, and had a teaspoonful apiece. It tasted like ink. *Vinum insaluberrimum.* But there it was, wine already old before Rome was an empire."

"Vuletich, where is he?"

"In Sofia."

"I'll go there in a plane myself and bring him and the Opimian."

"If that precious, that unique, relic should fall—"

"Then we shall both perish with it!"

"What I want to know," said François patiently, "is, how many will be there?"

It took longer to draw up the list than to invent the Pleistocene menu.

Not all scientists approve of every other scientist in the world. Mayor Lambert suggested twenty names. The old Academician winced at all of them, as if he had bitten into a persimmon. So with twenty other names.

"Well, then," said Georges, "let us have other than malefactors."

He sipped delicately from his little jar. It was of a pagan loveliness, with lip flared as in a Grecian lamp, and a design in faded red on its black, glazed body, so thin and time-hardened that the liqueur swirling in it gave forth an elfin ring.

"A fitting ceramique for the brandy," he murmured. "Let me congratulate you on your pots."

"You have discernment, M'sieu." Mayor Lambert held a light to a fresh cigar. "Spiteri, the Maltese archaeologist, found these in a tomb. They are Pompeiian tear jars."

By midnight we were agreed on the choice of guests. Twelve in all, taken from the first list. The brandy gone, we left and I said good night to the diners before their taxicabs at the curb. François was the last to go. He smote his chest, then stared at me.

"The dessert!" he shouted. "The Pleistocene dessert! What shall we have for that?"

He leaped in, the door slammed like a pistol shot, and the taxicab sped in pursuit of Georges and the Academicians.

This banquet, where should it be held? The major-domo was for the Talleyrand salon; Pierre for the Blue Room, with its Gobelins and plush chairs, its Fragonards and ormolu. Urbain's assistant was for screening off a corner of the great dining room, where a door led directly into the kitchen. I was talking with him and François in the crypt, when light came upon me.

"I have it! The cellar!"

We clattered down the stairs. Across from the wine cave was an unused chamber as dark as an oubliette, empty except for a half dozen broken hogsheads. I caught up a lantern and fetched it in. Cobbles bulged from the walls of crude and solid masonry; the paving was of large flagstones; the rafters had been hacked into shape with an adze.

"Is this Pleistocene enough?"

The chamber was thirty yards square, and its fireplace could have housed a coach. François struck a match and peered up the chimney. The draft was perfect. He vowed he could hear owls up above, in the trees. The place might have been built to purpose for the tryst with the musk ox.

"To think I've been in the Faisan d'Or since I was a *piccolo,* and never once heard of it," said Urbain's assistant.

His energy was prodigious. He had the cellar washed out; hung candelabra in the shape of cartwheels from the rafters; put a grid and turnspit in the fireplace; set up rough pine tables and chairs. Thirty chairs, not twelve: the Minister of Instruction was coming as a guest of Georges, and since that made it a diplomatic affair five Senators had had to be invited. The *chefs de cuisine* of the Roi Nantois, the Dauphin-Splendide, and the Noel Peters—these I invited on behalf of the Faisan d'Or.

The dungeon was thrown open. The light came from flames in braziers; the floor was carpeted with yew twigs. Heading the guests who filed in between rocks, as into a cave, were the Minister of Instruction and the Rector of the Sorbonne.

François entered, with him an upright, small man in white mustachios, with puckered, wise face, a frock coat and a rosette in his lapel. A supreme moment! Ah, Monsieur Paul, you should have been there! The guests rose in homage. Flashlights blazed. It was the great Maître Escoffier himself, writer of *La Guide Culinaire Moderne,* who bowed to the assemblage, and with grace seated himself between Melun-Perret and the ducal Doctor di Valmonte. . . .

The dinner was high in merit, considering the obstacles, but far higher in singularity. Fire thrummed on the hearth, and on the spit a haunch of musk ox revolved slowly, François basting it with ladles of sour cream. He had marinated it two days and nights. The immensity of that haunch which had propelled the beast over pastures when Europe was a tundra fresh from the receding ice cap was enough to inspire the diners with awe, with the most oppressive feelings of antiquity. It did, until the post-prandial champagne was poured out, to go along with the wafers of smoked Arctic dolphin on thin rice cakes.

The Palmyran rice, brought in by the old Academician, had resembled nothing so much as buckshot. We had ground it up with the fossil moss, a vegetable like hard coral, steeped it a fortnight in hot water, and made batter cakes. We had much left for a soufflé made with the beaten whites of cormorant eggs.

François carved the haunch with a sword-shaped blade, from which the slices fell, handsome and succulent, as dark as the red Argentine beef, onto plates so hot that the plates sputtered with the juice. The Duc di Valmonte, hero of a dozen banquets almost as epochal, sat as if hypnotized.

From stone jugs the waiters poured out a wine tinctured with the enamel dissolved in spirits, brought safely in Melun-Perret's plane from Sofia. It had a taste of museums, naturally.

Then followed quenelles of musk-ox liver à la maréchale, with Finnish cucumbers, aromatic as smelts, ripened in the long midnight sun. Then a salad of sea moss, cockles, and roe—all from the Arctic. Then a dessert of sherbet, made of a large chunk of fossil ice, as old as the musk ox itself, and coal-black. I had rendered it to powder and whipped it up with lime juice and syrup. Very handsome it looked under the soft lights.

Our *sommelier* brought in jeroboams of Perrier-Jouet, that poured out flashing amber and green, like the fountains at Versailles. Musicians came in to play flutes, bassoons, and hautboys—archaic, distant music, yet fanciful and gay.

The crowds outside the Faisan d'Or were enormous, for the journals had lifted interest still higher; and there were searchlights and an ambulance, sent down by the *Excelsior* newspaper, which had first claim to reports of disaster. Behind the rope in the cellar were spectators and reporters. Flashlights blinked every second, and the place filled with smoke. The Academicians, clutching at their throats, coughed and wheezed. Pierre, to save us from asphyxiation, dashed in with electric fans. Newsreel cameras whirred. Journalists climbed over the rope to interview Georges Melun-Perret, who, instead, led them to speak with Mayor Lambert, sitting at the head of the table, though his lapel was bare of decoration. They scribbled endless notes.

After that, speeches: first Mayor Lambert, then the Minister of Instruction. Then the fragile-ivory old Academician, with fingers plunging into his snuffbox, gave a speech, and it was the oddest of all.

"Fellow citizens," he began, "the Pleistocene was an intractable age. I assume that was the era of which we have been the guests.

"Of all its fauna the musk ox was the most admirable. One can only regret that it was overwhelmed by avalanches. I hope that explorers, instead of hunting in the boreal regions for beds of coal, or future airplane fields, will discover deep strata of musk oxen, inexhaustible mines of beef, enough to keep man well fed for twenty generations!

"As an archaeologist I should like to praise tonight's particular haunch. It proves that the bovine species was even before the dawn of antiquity perfect; that it had attained perfection when mankind was indistinguishable from orangutans. Man's defects are a scandal of the globe. Theologians have little good to say of him. Perhaps, through wars, he is headed for extinction. But—but—one good thing must be said for this grotesque but often well-meaning biped: he invented wine!

"Messieurs!" He lifted his glass. "To Noah, who first planted the grape!"

And that was the toast. The Academician sat down heavily. He smiled blissfully into space. He was really very drunk.

We heard much about the Pleistocene the next day, and several days after—perhaps too much. Enough Academicians, gourmets, scientists, and deputies to consume a herd of musk oxen were irritated at having been overlooked. The papers broke out in dithyrambs on the banquet, and printed every detail and speech. The Faisan d'Or might have been the only restaurant in Paris, in the world, and François the chef of the age. You saw him in the newsreels; you heard him on the radio; he was notorious. The Club des Cent, that premier gastronomic council, gave him a luncheon in the Faubourg St. Honoré. As for Mayor Lambert, both the *Candide* and the *Nouvelles Littéraires* declared that a ribbon must be bestowed upon him at once.

Patronage at the Faisan d'Or doubled overnight. It increased as the week went on. Then Monsieur Paul came back suddenly from his English tour, stalked through the kitchen to his office, and called me in.

"I fail, Monsieur Gallois," he said coldly, dashing his hand on a pile of newspapers spread out on his desk, "I fail to understand the meaning of all this."

He turned over one cartoon after another. There was François grilling steaks for Stone Age men shivering amid icebergs. There was François shaking hands with senators—and with the immortal Escoffier himself, an honor reserved for generals, statesmen, and ruling heads.

"And this—and this!"

Monsieur Paul looked up at me with the hurt and reproachful eyes of a spaniel that had been treated harshly.

"Monsieur," I said, "I began it for the good of the Faisan d'Or. In a way, it was a jest that paid, and I am sorry if—"

"Ring the bell for François!"

I did. As François moved in, with his slow, bargelike gait, wiping his hands upon his apron, I withdrew and closed the door. His summoning was indicative of Monsieur Paul's sharp displeasure. I looked about me, but saw that no one else in the kitchen was aware trouble was afoot, for they were all intent on their tasks. . . .

François was still in the office, and his measured rumbling went through the kitchen like thunder. He was resigning. In his demissory address, his arm going up and down, he was giving each sentence the weight, the edge of an artist as matchless in invective as in the roasting of meats. He spoke with deliberation in a French that was as bookish as a speech at the Academy. At intervals he gave his deep chest a thump like the impact of a battering ram. He had, he said, created history. And it was true. Habitués of the Faisan d'Or measured history, not by battles and reigns, but by dinners, banquets, and the triumphs of its artists in the kitchen.

"And now, Monsieur Paul, personally—"

Both François' arms went up into the air, and vibrated. He threw aside declamation, and went in for pure feeling, unpacking his heart in a bayou

Creole with the miasma of Africa upon it. His language would have frozen the scalp of a drill sergeant. In the garden Jules put hands over his ears. The Singhalese leaned his broom against the wall and shook with unaffected terror. Monsieur Paul—we could see him through the glass partition—bowed over the desk, covering his face. François emerged. The door clicked behind him. He adjusted his neckcloth, gave it a light pat, and strode off. Clear it was from his swagger and the rake of his bonnet over an eyebrow, that for this phoenix, this paragon of chefs, there was no more room at the Faisan d'Or.

His Pleistocene laurels still fresh, François betook himself to the Roi Nantois, and instantly was accorded a rank as high as Monsieur Paul's. Fortunate was the Roi Nantois, fortunate, too, its shareholders as well as its patrons, for it was soon to be emblazoned in the *Guide Michelin* with the rating of three stars. Perhaps I should add, with such tincture of modesty as might seem fit, that on the day after François' arrival I was myself installed there as master *saucier,* and supervisor of the roasts and fish.

As for Mayor Lambert, the upshot of the musk-ox feast was that he was invited to deliver five lectures on the Stone Age, and in the spring was given his decoration.

France honors those who in the fields of learning and the arts heap further luster upon her national glory. She seizes upon them with jealous possession. "France," says Balzac, "drinks the brains of men as savagely as she once chopped off their heads."

Perhaps, in the Golden Age to come, France may even honor a chef. . . .

A BLACK MYSTERIOUS SERPENT

FROM *Far Away and Long Ago*

W. H. HUDSON

There are few literary judgments that touch so nearly the heart of the matter as Joseph Conrad's assessment of W. H. Hudson. "Hudson writes as the grass grows. The good God makes it be there. And that is all there is to it."

Green Mansions, by which most readers know Hudson, is his mystical pantheism in fiction. The same concept of all of living Nature as God is blended into his superb essays of plant, bird, and animal life. In this selection from his *Far Away and Long Ago* we see that even in his childhood, much of which was spent in the Argentine pampas, he felt a sense of communion with all of earth's living things.

THERE EXISTED AT THAT TIME A SMALL PIECE OF WASTE GROUND ABOUT HALF an acre in extent, where there were no trees and where nothing planted by man would grow. It was at the far end of the plantation, adjoining the thicket of fennel and the big red willow tree on the edge of the moat. . . . This ground had been ploughed and dug up again and again, and planted with trees and shrubs of various kinds which were supposed to grow on any soil, but they had always languished and died, and no wonder, since the soil was a hard white clay resembling china clay. But although trees refused to grow there it was always clothed in vegetation of its own; all the hardiest weeds were there, and covered the entire barren area to the depth of a man's knees. These weeds had thin wiry stalks and small sickly leaves and flowers, and would die each summer long before their time. This barren piece of ground had a great attraction for me as a small boy, and I visited it daily and would roam about it among the miserable half-dead weeds with the sun-baked clay showing between the brown stalks, as if it delighted me as much as the alfalfa field, blue and fragrant in its flowering-time and swarming with butterflies.

One hot day in December I had been standing perfectly still for a few minutes among the dry weeds when a slight rustling sound came from near my feet, and glancing down I saw the head and neck of a large black serpent moving slowly past me. In a moment or two the flat head was lost to sight among the close-growing weeds, but the long body continued its moving slowly by—so slowly that it hardly appeared to move, and as the creature must have been not less than six feet long, and probably more, it took a very long time, while I stood thrilled with terror, not daring to make the slightest movement, gazing down upon it. Although so long it was not a thick snake, and as it moved on over the white ground it had the appearance of a coal-black current flowing past me—a current not of water or other liquid but of some such element as quicksilver moving on in a rope-like stream. At last it vanished, and turning I fled from the ground, thinking that never again would I venture into or near that frightfully dangerous spot in spite of its fascination.

Nevertheless I did venture. The image of that black mysterious serpent was always in my mind from the moment of waking in the morning until I fell asleep at night. Yet I never said a word about the snake to anyone: it was my secret, and I knew it was a dangerous secret, but I did not want to be told not to visit that spot again. And I simply could not keep away from it; the desire to look again at that strange being was too strong. I began to visit the place again, day after day, and would hang about the borders of the barren weedy ground watching and listening, and still no black serpent appeared. Then one day I ventured, though in fear and trembling, to go right in among the weeds, and still finding nothing began to advance step by step until I was right in the middle of the weedy ground and stood there a long time, waiting and watching. All I wanted was just to see it once more, and I had made up my mind that immediately on its appearance, if it did appear, I would take to my heels. It was when standing in this central spot that once again that slight rustling sound, like that of a few days before, reached my straining sense and sent an icy chill down my back. And there, within six inches of my toes, appeared the black head and neck, followed by the long, seemingly endless body. I dared not move, since to have attempted flight might have been fatal. The weeds were thinnest here, and the black head and slow-moving coil could be followed by the eye for a little distance. About a yard from me there was a hole in the ground about the circumference of a breakfast cup at the top, and into this hole the serpent put his head and slowly, slowly drew himself in, while I stood waiting until the whole body to the tip of the tail had vanished and all danger was over.

I had seen my wonderful creature, my black serpent unlike any serpent in the land, and the excitement following the first thrill of terror was still on me, but I was conscious of an element of delight in it, and I would not now resolve not to visit the spot again. Still, I was in fear, and kept away three or four days. Thinking about the snake I formed the conclusion that the hole he had taken refuge in was his den, where he lived, that he was often out roaming about in search of prey, and could hear footsteps at a considerable distance, and that when I walked about at that spot my footsteps disturbed him and caused him to go straight to his hole to hide himself from a possible danger. It struck me that if I went to the middle of the ground and stationed myself near the hole, I would be sure to see him. It would indeed be difficult to see him any other way, since one could never know in which direction he had gone out to seek for food. But no, it was too dangerous: the serpent might come upon me unawares and would probably resent always finding a boy hanging about his den. Still, I could not endure to think I had seen the last of him, and day after day I continued to haunt the spot, and going a few yards into the little weedy wilderness would stand and peer, and at the slightest rustling sound of an insect or falling leaf would experience a thrill of fearful joy, and still the black majestical creature failed to appear.

One day in my eagerness and impatience I pushed my way through the crowded weeds right to the middle of the ground and gazed with a mixed delight and fear at the hole: would he find me there, as on a former occasion? Would he come? I held my breath, I strained my sight and hearing in vain, the hope and fear of his appearance gradually died out, and I left the place bitterly disappointed and walked to a spot about fifty yards away, where mulberry trees grew on the slope of the mound inside the moat.

Looking into the masses of big clustering leaves over my head I spied a bat hanging suspended from a twig. The bats, I must explain, in that part of the world, that illimitable plain where there are no caverns and old buildings and other dark places to hide in by day, are not so intolerant of the bright light as in other lands. They do not come forth until evening, but by day they are content to hitch themselves to the twig of a tree under a thick cluster of leaves and rest there until it is dark.

Gazing up at this bat suspended under a big green leaf, wrapped in his black and buff-coloured wings as in a mantle, I forgot my disappointment, forgot the serpent, and was so entirely taken up with the bat that I paid no attention to a sensation like a pressure or a dull pain on the instep of my right foot. Then the feeling of pressure increased and was very curious and was as if I had a heavy object like a crowbar lying across my foot, and at length I looked down at my feet, and to my amazement and horror spied the great black snake slowly drawing his long coil across my instep! I dared not move, but gazed down fascinated with the sight of that glistening black cylindrical body drawn so slowly over my foot. He had come out of the moat, which was riddled with rat-holes, and had most probably been there hunting for rats when my wandering footsteps disturbed him and sent him home to his den; and making straight for it, as his way was, he came to my foot, and instead of going round drew himself over it. After the first spasm of terror I knew I was perfectly safe, that he would not turn upon me so long as I remained quiescent, and would presently be gone from sight. And that was my last sight of him; in vain I watched and waited for him to appear on many subsequent days: but that last encounter had left in me a sense of a mysterious being, dangerous on occasion as when attacked or insulted, and able in some cases to inflict death with a sudden blow, but harmless and even friendly or beneficent towards those who regarded it with kindly and reverent feelings in place of hatred. It is in part the feeling of the Hindu with regard to the cobra which inhabits his house and may one day accidentally cause his death, but is not to be persecuted.

THE PLANET EARTH FROM 100 MILES AWAY

Official United States Navy Photograph

Pazovski: Monkmeyer

POMPEII

STONEHENGE, A CIRCULAR GROUP OF STONES OF GREAT ANTIQUITY ON SALISBURY PLAIN IN SOUTHERN ENGLAND

Monkmeyer

THE CANYON DE SCHELLY IN ARIZONA. AT THE BASE OF THE WHITE HOUSE ARE THE RUINS OF OTHER DWELLINGS. THE TWO-THOUSAND-FOOT CLIFF ABOVE OVERHANGS SO FAR THAT RAIN NEVER BEATS UPON ITS FACE

Underwood and Underwood

Underwood and Underwood

left: THE CAULIFLOWER ROCK IN NEW MEXICO. FORMED BY EROSION, THE TOP IS HARDER THAN THE FOUNDATION AND THE WHOLE ROCK IS ABOUT AS HIGH AS A FOUR-STORY BUILDING

below: ERODED HILLSIDE IN TENNESSEE

Underwood and Underwood

Engelhard: Monkmeyer

right: CASTLE GEYSER IN YELLOWSTONE NATIONAL PARK

below: MAMMOTH HOT SPRINGS IN YELLOWSTONE, WYOMING, SURROUNDED BY ROLLING GREEN HILLS AND FORESTS

Engelhard: Monkmeyer

FPG

FPG

above: WILDFLOWERS

left: SNOWDROPS

A FIELD OF DANDELIONS

Jesse Lunger: FPG

right: PRAIRIE DOG

below: A NEST OF FOX CUBS

Daniel L. Burkett: Black Star

Lanks: Monkmeyer

Pinney: Monkmeyer

LARVA OF SEVENTEEN-YEAR LOCUST. IT FEEDS ON THE TENDER ROOTS OF PLANTS

Frederic Lew

MOUND ANTHILL

A CHAIN OF LIFE

Gerard: Monkmeyer

THE STUFF OF THE EARTH

FROM *A Land*

JACQUETTA HAWKES

It is an unorthodox version of creation that Jacquetta Hawkes gives us in this selection, infinitely more ancient than that of the Old Testament (though in its way no less reverent)—the one geology and archaeology offer for the origin of the land surfaces of the earth.

Jacquetta Hawkes says elsewhere in her book that she has used these two sciences "for purposes altogether unscientific." She has tried to convey a picture of the unity of "past and present: nature, man and art"—to show that the interrelation between the fossil trolobite and modern man is more deeply significant than can be explained by the language of science.

The writer is the wife of the much-read English novelist, J. B. Priestley. Her graceful and erudite writing has won a large audience for Mrs. Priestley in her own right.

ALTHOUGH I WAS BORN INTO A WORLD WHICH, AT LEAST IN MY PART OF IT, HAD long made itself aware that it was not a plate but a sphere, and that it was the servant and not the master of the sun, I was not born too late to absorb misconceptions from my nurse. Indeed I kept an unquestioned belief in one of these errors until only the other day, and I am therefore probably right to assume that many of my fellows believe in it still. I grew up with the simple image of Earth as a globe with an outer skin that was hard and cool but which grew progressively hotter and more wholly molten towards an unimaginably hot and molten centre. This picture, I now learn, is incorrect. Enormously the greater part of the earth's sphere is very dense, perhaps an alloy of iron and nickel. It is this metallic mass which draws the compass needle so faithfully to the north and which made the iron filings scattered by our physics mistress on a sheet of foolscap dance so mysteriously and form radiate patterns over the northern end of the magnet lying below the paper. The core is enclosed in an outer layer about seven hundred miles thick which may have risen to the surface when the earth was still fiery hot, as the dross rises when ores are smelted, or as scum rises on boiling jam.

The dross layer as it formed further divided itself into two parts, a heavy lower one of basalt and an upper one which on cooling crystallized into granite. This granite froth formed the first land masses of the world.

In deep mines men work naked and stream with sweat even when far above snow is falling on their houses. A few miles further down and the heat would become insupportable, deeper again and any shaft would begin to heave and close in, for it would have reached a depth at which the rock substance was molten. Whatever the temperature at the heart of the globe may be, radio-activity in the lower parts of its outer layer produces heat that accumulates in its deep imprisonment until it reaches such intensity that the substance melts. Only a score of miles below the surface on which we walk the crust is molten, though probably held rigid by the pressure of the solid rocks above. So the picture I formed in the nursery is not fundamentally misleading; we do in fact maintain our fragile lives on a wafer balanced between a hellish morass and unlimited space. Even that wafer wears thin, a fact accounting for many of the most stirring events in the history of the earth. In spite of the claims of gravestone merchants, granite can be gradually worn away by the combined and almost continuous assault of sun and frost, wind and water, and Earth's skin of granite was so worn. But what is weathered away is not lost, it must be redeposited elsewhere at a lower level, often under water. It was in this way that granite became the basic stuff of the sedimentary rocks that now form the greater part of our landscape. Since life began it has, of course, added immeasurably to these rocks, building up vast thicknesses from shells, corals, the minute bodies of foraminifera, chemical deposits provoked by algae, from the accumulation of forests and peat bogs. But it began with granite and the basalt that gouted up when the hard skin cracked. It is curious to think that granite and basalt, with H_2O, N, and CO_2, the water and early atmosphere of earth, have made all the material paraphernalia with which man now surrounds himself, the skyscraper, the wine-glass, the vacuum cleaner, jewels, the mirror into which I look. And the woman who looks? Where did it come from, this being behind the eyes, this thing that asks? How has this been gleaned from a landscape of harsh rock and empty seas?

But to return to the wafer, and to the statement that it wears thin. The irregularities of the earth's surface at the present time are slight enough—five miles up to the summit of the highest mountains, six miles down to the deepest sea-beds—less relatively than those of a smooth-skinned orange. Yet even this slight irregularity is always under attack by the powers already named, by sun and frost, wind and water, which erode the heights, transporting them grain by grain and molecule by molecule to add them to the low ground or to fill the hollows of the sea. Could this go on long enough a dead level would result and we should all perforce be plain-dwellers. There are many agencies working towards the achievement of rest, of quiescence. Gravity itself does much, through landslides, through streams and torrents that tear and batter their beds and carry down grits, pebbles, stones and boulders as their waters rush back to sea level. Frost splits, wind catches up grits and uses them like sandpaper to smooth and wear down exposed rock surfaces. The alternating heat and cold of day and night causes rock to swell and to retract until, weary of the process, its outer skin flakes off and is carried away by wind or water. To this last form of levelling down the geologists, who usually prefer such terms as isostatic readjustment, have given the pleasing name of onion weathering.

So, during a period of denudation, the levelling goes on. (Let it be remembered that the entire human episode has coincided with a very short stretch of a single geological period of denudation.) Everywhere the higher levels are being attacked, and their substance, broken into pieces ranging from dust grains to boulders, carried downwards. Most of the carrying is done by rivers that either redeposit the stuff along their lower reaches, fan it out in deltas, or sweep it right out to sea. It is the finer particles that reach the sea where they fall cloudily through the water and settle on the bottom, layer after layer slowly hardening into new rocks. New lands for old. There are two distinct kinds of sedimentary rocks. The rivers do not only carry these insoluble particles; some parts of the substance of the denuded lands are soluble and these are brought down in solution and then precipitated by chemical action. All the many varieties of sandstones and clays are formed by simple deposition, the limestones and dolomites mainly by precipitation. Chalk, once believed to have been built entirely from the bodies of minute sea creatures, is now recognized as a chemical precipitate, probably, however, created by the action of living algae and certainly crowded with the minute but elegant forms of the foraminifera. I like to think of the seas where chalk was forming clouded with white as though from a snow storm—a fall that lasted for thirty million years and lay to a depth of a thousand feet.

The character of new rocks accumulating on the sea bottom was naturally influenced by the character of the denuded lands that were their parents. Much of the New Red Sandstone still glowing warmly through Midland rain was laid down in great lakes or land-locked seas that covered central and northern England at a time when the surrounding lands were sun-baked deserts. The soft, bluish clay known as the Lias was accumulating when slow rivers were meandering down from a country of lakes and forests or swampy plains.

It is impossible to think of the blue Lias, of the mouldering cliffs of it along the Dorset coast, without thinking also of its fossils, of coiled ammonites, bullet-like belemnites, the huge skeletons of ichthyosaurs, and so also of fossils in general. The young are now kinder than they were and are more tender towards old age, more aware perhaps with the growth of self-consciousness that it will come also to them. But once old men were often called fossils, a most misleading usage, for the chance that any of us, dying at however advanced an age, having been given decent burial, will be fossilized is remote indeed. Sailors, perhaps, have the strongest hope. The true fossil is a creature of the sedimentary rocks, and the privilege of fossilization was given erratically, incalculably. Sometimes whole populations of molluscs or corals would be fossilized and their bodies build up thick beds of rock; sometimes only one in millions would gain this form of immortality in death.

In the right conditions the dead body of any organism, however frail, even delicate leaves, stems, fronds, might sink down to the sea bottom, or be held in swamps or the mud of rivers and there be petrified in the finest perfection of detail. When we come upon them again it seems as though time has revealed itself in a different dimension, as though the particles that smothered and preserved them were not grains of matter in space, but passing minutes; that these are infinitesimal lives "fast fixed in time."

So, layer upon layer, all the sedimentary rocks have been laid down, sometimes attaining thousands of feet in thickness—the limestones and sandstones, the chalk and clays that make so great a part of the landscape of Britain. It makes my flesh weary to recall this seemingly endless levelling down. In fact it is not endless. So long as the hard skin on which we live rests upon a morass of molten magma, there must come a moment when it will weaken and ruck up, and, as the energy long curbed below is freed, the sedimentary rocks that have been laid down so slowly and quietly on the sea floor may be thrust up raggedly into the air. The molten stuff itself finds openings where it can erupt through volcanic craters, seep through cracks, or, failing to reach the surface, push its way horizontally between the strata of sedimentary rocks. At a thousand degrees centigrade it may well through a crater in so fluid a state that it spreads over the surrounding land in wide, reeking seas. It must have been a grim scene in daylight and a lurid one at night when a great part of Ulster was overwhelmed by such a flow. This was more than fifteen million years before tourists began to crowd to the Giant's Causeway drawn by the strangeness of the hexagonal columns into which at that place the basalt and lava had solidified.

If the magma rises at a milder temperature it may hump itself into the neck of the crater as a stiff and already coagulating mass. Ailsa Crag, the huge rock which rises sheer from the sea south of Arran, is a hump of this kind. Now it is stained white by thousands of nesting gannets, aloof, pale-eyed birds pressing their warm feathers against the once boiling granite. Another volcanic creation is St. Kilda, the most westerly of the British Isles, where men clung tenaciously for a time, but which, grown weaker, they have now deserted.

Upheavals of the land surface may give the magma opportunities of a different kind. When a mountain range is formed by the folding of sedimentary rocks the partially molten substance pushes up into the soft or hollow places left below the folds. Long afterwards when a new cycle of denudation has worn away the spectacular peaks and ridges which covered it, this solidified core survives as the strongest feature of the landscape. Dartmoor, Bodmin Moor, Land's End and the Scillies are such exposed cores, after two hundred million years the only remains of the Armorican ranges that must in their day have been ten times their present height.

These, then, are the stuff of this land and of all lands: the sedimentary rocks formed during the long quiet periods of denudation, and the igneous or fiery rocks—granites, rhyolites, basalts and gabbros—which at many different times have penetrated or broken through them. A third group, the metamorphic rocks, have been created in part by the action of the fiery rocks upon the sedimentaries, in part by violent pressure caused by earth movement. The almost unimaginable pressure which may follow the buckling of an old surface into huge mountain ranges can change granites into gneiss, clay and shale into slate, limestone into marble and sandstone into true quartzite. The infernal heat of the nether world brought up by volcanic and other eruptions worked a comparable transformation on the sedimentary rocks with which it came in contact, tending to make them finer-grained, more shapely and rich. So it is that all igneous intrusions have an aureole of metamorphic rocks whose appearance and whole chemical structure they have changed.

The result of the intrusion of fiery rocks most fateful for the future life of human beings, and through them for the future of the earth's surface, was the production of minerals. Liquids and gases released by the heat escaped into surrounding fissures to form alluring metallic veins. The ancient furnace of the granite masses of Devon and Cornwall poured out the tin ore which was to draw men there, entice them to sink shafts and drive galleries until at last the countryside was left derelict with the elusive but powerful taint, the sense of degradation, that hangs about it today. Sometimes, rarely, the fissures were filled with gold.

The history of the earth's crust, then, has a rhythm. Denudation weakens it, the mountains are rucked up and the molten layer below forces itself towards the surface, then the storm dies away and denudation begins again. If the movement could be speeded up, as in a cinematograph, we should see a rise and fall as though of breathing:

> *The bosom of the landscape lifts and falls*
> *With its own leaden tide.*

SWEDISH TOMB OF THE LATE STONE AGE

BIRDS OF THE SUBTERRANEOUS PLACES

FROM *Personal Narrative of Travels to the Equinoctial Regions of America*

ALEXANDER VON HUMBOLDT

Next to Napoleon, Alexander von Humboldt was, probably, the greatest man in the Europe of his time. He was diplomat, philosopher, astronomer, physiologist, geographer, botanist, zoologist—but pre-eminently he was a scientific explorer. He prepared himself for this calling early in life by studies of commerce and foreign languages at Hamburg, anatomy at Jena, geology and the use of scientific instruments at Freiburg.

His expedition to South America to explore the course of the Orinoco and the Amazon laid the basis for future findings in meteorology, physical geography, and many others of the sciences. This selection from his American travels, an exploration of the Cavern of the Guacharo, demonstrates his great breadth of interest and his encyclopedic knowledge.

THAT WHICH CONFERS MOST CELEBRITY ON THE VALLEY OF CARIPE, BESIDES THE extraordinary coolness of its climate, is the great *Cueva,* or Cavern of the Guacharo. In a country where the people love the marvellous, a cavern which gives birth to a river, and is inhabited by thousands of nocturnal birds, the fat of which is employed in the Missions to dress food, is an everlasting object of conversation and discussion. The cavern, which the natives call "a mine of fat," is not in the valley of Caripe itself, but three short leagues distant from the convent, in the direction of west-south-west. It opens into a lateral valley, which terminates at the Sierra del Guacharo.

We set out for the Sierra on the 18th of September, accompanied by the alcaldes, or Indian magistrates, and the greater part of the monks of the convent. A narrow path led us at first towards the south, across a fine plain, covered with beautiful turf. . . .

The path winds in the direction of the river; and at the last turning we came suddenly before the immense opening of the grotto. The aspect of this spot is majestic, even to the eye of a traveller accustomed to the picturesque scenery of the higher Alps. I had before seen the caverns of the peak of

Derbyshire, where, lying down flat in a boat, we proceeded along a subterranean river, under an arch two feet high. I had visited the beautiful grotto of Treshemienshiz, in the Carpathian mountains, the caverns of the Hartz, and those of Franconia, which are vast cemeteries, containing bones of tigers, hyænas, and bears, as large as our horses. Nature in every zone follows immutable laws in the distribution of rocks, in the form of mountains, and even in those changes which the exterior crust of our planet has undergone. So great a uniformity led me to believe that the aspect of the cavern of Caripe would differ little from what I had observed in my preceding travels. The reality far exceeded my expectations. If the configuration of the grottoes, the splendour of the stalactites, and all the phenomena of inorganic nature, present striking analogies, the majesty of equinoctial vegetation gives at the same time an individual character to the aperture of the cavern.

The Cueva del Guacharo is pierced in the vertical profile of a rock. The entrance is towards the south, and forms an arch eighty feet broad and seventy-two high. The rock which surmounts the grotto is covered with trees of gigantic height. The mammee-tree and the genipa, with large and shining leaves, raise their branches vertically towards the sky; whilst those of the courbaril and the erythrina form, as they extend, a thick canopy of verdure. . . .

But this luxury of vegetation embellishes not only the external arch, it appears even in the vestibule of the grotto. We saw with astonishment plantain-leaved heliconias eighteen feet high, the praga palm-tree, and arborescent arums, following the course of the river, even to those subterranean places. The vegetation continues in the cave of Caripe as in those deep crevices of the Andes, half-excluded from the light of day, and does not disappear till, penetrating into the interior, we advance thirty or forty paces from the entrance. We measured the way by means of a cord; and we went on about four hundred and thirty feet without being obliged to light our torches. Daylight penetrates far into this region, because the grotto forms but one single channel, keeping the same direction, from south-east to north-west. Where the light began to fail, we heard from afar the hoarse sounds of the nocturnal birds; sounds which the natives think belong exclusively to those subterraneous places.

The guacharo is of the size of our fowls. . . . It would be difficult to form an idea of the horrible noise occasioned by thousands of these birds in the dark part of the cavern. Their shrill and piercing cries strike upon the vaults of the rocks, and are repeated by the subterranean echoes. The Indians showed us the nests of the guacharos by fixing a torch to the end of a long pole. These nests were fifty or sixty feet high above our heads, in holes in the shape of funnels, with which the roof of the grotto is pierced like a sieve. The noise increased as we advanced, and the birds were scared by the light of the torches of copal. When this noise ceased a few minutes around us, we heard at a distance the plaintive cries of the birds roosting in other ramifications of the cavern. It seemed as if different groups answered each other alternately.

The Indians enter the Cueva del Guacharo once a-year, near midsummer. They go armed with poles, with which they destroy the greater part of the nests. At that season several thousand birds are killed; and the old ones, as if to defend their brood, hover over the heads of the Indians, uttering terrible cries. The young, which fall to the ground, are opened on the spot. Their peritoneum is found extremely loaded with fat, and a layer of fat reaches from the abdomen to the anus, forming a kind of cushion between the legs of the bird. This quantity of fat in frugivorous animals, not exposed to the light, and exerting very little muscular motion, reminds us of what has been observed in the fattening of geese and oxen. It is well known how greatly darkness and repose favour this process. The nocturnal birds of Europe are lean, because, instead of feeding on fruits, like the guacharo, they live on the scanty produce of their prey. At the period commonly called, at Caripe, the oil harvest, the Indians build huts with palm-leaves, near the entrance, and even in the porch of the cavern. There, with a fire of brushwood, they melt in pots of clay the fat of the young birds just killed. This fat is known by the name of butter or oil (manteca, or aceite) of the guacharo. It is half liquid, transparent, without smell, and so pure that it may be kept above a year without becoming rancid. At the convent of Caripe no other oil is used in the kitchen of the monks but that of the cavern; and we never observed that it gave the aliments a disagreeable taste or smell.

The race of the guacharos would have been long ago extinct, had not several circumstances contributed to its preservation. The natives, restrained by their superstitious ideas, seldom have courage to penetrate far into the grotto. It appears also, that birds of the same species dwell in neighbouring caverns, which are too narrow to be accessible to man. Perhaps the great cavern is repeopled by colonies which forsake the small grottoes; for the missionaries assured us, that hitherto no sensible diminution of the birds have been observed. Young guacharos have been sent to the port of Cumana, and have lived there several days without taking any nourishment, the seeds offered to them not suiting their taste. When the crops and gizzards of the young birds are opened in the cavern, they are found to contain all sorts of hard and dry fruits, which furnish, under the singular name of guacharo seed (semilla del guacharo), a very celebrated remedy against intermittent fevers. The old birds carry these seeds to their young. They are carefully collected, and sent to the sick at Cariaco, and other places of the low regions, where fevers are generally prevalent.

As we continued to advance into the cavern, we followed the banks of the small river which issues from it, and is from twenty-eight to thirty feet wide. We walked on the banks, as far as the hills formed of calcareous incrustations permitted us. Where the torrent winds among very high masses of stalactites, we were often obliged to descend into its bed, which is only two feet deep. We learned with surprise, that this subterranean rivulet is the origin of the river Caripe, which, at the distance of a few leagues, where it joins the small river of Santa Maria, is navigable for canoes. It flows into the river Areo under the name of Caño de Terezen. We found on the banks of the subterranean rivulet a great quantity of palm-tree wood, the remains of trunks, on which the Indians climb to reach the nests hanging from the roofs of the cavern. The rings, formed by the vestiges of the old footstalks of the leaves, furnish as it were the steps of a ladder perpendicularly placed.

The Grotto of Caripe preserves the same direction, the same breadth, and its primitive height of sixty or seventy feet, to the distance of 472 metres, or 1458 feet, accurately measured. We had great difficulty in persuading the Indians to pass beyond the anterior portion of the grotto, the only part which they annually visit to collect the fat. The whole authority of "los padres" was necessary to induce them to advance as far as the spot where the soil rises abruptly at an inclination of sixty degrees, and where the torrent forms a small subterranean cascade. The natives connect mystic ideas with this cave, inhabited by nocturnal birds; they believe that the souls of their ancestors sojourn in the deep recesses of the cavern. "Man," say they, "should avoid places which are enlightened neither by the sun (zis), nor by the moon (nuna)." "To go and join the guacharos," is with them a phrase signifying to rejoin their fathers, to die. The magicians (piaches) and the poisoners (imorons) perform their nocturnal tricks at the entrance of the cavern, to conjure the chief of the evil spirits (ivorokiamo). Thus in every region of the earth a resemblance may be traced in the early fictions of nations, those especially which relate to two principles governing the world, the abode of souls after death, the happiness of the virtuous and the punishment of the guilty. The most different and most barbarous languages present a certain number of images, which are the same, because they have their source in the nature of our intelligence and our sensations. Darkness is everywhere connected with the idea of death. The Grotto of Caripe is the Tartarus of the Greeks; and the guacharos, which hover over the rivulet, uttering plaintive cries, remind us of the Stygian birds.

At the point where the river forms the subterranean cascade, a hill covered with vegetation, which is opposite to the opening of the grotto, presents a very picturesque aspect. It is seen at the extremity of a straight passage, 240 toises in length. The stalactites descending from the roof, and resembling columns suspended in the air, are relieved on a back-ground of verdure. The opening of the cavern appeared singularly contracted, when we saw it about the middle of the day, illumined by the vivid light reflected at once from the sky, the plants, and the rocks. The distant light of day formed a strange contrast with the darkness which surrounded us in the vast cavern. We discharged our guns at a venture, wherever the cries of the nocturnal birds and the flapping of their wings, led us to suspect that a great number of nests were crowded together. After several fruitless attempts M. Bonpland succeeded in killing a couple of guacharos, which, dazzled by the light of the torches, seemed to pursue us. This circumstance afforded me the means of making a drawing of this bird, which had previously been unknown to naturalists. We climbed, not without difficulty, the small hill whence the subterranean rivulet descends. We saw that the grotto was perceptibly contracted, retaining only forty feet in height, and that it continued stretching to north-east, without deviating from its primitive direction, which is parallel to that of the great valley of Caripe. . . .

The missionaries, with all their authority, could not prevail on the Indians to penetrate farther into the cavern. As the roof became lower the cries of the guacharos were more and more shrill. We were obliged to yield to the pusillanimity of our guides, and trace back our steps. The appearance of the cavern was however very uniform. We found that a bishop of St. Thomas of Guiana had gone farther than ourselves. He had measured nearly 2500 feet from the mouth to the spot where he stopped, but the cavern extended still farther. The remembrance of this fact was preserved in the convent of Caripe, without the exact period being noted. The bishop had provided himself with great torches of white Castile wax. We had torches composed only of the bark of trees and native resin. The thick smoke which issued from these torches, in a narrow subterranean passage, hurts the eyes and obstructs the respiration.

On turning back to go out of the cavern, we followed the course of the torrent. Before our eyes became dazzled with the light of day we saw on the outside of the grotto the water of the river sparkling amid the foliage of the trees which shaded it. It was like a picture placed in the distance, the mouth of the cavern serving as a frame. Having at length reached the entrance, we seated ourselves on the bank of the rivulet, to rest after our fatigues. We were glad to be beyond the hoarse cries of the birds, and to leave a place where darkness does not offer even the charm of silence and tranquillity. We could scarcely persuade ourselves that the name of the Grotto of Caripe had hitherto been unknown in Europe, for the guacharos alone might have sufficed to render it celebrated. These nocturnal birds have been no where yet discovered, except in the mountains of Caripe and Cumanacoa. The missionaries had prepared a repast at the entry of the cavern. Leaves of the banana and the vijao, which have a silky lustre, served us as a table-cloth, according to the custom of the country. Nothing was wanting to our enjoyment, not even remembrances, which are so rare in those countries, where generations disappear without leaving a trace of their existence.

THE SEEDS OF TRUNKBACKS

FROM *The Windward Road*

ARCHIE CARR

For a few hours once each year the giant turtles leave the sea, dig great holes in the tropic beaches to deposit their eggs, and then return to their natural habitat. This impulse, urge, instinct—whatever other word we use to describe our ignorance—is as little understood, and as intriguing as the natural force which moves the great flocks of birds on their seasonal migrations.

In this selection, Archie Carr, biologist, as warmly cognizant of people as he is of plants and animals, takes us to one of the solitary beaches of the Caribbean on a search for turtle eggs.

I WAS LOOKING FOR NESTS OF TRUNKBACK TURTLES. I HAD WALKED FIVE MILES and had found no sign—no fresh trail that was not clearly that of hawksbill or green turtle. Even the greens were scarce. There was just a sprinkling of early layers in the van of the big nesting migration—the "fleet," as the people on the beach call it—which was already long overdue. It was nearing noon of a flaming cloudless day and the land breeze had killed the trade wind.

Two miles back I had met the Siquirres dogs—the seasonally feral packs of curs that Paco had pointed out from the plane two days before. Each May or June the dogs gather on the beach from Siquirres and the other towns along the railroad far inland, called by some unknown cue to cross as much as thirty miles of jungle, marsh, and mangrove swamp and meet the fleet, and batten on turtle eggs for the season. There were eight dogs in the pack I met, and they were hungry and irritable. They ran yapping before me for a while, as if they thought I was somehow to blame for the lateness of the fleet, and then they dashed off over the low dunes and disappeared among the coco plums. Besides the dogs and a scurrying sand crab now and then, I had seen no living thing on land. . . .

I shuffled on through the fine hot sand. It was light, powdery dust of pumice and black glass that let you sink ankle-deep. It was so hot it burned my shanks above my shoe tops. The beach was piled with stranded timber —immense, silver trunks of cedar and *laurel* and *cedro macho* from the

Costa Rican rivers and mahogany from Panama or Nicaragua, stolen from the loggers by decades of June floods and then thrown back again onto the black beach by the wild seas that batter this open coast. No tropical beach is fun to walk on at cloudless, windless midday. This one, with its endless monstrous jetsam to send you weaving from the deep, hot dunes down into the brawling surf and back again, made following the narrow strip above high-water mark, where turtle trails are laid, a trying job. My ardor for trunkback nests was failing under the sun and I was on the point of crawling beneath a propped log to sleep out the midday calm when I saw what I had come after.

It was a short, broad-limbed V, deeply engraved in the beach above the tide zone. The open end of the wedge had been truncated by the lap of the last, highest wave, and the apex merged with a broad plowed and scuffed patch in the soft blown sand just seaward of the dune front. The limbs of the V—the trails to and from the disturbed patch—were nearly as wide as the wheel trail of a tractor, and indeed the whole system of marks seemed to show that a heavy, wheeled vehicle had come up from the sea, had sunk deep in the sand drift, and after a great deal of backing and filling and churning had returned to the water.

It was the nest of a trunkback. It was the first I had ever seen but there was no mistaking it. It was the first ever recorded for Central America, but its significance to me far transcended that statistic. To me it was the long-sought land-sign of a sea creature I had looked for since childhood—a monster of the deep ocean guided ashore one time in each year by the primal reptile drive to dig a hole in earth and drop in it the seeds of trunkbacks for tomorrow, and cover the hole with toeless flat feet, and pound back down to the sea never looking behind. It was the work of a water reptile pelagic as a whale or a plesiosaur and at home in the oceans of the world—the last vestige of landcraft left to a bloodline seabound for a hundred million years, and left then but to one sex for one hour on one night in the year.

You will gather that I am curiously, perhaps almost psychotically, susceptible to the color of the trunkback. For a while, then, what with my thoughts and the sun and the quaking air, I just stood and looked at the nest.

After a while the trance of lightheaded exultation ran out and I put down my camera bag and canteen and set about appraising the site where the turtle had worked. There was a great deal of it. A female trunkback often weighs a thousand pounds or more and is full of a fanatical kind of gland-given zeal that would almost pass for ingenuity. Everything she does is calculated, in a purely mechanistic sense of course, to keep her eggs from being dug up again, by either herpetologist or coatimundi. She can't hide the fact that she was out on the beach, so she confounds the egg-hunter with a plethora of clues. In this case the area of flung sand in which I had to prospect for the egg chamber was at least fifteen feet in diameter and roughly circular in outline. Since it offered no evidence, at least to my eye, by which the field for search might be narrowed down, I had to cover every square foot of it; and since the clutch of eggs might lie waist-deep beneath the sand, the job ahead was imposing.

I took up my egg stick. After making a few random test holes here and there, I began moving systematically back and forth across the site, punching as deeply as I could drive the stick. When I had completed a regular and closely spaced gridwork of holes and had found nothing, I began to realize that the slim section of cane that I had found effective enough in prospecting for the nests of hawksbills and green turtles was too feeble for the work at hand. To get down through the hard sand that lay below the surface drift I needed a pole with backbone—something I could plant and swing my weight on.

I began looking about the beach for something suitable. This was an open shore and a heavy sea washed it, and there was no dearth of driftwood, as I have said. I tested one silvery stick after another, but all were either crooked as a snake or punky and spineless from salt water and sun. I found a section of timber bamboo that was sound, but you don't split stuff like that with a pocketknife, which was the only tool I carried. Halfheartedly I trimmed and sharpened a leaf stem of coco palm, and this collapsed at the first thrust.

I wanted the nest badly, and with the mounting realization that I probably would not get it my frustration grew apace. I cursed my lack of foresight in not bringing a machete. I grabbed up a sphere of drifted pumice stone and tried to put an edge on my knife blade with it, but the rounded face of the stone collapsed like sugar candy and only polished the metal. In a peevish fit I threw the stone at the face of a *laurel* log and it went to pieces there.

Suddenly, a slight, blue feist dog burst from behind the log and started shrieking at me, lifting its feet in indignation and looking backwards at intervals as if for support from a source hidden from me by the rise of the log.

Then, for an instant, I saw a face above the six-foot loom of the trunk, and then the face was gone. I ran around the end of the log and saw a woman on horseback retreating at a dead run in the direction from which she had come. I could hear the splatting of the horse's feet in the wave wash and I could see in the slant of the rider's back that she was not party to the flight but was trying to stop and turn the horse. It was the horse who was alarmed at the sudden, unprecedented sight and stink of gringo behind a log on the black beach—not Mrs. Ybarra.

Mrs. Ybarra no doubt took an unenthusiastic view of me too. But she was a woman inured to the shocks of life on this beach. She was not the sort to turn back because of a stranger there, no matter how unaccounted for. She gradually dominated the horse and brought it to a grudging halt a hundred yards down the beach and turned it. I could see that it was an ash-colored *criollo* stallion—one of the tough, runty, and cruelly selected remnant of the old Spanish horse that somehow survived the odds against horseflesh on this tropical shore and that now, salt-cured, parasite-proof, and vampire-tolerant, and economical with its tissue-water as a camel, will single-foot all night in sand fetlock deep. The horse of the Mosquitia is almost a breed apart. Æsthetically it compares unfavorably with a true horse, but it is right for its milieu.

The example under Mrs. Ybarra had the odd, ratlike face and ewe-necked silhouette they all have. He came back toward me under pressure, against his judgment, his eyes rolling. He came because the will of his rider was stronger than his will.

As she approached, Mrs. Ybarra steered her mount down beach to pass well seaward of me, gripping the reins firmly and drumming at the horse's tight belly with her heels. She gave me a quick look.

"Adios," she said.

Adios said that way means you are going on by. In a matrix of circumstance such as this it becomes a bivalent greeting, a salutation with connotation that a parting will follow immediately. It is a hello-goodby, and a word that, as far as I know, has no counterpart in English or North American. Spanish can be shaded delicately. It is nowhere near so simple as my textbooks and teachers made out.

There was of course no reason at all why Mrs. Ybarra should not go on by. But at the moment she spoke I saw the pearly gleam of new turtle eggs in two arroba baskets swinging from her saddle; and this made it unthinkable that she should ride on and leave me with my dilemma.

So I said: *"Buenas tardes,"* and the shift in salutation changed our relationship at once and made it a point of courtesy for her to rein up, a bit warily, and see what my intentions were.

She was not the sort of woman you would expect to see on this beach, even supposing you were expecting women of any sort. She was a short, turnip-shaped woman with a thin-lipped Madonna's face and a mass of snuff-colored hair piled under a man's old felt hat tied on with a scarf. She had spindly Spanish legs and a big bosom bound in by a bodice of muslin.

She wore a brown cotton smock, and a skirt of the same stuff was cleverly tucked under and around her legs, because she rode astride and not side-saddle like the women in Honduras. Her racial origin and place in life were not evident from her appearance. Her skin was very dark, but she had nothing to do with the dark people of Tortuguero, who run mostly to Mosquito and Black Carib interbreeds with a sprinkling of black creoles from Bluefields and San Andrés. She looked like no Costa Rican I ever saw. Except for her almost black skin and reddish hair, and for the shameless way she straddled the high wooden packsaddle, she more closely approached the kind of women you see in the mountains of Matagalpa or of southern Honduras, where the century of hardship the old revolutions brought bred thin-faced women with more than their share of character. She had much in common with them and much in common with her horse. She was weather-beaten, but she had the quiet confidence that goes with a full stomach.

"Buenas tardes," she said, stopping her horse. "The widow of Ybarra from Panal, this side of Parismina."

I told her my name. I said I was studying the ways of turtles. I motioned toward the trunkback nest.

"Do you know what kind of turtle did that?" I said.

"Why not? *Es de canal*—a trunkback."

"That's what I thought," I said. "How do you know?"

"Only a trunkback tears up the beach like that. All this beach is torn up by trunkbacks. It's hard to ride except near the water."

I looked up and down the beach and for the first time noticed that the sand in front of the dunes had an oddly uneven topography that was not part of the wind-piled dune system, and not like any beach I had ever seen before.

"Some of that is where animals dig for eggs when the fleet of green turtles comes, but mostly it's trunkbacks that pile the sand like that. Like this nest here . . . But why don't you go on a way? I saw several carey nests in the light sand yonder, and some of green turtles—various. I dug two." She patted the side of one of the egg baskets.

"I don't want hawksbill eggs," I said, "or green turtle either. I'm looking for trunkback eggs."

"They're not as good as carey eggs. They have a little taste."

"I don't want to eat them," I said. "I want to measure them."

She looked at me deprecatingly. "They're this big. *Así de grande.*" She cupped her hand to show me how big.

"I mean exactly. And I want to take pictures of them."

"They are very deep. A yard—yard and a half. The animals can't find them. Even the tigers. Even the Siquirres dogs that dig out all the rest don't try to dig trunkback eggs."

"I don't care how long it takes," I said. "I would dig all afternoon if I knew there was a nest there. Maybe this one scratched and went back. Loggerheads do that."

She studied the tumbled sand for a moment. Then she wagged her finger from side to side in front of her face in the gesture of negation that all Latins use.

"Puso—" she said. *"Ahí puso."*

"But how do you find the nest?" I asked. "I've punched all around here and couldn't find a soft place anywhere."

Again she wagged her finger at me. "You didn't punch deep enough. There is no soft place in a *canal* nest. You just have to find it. Please, what time is it? Midday?"

I brushed the sweat-soaked sand from the face of my watch.

"A quarter after. Are you in a hurry?"

"Today the Spaniard pays the Mosquitos. I am going to collect a debt and I want to get there before they are all drunk. I saw the airplane Thursday, and they will all be drunk by dark."

I thought of the milk can of rum I had flown with and saw that she was probably right. The Spaniard she was talking about was Don Pedro, Yoyo's *mayordomo* at the Atlantic Trading Company at Tortuguero.

"How much is the debt?" I said.

"There are two of them. They add up to eight colones."

"All right, look. I'll pay you ten if you will help me find the turtle nest."

She looked at the sand in front of horse again, and then up at the sun. She sighed and swung a leg over the tall saddle frame and stepped to the ground.

"We will try it." She said it with no great enthusiasm.

She led the horse into the sprinkled shade of a ragged old mangineel, the only real tree anywhere on the foreshore, and tied the reins to a branch.

"That is a poison tree," I said.

"It doesn't molest horses."

"But how about your hands? You have to hold the reins."

"Don't worry. It doesn't molest me either. Only the juice, or the smoke when it burns."

"I wouldn't tie a horse to that tree for anything," I said.

"It's all right. You are a stranger here and haven't found yourself."

She drew a wasted sliver of a machete from a rawhide scabbard tied to the saddle. She walked back to the turtle nest and called to the feist and it came bouncing down from the beach grass, eager to serve her with all its talents. She leaned and scratched suggestively at the sand to interest the dog in the place.

"Huevos," she said.

I winced, because this word said by itself like that usually means something quite different; but the dog understood and began to dig in a crab hole six feet from the turtle nest.

"Don't be an imbecile," Mrs. Ybarra said. "Here—dig here!"

The dog dropped his ears, hurt by the tone of the words; then he moved over and started digging in the turtle nest.

"With green turtles and *careyes* Filin never deceives himself. With trunkbacks he doesn't serve. Let him dig here awhile. I have to go back there." She waved a hand toward the low scrub a hundred yards inland.

"Bueno." I thought she was excusing herself from me and prepared to stay and give what encouragement I could to the dog.

"No—I have to cut a stick. You come too. You can climb better."

We pushed through the sea grapes and sea oats and coco plums, and behind the dunes we came to a coppice of tightly spaced saplings. We stopped and Mrs. Ybarra peered about in the dense thicket until she found what she wanted.

"Aquel." She pointed into the dim interior of the thicket. "If you climb that *palito* and trim it, we can get it out."

I shinnied up the slim, smooth stem and trimmed off all the branches I could reach. Then I slid down and cut the trunk through at the ground and dragged it out into the clear. Mrs. Ybarra cut a five-foot section from the stem, skinned the bark from it, and tapered one end to a point.

"Ya," she said. "Maybe with this."

When we got back, the feist had lost interest in the turtle nest and was digging out another sand-crab hole.

"He doesn't serve," Mrs. Ybarra said.

She planted the tip of the stick in the center of the nest and pushed. The point grated to a stop in the dense sand two feet down. She tried again a foot away, with the same result. She punched a dozen holes and from each the stick emerged only dusted with the fine sand. She stopped and studied the site again on hands and knees, plucking at each twig or bit of debris that protruded above the plowed surface. After a while she found a newly broken end of beach morning-glory stem, and when she pulled on this a good three feet of green vine came out of the sand.

"Maybe here," she said. "The *canal* buried the vine."

She took up the stick and probed carefully all around where the vine had been. Still the rod broke through no nest roof and came out smeared with no yolk. Finally she stopped and shook her head, and sweat silently.

"It is *fregada,* this question of the *canal* nests," she said.

She wiped her eyes with the backs of her forearms. Her hair was falling out from under her hat, and the sweat-stuck sand had frosted the dark shine of her face. I thought I could see misgiving in her expression. I thought she must be leaning toward my view that this was a trial nest without eggs, such as loggerheads make.

"I don't believe there's anything here," I said.

"Don't deceive yourself. *Aquí puso*—she laid here. It is sure. Always it is like this. The *canal* is—ooo—very big. Her leg is like this—" She measured against her own thigh. "She reaches to a great depth, and she is heavy and she packs the sand back with her belly, harder than it was before. And the worst is, she plows so much ground it is hard to locate the nest. If you do find the eggs they are too big to eat with comfort. It is not worth the trouble. But maybe if we both pushed on the stick— The place should be exactly there."

I have seen a water-witch point out the spot for a well with the judicious precision with which Mrs. Ybarra aimed the tip of her stick. She sighted as if she were aiming a rifle at the head of a snake.

"Exactly there," she repeated.

She stuck the point in the sand and we both leaned on the shaft. It broke with a snap and split back to our hands.

"It broke," Mrs. Ybarra said. "The wood was tender. Look, do you want to try any more? I think it will be easier if you go out at night and find the *canal* when she is laying and before she has covered. Any time when the moon is over the sea, not over the land. In the black sand pieces they come out every night—one, two, three—to lay."

I said I thought she was right. I dug in my pocket and from under the sand there brought out some Costa Rican bills. I counted ten colones and held them out to her, saying that I was grateful for her help and was sorry she had got so hot and sandy.

"Ah, no," she said. "I can't accept that. I said I would find the eggs. You owe me nothing. I'll reach the village in plenty of time."

"No, look—I stopped you. I'm going to put the money in your saddlebag." . . .

I told her I was going on. I must have seemed depressed at the prospect, because she said:

"All right, there's a *cocal* [a coco fringe] no more than there—just a little way. You can get a *pipa* there [a drinking coconut], and there is shade. Then if you go on six miles there is another *cocal,* and my house is there.

If you go that far, it is almost certain that I can show you a *canal* tonight, laying on the high tide."

I thanked her and said I couldn't go that far. Without her noticing, I slipped the money into the basket where her shoes were.

"I'm going to dig another *canal* nest," I said. "I don't believe this one laid."

"Ay-eeee," she yelped. "You will kill yourself for nothing. She laid. This one laid. Right there. No *canal* nest will be easier to dig than this one."

"O.K.," I said. "But I'm not going to dig here any more. I'll be seeing you."

She gave me a look of what I think was pity, then set her mount in motion with her bare heels, guided him into the surf-wash, and squeezed him into the mincing single-foot he would hold all the way to Tortuguero. Then she turned and waved.

"Adios, pues," she said.

The little feist saw her leaving and ran to take the lead. A first sudden breath of the afternoon breeze wiped the gleam from the water and turned it black. The hoof-splash of the horse faded in the distance, and when it was gone the only sounds were the roll of the waves and the fitful piping of the tern as it slipped and tilted on the swelling trade wind.

HE SHOULD HAVE BECOME EXTINCT

FROM *The Voice of the Desert*

JOSEPH WOOD KRUTCH

Like Mary Austin and D. H. Lawrence before him, Joseph Wood Krutch would seem to have found in the American Southwest a land of deeper meanings, uncluttered by the passing orthodoxies of our machined contemporary life. The desert is a land of long and distant views, its seasons slow and inevitable, its flora and fauna involved in an endless adaptation.

Krutch was a professor of drama and a theatre critic. It was some half-dozen years ago that he gave up both professions and moved to Arizona. In *The Voice of the Desert,* from which this selection is taken, he writes of this sun-baked land he has chosen with the contented passion of a middle-aged man who has quietly and unexpectedly fallen in love.

ACCORDING TO AN ANCIENT AND ANONYMOUS JOCOSITY THE BRAVEST MAN WHO ever lived must have been the first to eat an oyster—alive.

A soberer judgment might want to make a case for that equally forgotten hero of paleolithic times who first domesticated fire. It must have been one of the first of his home-building achievements, but no wolf destined to turn into a dog and no buffalo destined to become a cow can possibly have seemed one-tenth so dangerous as devouring flame. Early man, like every other animal, must have long been accustomed to flee from it in abject terror. We shall never know what Prometheus first dared snatch a bit from some forest fire or some erupting volcano. But when he put it down in the middle of the domestic circle he must have said, "This I can tame and use."

Long before even his day, courage of some sort must have been a characteristic of living things and even the tamer of fire was not the first hero. Perhaps the first and greatest of all was whatever little blob of jelly—not yet either plant or animal but a little of both—first consented to take on the responsibility of being alive at all. And surely the second greatest was that plant or animal which first dared leave the water where, ever since the very dawn of creation, every other organism before it had been born and died. Men are talking now about journeys to the moon or to Mars, but neither is more unsuited to human life than the bare earth was to the first creatures who risked it.

For millions of years only the submerged areas of the earth had been habitable. It was in water that the first hypothetical one-celled creatures, too insubstantial to leave fossil remains, must have been generated. None ventured out of it during millions of years while stony skeletons were evolved and became the earliest sure evidence of life in some of the oldest rocks. In water also stayed all the wormlike and squidlike and shrimplike creatures which represented, in their day, the highest development of life. Meanwhile, during the major part of the earth's history, during considerably more than half the time since life began, all dry land was desert to a degree almost inconceivable—without soil of any kind, as bare as the moon, and subject to no changes except those produced by geological forces. Volcanoes flowed and mountains heaved. Rain falling on an earth without any plant cover to protect it washed cruel gullies as remorselessly as they are cut in the most unqualified "bad lands" of today. Had any creature of that time been capable of thought, life in any medium other than water would have seemed as fantastic as life without an atmosphere would seem to us.

Then at some time, geologists say it was probably something like three hundred million years ago, the first living thing dared to expose itself temporarily to the deadly air. If it was an animal, as some think most probable, then it must have rushed back (or perhaps ducked back) before the gills through which it breathed could dry out. It could hardly have done much more during many thousands of years after the first bold venture, because it could not actually live beyond easy reach of water until its whole anatomy and physiology had undergone fundamental changes. But patience is a quality which the universe seems never to have lacked (until man came along) and it was always the animal which broke most rashly with all previous tradition, which presently became the most highly developed and the most competent—as well as the least patient.

So far as I am concerned I see no reason to apologize for calling that animal a "hero" or for referring to his "courage." Such terms can have no real meaning except in connection with something which is alive and when we talk about "the suffering earth" or the "nobility" of a mountain range we are merely using a figure of speech. But it is hard to say just where reality begins or to decide just which animal or even which plant is still too simple to be capable of something genuinely analogous to daring and courage. If these virtues are real in man, then they are real because they began to be so as soon as there was anything in the universe which could defy law and habit by risking something which had never been done before.

Few of us are so committed to a merely mechanical behaviorism that we would refuse to call brave and adventurous the first human pioneers who came to live in the American West. So in their own way were the plants and animals who had preceded them there. And so, *a fortiori,* were those far back in time who first dared learn how to adapt themselves to that desert which all dry land then was. If daring to do what our intelligence recognizes as dangerous constitutes "courage," then the animal who similarly rejects the imperatives of its instinct is exhibiting a virtue at least analogous, and so, in some still dimmer fashion, is the simplest creature, animal or even vegetable, which refuses to obey its long established reflexes. The whole course of evolution is directed by just such courageous acts. It must have its countless unremembered heroes who created diversity by daring to do what no member of its species had ever done before.

Most scientists, I am well aware, would object strenuously to any such line of reasoning. But then many scientists are firmly convinced that in man himself there is also no such thing as either daring or courage as distinguished from a reflex, congenital or conditioned. And perhaps that conclusion is inevitable if you begin by denying their reality to all creatures "lower" than man. If every other animal is a machine then why shouldn't human beings be machines also. And if to speak of the "courage" of some very lowly creature is to indulge in exaggeration, it is at least an exaggeration opposite and corrective to a more usual one.

Is it possible, one may ask, to guess at the identity of the first great pioneer and radical who came to dry land? Or is it, like the song the Sirens sang, "beyond all conjecture?" Does he have a name and can we honor him by saying, "But for you and your enterprise I might still be a fish"? At least our own direct amphibious ancestors came to land only because that pioneer's descendants were there to be eaten!

Well, if the paleontologists are right—and their evidence seems pretty good—we can answer this question. As a matter of fact, I met only the day before yesterday one of the almost unchanged relatives of the first air-breathing creatures, and he did not seem especially proud. He crawled on eight legs out from under a board in my storeroom and I confess that, though I do not do such things lightly, I put my foot upon him. Before he was crushed into nothing he was about two inches long and pale straw in color. He carried two pinchers before him and over his back he carried a long tail with a sting at its end. He was, in short, one of the least popular of desert dwellers—a scorpion.

Finding out about one's ancestors, especially correlative ones, is often a risky business and perhaps most people would rather not know how much all of us are indebted to this rather unattractive creature. But so far as geologists can tell from the fossils they study and date, the first animal actually capable of breathing air was not only a member of the scorpion kind but amazingly like the one we step on when we find him.

To even the most uninstructed eye a scorpion fossilized during the Silurian or Devonian epoch—say something like three hundred million years ago—is unmistakably a scorpion. If one of them were to come to life again and crawl out of his stone sarcophagus into your desert patio, you would not be particularly surprised by his appearance unless you happened to be a biologist especially devoted to the study of that group of animals called arachnids to which the scorpion belongs. There are several species now common hereabout—some, like the victim of my brutality, only two inches long and some several times that length. A three hundred million year old specimen would look to the casual eye like merely a sort one had not happened to see before and not much more different from the familiar kinds than they are from one another.

In the highly improbable event that a living dinosaur should be found in some African or South American hiding place, it would create quite a stir in even the popular press and any big-game hunter would count it a high distinction to shoot one. Yet anyone who happens to live in one of the many parts of the earth where scorpions abound can have the privilege of stepping upon a creature who has been going about his business (such as it is) far longer than any dinosaur went about dinosaur business. As a matter of fact, scorpions put in their appearance more years before the first dinosaur than have slipped away since the last known dinosaur decided that he and his kind had had their day.

The horseshoe crab and the gingko tree are sometimes called "living fossils," and the epithet has more recently been applied to that strange fish known as Latimeria which was taken not many years ago off the coast of Africa in spite of the fact that it, as well as all its immediate relatives, was supposed to have become extinct a very long time ago. Yet no sort of fish is much older than the scorpion, and the horseshoe crab is not as nearly like any very ancient form as the scorpion in my storeroom is like his Silurian ancestor. He may not be much to look at, but the least we can do is to regard him in the spirit of the naturalist Sutherland when he contemplated the living members of a tribe somewhat less ancient than the scorpions: "If the test of nobility is antiquity of family, then the cockroach that hides behind the kitchen sink is the true aristocrat. He does not date back merely to the three brothers who came over in 1640 or to William the Conqueror. Wherever there have been great epoch-making movements of people he has been with them heart and soul. . . . Since ever a ship turned a foamy furrow in the sea he has been a passenger, not a paying one certainly but still a passenger. But man himself is but a creature of the last twenty minutes or so compared with the cockroach, for, from its crevice by the kitchen sink, it can point its antennae to the coal in the hod and say: 'When that was being made my family was already well established.' " Scorpions have never been as closely associated with man as the cockroach, but they may not consider that anything to be ashamed of and on the score of antiquity they have a right to snub the cockroaches as upstarts, relatively speaking at least.

It may seem odd that they have hung on so long while changing so little. It may seem even odder that they should be found in deserts despite the fact that they are so similar to the scorpions which had recently left the water. But they do not insist upon its being dry and some species will even tolerate a certain amount of cold. Though there are none in New England or in the Great Lakes region, they are found in the Alps and on our continent as far north as southern Canada. On the whole, however, they prefer warm climates and they have been in the Southwest for a long, long time. Tracks almost precisely like those made by a living species have been found in the Coconino sandstone which was laid down in Permian times or not more than a million or a million and a half years after scorpions took the first drastic step out of the water.

Most people today underestimate the intelligence and awareness of most creatures other than man because recent official science has often encouraged them to do so. But the scorpion is probably even dumber than he looks. At first sight you would have no reason to suppose that his senses were much less keen or his awareness much less dim than those of any common insect. But they are. By comparison even a beetle, to say nothing of a bee, an ant or a fly, is a miracle of alertness and competence. The life which I extinguished when I stepped on my specimen was about as dim as we can imagine life to be. The scorpion's brain stopped growing not long after he left the water and braininess had not got very far by then. . . .

So much, then, for this creature which, only a few pages back, I insisted upon endowing with "daring" and with "courage" because it ventured upon the land some three hundred millions of years ago. Judged even by the acuteness of its senses, much less by its intelligence, it belongs very low indeed in the hierarchy of life. What a long, long way it was from, say, the scorpion's eye—too primitive almost to deserve the name—to the eye of even so primitive an insect as the praying mantis. Yet the fact remains that between the scorpion and man himself the distance is not nearly so great as it is between the scorpion and anything which does not live at all. The difference between seeing, no matter how dimly, and not seeing at all is greater than the difference between the scorpion's vision and ours. It is easier to imagine how, given time enough, a scorpion could become a man than it is to imagine how sea water and mineral substances could have become a scorpion. Primitive as his eye is, it is indubitably an eye. Its owner can see with it—however dimly. And seeing itself is a process beyond comprehension. It involves awareness of some sort. Perhaps the difference between the scorpion's courage and what is possible for us is no greater than that between his eyesight and ours. Yet who would refuse to use the word "seeing" to describe what even a scorpion can do? Why should we not assume that his courage and ours are no less essentially, though remotely, the same?

Granting all this it is, however, still possible to wonder why this once so adventurous creature became so soon a very paragon of conservatism. As the first air-breather he may very well have been the remote ancestor of all the insects who were to proceed from originality to originality until they became capable of achievements which even man cannot wholly grasp. But this prototype of the insect himself continues to crawl upon the desert and to poison human beings with his ancient venom millions of years after almost all the other creatures which were even his near contemporaries gave up their effort to survive in their original forms. Like the horseshoe crab and the gingko tree, he should have become extinct eons ago. But he has changed even less than they and become one of the most striking examples not of evolution but of a refusal to evolve. Some of the irrational distaste and fear which the sight of him inspires in most people is partly the result of their dim half-realization that he comes down from a past too remote not to suggest unimaginable horrors. He is a living reminder of "the dark and backward abysm of time" and, like the earliest myths of the human race, he suggests the monstrous beginnings of instinct and mind and emotion. He is altogether too much like some bad dream and we would rather not be reminded of it.

As to the mystery of why he is still here, we shall have to be content to put him down as a left-over without knowing precisely how he managed to achieve that humble status. A long time ago he wandered into the desert pretty much what he is now and found that he could survive there, partly no doubt because his demands are modest and he can satisfy them without exposing himself very much. He eats insects which are plentiful and he can do without water as well as without food for long periods. Like the members of certain very old human families he has little to be proud of except the achievements of his remote ancestors, and if he were capable of pride he might, like them, grow prouder just in proportion as he comes to be more and more remote in time from them and their virtues. Like such people, he also makes us wonder what became of all the greatness which was once in his race. Did the scorpion use up all the daring of his tribe in his one great exploit all those millions of years ago? Did he squander it all at once like the wits at the Mermaid Tavern, each of whom seemed resolved to:

Put his whole wit in one jest
And live a fool the rest of his dull life?

It is a pleasant fancy but one had better not put it into words when there are any paleontologists about. We honor the scorpion for his early achievement but it has to be admitted that he doesn't seem to have done much to be proud of in recent years.

5

Men Fight on the Earth

Whether war is a necessary element in human evolution as some have claimed may be questioned, but that it has been one of man's governing preoccupations since the earliest days of recorded history is a matter of record. The first of the organized wars of which our archaeologists have uncovered evidences were fought in the fertile crescent of the Nile and the Caspian steppe lands between the primeval argricultural and pastoral communities. After Lepanto in 1571 the battleground shifted to the Mediterranean lands and southwest Asia, then to the coastal lands of the Atlantic. With the industrial revolution the stage for battle extended to take in the whole of the known world. The trenches that ancient man once dug around his village now stretch across a continent, the crater blasted by a shell will now engulf a town, and a single atom bomb will poison the earth on which a city stands. The dictionary of war too has altered in these last hundred years. Such words as glory, crusade, victory tend to give way, in contemporary literature, to rubble, waste, and random killing. It is from this modern literature, more rigorously defined by death and devastation, that we have for the most part made our choices.

ROBERT DE MAMINES, A FRENCH CAPTAIN OF THE 15TH CENTURY, IN HIS SUIT OF ARMOR

THE GEOGRAPHY OF THE TRENCH

FROM *Good-bye to All That*

ROBERT GRAVES

The first World War—it is terrifying to think how quickly we have grown used to this casual numbering—was a war of trenches. There were millions of men in these pits that were dug across Europe, and with a strangely resigned elasticity, they adapted to underground living, to mud and lice and dirt. In this selection from his wartime autobiography, Robert Graves sees the trenches for the first time.

Graves has won a large reputation both as poet and novelist. The London *Times Literary Supplement,* that arbiter of English writing, ranks him with the great for his unadorned, lucid prose style.

AT CAMBRIN VILLAGE, WHICH WAS ABOUT A MILE FROM THE FRONT TRENCHES, we were taken into a ruined house. It had been a chemist's shop and the coloured glass lights were still in the window. It was the billet of the Welsh company quartermaster-sergeants. Here we were issued with gas-respirators and field dressings. This was the first respirator issued in France. It was a gauze pad filled with chemically-treated cotton waste, to be tied across the mouth and nose. It seems it was useless against German gas. I never put it to the test. A week or two later came the "smoke-helmet," a greasy grey-felt bag with a talc window to look through, but no mouthpiece. This also was probably ineffective against gas. The talc was always cracking and there were leaks where it was stitched into the helmet.

These were early days of trench-warfare, the days of the jam-tin bomb and the gas-pipe trench-mortar. It was before Lewis or Stokes guns, steel helmets, telescopic rifle-sights, gas-shells, pill-boxes, tanks, trench-raids, or any of the later improvements of trench-warfare.

After a meal of bread, bacon, rum and bitter stewed tea sickly with sugar, we went up through the broken trees to the east of the village and up a long trench to battalion headquarters. The trench was cut through red clay. I had a torch with me which I kept flashed on the ground. Hundreds of field mice and frogs were in the trench. They had fallen in and had no way out. The light dazzled them and we could not help treading on them. So I put the torch back in my pocket. We had no picture of what the trenches would be like, and were not far off the state of mind in which one young soldier joined us a week or two later. He called out very excitedly to old Burford who was cooking up a bit of stew in a dixie, apart from the others: "Hi, mate, where's the battle? I want to do my bit."

The trench was wet and slippery. The guide was giving hoarse directions all the time. "Hole right." "Wire high." "Wire low." "Deep place here, sir." "Wire low." I had never been told about the field telephone wires. They were fastened by staples to the side of the trench, and when it rained the staples were always falling out and the wire falling down and tripping people up. If it sagged too much one stretched it across the top of the trench to the other side to correct the sag, and then it would catch one's head. The holes were the sump-pits used for draining the trenches. We were now under rifle-fire. I always found rifle-fire more trying than shell-fire. The gunner was usually, I knew, firing not at people but at map-references–cross-roads, likely artillery positions, houses that suggested billets for troops, and so on. Even when an observation officer in an aeroplane or captive balloon or on a church spire was directing the gun-fire it seemed unaimed, somehow. But a rifle bullet even when fired blindly always had the effect of seeming aimed. And we could hear a shell coming and take some sort of cover, but the rifle bullet gave no warning. So though we learned not to duck a rifle bullet, because once it was heard it must have missed, it gave us a worse feeling of danger. Rifle bullets in the open went hissing into the grass without much noise, but when we were in a trench the bullets, going over the hollow, made a tremendous crack. Bullets often struck the barbed wire in front of the trenches, which turned them and sent them spinning in a head-over-heels motion—ping! rockety-ockety-ockety-ockety into the woods behind.

Battalion headquarters was a dug-out in the reserve line about a quarter of a mile from the front companies. The colonel, a twice-wounded regular, shook hands with us and offered us the whisky bottle. He said that we were welcome, and hoped that we would soon grow to like the regiment as much as our own. It was a cosy dug-out for so early a stage of trench-warfare. (This sector had only recently been taken over from the French, who knew how to make themselves comfortable. It had been a territorial division of men in the forties who had a local armistice with the Germans opposite; there was no firing and apparently even civilian traffic through the lines.) There was an ornamental lamp, a clean cloth, and polished silver on the table. The colonel, adjutant, doctor, second-in-command, and signalling officer were at dinner. It was civilized cooking, with fresh meat and vegetables. Pictures were pasted on the walls, which were wallpapered; there were beds with spring mattresses, a gramophone, easy chairs. It was hard to reconcile this with accounts I had read of troops standing waist-deep in mud and gnawing a biscuit while shells burst all around. We were posted to our companies. I went to C Company. "Captain Dunn is your company commander," said the adjutant. "The soundest officer in the battalion. By the way, remind him that I want that list of D.C.M. recommendations for the last show sent in at once, but not more than two names, or else they won't give us any. Four is about the ration for the battalion in a dud show."

Our guide took us up to the front line. We passed a group of men huddled over a brazier. They were wearing waterproof capes, for it had now started to rain, and cap-comforters, because the weather was cold. They were little men, daubed with mud, and they were talking quietly together in Welsh. Although they could see we were officers, they did not jump to their feet and salute. I thought that this was a convention of the trenches, and indeed I knew that it was laid down somewhere in the military textbooks that the courtesy of the salute was to be dispensed with in battle. But I was wrong; it was just slackness. We overtook a fatigue-party struggling up the trench loaded with timber lengths and bundles of sandbags, cursing plaintively as they slipped into sump-holes and entangled their burdens in the telephone wire. Fatigue-parties were always encumbered by their rifles and equipment, which it was a crime ever to have out of reach. When we had squeezed past this party we had to stand aside to let a stretcher-case past. "Who's the poor bastard, Dai?" the guide asked the leading stretcher-bearer. "Sergeant Gallagher," Dai answered. "He thought he saw a Fritz in No Man's Land near our wire, so the silly b—r takes one of them new issue percussion bombs and shoots it at 'im. Silly b—r aims too low, it hits the top of the parapet and bursts back. Deoul! man, it breaks his silly f—ing jaw and blows a great lump from his silly f—ing face, whatever. Poor silly b—r! Not worth sweating to get him back! He's put paid to, whatever." The wounded man had a sandbag over his face. He was dead when they got him back to the dressing-station. I was tired out by the time I got to company headquarters. I was carrying a pack-valise like the men, and my belt was hung with all the usual furnishings—revolver, field-glasses, compass, whisky-flask, wire-cutters, periscope, and a lot more. A Christmas-tree that was called. (These were the days in which officers went out to France with swords and had them sharpened by the armourer before sailing. But I had been advised to leave my sword back in the billet where we had tea; I never saw it again or bothered about it.) I was hot and sweaty; my hands were sticky with the clay from the side of the trench. C Company headquarters was a two-roomed timber-built shelter in the side of a trench connecting the front and support lines. Here were table-cloth and lamp again, whisky-bottle and glasses, shelves with books and magazines, a framed picture of General Joffre, a large mirror, and bunks in the next room. I reported to the company commander.

I had expected him to be a middle-aged man with a breastful of medals, with whom I would have to be formal; but Dunn was actually two months younger than myself. He was one of the fellowship of "only survivors." Captain Miller of the Black Watch in the same division was another. Miller had only escaped from the Rue du Bois massacre by swimming down a flooded trench. He has carried on his surviving trade ever since. Only survivors have great reputations. Miller used to be pointed at in the streets when the battalion was back in reserve billets. "See that fellow. That's Jack Miller. Out from the start and hasn't got it yet." Dunn had not let the war affect his morale at all. He greeted me very easily with: "Well, what's the news from England? Oh, sorry, first I must introduce you. This is Walker–clever chap, comes from Cambridge and fancies himself as an athlete. This is Jenkins, one of those patriotic chaps who chucked up his job to come here. This is Price, who only joined us yesterday, but we like him; he brought some damn good whisky with him. Well, how long is the war going to last and who's winning? We don't know a thing out here. And what's all this talk about war-babies? Price pretends he knows nothing about them." I told them about the war and asked them about the trenches.

"About trenches," said Dunn. "Well, we don't know as much about trenches as the French do and not near as much as Fritz does. We can't expect Fritz to help, but the French might do something. They are greedy; they won't let us have the benefit of their inventions. What wouldn't we give for parachute-lights and their aerial torpedoes! But there's no connection between the two armies except when there's a battle on, and then we generally let each other down.

"When I was out here first, all that we did in the trenches was to paddle about in water and use our rifles. We didn't think of them as places to live in, they were just temporary inconveniences. Now we work all the time we are here, not only for safety but for health. Night and day. First, the firesteps, then building traverses, improving the communication trenches, and so on; lastly, on our personal comfort–shelters and dug-outs. There was a territorial battalion that used to relieve us. They were hopeless. They used to sit down in the trench and say: 'Oh, my God, this is the limit.' They'd pull out pencil and paper and write home about it. Did no work on the traverses or on fire positions. Consequence—they lost half their men from frostbite and rheumatism, and one day the Germans broke in and scuppered a lot more of them. They allowed the work we'd done in the trench to go to ruin and left the whole place like a sewage-farm for us to take over again.

We were sick as muck. We reported them several times to brigade headquarters, but they never got any better. Slack officers, of course. Well, they got smashed, as I say, and were sent away to be lines-of-communication troops. Now we work with the First South Wales Borderers. They're all right. Awful chaps those territorial swine. Usen't to trouble about latrines at all; left food about and that encouraged rats; never filled a sandbag. I only once saw a job of work that they did. That was a steel loop-hole they put in. But they put it facing square to the front and quite unmasked, so they had two men killed at it—absolute death-trap. About our chaps. They're all right, but not as right as they ought to be. The survivors of the show ten days ago are feeling pretty low, and the big new draft doesn't know anything yet."

"Listen," said Walker, "there's too much firing going on. The men have got the wind up over something. Waste of ammunition, and if Fritz knows we're jumpy he'll give us an extra bad time. I'll go up and stop them."

Dunn went on. "These Welshmen are peculiar. They won't stand being shouted at. They'll do anything if you explain the reason for it. They will do and die, but they have to know their reason why. The best way to make them behave is not to give them too much time to think. Work them off their feet. They are good workmen. Officers must work too, not only direct the work. Our time-table is like this. Breakfast at eight o'clock in the morning, clean trenches and inspect rifles, work all morning; lunch at twelve, work again from one till about six, when the men feed again. "Stand-to" at dusk for about an hour, work all night, "stand-to" for an hour before dawn. That's the general program. Then there's sentry duty. The men do two-hour sentry spells, then work two hours, then sleep two hours. At night sentries are doubled, so our working parties are smaller. We officers are on duty all day and divide up the night in three-hourly watches." He looked at his wrist watch. "I say," he said, "that carrying-party must have got the R.E. stuff by now. Time we all got to work. Look here, Graves, you lie down and have a doss on that bunk. I want you to take the watch before "stand-to." I'll wake you up and show you round. Where the hell's my revolver? I don't like to go out without that. Hello, Walker, what was wrong?"

Walker laughed. "A chap from the new draft. He had never fired his musketry course at Cardiff, and tonight he fired ball for the first time. It seemed to go to his head. He'd had a brother killed up at Ypres and he said he was going to avenge him. So he blazed off all his own ammunition at nothing, and two bandoliers out of the ammunition-box besides. They call him the Human Maxim now. His foresight's misty with heat. Corporal Parry should have stopped him; but he was just leaning up against the traverse and shrieking with laughter. I gave them both a good cursing. Some other new chaps started blazing away, too. Fritz retaliated with machine-guns and whizz-bangs. No casualties. I don't know why. It's all quiet now. Everybody ready?"

They went out and I rolled up in my blanket and fell asleep. Dunn woke me about one o'clock. "Your watch," he said. I jumped out of the bunk with a rustle of straw; my feet were sore and clammy in my boots. I was cold, too. "Here's the rocket-pistol and a few flares. Not a bad night. It's stopped raining. Put your equipment on over your raincoat or you won't be able to get at your revolver. Got a torch? Good. About this flare business. Don't use the pistol too much. We haven't many flares, and if there's an attack we will want as many as we can get. But use it if you think that there is something doing. Fritz is always sending up flare lights, he's got as many as he wants."

He showed me round the line. The battalion frontage was about eight hundred yards. Each company held two hundred of these with two platoons in the front line and two platoons in the support line about a hundred yards back. Dunn introduced me to the platoon sergeants, more particularly to Sergeant Eastmond of the platoon to which I was posted. He asked Sergeant Eastmond to give me any information that I wanted, then went back to sleep, telling me to wake him up at once if anything was wrong. I was left in charge of the line. Sergeant Eastmond was busy with a working-party, so I went round by myself. The men of the working-party, who were building up the traverses with sandbags (a traverse, I learned, was a safety-buttress in the trench), looked curiously at me. They were filling sandbags with earth, piling them up bricklayer fashion, with headers and stretchers alternating, then patting them flat with spades. The sentries stood on the fire-step at the corners of the traverses, stamping their feet and blowing on their fingers. Every now and then they peered over the top for a few seconds. Two parties, each of an N.C.O. and two men, were out in the company listening-posts, connected with the front trench by a sap about fifty yards long. The German front line was about three hundred yards beyond them. From berths hollowed in the sides of the trench and curtained with sandbags came the grunt of sleeping men.

I jumped up on the fire-step beside the sentry and cautiously raising my head stared over the parapet. I could see nothing except the wooden pickets supporting our protecting barbed-wire entanglement and a dark patch or two of bushes beyond. The darkness seemed to move and shake about as I looked at it; the bushes started travelling, singly at first, then both together. The pickets were doing the same. I was glad of the sentry beside me; his name, he told me, was Beaumont. "They're quiet tonight, sir," he said, "a relief going on; I think so, surely." I said: "It's funny how those bushes seem to move." "Aye, they do play queer tricks. Is this your first spell in trenches, sir?" A German flare shot up, broke into bright flame, dropped slowly and went hissing into the grass just behind our trench, showing up the bushes and pickets. Instinctively I moved. "It's bad to do that, sir," he said, as a rifle bullet cracked and seemed to pass right between us. "Keep still, sir, and they can't spot you. Not but what a flare is a bad thing to have fall on you. I've seen them burn a hole in a man."

I spent the rest of my watch in acquainting myself with the geography of the trench-section, finding how easy it was to get lost among *culs de sac* and disused alleys. Twice I overshot the company frontage and wandered among the Munsters on the left. Once I tripped and fell with a splash into deep mud. At last my watch was ended with the first signs of dawn. I passed the word along the line for the company to stand-to arms. The N.C.O.'s whispered hoarsely into the dug-outs: "Stand-to, stand-to," and out the men tumbled with their rifles in their hands. As I went towards company headquarters to wake the officers I saw a man lying on his face in a machine-gun shelter. I stopped and said: "Stand-to, there." I flashed my torch on him and saw that his foot was bare. The machine-gunner beside him said: "No good talking to him, sir." I asked: "What's wrong? What's he taken his boot and sock off for?" I was ready for anything odd in the trenches. "Look for yourself, sir," he said. I shook the man by the arm and noticed suddenly that the back of his head was blown out. The first corpse that I saw in France was this suicide. He had taken off his boot and sock to pull the trigger of his rifle with his toe; the muzzle was in his mouth. "Why did he do it?" I said. "He was in the last push, sir, and that sent him a bit queer, and on top of that he got bad news from Limerick about his girl and another chap." He was not a Welshman, but belonged to the Munsters; their machine-guns were at the extreme left of our company. The suicide had already been reported and two Irish officers came up. "We've had two or three of these lately," one of them told me. Then he said to the other: "While I remember, Callaghan, don't forget to write to his next-of-kin. Usual sort of letter, cheer them up, tell them he died a soldier's death, anything you like. I'm not going to report it as suicide."

At stand-to rum and tea were served out. I had a look at the German trenches through a periscope—a streak of sandbags four hundred yards away. Some of these were made of coloured stuff, whether for camouflage or from a shortage of plain canvas I do not know. There was no sign of the enemy, except for a wisp or two of wood-smoke where they, too, were boiling up a hot drink. Between us and them was a flat meadow with cornflowers, marguerites and poppies growing in the long grass, a few shell holes, the bushes I had seen the night before, the wreck of an aeroplane, our barbed wire and theirs. A thousand yards away was a big ruined house, behind that a red-brick village (Auchy), poplars and haystacks, a tall chimney, another village (Haisnes). Half-right was a pithead and smaller slag-heaps. La Bassée lay half-left; the sun caught the weathervane of the church and made it twinkle.

I went off for a sleep.

RAVAGING A MEDIEVAL TOWN

A SHEER WALL OF MOVING EARTH

FROM *Crevasse*

WILLIAM FAULKNER

This story of soldiers trapped in a cave-in is William Faulkner in an unexpected dimension, one unfamiliar to the large public for whom his name is associated with the clinical novels of degeneracy and corruption in the deep South which won him the Nobel Prize. Here he writes in a simpler prose and with a compassion rarely to be found in his Sartoris novels, but even this earlier writing has a nightmare quality, as though one were looking at a world darkly reflected through distorting lenses.

THE PARTY GOES ON, SKIRTING THE EDGE OF THE BARRAGE WEAVING DOWN INTO shell craters old and new, crawling out again. Two men half drag, half carry between them a third, while two others carry the three rifles. The third man's head is bound in a bloody rag; he stumbles his aimless legs along, his head lolling, sweat channeling slowly down his mud-crusted face.

The barrage stretches on and on across the plain, distant, impenetrable. Occasionally a small wind comes up from nowhere and thins the dun smoke momentarily upon clumps of bitten poplars. The party enters and crosses a field which a month ago was sown to wheat and where yet wheatspears thrust and cling stubbornly in the churned soil, among scraps of metal and seething hunks of cloth.

It crosses the field and comes to a canal bordered with tree stumps sheared roughly at a symmetrical five-foot level. The men flop and drink of the contaminated water and fill their water bottles. The two bearers let the wounded man slip to earth; he hangs lax on the canal bank with both arms in the water and his head too, had not the others held him up. One of them raises water in his helmet, but the wounded man cannot swallow. So they set him upright and the other holds the helmet brim to his lips and refills the helmet and pours the water on the wounded man's head, sopping the bandage. Then he takes a filthy rag from his pocket and dries the wounded man's face with clumsy gentleness.

The captain, the subaltern and the sergeant, still standing, are poring over a soiled map. Beyond the canal the ground rises gradually; the canal cutting reveals the chalk formation of the land in pallid strata. The captain puts the map away and the sergeant speaks the men to their feet, not loud. The two bearers raise the wounded man and they follow the canal bank, coming after a while to a bridge formed by a water-logged barge hull lashed bow and stern to either bank, and so pass over. Here they halt again while once more the captain and the subaltern consult the map.

Gunfire comes across the pale spring noon like a prolonged clashing of hail on an endless metal roof. As they go on the chalky soil rises gradually underfoot. The ground is dryly rough, shaling, and the going is harder still for the two who carry the wounded man. But when they would stop the wounded man struggles and wrenches free and staggers on alone, his hands at his head, and stumbles, falling. The bearers catch and raise him and hold him muttering between them and wrenching his arms. He is muttering ". . . bonnet . . ." and he frees his hands and tugs again at his bandage. The commotion passes forward. The captain looks back and stops; the party halts also, unbidden, and lowers rifles.

"A's pickin at's bandage, sir-r," one of the bearers tells the captain. They let the man sit down between them; the captain kneels beside him.

". . . bonnet . . . bonnet," the man mutters. The captain loosens the bandage. The sergeant extends a water bottle and the captain wets the bandage and lays his hand on the man's brow. The others stand about, looking on with a kind of sober, detached interest. The captain rises. The bearers raise the wounded man again. The sergeant speaks them into motion.

They gain the crest of the ridge. The ridge slopes westward into a plateau slightly rolling. Southward, beneath its dun pall, the barrage still rages; westward and northward about the shining empty plain smoke rises lazily here and there above clumps of trees. But this is the smoke of burning things, burning wood and not powder, and the two officers gaze from beneath their hands, the men halting again without order and lowering arms.

"Gad, sir," the subaltern says suddenly in a high, thin voice; "it's houses burning! They're retreating! Beasts! Beasts!"

" 'Tis possible," the captain says, gazing beneath his hand. "We can get around that barrage now. Should be a road just yonder." He strides on again.

"For-rard," the sergeant says, in that tone not loud. The men slope arms once more with unquestioning docility.

The ridge is covered with a tough, gorselike grass. Insects buzz in it, zip from beneath their feet and fall to slatting again beneath the shimmering noon. The wounded man is babbling again. At intervals they pause and give him water and wet the bandage again, then two others exchange with the bearers and they hurry the man on and close up again.

The head of the line stops; the men jolt prodding into one another like a train of freight cars stopping. At the captain's feet lies a broad shallow depression in which grows a sparse, dead-looking grass like clumps of bayonets thrust up out of the earth. It is too big to have been made by a small shell, and too shallow to have been made by a big one. It bears no traces of having been made by anything at all, and they look quietly down into it. "Queer," the subaltern says. "What do you fancy could have made it?"

The captain does not answer. He turns. They circle the depression, looking down into it quietly at they pass it. But they have no more than passed it when they come upon another one, perhaps not quite so large. "I didn't know they had anything that could make that," the subaltern says. Again the captain does not answer. They circle this one also and keep on along the crest of the ridge. On the other hand the ridge sheers sharply downward stratum by stratum of pallid eroded chalk.

A shallow ravine gashes its crumbling yawn abruptly across their path. The captain changes direction again, paralleling the ravine, until shortly afterward the ravine turns at right angles and goes on in the direction of their march. The floor of the ravine is in shadow; the captain leads the way down the shelving wall, into the shade. They lower the wounded man carefully and go on.

After a time the ravine opens. They find that they have debouched into another of those shallow depressions. This one is not so clearly defined, though, and the opposite wall of it is nicked by what is apparently another depression, like two overlapping disks. They cross the first depression, while more of the dead-looking grass bayonets saber their legs dryly, and pass through the gap into the next depression.

This one is like a miniature valley between miniature cliffs. Overhead they can see only the drowsy and empty bowl of the sky, with a few faint smoke smudges to the northwest. The sound of the barrage is now remote and far away: a vibration in earth felt rather than heard. There are no recent shell craters or marks here at all. It is as though they had strayed suddenly into a region, a world where the war had not reached, where nothing had reached, where no life is, and silence itself is dead. They give the wounded man water and go on.

The valley, the depression, strays vaguely before them. They can see that it is a series of overlapping, vaguely circular basins formed by no apparent or deducible agency. Pallid grass bayonets saber at their legs, and after a time they are again among old healed scars of trees to which there cling sparse leaves neither green nor dead, as if they too had been overtaken and caught by a hiatus in time, gossiping dryly among themselves though there is no wind. The floor of the valley is not level. It in itself descends into vague depressions, rises again as vaguely between its shelving walls. In the center of these smaller depressions whitish knobs of chalk thrust up through the thin topsoil. The ground has a resilient quality, like walking on cork; feet make no sound. "Jolly walking," the subaltern says. Though his voice is not raised, it fills the small valley with the abruptness of a thunderclap, filling the silence, the words seeming to hang about them as though silence here had been so long undisturbed that it had forgot its purpose; as one they look quietly and soberly about, at the shelving walls, the stubborn ghosts of trees, the bland, hushed sky. "Topping hole-up for embusqué birds and such," the subaltern says.

"Ay," the captain says. His word in turn hangs sluggishly and fades. The men at the rear close up, the movement passing forward, the men looking quietly and soberly about.

"But no birds here," the subaltern says. "No insects even."

"Ay," the captain says. The word fades, the silence comes down again, sunny, profoundly still. The subaltern pauses and stirs something with his foot. The men halt also, and the subaltern and the captain, without touching it, examine the half-buried and moldering rifle. The wounded man is babbling again.

"What is it, sir?" the subaltern says. "Looks like one of those things the Canadians had. A Ross. Right?"

"French," the captain says; "1914."

"Oh," the subaltern says. He turns the rifle aside with his toe. The bayonet is still attached to the barrel, but the stock has long since rotted away. They go on, across the uneven ground, among the chalky knobs thrusting up through the soil. Light, the wan and drowsy sunlight, is laked in the valley, stagnant, bodiless, without heat. The saberlike grass thrusts sparsely and rigidly upward. They look about again at the shaling walls, then the ones at the head of the party watch the subaltern pause and prod with his stick at one of the chalky knobs and turn presently upward its earth-stained eyesockets and its unbottomed grin.

"Forward," the captain says sharply. The party moves; the men look quietly and curiously at the skull as they pass. They go on, among the other whitish knobs like marbles studded at random in the shallow soil.

"All in the same position, do you notice, sir?" the subaltern says, his voice chattily cheerful; "all upright. Queer way to bury chaps: sitting down. Shallow, too."

"Ay," the captain says. The wounded man babbles steadily. The two bearers stop with him, but the others crowd on after the officers, passing the two bearers and the wounded man. "Dinna stop to gi's sup water," one of the bearers says. "A'll drink walkin." They take up the wounded man again and hurry him on while one of them tries to hold the neck of a water bottle to the wounded man's mouth, clattering it against his teeth and spilling the water down the front of his tunic. The captain looks back.

"What's this?" he says sharply. The men crowd up. Their eyes are wide, sober; he looks about at the quiet, intent faces. "What's the matter back there, Sergeant?"

"Wind-up," the subaltern says. He looks about at the eroded walls, the whitish knobs thrusting quietly out of the earth. "Feel it myself," he says. He laughs, his laughter a little thin, ceasing. "Let's get out of here, sir," he says. "Let's get into the sun again."

"You are in the sun here," the captain says. "Ease off there, men. Stop crowding. We'll be out soon. We'll find the road and get past the barrage and make contact again." He turns and goes on. The party gets into motion again.

Then they all stop as one, in the attitudes of walking, in an utter suspension, and stare at one another. Again the earth moves under their feet. A man screams, high, like a woman or a horse; as the firm earth shifts for a third time beneath them the officers whirl and see beyond the down-plunging man a gaping hole with dry dust still crumbling about the edges before the orifice crumbles again beneath a second man. Then a crack springs like a sword lash beneath them all; the earth breaks under their feet and tilts like jagged squares of pale fudge, framing a black yawn out of which, like a silent explosion, bursts the unmistakable smell of rotted flesh. While they scramble and leap (in silence now; there has been no sound since the first man screamed) from one cake to another, the cakes tilt and slide until the whole floor of the valley rushes slowly under them and plunges them downward into darkness. A grave rumbling rises into the sunlight on a blast of decay and of faint dust which hangs and drifts in the faint air about the black orifice.

The captain feels himself plunging down a sheer and shifting wall of moving earth, of sounds of terror and of struggling in the ink dark. Someone else screams. The scream ceases; he hears the voice of the wounded man coming thin and reiterant out of the plunging bowels of decay: "A'm no dead! A'm no dead!" and ceasing abruptly, as if a hand had been laid on his mouth.

Then the moving cliff down which the captain plunges slopes gradually off and shoots him, uninjured, onto a hard floor, where he lies for a time on his back while across his face the lightward- and airward-seeking blast of death and dissolution rushes. He has fetched up against something; it tumbles down upon him lightly, with a muffled clatter as if it had come to pieces.

Then he begins to see the light, the jagged shape of the cavern mouth high overhead, and then the sergeant is bending over him with a pocket torch. "McKie?" the captain says. For reply the sergeant turns the flash upon his own face. "Where's Mr. McKie?" the captain says.

"A's gone, sir-r," the sergeant says in a husky whisper. The captain sits up. "How many are left?"

"Fourteen, sir-r," the sergeant whispers.

"Fourteen. Twelve missing. We'll have to dig fast." He gets to his feet. The faint light from above falls coldly upon the heaped avalanche, upon the thirteen helmets and the white bandage of the wounded man huddled about the foot of the cliff. "Where are we?"

For answer the sergeant moves the torch. It streaks laterally into the darkness, along a wall, a tunnel, into yawning blackness, the walls faceted with pale glints of chalk. About the tunnel, sitting or leaning upright against the walls, are skeletons in dark tunics and bagging Zouave trousers, their moldering arms beside them; the captain recognizes them as Senegalese troops of the May fighting of 1915, surprised and killed by gas probably in the attitudes in which they had taken refuge in the chalk caverns. He takes the torch from the sergeant.

"We'll see if there's anyone else," he says. "Have out the trenching tools." He flashes the light upon the precipice. It rises into gloom, darkness, then into the faint rumor of daylight overhead. With the sergeant behind him he climbs the shifting heap, the earth sighing beneath him and shaling downward. The injured man begins to wail again, "A'm no dead! A'm no dead!" until his voice goes into a high sustained screaming. Someone lays a hand over his mouth. His voice is muffled, then it becomes laughter on a rising note, becomes screaming again, is choked again.

The captain and the sergeant mount as high as they dare, prodding at the earth while the earth shifts beneath them in long hushed sighs. At the foot of the precipice the men huddle, their faces lifted faint, white, and patient into the light. The captain sweeps the torch up and down the cliff. There is nothing, no arm, no hand, in sight. The air is clearing slowly. "We'll get on," the captain says.

"Ay, sir-r," the sergeant says.

In both directions the cavern fades into darkness, plumbless and profound, filled with the quiet skeletons sitting and leaning against the walls, their arms beside them.

"The cave-in threw us forward," the captain says.

"Ay, sir-r," the sergeant whispers.

"Speak out," the captain says. "It's but a bit of a cave. If men got into it, we can get out."

"Ay, sir-r," the sergeant whispers.

"If it threw us forward, the entrance will be yonder."

"Ay, sir-r," the sergeant whispers.

The captain flashes the torch ahead. The men rise and huddle quietly behind him, the wounded man among them. He whimpers. The cavern goes on, unrolling its glinted walls out of the darkness; the sitting shapes grin quietly into the light as they pass. The air grows heavier; soon they are trotting, gasping, then the air grows lighter and the torch sweeps up another slope of earth, closing the tunnel. The men halt and huddle. The captain mounts the slope. He snaps off the light and crawls slowly along the crest of the slide, where it joins the ceiling of the cavern, sniffing. The light flashes on again. "Two men with trenching tools," he says.

Two men mount to him. He shows them the fissure through which air seeps in small, steady breaths. They begin to dig, furiously, hurling the dirt back. Presently they are relieved by two others; presently the fissure becomes a tunnel and four men can work at once. The air becomes fresher. They burrow furiously, with whimpering cries like dogs. The wounded man, hearing them perhaps, catching the excitement perhaps, begins to laugh again, meaningless and high. Then the man at the head of the tunnel bursts through. Light rushes in around him like water; he burrows madly; in silhouette they see his wallowing buttocks lunge from sight and a burst of daylight surges in.

The others leave the wounded man and surge up the slope, fighting and snarling at the opening. The sergeant springs after them and beats them away from the opening with a trenching spade, cursing in his hoarse whisper.

"Let them go, Sergeant," the captain says. The sergeant desists. He stands aside and watches the men scramble into the tunnel. Then he descends, and he and the captain help the wounded man up the slope. At the mouth of the tunnel the wounded man rebels.

"A'm no dead! A'm no dead!" he wails, struggling. By cajolery and force they thrust him, still wailing and struggling, into the tunnel, where he becomes docile again and scuttles through.

"Out with you, Sergeant," the captain says.

"After you, sir-r," the sergeant whispers.

"Out wi ye, man!" the captain says. The sergeant enters the tunnel. The captain follows. He emerges onto the outer slope of the avalanche which had closed the cave, at the foot of which the fourteen men are kneeling in a group. On his hands and knees like a beast, the captain breathes, his breath making a hoarse sound. "Soon it will be summer," he thinks, dragging the air into his lungs faster than he can empty them to respire again. "Soon it will be summer, and the long days." At the foot of the slope the fourteen men kneel. The one in the center has a Bible in his hand, from which he is intoning monotonously. Above his voice the wounded man's gibberish rises, meaningless and unemphatic and sustained.

ETRUSCAN WARRIORS

THE CAVE OF THE CYCLOPS

FROM *Odyssey*

HOMER

Whether Homer was a mythical figure—a name that drew around itself the songs with which the ancients celebrated their heroic deeds—or whether he was a man, blind, the first of Greek poets, we shall probably never be certain. We know that the Homeric epics were recited a thousand years before the Christian era. The influence of the *Iliad* and *Odyssey* upon the form and substance of all our literature has been immeasurably great.

If one looks for symbols, Odysseus is man driven by an endless, restless search; if one does not, he is the hero in a story of high adventure, the most enduring ever fashioned. In this selection, Odysseus—man—pits his craft and wit against the monstrous strength of the Cyclops, or against giant and insensate Nature, if one prefers.

WITH THE FIRST ROSY LIGHT OF DAWN, I ASSEMBLED MY COMPANY AND GAVE them their orders. "My good friends," I said, "for the time being I want you to stay here, while I go in my own ship with my own crew to find out what kind of men are over there, and whether they are brutal and lawless savages or hospitable and god-fearing people."

Then I climbed into my ship and told my men to follow me and loose the hawsers. They came on board at once, went to the benches, sat down in their places and churned the grey water with their oars. It was no great distance to the mainland coast. As we approached its nearest point, we made out a cave there, close to the sea, with a high entrance overhung by laurels. Here large flocks of sheep and goats were penned at night, and round the mouth a yard had been built with a great wall of stones bedded deep between tall pines and high-branched oaks. It was the den of a giant, the lonely shepherd of sequestered flocks, who had no truck with others of his kind but lived aloof in his own lawless way. And what a formidable monster he was! No one would have taken him for a man who ate bread like ourselves; he reminded one rather of some wooded peak in the high hills, lifting itself in solitary state.

At this point, I told the rest of my loyal following to stay there on guard by the ship while I myself picked out the twelve best men in the company and advanced. I took with me in a goatskin some dark and mellow wine which had been given to me by Maron son of Euanthes, the priest of Apollo (who was patron-deity of Ismarus), because we had protected him and his child and wife out of respect for his office, when we came upon his home in a grove of trees sacred to Phoebus Apollo. This man made me some fine presents: he gave me seven talents of wrought gold, with a mixing-bowl of solid silver, and he drew off for me as well a full dozen jars of mellow unmixed wine. And a wonderful drink it was. It had been kept secret from all his serving-men and maids, in fact from everyone in the house but himself, his good wife, and a single stewardess. When they drank this red and honeyed vintage, he used to pour one cupful of wine into twenty of water, and the sweet fumes that came up from the bowl were irresistible—those were occasions when abstinence could have no charms.

Well, I filled a big bottle with this wine and took some food in a wallet along with me also; for I had an instant foreboding, though I am no coward, that we were going to find ourselves face to face with some being of colossal strength and ferocity, to whom the laws of man and god meant nothing. It took us very little time to reach the cave, but we did not find its owner at home: he was tending his fat sheep in the pastures. So we went inside and had a good look round. There were baskets laden with cheeses, and the folds were thronged with lambs and kids, each class, the firstlings, the summer lambs, and the little ones, being separately penned. All his well-made vessels, the pails and bowls he used for milking, were swimming with whey.

Now my men's idea was first to make off with some of the cheeses, then come back, drive the kids and lambs quickly out of the pens down to the good ship, and so set sail across the salt water. They pleaded with me; but though it would have been far better so, I was not to be persuaded. I wished to see the owner of the cave and had hopes of some friendly gifts from my host. As things fell out, my company were to have an unpleasant surprise when he did put in an appearance.

We lit a fire, killed a beast and made offerings, took some cheeses just for ourselves, and when we had eaten, sat down in the cave to await his arrival. At last he came up, shepherding his flocks and carrying a huge bundle of dry wood to burn at supper-time. With a great din he cast this down inside the cavern, giving us such a fright that we hastily retreated to an inner recess. Meanwhile he drove his fat sheep into the wider part of the cave—I mean all the ewes that he milked: the rams and he-goats he left out of doors in the walled yard. He then picked up a huge stone, with which he closed the entrance. It was a mighty slab, such as you couldn't have budged from the ground, not with a score of heavy four-wheeled waggons to help you. That will give you some idea of the monstrous size of the rock with which he closed the cave. Next he sat down to milk his ewes and bleating goats, which he did methodically, putting her young to each mother as he finished. He then curdled half the white milk, gathered it all up, and stored it in wicker baskets; the remainder he left standing in pails, so that it would be handy at supper-time and when he wanted a drink. When he had done with his business and finished all his jobs, he lit up the fire, spied us, and began asking questions.

"Strangers!" he said. "And who may you be? Where do you hail from over the highways of the sea? Is yours a trading venture; or are you cruising the main on chance, like roving pirates, who risk their lives to ruin other people?"

Our hearts sank within us. The booming voice and the very sight of the monster filled us with panic. Still, I managed to find words to answer him.

"We are Achaeans," I said, "on our way back from Troy, driven astray by contrary winds across a vast expanse of sea. Far from planning to come here, we meant to sail straight home; but we lost our bearings, as Zeus, I suppose, intended that we should. We are proud to belong to the forces of Agamemnon, Atreus' son, who by sacking the great city of Ilium and destroying all its armies has made himself the most famous man in the world today. We, less fortunate, are visiting you here as suppliants, in the hope that you may give us friendly entertainment or even go further in your generosity. You know the laws of hospitality: I beseech you, good sir, to remember your duty to the gods. For we throw ourselves on your mercy: and Zeus is there to avenge the suppliant and the guest. He is the travellers' god: he guards their steps and he invests them with their rights."

So said I, and promptly he answered me out of his pitiless heart: "Stranger, you must be a fool, or must have come from very far afield, to preach to me of fear or reverence for the gods. We Cyclopes care not a jot for Zeus with his aegis, nor for the rest of the blessed gods, since we are much stronger than they. It would never occur to me to spare you or your men against my will for fear of trouble from Zeus. But tell me where you moored your good ship when you came. Was it somewhere up the coast, or near by? I should like to see her."

He was trying to get the better of me, but I knew enough of the world to see through him and I met him with deceit.

"As for my ship," I answered, "it was wrecked by the Earth-shaker Poseidon on the confines of your land. The wind had carried us onto a lee shore. He drove the ship up to a headland and hurtled it on the rocks. But I and my friends here managed to escape with our lives."

To this the cruel brute made no reply. Instead, he jumped up, and reaching out towards my men, seized a couple and dashed their heads against the floor as though they had been puppies. Their brains ran out on the ground and soaked the earth. Limb by limb he tore them to pieces to make his meal, which he devoured like a mountain lion, never pausing till entrails and flesh, marrow and bones, were all consumed, while we could do nothing but weep and lift up our hands to Zeus in horror at the ghastly sight, paralysed by our sense of utter helplessness. When the Cyclops had filled his great belly with this meal of human flesh, which he washed down with unwatered milk, he stretched himself out for sleep among his flocks inside the cave. And now my manhood prompted me to action: I thought I would draw my sharp sword from the scabbard at my side, creep up to him, feel for the right place with my hand and stab him in the breast where the liver is supported by the midriff. But on second thoughts I refrained, realizing that we should have perished there as surely as the Cyclops, for we should have found it impossible with our unaided hands to push aside the huge rock with which he had closed the great mouth of the cave. So for the time being we just sat groaning there and waited for the blessed light of day.

No sooner had the tender Dawn shown her roses in the East, than the Cyclops lit up the fire and milked his splendid ewes, all in their proper order, putting her young to each. This business over and his morning labours done, he once more snatched up a couple of my men and prepared his meal. When he had eaten, he turned his fatted sheep out of the cave, removing the great doorstone without an effort. But he replaced it immediately, as easily as though he were putting the lid on a quiver. Then, with many a whistle, he drove his rich flocks off towards the high pasture, while I was left, with murder in my heart, beating about for some scheme by which I might pay him back if only Athene would grant me my prayer. The best plan I could think of was this. Lying by the pen, the Cyclops had a huge staff of green olive-wood, which he had cut to carry in his hand when it was seasoned. To us it looked more like the mast of some black ship of twenty oars, a broad-bottomed freighter such as they use for long sea voyages. That was the impression which its length and thickness made on us. On this piece of timber I set to work and cut off a fathom's length, which I handed over to my men and told them to smooth down. When they had dressed it, I took a hand and sharpened it to a point. Then I poked it into the blazing fire to make it hard, and finally I laid it carefully by, hiding it under the dung, of which there were heaps scattered in profusion throughout the cave. I then told my company to cast lots among themselves for the dangerous task of helping me to lift the pole and twist it in the Cyclops' eye when he was sound asleep. The lot fell on the very men that I myself should have chosen, four of them, so that counting myself we made a party of five.

Evening came, and with it the Cyclops, shepherding his woolly sheep, every one of which he herded into the broad part of the cave, leaving none out in the walled yard, either because he suspected something or because a god had warned him. He raised the great doorstone, set it in its place, and then sat down to milk his ewes and bleating goats, which he did in an orderly way, giving each mother its young one in due course. When this business was over and his work finished, he once more seized upon two of us and prepared his supper. Then came my chance. With an ivy-wood bowl of my dark wine in my hands, I went up to him and said: "Here, Cyclops, have some wine to wash down that meal of human flesh, and find out for yourself what kind of vintage was stored away in our ship's hold. I brought it for you by way of an offering in the hope that you would be charitable and help me on my homeward way. But your savagery is more than we can bear. Cruel monster, how can you expect ever to have a visitor again from the world of men, after such deeds as you have done?"

The Cyclops took the wine and drank it up. And the delicious draught gave him such exquisite pleasure that he asked me for another bowlful.

"Be good enough," he said, "to let me have some more; and tell me your name, here and now, so that I may make you a gift that you will value. We Cyclopes have wine of our own made from the grapes that our rich soil and timely rains produce. But this vintage of yours is nectar and ambrosia distilled."

So said the Cyclops, and I handed him another bowlful of the ruddy wine. Three times I filled up for him; and three times the fool drained the bowl to the dregs. At last, when the wine had fuddled his wits, I addressed him with disarming suavity.

"Cyclops," I said, "you wish to know the name I bear. I'll tell it to you; and in return I should like to have the gift you promised me. My name is Nobody. That is what I am called by my mother and father and by all my friends."

The Cyclops answered me with a cruel jest. "Of all his company I will eat Nobody last, and the rest before him. That shall be your gift."

He had hardly spoken before he toppled over and fell face upwards on the floor, where he lay with his great neck twisted to one side, conquered, as all men are, by sleep. His drunkenness made him vomit, and a stream of wine mixed with morsels of men's flesh poured from his throat. I went at once and thrust our pole deep under the ashes of the fire to make it hot, and meanwhile gave a word of encouragement to all my men, to make sure that no one should play the coward and leave me in the lurch. When the fierce glow from the olive stake warned me that it was about to catch alight in the flames, green as it was, I withdrew it from the fire and brought it over to the spot where my men were standing ready. Heaven now inspired them with a reckless courage. Seizing the olive pole, they drove its sharpened end into the Cyclops' eye, while I used my weight from above to twist it home, like a man boring a ship's timber with a drill which his mates below him twirl with a strap they hold at either end, so that it spins continuously. In much the same way we handled our pole with its red-hot point and twisted it in his eye till the blood boiled up round the burning wood. The fiery smoke from the blazing eyeball singed his lids and brow all round, and the very roots of his eye crackled in the heat. I was reminded of the loud hiss that comes from a great axe or adze when a smith plunges it into cold water—to temper it and give strength to the iron. That is how the Cyclops' eye hissed round the olive stake. He gave a dreadful shriek, which echoed round the rocky walls, and we backed away from him in terror, while he pulled the stake from his eye, streaming with blood. Then he hurled it away from him with frenzied hands and raised a great shout for the other Cyclopes who lived in neighbouring caves along the windy heights. These, hearing his screams, came up from every quarter, and gathering outside the cave asked him what ailed him:

"What on earth is wrong with you, Polyphemus? Why must you disturb the peaceful night and spoil our sleep with all this shouting? Is a robber driving off your sheep, or is somebody trying by treachery or violence to kill you?"

Out of the cave came Polyphemus' great voice in reply: "O my friends, it's Nobody's treachery, no violence, that is doing me to death."

"Well then," they answered in a way that settled the matter, "if nobody is assaulting you in your solitude, you must be sick. Sickness comes from almighty Zeus and cannot be helped. All you can do is to pray to your father, the Lord Poseidon."

And off they went, while I chuckled to myself at the way in which my happy notion of a false name had taken them in. The Cyclops, still moaning in agonies of pain, groped about with his hands and pushed the rock away from the mouth of the cave. But then he sat himself down in the doorway and stretched out both arms in the hope of catching us in the act of slipping out among the sheep. What a fool he must have thought me! Meanwhile I was cudgelling my brains for the best possible course, trying to hit on some way of saving my friends as well as my own skin. Plan after plan, dodge after dodge, passed through my mind. It was a matter of life or death: we were in mortal peril. And this was the scheme I eventually chose. There were in the flock some well-bred, thick-fleeced rams, fine, big animals in their coats of black wool. These I quietly lashed together with the plaited withes which the savage monster used for his bed. I took them in threes. The middle one in each case was to carry one of my followers, while its fellows went on either side to protect him. Each of my men thus had three sheep to bear him. But for myself I chose a full-grown ram who was the pick of the whole flock. Seizing him by the back, I curled myself up under his shaggy belly and lay there upside down, with a firm grip on his wonderful fleece and with patience in my heart. Thus in fear and trembling we waited for the blessed Dawn.

As soon as she arrived and flecked the East with red, the rams of the flock began to scramble out and make for the pastures, but the ewes, unmilked as they were and with udders full to bursting, stood bleating by the pens. Their master, though he was worn out by the agonies he had gone through, passed his hands along the backs of all the animals as they came to a stand before him; but the idiot never noticed that my men were tied up under the breasts of his own woolly sheep. The last of the flock to come up to the doorway was the big ram, burdened by his own fleece and by me with my teeming brain. As he felt him with his hands the great Polyphemus broke into speech:

"Sweet ram," he said, "what does this mean? Why are you the last of the flock to pass out of the cave, you who have never lagged behind the sheep, you who always step so proudly out and are the first of them to crop the lush shoots of the grass, first to make your way to the flowing stream, and first to turn your head homewards to the sheepfold when the evening falls? Yet today you are the last of all. Are you grieved for your master's eye, blinded by a wicked man and his accursed friends, when he had robbed me of my wits with wine? Nobody was his name; and I swear that he has not yet saved his skin! Ah, if only you could feel as I do and find a voice to tell me where he's hiding from my fury! Wouldn't I hammer him and splash his brains all over the floor of the cave, till that miserable Nobody had eased my heart of the suffering I owe to him!"

So he passed the ram out; and when he had put a little distance between ourselves and the courtyard of the cave, I first freed myself from under my ram and next untied my men from theirs. Then, quickly, though with many a backward look, we drove our long-legged sheep right down to the ship—and a rich, fat flock they made. My dear companions were overjoyed when they caught sight of us survivors, though their relief soon changed to lamentation for their slaughtered friends. I would have none of this weeping, however, and with a nod made clear my will to each, bidding them make haste instead to tumble all the fleecy sheep on board and put to sea. So in they jumped, ran to the benches, sorted themselves out, and plied the grey water with their oars.

But before we were out of earshot, I let Polyphemus have a piece of my mind. "Cyclops!" I called. "So he was not such a weakling after all, the man whose friends you meant to overpower and eat in that snug cave of yours! And your crimes came home to roost, you brute, who have not even the decency to refrain from devouring your own guests. Now Zeus and all his fellow-gods have paid you out."

A SPOUTING COLUMN OF DUST AND SMOKE

FROM *Revolt in the Desert*

T. E. LAWRENCE

T. E. Lawrence was attached to the British Intelligence Service during the first World War. He worked out and carried through an almost legendary campaign against the Turks. Singlehanded he organized the revolt of widely scattered Arab tribes against Turkish rule. His were commando tactics—surprise raids, mining of enemy positions, destroying supplies. This selection from *Revolt in the Desert* describes his method and tactics.

IN THE MORNING WE DELAYED TO EAT AGAIN, HAVING ONLY SIX HOURS OF march before us; and then pushed across the mud-flat to a plain of firm limestone rag, carpeted with brown, weather-blunted flint. This was succeeded by low hills, with occasional soft beds of sand, under the steeper slopes where eddying winds had dropped their dust. Through these we rode up shallow valleys to a crest; and then by like valleys down the far side, whence we issued abruptly, from dark, tossed stone-heaps into the sun-steeped wideness of a plain. Across it an occasional low dune stretched a drifting line.

We had made our noon halt at the first entering of the broken country; and, rightly, in the late afternoon came to the well. It was an open pool, a few yards square, in a hollow valley of large stone-slabs and flint and sand. The stagnant water looked uninviting. Over its face lay a thick mantle of green slime, from which swelled curious bladder-islands of floating fatty pink. The Arabs explained that the Turks had thrown dead camels into the pool to make the water foul; but that time had passed and the effect was grown faint. It would have been fainter had the criterion of their effort been my taste.

Yet it was all the drink we should get up here unless we took Mudowwara, so we set to and filled our waterskins. One of the Howeitat, while helping in this, slipped off the wet edge into the water. Its green carpet closed oilily over his head and hid him for an instant: then he came up, gasping vigorously, and scrambled out amid our laughter; leaving behind him a black hole in the scum from which a stench of old meat rose like a visible pillar, and hung about us and him and the valley, disconcertingly.

At dusk, Zaal and I, with the sergeants and others, crept forward quietly. In half an hour we were at the last crest, in a place where the Turks had dug trenches, and stoned up an elaborate outpost of engrailed sangars, which on this black new-moon night of our raid were empty. In front and below lay the station, its doors and windows sharply marked by the yellow cooking fires and lights of the garrison. It seemed close under our observation; but the Stokes gun would carry only three hundred yards. Accordingly we went nearer, hearing the enemy noises, and attentively afraid lest their barking dogs uncover us. Sergeant Stokes made casts out to left and right, in search of gun-positions, but found nothing that was satisfactory.

Meanwhile, Zaal and I crawled across the last flat, till we could count the unlighted tents and hear the men talking. One came out a few steps in our direction, then hesitated. He struck a match to light a cigarette, and the bold light flooded his face, so that we saw him plainly, a young, hollow-faced sickly officer. He squatted, busy for a moment, and returned to his men, who hushed as he passed.

We moved back to our hill and consulted in whispers. The station was very long, of stone buildings, so solid that they might be proof against our time-fused shell. The garrison seemed about two hundred. We were one hundred and sixteen rifles and not a happy family. Surprise was the only benefit we could be sure of.

So, in the end, I voted that we leave it, unalarmed, for a future occasion, which might be soon. But, actually, one accident after another saved Mudowwara; and it was not until August, 1918, that Buxton's Camel Corps at last measured to it the fate so long overdue.

Quietly we regained our camels and slept. Next morning we returned on our tracks to let a fold of the plain hide us from the railway, and then marched south across the sandy flat; seeing tracks of gazelle, oryx and ostrich; with, in one spot, stale padmarks of leopard. We were making for the low hills bounding the far side, intending to blow up a train; for Zaal said that where these touched the railway was such a curve as we needed for minelaying, and that the spurs commanding it would give us ambush and a field of fire for our machine-guns.

So we turned east in the southern ridges till within half a mile of the line. There the party halted in a thirty-foot valley, while a few of us walked down to the line, which bent a little eastward to avoid the point of higher ground under our feet. The point ended in a flat table fifty feet above the track, facing north across the valley.

The metals crossed the hollow on a high bank, pierced by a two-arched bridge for the passage of rain-water. This seemed an ideal spot to lay the charge. It was our first try at electric mining and we had no idea what would happen; but it stood to our reason that the job would be more sure with an arch under the explosive because, whatever the effect on the locomotive, the bridge would go, and the succeeding coaches be inevitably derailed.

Back with our camels, we dumped the loads, and sent the animals to safe pasture near some undercut rocks from which the Arabs scraped salt. The freedmen carried down the Stokes gun with its shells; the Lewis guns; and the gelatine with its insulated wire, magneto and tools to the chosen place. The sergeants set up their toys on a terrace, while we went down to the bridge to dig a bed between the ends of two steel sleepers, wherein to hide my fifty pounds of gelatine. We had stripped off the paper wrapping of the individual explosive plugs and kneaded them together by help of the sun heat into a shaking jelly in a sandbag.

The burying of it was not easy. The embankment was steep, and in the sheltered pocket between it and the hillside was a wind-laid bank of sand. No one crossed this but myself, stepping carefully; yet I left unavoidable great prints over its smoothness. The ballast dug out from the track I had to gather in my cloak for carriage in repeated journeys to the culvert, whence it could be tipped naturally over the shingle bed of the water-course.

It took me nearly two hours to dig in and cover the charge: then came the difficult job of unrolling the heavy wires from the detonator to the hills whence we would fire the mine. The top sand was crusted and had to be broken through in burying the wires. They were stiff wires, which scarred the wind-rippled surface with long lines like the belly marks of preposterously narrow and heavy snakes. When pressed down in one place they rose into the air in another. At last they had to be weighted down with rocks which, in turn, had to be buried at the cost of great disturbance of the ground.

Afterwards it was necessary, with a sandbag, to stipple the marks into a wavy surface; and, finally, with a bellows and long fanning sweeps of my cloak, to simulate the smooth laying of the wind. The whole job took five hours to finish; but then it was well finished: neither myself nor any of us could see where the charge lay, or that double wires led out underground from it to the firing-point two hundred yards off, behind the ridge marked for our riflemen.

The wires were just long enough to cross from this ridge into a depression. There we brought up the two ends and connected them with the electric exploder. It was an ideal place both for it and for the man who fired it, except that the bridge was not visible thence.

However, this only meant that some one would have to press the handle at a signal from a point fifty yards ahead, commanding the bridge and the ends of the wires alike. Salem, Feisal's best slave, asked for this task of honour, and was yielded it by acclamation. The end of the afternoon was spent in showing him (on the disconnected exploder) what to do, till he was act-perfect and banked down the ratchet precisely as I raised my hand with an imaginary engine on the bridge.

We walked back to camp, leaving one man on watch by the line. Our baggage was deserted, and we stared about in a puzzle for the rest, till we saw them suddenly sitting against the golden light of sunset along a high ridge. We yelled to them to lie down or come down, but they persisted up there on their perch like a school of hooded crows, in full view of north and south.

At last we ran up and threw them off the skyline, too late. The Turks in a little hillpost by Hallat Ammar, four miles south of us, had seen them, and opened fire in their alarm upon the long shadows which the declining sun was pushing gradually up the slopes towards the post. Beduin were past-masters in the art of using country, but in their abiding contempt for the stupidity of the Turks they would take no care to fight them. This ridge was visible at once from Mudowwara and Hallat Ammar, and they had frightened both places by their sudden ominous expectant watch.

However, the dark closed on us, and we knew we must sleep away the night patiently in hope of the morrow. Perhaps the Turks would reckon us gone if our place looked desert in the morning. So we lit fires in a deep hollow, baked bread and were comfortable. The common tasks had made us one party, and the hill-top folly shamed every one into agreement that Zaal should be our leader.

Day broke quietly, and for hours we watched the empty railway with its peaceful camps. The constant care of Zaal and of his lame cousin, Howeimil, kept us hidden, though with difficulty, because of the insatiate restlessness of the Beduin, who would never sit down for ten minutes, but must fidget and do or say something. This defect made them very inferior to the stolid English for the long, tedious strain of a waiting war. Also it partly accounted for their uncertain stomachs in defence. Today they made us very angry.

Perhaps, after all, the Turks saw us, for at nine o'clock some forty men came out of the tents on the hill-top by Hallat Ammar to the south and advanced in open order. If we left them alone, they would turn us off our mine in an hour; if we opposed them with our superior strength and drove them back, the railway would take notice, and traffic be held up. It was a quandary, which eventually we tried to solve by sending thirty men to check the enemy patrol gradually; and, if possible, to draw them lightly aside into the broken hills. This might hide our main position and reassure them as to our insignificant strength and purpose.

For some hours it worked as we had hoped; the firing grew desultory and distant. A permanent patrol came confidently up from the south and walked past our hill, over our mine and on towards Mudowwara without noticing us. There were eight soldiers and a stout corporal, who mopped his brow against the heat, for it was now after eleven o'clock and really warm. When he had passed us by a mile or two the fatigue of the tramp became too much for him. He marched his party into the shade of a long culvert, under whose arches a cool draught from the east was gently flowing, and there in comfort they lay on the soft sand, drank water from their bottles, smoked, and at last slept. We presumed that this was the noon-day rest which every solid Turk in the hot summer of Arabia took as a matter of principle, and that their allowing themselves the pause showed that we were disproved or ignored. However, we were in error.

Noon brought a fresh care. Through my powerful glasses we saw a hundred Turkish soldiers issue from Mudowwara Station and make straight across the sandy plain towards our place. They were coming very slowly, and no doubt unwillingly, for sorrow at losing their beloved midday sleep: but at their very worst marching and temper they could hardly take more than two hours before they reached us.

We began to pack up, preparatory to moving off, having decided to leave the mine and its leads in place on chance that the Turks might not find them, and we be able to return and take advantage of all the careful work. We sent a messenger to our covering party on the south, that they should meet us farther up, near those scarred rocks which served as screen for our pasturing camels.

Just as he had gone, the watchman cried out that smoke in clouds was rising from Hallat Ammar. Zaal and I rushed uphill and saw by its shape and volume that indeed there must be a train waiting in that station. As we were trying to see it over the hill, suddenly it moved out in our direction. We yelled to the Arabs to get into position as quick as possible, and there came a wild scramble over sand and rock. Stokes and Lewis, being booted, could not win the race; but they came well up, their pains and dysentery forgotten.

The men with rifles posted themselves in a long line behind the spur running from the guns past the exploder to the mouth of the valley. From it they would fire directly into the derailed carriages at less than one hundred and fifty yards, whereas the ranges for the Stokes and Lewis guns were about three hundred yards. An Arab stood up on high behind the guns and shouted to us what the train was doing—a necessary precaution, for if it carried troops and detrained them behind our ridge we should have to face about like a flash and retire fighting up the valley for our lives. Fortunately it held on at all the speed the two locomotives could make on wood fuel.

It drew near where we had been reported, and opened random fire into the desert. I could hear the racket coming, as I sat on my hillock by the bridge to give the signal to Salem, who danced round the exploder on his knees, crying with excitement, and calling urgently on God to make him fruitful. The Turkish fire sounded heavy, and I wondered with how many men we were going to have affair, and if the mine would be advantage enough for our eighty fellows to equal them. It would have been better if the first electrical experiment had been simpler.

However, at that moment the engines, looking very big, rocked with screaming whistles into view around the bend. Behind them followed ten box-wagons, crowded with rifle-muzzles at the windows and doors; and in little sandbag nests on the roofs Turks precariously held on, to shoot at us. I had not thought of two engines, and on the moment decided to fire the charge under the second, so that however little the mine's effect, the uninjured engine should not be able to uncouple and drag the carriages away.

Accordingly, when the front "driver" of the second engine was on the bridge, I raised my hand to Salem. There followed a terrific roar, and the line vanished from sight behind a spouting column of black dust and smoke a hundred feet high and wide. Out of the darkness came shattering crashes and long, loud metallic clangings of ripped steel, with many lumps of iron and plate; while one entire wheel of a locomotive whirled up suddenly black out of the cloud against the sky, and sailed musically over our heads to fall slowly and heavily into the desert behind. Except for the flight of these, there succeeded a deathly silence, with no cry of men or rifle-shot, as the now-grey mist of the explosion drifted from the line towards us, and over our ridge until it was lost in the hills.

In the lull, I ran southward to join the sergeants. Salem picked up his rifle and charged out into the murk. Before I had climbed to the guns the hollow was alive with shots, and with the brown figures of the Beduin leaping forward to grips with the enemy. I looked round to see what was happening so quickly, and saw the train stationary and dismembered along the track, with its wagon sides jumping under the bullets which riddled them, while Turks were falling out from the far doors to gain the shelter of the railway embankment.

As I watched, our machine-guns chattered out over my head, and the long rows of Turks on the carriage roofs rolled over, and were swept off the top like bales of cotton before the furious shower of bullets which stormed along the roofs and splashed clouds of yellow chips from the planking. The dominant position of the guns had been an advantage to us so far.

When I reached Stokes and Lewis the engagement had taken another turn. The remaining Turks had got behind the bank, here about eleven feet high, and from cover of the wheels were firing point-blank at the Beduin twenty yards across the sand-filled dip. The enemy in the crescent of the curving line were secure from the machine-guns; but Stokes slipped in his first shell, and after a few seconds there came a crash as it burst beyond the train in the desert.

He touched the elevating screw, and his second shot fell just by the trucks in the deep hollow below the bridge where the Turks were taking refuge. It made a shambles of the place. The survivors of the group broke out in a panic across the desert, throwing away their rifles and equipment as they ran. This was the opportunity of the Lewis gunners. The sergeant grimly traversed with drum after drum, till the open sand was littered with bodies. Mushagraf, the Sherari boy behind the second gun, saw the battle over, threw aside his weapon with a yell, and dashed down at speed with his rifle to join the others who were beginning, like wild beasts, to tear open the carriages and fall to plunder. It had taken nearly ten minutes.

I ran down to the ruins to see what the mine had done. The bridge was gone; and into its gap was fallen the front wagon, which had been filled with sick. The smash had killed all but three or four and had rolled dead and dying into a bleeding heap against the splintered end. One of those yet alive deliriously cried out the word typhus. So I wedged shut the door, and left them there, alone.

Succeeding wagons were derailed and smashed: some had frames irreparably buckled. The second engine was a blanched pile of smoking iron. Its driving wheels had been blown upward, taking away the side of the fire-box. Cab and tender were twisted into strips, among the piled stones of the bridge abutment. It would never run again. The front engine had got off better: though heavily derailed and lying half-over, with the cab burst, yet its steam was at pressure, and driving-gear intact.

The valley was a weird sight.

''THERE'S NO TRENCH—THERE'S NOTHING''

FROM *Under Fire*

HENRI BARBUSSE

Under Fire, the novel by Henri Barbusse from which this selection on trench warfare comes, is a shattering indictment of war. Barbusse fought as a private in the first World War and was three times cited for bravery. He spent the rest of his life "making war on war."

The book exerted an enormous moral influence for peace. It was awarded the Prix Goncourt in 1917, says one commentator, "just when it was being refused publication in America, a decision which was hastily reversed."

"WE'RE IN FRONT OF THE FIRST LINES," THEY WHISPER ROUND ME. "NO," MURmur other voices, "we're just behind."

No one knows. The rain still falls, though less fiercely than at some moments on the march. But what matters the rain! We have spread ourselves out on the ground. Now that our backs and limbs rest in the yielding mud, we are so comfortable that we are unconcerned about the rain that pricks our faces and drives through to our flesh, indifferent to the saturation of the bed that contains us.

But we get hardly time enough to draw breath. They are not so imprudent as to let us bury ourselves in sleep. We must set ourselves to incessant labor. It is two o'clock of the morning; in four hours more it will be too light for us to stay here. There is not a minute to lose.

"Every man," they say to us, "must dig five feet in length, two and a half feet in width, and two and three-quarter feet in depth. That makes fifteen feet in length for each team. And I advise you to get into it; the sooner it's done, the sooner you'll leave."

We know the pious claptrap. It is not recorded in the annals of the regiment that a trenching fatigue-party ever once got away before the moment when it became absolutely necessary to quit the neighborhood if they were not to be seen, marked and destroyed along with the work of their hands.

We murmur, "Yes, yes—all right; it's not worth saying. Go easy."

But everybody applies himself to the job courageously, except for some invincible sleepers whose nap will involve them later in superhuman efforts.

We attack the first layer of the new line—little mounds of earth, stringy with grass. The ease and speed with which the work begins—like all entrenching work in free soil—foster the illusion that it will soon be finished, that we shall be able to sleep in the cavities we have scooped; and thus a certain eagerness revives.

But whether by reason of the noise of the shovels, or because some men are chatting almost aloud, in spite of reproofs, our activity wakes up a rocket, whose flaming vertical line rattles suddenly on our right.

"Lie down!" Every man flattens himself, and the rocket balances and parades its huge pallor over a sort of field of the dead.

As soon as it is out one hears the men, in places and then all along, detach themselves from their secretive stillness, get up, and resume the task with more discretion.

Soon another star-shell tosses aloft its long golden stalk, and still more brightly illuminates the flat and motionless line of trenchmakers. Then another and another.

Bullets rend the air around us, and we hear a cry, "Some one wounded!" He passes, supported by comrades. We can just see the group of men who are going away, dragging one of their number.

The place becomes unwholesome. We stoop and crouch, and some are scratching at the earth on their knees. Others are working full length; they toil, and turn, and turn again, like men in nightmares. The earth, whose first layer was light to lift, becomes muddy and sticky; it is hard to handle, and clings to the tool like glue. After every shovelful the blade must be scraped.

Already a thin heap of earth is winding along, and each man has the idea of reinforcing the incipient breastwork with his pouch and his rolled-up greatcoat, and he hoods himself behind the slender pile of shadow when a volley comes—

While we work we sweat, and as soon as we stop working we are pierced through by the cold. A spell seems to be cast on us, paralyzing our arms. The rockets torment and pursue us, and allow us but little movement. After every one of them that petrifies us with its light we have to struggle against a task still more stubborn. The hole only deepens into the darkness with painful and despairing tardiness.

The ground gets softer; each shovelful drips and flows, and spreads from the blade with a flabby sound. At last some one cries, "Water!" The repeated cry travels all along the row of diggers—"Water—that's done it!"

"Mélusson's team's dug deeper, and there's water. They've struck a swamp."—"No help for it."

We stop in confusion. In the bosom of the night we hear the sound of shovels and picks thrown down like empty weapons. The non-coms. go gropingly after the officer to get instructions. Here and there, with no desire for anything better, some men are going deliciously to sleep under the caress of the rain, under the radiant rockets.

It was very nearly at this minute, as far as I can remember, that the bombardment began again. The first shell fell with a terrible splitting of the air, which seemed to tear itself in two; and other whistles were already converging upon us when its explosion uplifted the ground at the head of the detachment in the heart of the magnitude of night and rain, revealing gesticulations upon a sudden screen of red.

No doubt they had seen us, thanks to the rockets, and had trained their fire on us.

The men hurled and rolled themselves towards the little flooded ditch that they had dug, wedging, burying, and immersing themselves in it, and placed the blades of the shovels over their heads. To right, to left, in front and behind, shells burst so near that every one of them shook us in our bed of clay; and it became soon one continuous quaking that seized the wretched gutter, crowded with men and scaly with shovels, under the strata of smoke and the falling fire. The splinters and débris crossed in all directions with a network of noise over the dazzling field. No second passed but we all thought what some stammered with their faces in the earth, "We're done, this time!"

A little in front of the place where I am, a shape has arisen and cried, "Let's be off!" Prone bodies half rose out of the shroud of mud that dripped in tails and liquid rags from their limbs, and these deathful apparitions cried also, "Let's go!" They were on their knees, on all-fours, crawling towards the way of retreat: "Get on, *allez,* get on!"

But the long file stayed motionless, and the frenzied complaints were in vain. They who were down there at the end would not budge, and their inactivity immobilized the rest. Some wounded passed over the others, crawling over them as over débris, and sprinkling the whole company with their blood.

We discovered at last the cause of the maddening inactivity of the detachment's tail—"There's a barrage fire beyond."

A weird imprisoned panic seized upon the men with cries inarticulate and gestures stillborn. They writhed upon the spot. But little shelter as the incipient trench afforded, no one dared leave the ditch that saved us from protruding above the level of the ground, no one dared fly from death to-

FPG

U. S. MARINES ADVANCE IN KOREA

DETAIL FROM THE BAYEUX TAPESTRY

Sperr: Frederic Lewis

MRS. SCHUYLER FIRES HER CORNFIELDS AT THE APPROACH OF THE BRITISH DURING THE AMERICAN REVOLUTION

THE BATTLE OF MONTEBELLO, IN WHICH THE FRENCH DEFEATED THE AUSTRIANS ON ITALIAN SOIL

Sperr: Frederic Lewis

Underwood and Underwood

A GERMAN BARRICADE OF WORLD WAR I

Underwood and Underwood

SHATTERED EARTH

THE 9TH BRITISH LANCERS CHARGE GERMAN ARTILLERY, WORLD WAR I

Underwood and Underwood

Underwood and Underwood

THE BRITISH BUILD A PARAPET

ALLIED TROOPS HOLD A TRENCH, WORLD WAR I

Frederic Lewis

Underwood and Underwood

RUSSIANS IN THEIR TRENCHES, WORLD WAR I

ELABORATE DUGOUTS, CONVERTED BY THE GERMANS FROM A ROADWAY AND CAPTURED BY THE BRITISH IN WORLD WAR I

Underwood and Underwood

Frederic Lewis

FIFTH DIVISION MARINES WORM UP A SANDY SLOPE FROM THE BEACH AT IWO JIMA

THE BURMA ROAD

FPG

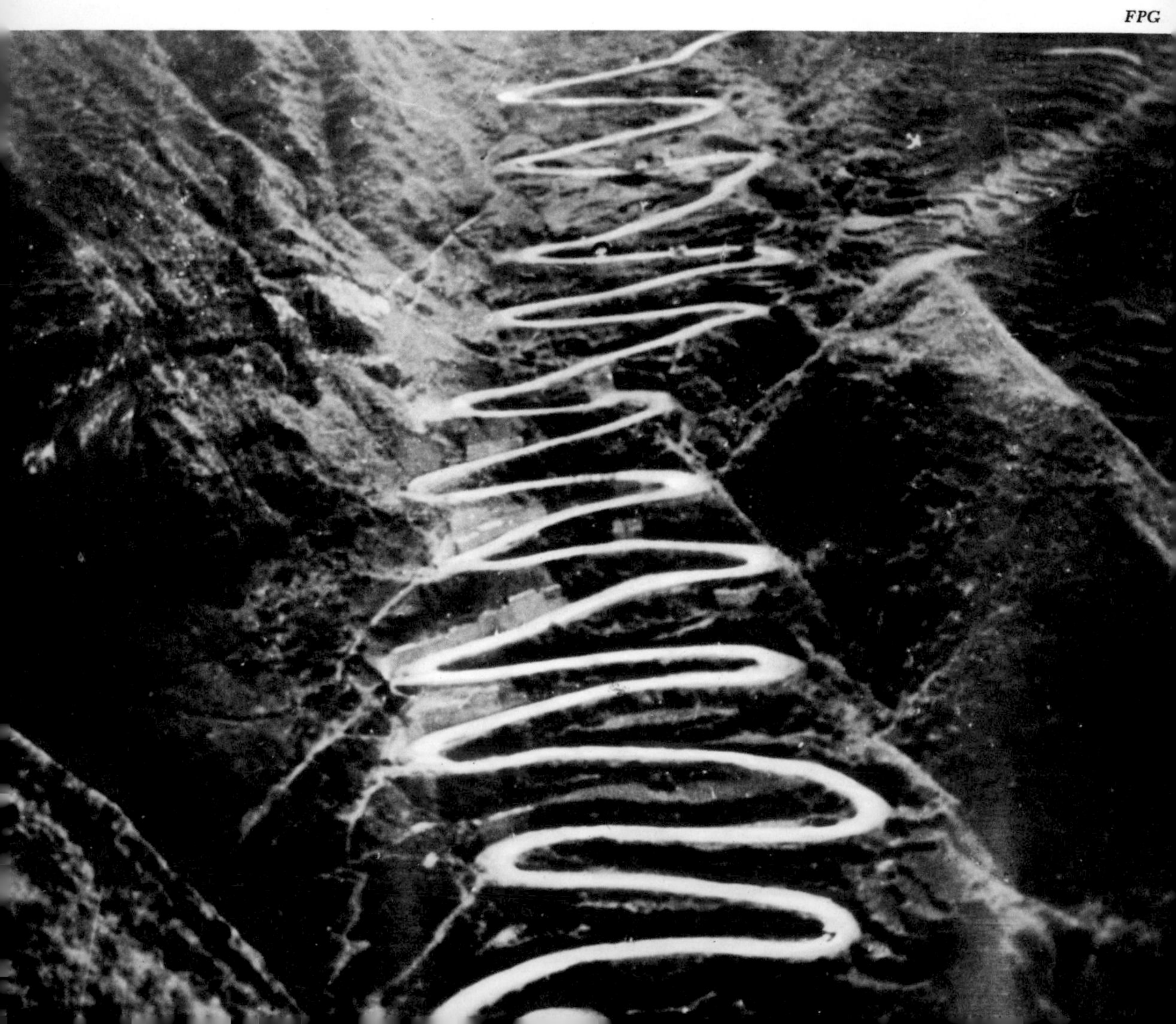

FPG

left: PVT. JIM SULLIVAN, OF MODESTA, CALIFORNIA, RELIEVES HIS BUDDY NEAR CHIN JU, KOREA

MARINES CHARGE ON TARAWA

Frederic Lewis

FPG

GRIEF AT THE DEATH OF A COMRADE AS AN ORDERLY RECORDS A SERIAL NUMBER

wards the traverse that should be down there. Great were the risks of the wounded who had managed to crawl over the others, and every moment some were struck and went down again.

Fire and water fell blended everywhere. Profoundly entangled in the supernatural din, we shook from neck to heels. The most hideous of deaths was falling and bounding and plunging all around us in waves of light, its crashing snatched our fearfulness in all directions—our flesh prepared itself for the monstrous sacrifice! In that tense moment of imminent destruction, we could only remember just then how often we had already experienced it, how often undergone this outpouring of iron, and the burning roar of it, and the stench. It is only during a bombardment that one really recalls those he has already endured.

And still, without ceasing, newly-wounded men crept over us, fleeing at any price. In the fear that their contact evoked we groaned again, "We shan't get out of this; nobody will get out of it."

Suddenly a gap appeared in the compressed humanity, and those behind breathed again, for we were on the move.

We began by crawling, then we ran, bowed low in the mud and water that mirrored the flashes and the crimson gleams, stumbling and falling over submerged obstructions, ourselves resembling heavy splashing projectiles, thunder-hurled along the ground. We arrive at the starting-place of the trench we had begun to dig.

"There's no trench—there's nothing."

In truth the eye could discern no shelter in the plain where our work had begun. Even by the stormy flash of the rockets we could only see the plain, a huge and raging desert. The trench could not be far away, for it had brought us here. But which way must we steer to find it?

The rain redoubled. We lingered a moment in mournful disappointment, gathered on a lightning-smitten and unknown shore—and then the stampede.

Some bore to the left, some to the right, some went straight forward—tiny groups that one only saw for a second in the heart of the thundering rain before they were separated by sable avalanches and curtains of flaming smoke.

The bombardment over our heads grew less; it was chiefly over the place where we had been that it was increasing. But it might any minute isolate everything and destroy it.

The rain became more and more torrential—a deluge in the night. The darkness was so deep that the star-shells only lit up slices of water-seamed obscurity, in the depths of which fleeing phantoms came and went and ran round in circles.

I cannot say how long I wandered with the group with which I had remained. We went into morasses. We strained our sight forward in quest of the embankment and the trench of salvation, towards the ditch that was somewhere there, as towards a harbor.

A cry of consolation was heard at last through the vapors of war and the elements—"A trench!" But the embankment of that trench was moving; it was made of men mingled in confusion, who seemed to be coming out and abandoning it.

"Don't stay there, mates!" cried the fugitives; "clear off, don't come near! It's hell—everything's collapsing—the trenches are legging it and the dug-outs are bunged up—the mud's pouring in everywhere. There won't be any trenches by the morning—it's all up with them about here!"

They disappeared. Where? We forgot to ask for some little direction from these men whose streaming shapes had no sooner appeared than they were swallowed up in the dark.

Even our little group crumbled away among the devastation, no longer knowing where they were. Now one, now another, faded into the night, disappearing towards his chance of escape.

We climbed slopes and descended them. I saw dimly in front of me men bowed and hunchbacked, mounting a slippery incline where mud held them back, and the wind and rain repelled them under a dome of cloudy lights.

Then we flowed back, and plunged into a marsh up to our knees. So high must we lift our feet that we walked with a sound of swimming. Each forward stride was an enormous effort which slackened in agony.

It was there that we felt death drawing near. But we beached ourselves at last on a sort of clay embankment that divided the swamp. As we followed the slippery back of this slender island along, I remember that once we had to stoop and steer ourselves by touching some half-buried corpses, so that we should not be thrown down from the soft and sinuous ridge. My hand discovered shoulders and hard backs, a face cold as a helmet, and a pipe still desperately bitten by dead jaws.

As we emerged and raised our heads at a venture we heard the sound of voices not far away. "Voices! Ah, voices!" They sounded tranquil to us, as though they called us by our names, and we all came close together to approach this fraternal murmuring of men.

The words became distinct. They were quite near—in the hillock that we could dimly see like an oasis; and yet we could not hear what they said. The sounds were muddled, and we did not understand them.

"What are they saying?" asked one of us in a curious tone.

Instinctively we stopped trying to find a way in. A doubt, a painful idea was seizing us. Then, clearly enunciated, there rang out these words—

"Achtung!—Zweites Geschütz—Schuss—"

Farther back, the report of a gun answered the telephonic command.

Horror and stupefaction nailed us to the spot at first—"Where are we? Oh, Christ, where are we?" Turning right about face, slowly in spite of all, borne down anew by exhaustion and dismay, we took flight, as overwhelmed by weariness as if we had many wounds, pulled back by the mud towards the enemy country, and retaining only just enough energy to repel the thought of the sweetness it would have been to let ourselves die.

We came to a sort of great plain. We halted and threw ourselves on the ground on the side of a mound, and leaned back upon it, unable to make another step.

And we moved no more, my shadowy comrades nor I. The rain splashed in our faces, streamed down our backs and chests, ran down from our knees and filled our boots.

We should perhaps be killed or taken prisoners when day came. But we thought no more of anything. We could do no more; we knew no more.

We are waiting for daylight in the place where we sank to the ground. Sinister and slow it comes, chilling and dismal, and expands upon the livid landscape.

The rain has ceased to fall—there is none left in the sky. The leaden plain and its mirrors of sullied water seem to issue not only from the night but from the sea.

Drowsy or half asleep, sometimes opening our eyes only to close them again, we attend the incredible renewal of light, paralyzed with cold and broken with fatigue.

Where are the trenches?

We see lakes, and between the lakes there are lines of milky and motionless water. There is more water even than we had thought. It has taken everything and spread everywhere, and the prophecy of the men in the night has come true. There are no more trenches; those canals are the trenches enshrouded. It is a universal flood. The battlefield is not sleeping; it is dead. Life may be going on down yonder perhaps, but we cannot see so far.

Swaying painfully, like a sick man, in the terrible encumbering clasp of my greatcoat, I half raise myself to look at it all. There are three monstrously shapeless forms beside me. One of them—it is Paradis, in an amazing armor of mud, with a swelling at the waist that stands for his cartridge pouches—gets up also. The others are asleep, and make no movement.

And what is this silence, too, this prodigious silence? There is no sound, except when from time to time a lump of earth slips into the water, in the middle of this fantastic paralysis of the world. No one is firing. There are no shells, for they would not burst. There are no bullets, either, for the men—

Ah, the men! Where are the men?

We see them gradually. Not far from us there are some stranded and sleeping hulks so molded in mud from head to foot that they are almost transformed into inanimate objects.

Some distance away I can make out others, curled up and clinging like snails all along a rounded embankment, from which they have partly slipped back into the water. It is a motionless rank of clumsy lumps, of bundles placed side by side, dripping water and mud, and of the same color as the soil with which they are blended.

I make an effort to break the silence. To Paradis, who also is looking that way, I say, "Are they dead?"

"We'll go and see presently," he says in a low voice; "stop here a bit yet. We shall have the heart to go there by and by."

We look at each other, and our eyes fall also on the others who came and fell down here. Their faces spell such weariness that they are no longer faces so much as something dirty, disfigured and bruised, with blood-shot eyes. Since the beginning we have seen each other in all manner of shapes and appearances, and yet—we do not know each other.

Paradis turns his head and looks elsewhere.

Suddenly I see him seized with trembling. He extends an arm enormously caked in mud. "There—there—" he says.

On the water which overflows from a stretch particularly cross-seamed and gullied, some lumps are floating, some round-backed reefs.

We drag ourselves to the spot. They are drowned men. Their arms and heads are submerged. On the surface of the plastery liquid appear their backs and the straps of their accouterments. Their blue cloth trousers are inflated, with the feet attached askew upon the ballooning legs, like the black wooden feet on the shapeless legs of marionettes. From one sunken head the hair stands straight up like water-weeds. Here is a face which the water only lightly touches; the head is beached on the marge, and the body disappears in its turbid tomb. The face is lifted skyward. The eyes are two white holes; the mouth is a black hole. The mask's yellow and puffed-up skin appears soft and creased, like dough gone cold.

They are the men who were watching there, and could not extricate themselves from the mud. All their efforts to escape over the sticky escarpment of the trench that was slowly and fatally filling with water only dragged them still more into the depth. They died clinging to the yielding support of the earth.

There, our first lines are; and there, the first German lines, equally silent and flooded. On our way to these flaccid ruins we pass through the middle of what yesterday was the zone of terror, the awful space on whose threshold the fierce rush of our last attack was forced to stop, the No Man's Land which bullets and shells had not ceased to furrow for a year and a half, where their crossed fire during these latter days had furiously swept the ground from one horizon to the other.

Now, it is a field of rest. The ground is everywhere dotted with beings who sleep or who are on the way to die, slowly moving, lifting an arm, lifting the head.

The enemy trench is completing the process of foundering into itself, among great marshy undulations and funnel-holes, shaggy with mud; it forms among them a line of pools and wells. Here and there we can see the still overhanging banks begin to move, crumble, and fall down. In one place we can lean against it.

In this bewildering circle of filth there are no bodies. But there, worse than a body, a solitary arm protrudes, bare and white as a stone, from a hole which dimly shows on the other side of the water. The man has been buried in his dug-out and has had only the time to thrust out his arm.

Quite near, we notice that some mounds of earth aligned along the ruined ramparts of this deep-drowned ditch are human. Are they dead—or asleep? We do not know; in any case, they rest.

Are they German or French? We do not know. One of them has opened his eyes, and looks at us with swaying head. We say to him, "French?"—and then, "*Deutsch?*" He makes no reply, but shuts his eyes again and relapses into oblivion. We never knew what he was.

We cannot decide the identity of these beings, either by their clothes, thickly covered with filth, or by their head-dress, for they are bareheaded or swathed in woolens under their liquid and offensive cowls; or by their weapons, for they either have no rifles or their hands rest lightly on something they have dragged along, a shapeless and sticky mass, like to a sort of fish.

All these men of corpse-like faces who are before us and behind us, at the limit of their strength, void of speech as of will, all these earth-charged men who you would say were carrying their own winding-sheets, are as much alike as if they were naked. Out of the horror of the night apparitions are issuing from this side and that who are clad in exactly the same uniform of misery and mud.

It is the end of all. For the moment it is the prodigious finish, the epic cessation of the war.

I once used to think that the worst hell in war was the flame of shells; and then for long I thought it was the suffocation of the caverns which eternally confine us. But it is neither of these. Hell is water.

A CONFEDERATE SOLDIER RESTS AT STONE RIVER, TENNESSEE

THE SOLID EARTH WENT UP

FROM *A Stillness at Appomattox*

BRUCE CATTON

Bruce Catton tells the little-known story of the Pennsylvania miners who dug four hundred feet of tunnel through a hill to dynamite a Confederate redoubt, one of the most dramatic incidents of the Civil War. *A Stillness at Appomattox,* from which this selection is taken, won the 1954 Pulitzer award for history, besides numerous other prizes. Catton has the rare talent for weaving the raw material of history—diaries, letters and army reports—into the many-textured fabric of literature.

COMING FROM MINING COUNTRY AND HAVING MANY MINERS, THE 48TH KNEW A thing or two about digging in the earth. One day its commander, passing along the trench, came on a soldier who was peering through the firing slit at the Rebel works. The man stepped down, turned to a comrade, and said: "We could blow that damned fort out of existence if we could run a mine shaft under it."

The commanding officer was Lieutenant Colonel Henry Pleasants, and that was talk he could understand because he was a mining engineer himself and before being a mining engineer he had done railroad construction work, and he had tunneled under obstructions before now. Born in the Argentine, the son of a Philadelphia businessman who married a Spanish woman and spent many years in South America, he was thirteen before he was brought to Philadelphia for a North American education. Trained as a civil engineer, he worked for the Pennsylvania Railroad in the early 1850s and he had had a hand in driving a 4,200-foot tunnel through the Alleghenies. A few years before the war he quit the railroad for coal mining and made his home in Schuylkill County. He was thirty-one now—slim, dapper, dark, and bearded—and as he passed along the trench he kept thinking about what the soldier had said. A little later he went down the ravine to a bombproof where the regimental officers lived, and he introduced the subject to them by saying bluntly: "That God-damned fort is the only thing between us and Petersburg, and I have an idea we can blow it up."

Not long after this, Pleasants passed the suggestion along, more formally, to his division commander, Brigadier General Robert Potter, and Potter sent a staff officer around to see what this was all about. Pleasants took the man to a place in the trench where they could get a good view of the Rebel fort. While they were looking over the parapet, the staff man unfortunately was hit in the face by a Confederate bullet, but after he had been carried away Pleasants drew a rough sketch of the terrain and sent it to Potter, and a few days later Potter sent for him and took him back to corps headquarters to see Burnside.

It was a sweltering hot night, and the two officers found Burnside sitting in his tent, coat off, bald head glistening in the candlelight, a long cigar cocked up at the side of his mouth. Burnside put the young colonel at his ease at once, and listened intently while the plan was explained, mopping beads of sweat off his forehead with a big silk bandanna while they talked.

Modestly enough, Pleasants admitted getting his idea from a chance remark dropped by an enlisted man. He then went on to explain how they could begin a tunnel on a sheltered spot on the hillside, forty or fifty yards behind their trench, where the Rebels would not be able to see what they were doing. The shaft would slant uphill, which would take care of the drainage problem, and although it would probably have to be more than 500 feet long, Pleasants thought he could devise a means of ventilating it.

Burnside liked the idea and he said he would take it up with Meade. Meanwhile, he said, Pleasants should go ahead with it. So the next day Pleasants organized his coal miners into details, led them to a spot on the protected side of the ravine, and put them to work. Lacking picks, they began by using their bayonets, and in no time at all they were underground.

Meade took very little stock in the project, but he felt that it was good to keep the troops busy. Also, his engineers had just reported that "the new era in field works has so changed their character as in fact to render them almost as strong as permanent ones," and every professional soldier knew that the only way to take permanent fortifications was through the long, ritualized processes of siege warfare. This involved an almost endless dig-and-fill routine—an advance by regular approaches, in military jargon—the general object of which was to inch one's own lines forward far enough so that heavy guns could be mounted where they could flatten the enemy's works at short range. The trouble was that the conditions which would make siege warfare successful simply did not exist here. Petersburg was by no means surrounded, and the Federals did not begin to have the necessary preponderance of force.

So when Burnside came in with this new idea, Meade was prepared to be receptive. The same could not be said for his engineers, who pooh-

poohed the whole proposal and said it was clap-trap and nonsense. They said loftily that there was nothing novel about mining the enemy's works —it was standard operating procedure, once the besieging party had brought its own trenches up to within a few yards of the objective point—but they declared that no army on earth had ever tried to do it at anything like the distance involved on Burnside's front. A mine shaft of that length, they went on, could not possibly be ventilated and the men who had to dig it would all be suffocated, if they were not first crushed under falling earth. Besides, the Rebels would find out about it and would interfere. The army's engineers, in short, would have none of it.

Meade himself felt much the same way, but Grant was anxious to get on with the war and he was pressing Meade to see if there was not some way to break the Rebel front. Meade had to confess that there did not seem to be any way, but he did tell Grant that Burnside had some men digging a mine "which General B. thinks when exploded will enable him by a formidable assault to carry the line of works." So with this cautious endorsement, and largely because there was nothing else in sight, the Schuylkill miners suddenly began to be very important people.

Pleasants began by getting from each of his company commanders a list of all the men who were actually coal miners. He organized these men into shifts, with a non-com named Harry Reese as mine boss, precisely as if he were going to mine for coal, and he put them to work round the clock, seeing to it that each man got a dram of commissary whisky when he finished his stint. Picks and shovels were supplied, and although the picks were not the kind used in coal mines, there were plenty of blacksmiths in IX Corps artillery units and Pleasants persuaded them to remodel the implements. The work went faster than he had anticipated, and in a short time he needed timbers to shore up the ceiling and walls.

At this point he found that the army was letting him do this job rather than helping him do it. Meade had promised Burnside to send a company of engineers and any other aid that might be needed, but the company never showed up and when Pleasants asked for some timber nothing seemed to happen. So Pleasants sent a detail from his regiment down into the ravine behind the lines, tore down a railroad bridge, and used those timbers as long as they lasted. Then he discovered an abandoned sawmill four or five miles to the rear. He got Burnside to issue a pass and provide some horses and wagons, and he sent two companies back to operate the mill and cut the necessary lumber.

Pleasants also needed handbarrows to carry the dirt out of the tunnel and dispose of it in some place where Rebel lookouts would not see it. Army headquarters had promised sandbags, but the sandbags never arrived, so

Pleasants collected cracker boxes, reinforced them with iron hoops taken from pork barrels, nailed stout handles on them, and detailed parties to lug these in and out of the shaft.

After a week progress came to a halt when the miners struck a belt of wet clay and the ceiling sagged, breaking the timbers and nearly closing the tunnel. Pleasants retimbered the shaft, shored up the ceiling with stouter props, and drove on. Next he struck a bed of marl which had a way of turning to rock soon after the air struck it. The soldiers amused themselves by carving tobacco pipes out of this in their spare time, but it was mean stuff to tunnel through and the colonel finally had to increase the tunnel's angle of climb so as to get into a softer earth stratum. He was making his tunnel five feet high, four feet wide at the bottom, and some two and one half feet wide at the top, and it was strongly timbered all the way—ceiling, both sides, and floor. Cutting and transporting all of this timber and getting it inside the mine, and taking all of the dirt out and concealing it in the ravine under fresh-cut bushes, kept calling for more and more hands, and before long practically the entire regiment was at work.

When the shaft had gone a couple of hundred feet into the hillside, Pleasants felt that it was time to make some exact calculations about the spot where the powder magazine ought to go. (Obviously he would accomplish nothing if he dug past the Rebel fort or stopped short of it.) So he applied to the engineers for the instruments with which he could make the necessary triangulations. The engineers laughed this off, and a plea to Meade's headquarters was lost in the shuffle somewhere, and at last Burnside—who seems to have been the only important officer in the army who was disposed to be helpful—wired to a friend in Washington and had him send down a theodolite.

Pleasants had to take this into the front line to make his observations, and of course Rebel snipers were apt to shoot him while he was doing it. He got around this by having half a dozen soldiers put their caps on ramrods and raise them just above the parapet. While the sharpshooters peppered away at these, hitting them quite regularly and no doubt imagining that they were hitting human heads inside of them, Pleasants draped some burlap over his head and his instrument, got unobserved over the parapet level a few yards away, and made his observations.

Farther and farther into the hillside went the tunnel. As the engineers had prophesied, ventilation was a problem, but Pleasants solved it. Close beside the tunnel, at a point just behind the main Federal trench, he dug a vertical shaft whose lower end opened into a little recess in the tunnel wall and whose upper end discharged unobtrusively into a clump of bushes. Then he built a square tube of boards, reaching from the mouth of the tunnel all the way to its inner end, and he prepared a door by which the outer end of the tunnel could be sealed shut, leaving the open end of the wooden tube protruding out into the air. The rest was simple: close the door and build a fire in the little recess at the bottom of the vertical shaft. The smoke and heated air went up this chimney, the resultant draft pulled the bad air out of the tunnel, and fresh air from the outside was drawn in through the wooden tube.

On July 17, three weeks after the job had been begun, the inner end of the tunnel was squarely beneath the Confederate redoubt, twenty-odd feet underground and 510 feet from the entrance, and the miners could hear Confederate soldiers tramping about overhead. Pleasants then had his men dig a 75-foot shaft running across the end of the tunnel; a diagram of his work now would look like a capital *T* with a very long shank, with a crossbar of the *T* running along directly beneath the Confederate works.

Pleasants then reported that the mine was ready for its charge of powder—at which point further operations were temporarily suspended because the Rebels had discovered that the Yankees were digging a mine and were sinking shafts of their own trying to find it.

Confederate luck right here was bad. Their engineers misjudged the direction the tunnel was taking, and their countermining shafts failed to intersect it. When Pleasants had his men stop working, the Rebels in underground listening posts could hear nothing, and in the end all of their protective measures failed. Meanwhile, the Southern privates who were going about their business directly above the dark sinister gallery began to treat the whole affair as another camp rumor, and now and then they would call across and ask the Yankees when the big show was going to begin.

After a pause, with the digging and timbering all finished, Pleasants went to work to lay the powder charges. Burnside wanted to use eight tons of powder, but the army engineers had one good suggestion here—the use of explosives in quantity was a subject they really knew something about—and they pointed out that a smaller charge would actually be more effective. In the end, Burnside settled for four tons, and Pleasants had his men build eight open-topped wooden boxes in the lateral gallery for magazines. The powder was delivered behind the lines in 320 kegs, each containing 25 pounds, and there was day-and-night work carrying these into the mine and pouring the charges into the magazines.

All of the magazines were connected by wooden troughs half filled with powder, and these troughs met at the place where the gallery crossed the inner end of the main shaft. The engineers had promised Pleasants a supply of wire and a "galvanic battery" to touch off the charge, but this was another delivery that was never made, so Pleasants got a supply of ordinary fuses, spliced them together, introduced one end into the powder in the trough, and strung the rest of the fuse back along the tunnel for about one hundred feet. As a final step, earth was solidly tamped into place, filling the main shaft for thirty-eight feet from the place where it met the lateral gallery. . . .

The night wore away, silent except for the shuffling of thousands of men moving to their places, and a little after three o'clock in the morning Pleasants sent a man into the mine and shaft to set fire to the fuse. . . .

Half-past three came, with the high command fingering watches and staring off into the dark, and nothing happened. Another half hour went by, and half an hour more on top of that, and the silence was unbroken, except for the occasional discharge of some wakeful picket's musket. Grant got impatient, and at last he told Meade to have Burnside make his charge regardless: something had gone wrong with the mine, and there was no use waiting any longer. In the east the sky was turning gray—and five eighths of Lee's army was north of the James River, with the full strength of the Army of the Potomac massed to smash through the fraction that was left.

Grant was impatient, and Meade was impatient, and probably even Burnside was getting a little restless; but the man who was really excited was Colonel Pleasants. About the time Grant was saying that the charge had better go ahead without the explosion, Pleasants called Sergeant Harry Reese, the mine boss, and told him to go into the tunnel and see what was the matter.

In went Reese, on as nerve-racking an assignment as the war could produce, groping forward all bent over along 400 feet of a dark tunnel, never sure that the solid earth ahead was not going to quake and heave and tumble to bury him forever. He got to the fuse, traced it, and found that the spark had died at a place where one fuse had been spliced to another. He started back to get a new fuse, found Lieutenant Jacob Douty coming in, at Pleasants's direction, with the material he needed, and he and Douty went back to the splice and made a new connection. Then he lit the spark again, and he and Lieutenant Douty came out of the tunnel as fast as they could travel—and the sky grew lighter in the east, so that ridges and trees and hillocks became dark shadows outlined against the dying night, and the whole Army of the Potomac stood by gripping its muskets, waiting for nobody knew just what.

Four forty-five: and at last it happened.

To the men who were waiting in the front line it seemed to occur in slow motion: first a long, deep rumble, like summer thunder rolling along a faraway horizon, then a swaying and swelling of the ground up ahead, with the solid earth rising to form a rounded hill, everything seeming very gradual and leisurely. Then the rounded hill broke apart, and a prodigious spout of flame and black smoke went up toward the sky, and the air was full of enormous clods of earth as big as houses, of brass cannon and detached artillery wheels, of wrecked caissons and fluttering tents and weirdly tumbling human bodies; and there was a crash "like the noise of great thunders," followed by other, lesser explosions, and all of the landscape along the firing line had turned into dust and smoke and flying debris, choking and blinding men and threatening to engulf Burnside's whole army corps.

Different men saw it and felt it in different ways. A soldier in the 36th Massachusetts wrote that "we witnessed a volcano and experienced an earthquake," yet an officer in Ferrero's division, standing not a third of a mile away from the explosion, recalled it as "a dull, heavy thud, not at all startling . . . a heavy, smothered sound, not nearly so distinct as a musket shot." A man in Pleasants's own 48th Pennsylvania remembered it as "a magnificent spectacle," and another soldier recalled that a bronze cannon was tossed nearly over to the Union line. To one man the whole thing looked like "a waterspout as seen at sea," another felt it as "a heavy shaking of the earth, with a rumbling, muffled sound," and to men in Hancock's corps, waiting behind the artillery, it seemed that the solid earth went up "like an enormous whirlwind."

THERE WAS A LULL IN THE RAID

FROM *London Calling*

STORM JAMESON

There are no heroics in this incident of the London bombings told by Storm Jameson, no great air battles or divisions in combat or titanic naval engagements. Nothing more than a bomb hole and rubble and a child. But it is war in all its horror none the less.

Storm Jameson has known war too well. Her brother was killed in the first World War and her son fought in the R.A.F. in the second. She herself worked through the worst of the London blitz as president of the English branch of P.E.N. in close touch with writers in countries overrun by the German armies.

IT WAS A MODERATELY BAD RAID. A WOMAN ARRIVED IN LONDON BY A LATE train, long after dark. The darkness was naturally relative; there were fires, tracer bullets, flares, and the rest of it. She could have sheltered in the tube, but she had a tic about sleeping in her bed. There was a lull in the raid, a something enough like silence to be mistaken for it. She set out to walk home. Turning into one street, she saw that it had caught it earlier in the night; there was a crashed house lying partly in the road. She was too tired to take a longer way round and went forward hoping to be allowed to scramble past. Men had been digging, and they had stopped. Just as she reached this, in those days very ordinary place, a raid warden separated himself from the rubble and said, "Can anyone here sing?" A moment of stupefied silence. Someone said, "Nay, I can't." But the question seemed to make the woman's presence there respectable. She asked, "What do you want?" In a matter-of-fact voice the warden explained that a child was alive under the house, a little girl, she did not seem to be hurt at all—at any rate, when he asked, she said No—and she was not frightened, but she kept on asking for someone to sing to her. The woman had no singing voice at all, oh not at all. But she had been used, she said, to sing to her son when he was a baby. "That would perhaps do," the warden said.

"Very well, where shall I go?"

"Here. You don't mind the chance of the rest of the wall coming down on you, I suppose."

It was a quite unwarranted supposition. The woman was thoroughly alarmed. She lay down where she was told, on the rubble, to bring her mouth to the end of the way by which the child's voice had reached the upper world. There is no other way to describe it. Imagine yourself hearing a voice from ground you are crossing at night. . . . The warden crouched down. "You're all right, you're not hurting?" he said gently. The reedy voice came up. "No."

"What shall I sing?"

"Sing about the old woman," the child said.

"There was an old woman who went up in a basket?" the woman said, "do you mean that one?"

"Yes." The child sounded impatient that anyone could doubt she meant that old woman and no other.

"They're going to try digging at the other side," the warden said, "this here looks like coming down on her."

There was an old woman went up in a basket
Ninety times as high as the moon,
And where she was going I couldn't but ask it,
For in her hand she carried a broom.
Old woman, old woman, said I
Whither, O whither, away so high?
To sweep the cobwebs out of the sky
And I shall come back again by and by. . . .

This woman's mother had taught her the tune and the words; she in turn had taught them to her son, who very likely did not remember them. All these memories have to end somewhere, or the world would be choked with them. The almost tuneless old tunes, the rubbed stone of old walls, the innocent curve of old lanes, must be effaced to make room for the future. And if the future is less charming? So much the worse for it. . . . The raid had started again, but her voice, thin as it was, reached the child by a line shorter than the lines joining the German planes to the houses and streets of London. She sang it through once and stopped. She knew what the child would say. The child said it.

"Again."

It is one of the first words a child learns. Why? Perhaps it guesses that there are not enough new joys to go round. She sang it again.

"Again. . . ."

She sang it three, four, five times. This time there was no answer. "Shall I sing something else?" No answer. She twisted round to speak to the warden. "I think she is dead."

He was suddenly and bitterly angry. "Oh, no, she isn't! She'll have dropped off to sleep."

It was daylight when the men digging were able to lower a doctor and another man into the cellar. The first thing to be brought back was a curious monster, formed of two women crushed together and covered thickly with plaster. Then the dead child. The lower half of her little body had been crushed. How had she lived for four hours? The warden was angry again.

"You're not going to tell me . . ." he sputtered.

Tell him what? That the night sky is less innocent than it was in the days of old women in baskets, or that death is not death? He bent stubbornly over the stretcher. It is impossible that a child lives in such circumstances or dies after demanding again and again something quite idiotic. But everything, the woman wanted to tell him, is impossible in an air-raid. It is impossible that brave young men have been trained to crush the bodies of children, it is impossible that a song which served to put one child to bed serves just as well to put another one to die.

6 AUGUST 1945

FROM *Hiroshima Diary: The Journal of a Japanese Physician, August 6–September 30, 1945*

MICHIHIKO HACHIYA

In 1950 Warner Wells, the translator-and-editor-to-be of Dr. Hachiya's *Hiroshima Diary,* became a surgical consultant to the Atom Bomb Casuality Commission which operated in Hiroshima and Nagasaki. Dr. Wells learned that Dr. Hachiya, Director of the Hiroshima Communications Hospital, had written a diary of his experiences after the atomic bomb had struck Hiroshima. The Hiroshima Communications Hospital, of strong, reinforced concrete construction, was located about 1,500 meters from the hypocenter of the bomb. Dr. Hachiya's house was only a few hundred meters from the hospital.

Dr. Wells prepared the rough draft of the translation with the help of Dr. Neal Tsukifujii, and then spent three further years polishing and editing the diary in an effort to retain the simplicity and literary quality Dr. Hachiya achieved in his own tongue.

THE HOUR WAS EARLY; THE MORNING STILL, WARM, AND BEAUTIFUL. SHIMMERING leaves, reflecting sunlight from a cloudless sky, made a pleasant contrast with shadows in my garden as I gazed absently through wide-flung doors opening to the south.

Clad in drawers and undershirt, I was sprawled on the living room floor exhausted because I had just spent a sleepless night on duty as an air warden in my hospital.

Suddenly, a strong flash of light startled me—and then another. So well does one recall little things that I remember vividly how a stone lantern in the garden became brilliantly lit and I debated whether this light was caused by a magnesium flare or sparks from a passing trolley.

Garden shadows disappeared. The view where a moment before all had been so bright and sunny was now dark and hazy. Through swirling dust I could barely discern a wooden column that had supported one corner of my house. It was leaning crazily and the roof sagged dangerously.

Moving instinctively, I tried to escape, but rubble and fallen timbers barred the way. By picking my way cautiously I managed to reach the *rōka* and stepped down into my garden. A profound weakness overcame me, so I stopped to regain my strength. To my surprise I discovered that I was completely naked. How odd! Where were my drawers and undershirt?

What had happened?

All over the right side of my body I was cut and bleeding. A large splinter was protruding from a mangled wound in my thigh, and something warm trickled into my mouth. My cheek was torn, I discovered as I felt it gingerly, with the lower lip laid wide open. Embedded in my neck was a sizable fragment of glass which I matter-of-factly dislodged, and with the detachment of one stunned and shocked I studied it and my blood-stained hand.

Where was my wife?

Suddenly thoroughly alarmed, I began to yell for her: "Yaeko-san! Yaeko-san! Where are you?"

Blood began to spurt. Had my carotid artery been cut? Would I bleed to death? Frightened and irrational, I called out again: "It's a five-hundred-ton bomb! Yaeko-san, where are you? A five-hundred-ton bomb has fallen!"

Yaeko-san, pale and frightened, her clothes torn and blood-stained, emerged from the ruins of our house holding her elbow. Seeing her, I was reassured. My own panic assuaged, I tried to reassure her.

"We'll be all right," I exclaimed. "Only let's get out of here as fast as we can."

She nodded, and I motioned for her to follow me.

The shortest path to the street lay through the house next door so through the house we went—running, stumbling, falling, and then running again until in headlong flight we tripped over something and fell sprawling into the street. Getting to my feet, I discovered that I had tripped over a man's head.

"Excuse me! Excuse me, please!" I cried hysterically.

There was no answer. The man was dead. The head had belonged to a young officer whose body was crushed beneath a massive gate.

We stood in the street, uncertain and afraid, until a house across from us began to sway and then with a rending motion fell almost at our feet. Our own house began to sway, and in a minute it, too, collapsed in a cloud of dust. Other buildings caved in or toppled. Fires sprang up and whipped by a vicious wind began to spread.

It finally dawned on us that we could not stay there in the street, so we turned our steps towards the hospital. Our home was gone; we were wounded and needed treatment; and after all, it was my duty to be with my staff. This latter was an irrational thought—what good could I be to anyone, hurt as I was.

We started out, but after twenty or thirty steps I had to stop. My breath became short, my heart pounded, and my legs gave way under me. An overpowering thirst seized me and I begged Yaeko-san to find me some water. But there was no water to be found. After a little my strength somewhat returned and we were able to go on.

I was still naked, and although I did not feel the least bit of shame, I was disturbed to realize that modesty had deserted me. On rounding a corner we came upon a soldier standing idly in the street. He had a towel draped across his shoulder, and I asked if he would give it to me to cover my nakedness. The soldier surrendered the towel quite willingly but said not a word. A little later I lost the towel, and Yaeko-san took off her apron and tied it around my loins.

Our progress toward the hospital was interminably slow, until finally, my legs, stiff from drying blood, refused to carry me farther. The strength, even the will, to go on deserted me, so I told my wife, who was almost as badly hurt as I, to go on alone. This she objected to, but there was no choice. She had to go ahead and try to find someone to come back for me.

Yaeko-san looked into my face for a moment, and then, without saying a word, turned away and began running towards the hospital. Once, she looked back and waved and in a moment she was swallowed up in the gloom. It was quite dark now, and with my wife gone, a feeling of dreadful loneliness overcame me.

I must have gone out of my head lying there in the road because the next thing I recall was discovering that the clot on my thigh had been dislodged and blood was again spurting from the wound. I pressed my hand to the bleeding area and after a while the bleeding stopped and I felt better.

Could I go on?

I tried. It was all a nightmare—my wounds, the darkness, the road ahead. My movements were ever so slow; only my mind was running at top speed.

In time I came to an open space where the houses had been removed to make a fire lane. Through the dim light I could make out ahead of me the hazy outlines of the Communications Bureau's big concrete building, and beyond it the hospital. My spirits rose because I knew that now someone would find me; and if I should die, at least my body would be found.

I paused to rest. Gradually things around me came into focus. There were the shadowy forms of people, some of whom looked like walking ghosts. Others moved as though in pain, like scarecrows, their arms held out from their bodies with forearms and hands dangling. These people puzzled me until I suddenly realized that they had been burned and were holding their arms out to prevent the painful friction of raw surfaces rubbing together. A naked woman carrying a naked baby came into view. I averted my gaze.

Perhaps they had been in the bath. But then I saw a naked man, and it occurred to me that, like myself, some strange thing had deprived them of their clothes. An old woman lay near me with an expression of suffering on her face; but she made no sound. Indeed, one thing was common to everyone I saw—complete silence.

All who could were moving in the direction of the hospital. I joined in the dismal parade when my strength was somewhat recovered, and at last reached the gates of the Communications Bureau.

Familiar surroundings, familiar faces. There was Mr. Iguchi and Mr. Yoshihiro and my old friend, Mr. Sera, the head of the business office. They hastened to give me a hand, their expressions of pleasure changing to alarm when they saw that I was hurt. I was too happy to see them to share their concern.

No time was lost over greetings. They eased me onto a stretcher and carried me into the Communications Building, ignoring my protests that I could walk. Later, I learned that the hospital was so overrun that the Communications Bureau had to be used as an emergency hospital. The rooms and corridors were crowded with people, many of whom I recognized as neighbors. To me it seemed that the whole community was there.

My friends passed me through an open window into a janitor's room recently converted to an emergency first-aid station. The room was a shambles; fallen plaster, broken furniture, and debris littered the floor; the walls were cracked; and a heavy steel window casement was twisted and almost wrenched from its seating. What a place to dress the wounds of the injured.

To my great surprise who should appear but my private nurse, Miss Kado, and Mr. Mizoguchi, and old Mrs. Saeki. Miss Kado set about examining my wounds without speaking a word. No one spoke. I asked for a shirt and pajamas. They got them for me, but still no one spoke. Why was everyone so quiet?

Miss Kado finished the examination, and in a moment it felt as if my chest was on fire. She had begun to paint my wounds with iodine and no amount of entreaty would make her stop. With no alternative but to endure the iodine, I tried to divert myself by looking out the window.

The hospital lay directly opposite with part of the roof and the third floor sunroom in plain view, and as I looked up, I witnessed a sight which made me forget my smarting wounds. Smoke was pouring out of the sunroom windows. The hospital was afire!

"Fire!" I shouted. "Fire! Fire! The hospital is on fire!"

My friends looked up. It was true. The hospital *was* on fire.

The alarm was given and from all sides people took up the cry. The high-pitched voice of Mr. Sera, the business officer, rose above the others, and it seemed as if his was the first voice I had heard that day. The uncanny stillness was broken. Our little world was now in pandemonium.

I remember that Dr. Sasada, chief of the Pediatric Service, came in and tried to reassure me, but I could scarcely hear him above the din. I heard Dr. Hinoi's voice and then Dr. Koyama's. Both were shouting orders to evacuate the hospital and with such vigor that it sounded as though the sheer strength of their voices could hasten those who were slow to obey.

The sky became bright as flames from the hospital mounted. Soon the Bureau was threatened and Mr. Sera gave the order to evacuate. My stretcher was moved into a rear garden and placed beneath an old cherry tree. Other patients limped into the garden or were carried until soon the entire area became so crowded that only the very ill had room to lie down. No one talked, and the ominous silence was relieved only by a subdued rustle among so many people, restless, in pain, anxious, and afraid, waiting for something else to happen.

The sky filled with black smoke and glowing sparks. Flames rose and the heat set currents of air in motion. Updrafts became so violent that sheets of zinc roofing were hurled aloft and released, humming and twirling, in erratic flight. Pieces of flaming wood soared and fell like fiery swallows. While I was trying to beat out the flames, a hot ember seared my ankle. It was all I could do to keep from being burned alive.

The Bureau started to burn, and window after window became a square of flame until the whole structure was converted into a crackling, hissing inferno.

Scorching winds howled around us, whipping dust and ashes into our eyes and up our noses. Our mouths became dry, our throats raw and sore from the biting smoke pulled into our lungs. Coughing was uncontrollable. We would have moved back, but a group of wooden barracks behind us caught fire and began to burn like tinder.

The heat finally became too intense to endure, and we were left no choice but to abandon the garden. Those who could fled; those who could not perished. Had it not been for my devoted friends, I would have died, but again, they came to the rescue and carried my stretcher to the main gate on the other side of the Bureau.

Here, a small group of people were already clustered, and here I found my wife. Dr. Sasada and Miss Kado joined us.

Fires sprang up on every side as violent winds fanned flames from one building to another. Soon, we were surrounded. The ground we held in front of the Communications Bureau became an oasis in a desert of fire. As the flames came closer the heat became more intense, and if someone in our group had not had the presence of mind to drench us with water from a fire hose, I doubt if anyone could have survived.

Hot as it was, I began to shiver. The drenching was too much. My heart pounded; things began to whirl until all before me blurred.

"Kurushii," I murmured weakly. "I am done."

The sound of voices reached my ears as though from a great distance and finally became louder as if close at hand. I opened my eyes; Dr. Sasada was feeling my pulse. What had happened? Miss Kado gave me an injection. My strength gradually returned. I must have fainted.

Huge raindrops began to fall. Some thought a thunderstorm was beginning and would extinguish the fires. But these drops were capricious. A few fell and then a few more and that was all the rain we saw.

The first floor of the Bureau was now ablaze and flames were spreading rapidly toward our little oasis by the gate. Right then, I could hardly understand the situation, much less do anything about it.

An iron window frame, loosened by fire, crashed to the ground behind us. A ball of fire whizzed by me, setting my clothes ablaze. They drenched me with water again. From then on I am confused as to what happened.

I do remember Dr. Hinoi because of the pain, the pain I felt when he jerked me to my feet. I remember being moved or rather dragged, and my whole spirit rebelling against the torment I was made to endure.

My next memory is of an open area. The fires must have receded. I was alive. My friends had somehow managed to rescue me again.

A head popped out of an air-raid dugout, and I heard the unmistakable voice of old Mrs. Saeki: "Cheer up, doctor! Everything will be all right. The north side is burnt out. We have nothing further to fear from the fire."

I might have been her son, the way the old lady calmed and reassured me. And indeed, she was right. The entire northern side of the city was completely burned. The sky was still dark, but whether it was evening or midday I could not tell. It might even have been the next day. Time had no meaning. What I had experienced might have been crowded into a moment or been endured through the monotony of eternity.

Smoke was still rising from the second floor of the hospital, but the fire had stopped. There was nothing left to burn, I thought; but later I learned that the first floor of the hospital had escaped destruction largely through the courageous efforts of Dr. Koyama and Dr. Hinoi.

The streets were deserted except for the dead. Some looked as if they had been frozen by death while in the full action of flight; others lay sprawled as though some giant had flung them to their death from a great height.

Hiroshima was no longer a city, but a burnt-over prairie. To the east and to the west everything was flattened. The distant mountains seemed nearer than I could ever remember. The hills of Ushita and the woods of Nigitsu loomed out of the haze and smoke like the nose and eyes on a face. How small Hiroshima was with its houses gone.

The wind changed and the sky again darkened with smoke.

Suddenly, I heard someone shout: "Planes! Enemy planes!"

Could that be possible after what had already happened? What was there left to bomb? My thoughts were interrupted by the sound of a familiar name.

A nurse calling Dr. Katsube.

"It is Dr. Katsube! It's him!" shouted old Mrs. Saeki, a happy ring to her voice. "Dr. Katsube has come!"

It was Dr. Katsube, our head surgeon, but he seemed completely unaware of us as he hurried past, making a straight line for the hospital. Enemy planes were forgotten, so great was our happiness that Dr. Katsube had been spared to return to us.

Before I could protest, my friends were carrying me into the hospital. The distance was only a hundred meters, but it was enough to cause my heart to pound and make me sick and faint.

I recall the hard table and the pain when my face and lip were sutured, but I have no recollection of the forty or more other wounds Dr. Katsube closed before night.

They removed me to an adjoining room, and I remember feeling relaxed and sleepy. The sun had gone down, leaving a dark red sky. The red flames of the burning city had scorched the heavens. I gazed at the sky until sleep overtook me.

''I DID NOT WANT TO KILL YOU''

FROM *All Quiet on the Western Front*

ERICH MARIA REMARQUE

By far the most widely read novel to come out of the first World War was Erich Maria Remarque's *All Quiet on the Western Front.* In Germany alone it sold more than a million copies and in this country, in England and in France it had an enormous reading public. It is possible that its popularity derived from its implicit pacificism. It was published in 1929, ten years removed from the war, and with the world already making preparations for the second.

In this selection Remarque has two soldiers, enemies, caught in a shell hole. The enemy you bayonet, he says, must remain faceless. Once he acquires a face, you do not see the enemy, you see a man.

A PATROL HAS TO BE SENT OUT TO DISCOVER JUST HOW FAR THE ENEMY position is advanced. Since my leave I feel a certain strange attachment to the other fellows, and so I volunteer to go with them. We agree on a plan, slip out through the wire and then divide and creep forward separately. After a while I find a shallow shell-hole and crawl into it. From here I peer forward.

There is moderate machine-gun fire. It sweeps across from all directions, not very heavy, but always sufficient to make one keep down.

A parachute star-shell opens out. The ground lies stark in the pale light, and then the darkness shuts down again blacker than ever. In the trenches we were told there were black troops in front of us. That is nasty, it is hard to see them; they are very good at patrolling, too. And oddly enough they are often quite stupid; for instance, both Kat and Kropp were once able to shoot down a black enemy patrol because the fellows in their enthusiasm for cigarettes smoked while they were creeping about. Kat and Albert had simply to aim at the glowing ends of the cigarettes.

A bomb or something lands close beside me. I have not heard it coming and am terrified. At the same moment a senseless fear takes hold on me.

Here I am alone and almost helpless in the dark—perhaps two other eyes have been watching me for a long while from another shell-hole in front of me, and a bomb lies ready to blow me to pieces. I try to pull myself together. It is not my first patrol and not a particularly risky one. But it is the first since my leave, and besides, the lie of the land is still rather strange to me.

I tell myself that my alarm is absurd, that there is probably nothing at all there in the darkness watching me, because otherwise the missile would not have landed so flat.

It is in vain. In whirling confusion my thoughts hum in my brain—I hear the warning voice of my mother, I see the Russians with the flowing beards leaning against the wire fence, I have a bright picture of a canteen with stools, of a cinema in Valenciennes; tormented, terrified, in my imagination I see the grey, impalpable muzzle of a rifle which moves noiselessly before me whichever way I try to turn my head. The sweat breaks out from every pore.

I still continue to lie in my shallow bowl. I look at the time; only a few minutes have passed. My forehead is wet, the sockets of my eyes are damp, my hands tremble, and I am panting softly. It is nothing but an awful spasm of fear, a simple animal fear of poking out my head and crawling on farther.

All my efforts subside like froth into the one desire to be able just to stay lying there. My limbs are glued to the earth. I make a vain attempt;—they refuse to come away. I press myself down on the earth, I cannot go forward, I make up my mind to stay lying there.

But immediately the wave floods over me anew, a mingled sense of shame, of remorse, and yet at the same time of security. I raise myself up a little to take a look around.

My eyes burn with staring into the dark. A star-shell goes up;—I duck down again.

I wage a wild and senseless fight, I want to get out of the hollow and yet slide back into it again, I say: "You must, it is your comrades, it is not any idiotic command," and again: "What does it matter to me, I have only one life to lose—"

That is the result of all this leave, I reproach myself bitterly. But I cannot convince myself, I become terribly faint. I raise myself slowly and reach forward with my arms, dragging my body after me and then lie on the edge of the shell-hole, half in and half out.

There I hear sounds and drop back. Suspicious sounds can be detected clearly despite the noise of the artillery-fire. I listen; the sound is behind me. They are our people moving along the trench. Now I hear muffled voices. To judge by the tone that might be Kat talking.

At once a new warmth flows through me. These voices, these few quiet words, these footsteps in the trench behind me recall me at a bound from the terrible loneliness and fear of death by which I had been almost destroyed. They are more to me than life, these voices, they are more than motherliness and more than fear; they are the strongest, most comforting thing there is anywhere: they are the voices of my comrades.

I am no longer a shuddering speck of existence, alone in the darkness;—I belong to them and they to me, we all share the same fear and the same life, we are nearer than lovers, in a simpler, a harder way; I could bury my face in them, in these voices, these words that have saved me and will stand by me.

Cautiously I glide out over the edge and snake my way forward. I shuffle along on all fours a bit farther, I keep track of my bearings, look around me and observe the distribution of the gun-fire so as to be able to find my way back. Then I try to get in touch with the others.

I am still afraid, but it is an intelligent fear, an extraordinarily heightened caution. The night is windy and shadows flit hither and thither in the flicker of the gun-fire. It reveals too little and too much. Often I peer ahead, but always for nothing. Thus I advance a long way and then turn back in a wide curve. I have not established touch with the others. Every yard nearer our trench fills me with confidence;—and with haste, too. It would be bad to get lost now.

Then a new fear lays hold of me. I can no longer remember the direction. Quiet, I squat in a shell-hole and try to locate myself. More than once it has happened that some fellow has jumped joyfully into a trench only then to discover that it was the wrong one.

After a little time I listen again, but still I am not sure. The confusion of shell-holes now seems so bewildering that I can no longer tell in my agitation which way I should go. Perhaps I am crawling parallel to the lines, and that might go on for ever. So I crawl round once again in a wide curve.

These damned rockets! They seem to burn for an hour, and a man cannot make the least movement without bringing the bullets whistling round.

But there is nothing for it, I must get out. Falteringly I work my way farther, I move off over the ground like a crab and rip my hands sorely on the jagged splinters, as sharp as razor blades. Often I think that the sky is becoming lighter on the horizon, but it may be merely my imagination. Then gradually I realize that to crawl in the right direction is a matter of life or death.

A shell crashes. Almost immediately two others. And then it begins in earnest. A bombardment. Machine-guns rattle. Now there is nothing for it but to stay lying low. Apparently an attack is coming. Everywhere the rockets shoot up. Unceasing.

I lie huddled in a large shell-hole, my legs in the water up to the belly. When the attack starts I will let myself fall into the water, with my face as deep in the mud as I can keep it without suffocating. I must pretend to be dead.

Suddenly I hear the barrage lift. At once I slip down into the water, my helmet on the nape of my neck and my mouth just clear so that I can get a breath of air.

I lie motionless;—somewhere something clanks, it stamps and stumbles nearer—all my nerves become taut and icy. It clatters over me and away, the first wave has passed. I have but this one shattering thought: What will you do if someone jumps into your shell-hole?—Swiftly I pull out my little dagger, grasp it fast and bury it in my hand once again under the mud. If anyone jumps in here I will go for him; it hammers in my forehead; at once, stab him clean through the throat, so that he cannot call out; that's the only way; he will be just as frightened as I am, when in terror we fall upon one another, then I must be first.

Now our batteries are firing. A shell lands near me. That makes me savage with fury, all it needs now is to be killed by our own shells; I curse and grind my teeth in the mud; it is a raving frenzy; in the end all I can do is groan and pray.

The crash of the shells bursts in my ears. If our fellows make a counter-raid I will be saved. I press my head against the earth and listen to the muffled thunder, like the explosions of quarrying—and raise it again to listen for the sounds on top.

The machine-guns rattle. I know our barbed-wire entanglements are strong and almost undamaged;—parts of them are charged with a powerful electric current. The rifle-fire increases. They have not broken through; they have to retreat.

I sink down again, huddled, strained to the uttermost. The banging, the creeping, the clanging becomes audible. One single cry yelling amongst it all. They are raked with fire, the attack is repulsed.

Already it has become somewhat lighter. Steps hasten over me. The first. Gone. Again, another. The rattle of machine-guns becomes an unbroken chain. Just as I am about to turn round a little, something heavy stumbles, and with a crash a body falls over me into the shell-hole, slips down, and lies across me—

I do not think at all, I make no decision—I strike madly home, and feel only how the body suddenly convulses, then becomes limp, and collapses. When I recover myself, my hand is sticky and wet.

The man gurgles. It sounds to me as though he bellows, every gasping breath is like a cry, a thunder—but it is only my heart pounding. I want to stop his mouth, stuff it with earth, stab him again, he must be quiet, he is betraying me; now at last I regain control of myself, but have suddenly become so feeble that I cannot any more lift my hand against him.

So I crawl away to the farthest corner and stay there, my eyes glued on him, my hand grasping the knife—ready, if he stirs, to spring at him again. But he won't do so any more, I can hear that already in his gurgling.

I can see him indistinctly. I have but one desire, to get away. If it is not soon it will be too light; it will be difficult enough now. Then as I try to raise up my head I see it is impossible already. The machine-gun fire so sweeps the ground that I would be shot through and through before I could make one jump.

I test it once with my helmet, which I take off and hold up to find out the level of the shots. The next moment it is knocked out of my hand by a bullet. The fire is sweeping very low over the ground. I am not far enough from the enemy line to escape being picked off by one of the snipers if I attempt to get away.

The light increases. Burning I wait for our attack. My hands are white at the knuckles, I clench them so tightly in my longing for the fire to cease so that my comrades may come.

Minute after minute trickles away. I dare not look again at the dark figure in the shell-hole. With an effort I look past it and wait, wait. The bullets hiss, they make a steel net, never ceasing, never ceasing.

Then I notice my bloody hand and suddenly feel nauseated. I take some earth and rub the skin with it, now my hand is muddy and the blood cannot be seen any more.

The fire does not diminish. It is equally heavy from both sides. Our fellows have probably given me up for lost long ago.

It is early morning, clear and grey. The gurgling continues, I stop my ears, but soon take my fingers away again, because then I cannot hear the other sound.

The figure opposite me moves. I shrink together and involuntarily look at it. Then my eyes remain glued to it. A man with a small pointed beard lies there, his head is fallen to one side, one arm is half-bent, his head rests helplessly upon it. The other hand lies on his chest, it is bloody.

He is dead, I say to myself, he must be dead, he doesn't feel anything any more; it is only the body that is gurgling there. Then the head tries to raise itself, for a moment the groaning becomes louder, his forehead sinks back upon his arm. The man is not dead, he is dying, but he is not dead. I drag myself toward him, hesitate, support myself on my hands, creep a bit farther, wait, again a terrible journey of three yards, a long, a terrible journey. At last I am beside him.

Then he opens his eyes. He must have heard me and gazes at me with a look of utter terror. The body lies still, but in the eyes there is such an extraordinary expression of flight that for a moment I think they have power enough to carry the body off with them. Hundreds of miles away with one bound. The body is still, perfectly still, without sound, the gurgle has ceased, but the eyes cry out, yell, all the life is gathered together in them for one tremendous effort to flee, gathered together there in a dreadful terror of death, of me.

My legs give way and I drop on my elbows. "No, no," I whisper.

The eyes follow me. I am powerless to move so long as they are there.

Then his hand slips slowly from his breast, only a little bit, it sinks just a few inches, but this movement breaks the power of the eyes. I bend forward, shake my head and whisper: "No, no, no." I raise one hand, I must show him that I want to help him, I stroke his forehead.

The eyes shrink back as the hand comes, then they lose their stare, the eyelids droop lower, the tension is past. I open his collar and place his head more comfortably upright.

His mouth stands half open, it tries to form words. The lips are dry. My water bottle is not there. I have not brought it with me. But there is water in the mud, down at the bottom of the crater. I climb down, take out my handkerchief, spread it out, push it under and scoop up the yellow water that strains through into the hollow of my hand.

He gulps it down. I fetch some more. Then I unbutton his tunic in order to bandage him if it is possible. In any case I must do it, so that if the fellows over there capture me they will see that I wanted to help him, and so will not shoot me. He tries to resist, but his hand is too feeble. The shirt is stuck and will not come away, it is buttoned at the back. So there is nothing for it but to cut it off.

I look for the knife and find it again. But when I begin to cut the shirt the eyes open once more and the cry is in them again and the demented expression, so that I must close them, press them shut and whisper: "I want to help you. Comrade, *camerade, camerade, camerade—*" eagerly repeating the word, to make him understand.

There are three stabs. My field dressing covers them, the blood runs out under it, I press it tighter; there; he groans.

That is all I can do. Now we must wait, wait.

These hours. . . . The gurgling starts again—but how slowly a man dies! For this I know—he cannot be saved. Indeed, I have tried to tell myself that he will be, but at noon this pretence breaks down and melts before his groans. If only I had not lost my revolver crawling about, I would shoot him. Stab him I cannot.

By noon I am groping on the outer limits of reason. Hunger devours me, I could almost weep for something to eat, I cannot struggle against it. Again and again I fetch water for the dying man and drink some myself.

This is the first man I have killed with my hands, whom I can see close at hand, whose death is my doing. Kat and Kropp and Müller have experienced it already, when they have hit someone; it happens to many, in hand-to-hand fighting especially—

But every gasp lays my heart bare. This dying man has time with him, he has an invisible dagger with which he stabs me: Time and my thoughts.

I would give much if he would but stay alive. It is hard to lie here and to have to see and hear him.

In the afternoon, about three, he is dead.

I breathe freely again. But only for a short time. Soon the silence is more unbearable than the groans. I wish the gurgling were there again, gasping, hoarse, now whistling softly and again hoarse and loud.

It is mad, what I do. But I must do something. I prop the dead man up again so that he lies comfortably although he feels nothing any more. I close his eyes. They are brown, his hair is black and a bit curly at the sides.

The mouth is full and soft beneath his moustache; the nose is slightly arched, the skin brownish; it is now not so pale as it was before, when he was still alive. For a moment the face seems almost healthy;—then it collapses suddenly into the strange face of the dead that I have so often seen, strange faces, all alike.

No doubt his wife still thinks of him; she does not know what has happened. He looks as if he would often have written to her;—she will still be getting mail from him— Tomorrow, in a week's time—perhaps even a stray letter a month hence. She will read it, and in it he will be speaking to her.

My state is getting worse, I can no longer control my thoughts. What would his wife look like? Like the little brunette on the other side of the canal? Does she belong to me now? Perhaps by this act she becomes mine. I wish Kantorek were sitting here beside me. If my mother could see me—

The dead man might have had thirty more years of life if only I had impressed the way back to our trench more sharply on my memory. If only he had run two yards farther to the left, he might now be sitting in the trench over there and writing a fresh letter to his wife.

But I will get no further that way; for that is the fate of all of us: if Kemmerich's leg had been six inches to the right; if Haie Westhus had bent his back three inches further forward—

The silence spreads. I talk and must talk. So I speak to him and say to him: "Comrade, I did not want to kill you. If you jumped in here again, I would not do it, if you would be sensible too. But you were only an idea to me before, an abstraction that lived in my mind and called forth its appropriate response. It was that abstraction I stabbed. But now, for the first time, I see you are a man like me. I thought of your hand-grenades, of your bayonet, of your rifle; now I see your wife and your face and our fellowship. Forgive me, comrade. We always see it too late. Why do they never tell us that you are just poor devils like us, that your mothers are just as anxious as ours, and that we have the same fear of death, and the same dying and the same agony–Forgive me, comrade; how could you be my enemy? If we threw away these rifles and this uniform you could be my brother just like Kat and Albert. Take twenty years of my life, comrade, and stand up—take more, for I do not know what I can even attempt to do with it now."

It is quiet, the front is still except for the crackle of rifle-fire. The bullets rain over, they are not fired haphazard, but shrewdly aimed from all sides. I cannot get out.

"I will write to your wife," I say hastily to the dead man, "I will write to her, she must hear it from me, I will tell her everything I have told you, she shall not suffer, I will help her, and your parents too, and your child—"

His tunic is half open. The pocketbook is easy to find. But I hesitate to open it. In it is the book with his name. So long as I do not know his name perhaps I may still forget him, time will obliterate it, this picture. But his name, it is a nail that will be hammered into me and never come out again. It has the power to recall this for ever, it will always come back and stand before me.

Irresolutely I take the wallet in my hand. It slips out of my hand and falls open. Some pictures and letters drop out. I gather them up and want to put them back again, but the strain I am under, the uncertainty, the hunger, the danger, these hours with the dead man have confused me, I want to hasten the relief, to intensify and to end the torture, as one strikes an unendurably painful hand against the trunk of a tree, regardless of everything.

There are portraits of a woman and a little girl, small amateur photographs taken against an ivy-clad wall. Along with them are letters. I take them out and try to read them. Most of it I do not understand, it is so hard to decipher and I know scarcely any French. But each word I translate pierces me like a shot in the chest;—like a stab in the chest.

My brain is taxed beyond endurance. But I realize this much, that I will never dare to write to these people as I intended. Impossible. I look at the portraits once more; they are clearly not rich people. I might send them money anonymously if I earn anything later on. I seize upon that, it is at least something to hold on to. This dead man is bound up with my life, therefore I must do everything, promise everything, in order to save myself; I swear blindly that I mean to live only for his sake and his family, with wet lips I try to placate him—and deep down in me lies the hope that I may buy myself off in this way and perhaps even yet get out of this; it is a little stratagem: if only I am allowed to escape, then I will see to it. So I open the book and read slowly:—Gérard Duval, compositor.

With the dead man's pencil I write the address on an envelope, then swiftly thrust everything back into his tunic.

I have killed the printer, Gérard Duval. I must be a printer, I think confusedly, be a printer, printer—

By afternoon I am calmer. My fear was groundless. The name troubles me no more. The madness passes. "Comrade," I say to the dead man, but I say it calmly, "today you, tomorrow me. But if I come out of it, comrade, I will fight against this, that has struck us both down; from you, taken life —and from me—? Life also. I promise you, comrade. It shall never happen again."

The sun strikes low. I am stupefied with exhaustion and hunger. Yesterday is like a fog to me, there is no hope of getting out of this yet. I fall into a doze and do not at first realize that evening is approaching. The twilight comes. It seems to me to come quickly now. One hour more. If it were summer, it would be three hours more. One hour more.

Now suddenly I begin to tremble; something might happen in the interval. I think no more of the dead man, he is of no consequence to me now. With one bound the lust to live flares up again and everything that has filled my thoughts goes down before it. Now, merely to avert any ill-luck, I babble mechanically: "I will fulfil everything, fulfil everything I have promised you—" but already I know that I shall not do so.

Suddenly it occurs to me that my own comrades may fire on me as I creep up; they do not know I am coming. I will call out as soon as I can so that they will recognize me. I will stay lying in front of the trench until they answer me.

The first star. The front remains quiet. I breathe deeply and talk to myself in my excitement: "No foolishness now, Paul—quiet, Paul, quiet—then you will be saved, Paul." When I use my Christian name, it works as though someone else spoke to me, it has more power.

The darkness grows. My excitement subsides, I wait cautiously until the first rocket goes up. Then I crawl out of the shell-hole. I have forgotten the dead man. Before me lies the on-coming night and the pale gleaming field. I fix my eye on a shell-hole; the moment the light dies I scurry over into it, grope farther, spring into the next, duck down, scramble onward.

I come nearer. There, by the light of a rocket I see something move in the wire, then it stiffens and lies still. Next time I see it again, yes, they are men from our trench. But I am suspicious until I recognize our helmets. Then I call. And immediately an answer rings out, my name: "Paul—Paul—"

I call again in answer. It is Kat and Albert who have come out with a stretcher to look for me.

"Are you wounded?"

"No, no—"

We drop into the trench. I ask for something to eat and wolf it down. Müller gives me a cigarette. In a few words I tell what happened. There is nothing new about it; it happens quite often. The night attack is the only unusual feature of the business. In Russia Kat once lay for two days behind the enemy lines before he could make his way back.

I do not mention the dead printer.

But by next morning I can keep it to myself no longer. I must tell Kat and Albert. They both try to calm me. "You can't do anything about it. What else could you have done? That is what you are here for."

I listen to them and feel comforted, reassured by their presence. It was mere drivelling nonsense that I talked out there in the shell-hole.

"Look there for instance," points Kat.

On the fire-step stand some snipers. They rest their rifles with telescopic sights on the parapet and watch the enemy front. Once and again a shot cracks out.

Then we hear the cry: "That's found a billet!" "Did you see how he leapt in the air?" Sergeant Oellrich turns round proudly and scores his points. He heads the shooting list for today with three unquestionable hits.

"What do you say to that?" asks Kat.

I nod.

"If he keeps that up he will get a little coloured bird for his buttonhole by this evening," says Albert.

"Or rather he will soon be made acting-sergeant-major," says Kat.

We look at one another. "I would not do it," I say.

"All the same," says Kat, "it's very good for you to see it just now."

Sergeant Oellrich returns to the fire-step. The muzzle of his rifle searches to and fro.

"You don't need to lose any more sleep over your affair," nods Albert.

And now I hardly understand it myself any more.

"It was only because I had to lie there with him so long," I say. "After all, war is war."

Oellrich's rifle cracks out sharp and dry.

6

Men Wonder at the Earth

Bettman Archive

The scientists say that ours is a second-rate planet spinning about a third-rate sun. In the infinite distances of the sky, our great world shrinks to a speck and our proud millennia of civilization to an insignificant interlude. This humble judgment we have been forced to only recently. Generations before ours comforted themselves with the dream that their earth was the center of the universe. They built their mythology, their music, art and story about that dream. It was hard to let it go. Where was the wonder of an earth created out of the fortuitous conjunction of minute particles of matter? And of man, descended by two billion years of shaping from a blob of amphibious life?

But perhaps ours is the grander view by very virtue of its humility. For our wonder at the recurring mystery of the earth has not been diminished. It has only taken a new and, it may be, a more reverent form, premised on a creation that is continuous, an ever unfolding future, and the knowledge that man has only just begun to grow.

It is from the old writings and the new that we have chosen these selections in which men express their wonder at the mysteries of this earth they inhabit.

MORE THAN AN HOUR ON THE ROAD

FROM *Career*

KAY BOYLE

There are many levels of emotional meaning in Kay Boyle's stories. The reader will find it true of this account of a boy learning water divining. Her style is highly personal, experimental, and inevitably provocative. She has been described by more than one respectful reviewer as one of the more uncomfortably brilliant of American writers. But in spite of this rather wary characterization, she has won a not inconsiderable and a very steadfast body of discerning readers on both sides of the Atlantic.

THE DAY WAS QUITE FAIR AND THE GROUND SOFT AS SPRING UNDER FOOT, AND the boy and the diviner set off together to walk to the farm. The diviner was a tall man and he had on his face the look of serenity a religious man might wear, because of his belief in something that had covert life, that went strong as wind blowing, and as impervious, underground.

The diviner talked of water passing under a bridge, or passing under a boat, and if he stood on a bridge or stepped in the boat this water's flowing did not change the beating of his heart. But if he went into a house and water was passing unbeknown under it, his pulse told him this. The boy was so new to the work that everything the man said had a sound of wonder. The man said he had a friend who built a house and slept in a front room of it, and day after day his health faded and the doctors could find no reason why it should be so.

"When I went to see him," said the diviner, walking the road with the boy and chewing at a bit of grass between his teeth, "I saw his face and then I knew what it was. It was water."

"Was there water passing by the house?" said the boy quickly, and the man shook his head.

"Water going by means nothing," he said. "It's water running under the ground that counts. There was water running under the house on the side he slept on, but nobody knew anything about it. He couldn't get any rest at night and his appetite left him. Most people are dead to it," said the diviner. "But this man, he might have died. When I came into the room where he was the hair stood right up straight on my head, and the ends of my fingers started tingling. I knew what it was then and I took hold of his hand. But he had to let go of me and sit down because his heart was beating more than he could stand."

The boy listened to everything the man said, for he was setting out in life now; now he was going towards what work would bring him to. It seemed to him that he would have to be shaped thought by thought and bone by bone by whatever career he undertook, for he had no clear picture in his mind of what kind of a person he was or what he was intended to be. Whether he would be a man like his father, working as a builder, or like men he saw passing in the street or serving in a store, he did not know. But being young, he believed the choice had fallen on him: he said little, but he waited, knowing that the choice was made and that he could not be like the others, saying not a word but listening to the men who talked in his father's house, and to his father, knowing without vanity that he could not become the same.

The diviner himself was three men walking along the road, not one of them paying any heed to the black-faced sheep or the coarse, clay-red, small cattle they passed. He was first a man who lived to himself, and he was a man the engineering people employed as a locator of water, and he was as well a stranger speaking to the new boy as they went along to the farm where water was wanted. January is a warm time in Australia, and the farm was far, and the wet grass by the road was already beginning to stand up towards the sun when it came in sight.

The diviner was saying that the power extended to silver as well as to a twig of hazel he sometimes used, and he took a half-crown and a bit of bent wire from his pocket, and, in his hand as they walked, the wire drew straight of itself and reached out as if in hunger towards the piece of silver he had concealed in the palm of his other hand. Whichever way he moved the hand with the half crown in it, the wire changed its course and sought the direction of the silver. The man laughed a little, but still he was pleased by the look of awe in the new boy's face.

The boy stopped still in the road, and was staring, for whatever devotion to something else there was in him had been made impure by church taken as a weekly, dutiful thing. But this miracle he saw was what the miracle of voices singing and the high ribs of stone might have been if they had been kept, like gold, until he was old enough to see. The wire straightening out, like a reed in flowing water, and reaching for the coin was the mystery given a name at last. He stood still in the road, with his mouth open, watching the man put the half crown and the bit of wire back in his pocket again.

"Come along, now," said the man. "There's the farm off there where the trees are."

The sky and the sea below the line of land were one now, the same, fresh, loud, unbroken blue as if a wind had cleaned them out. The boy looked down, trying to see and follow the line that lay between them.

"I knew a rock once," he said, "where if you put your ear down against it you could hear the water running underneath."

"Water doesn't always say which way it's going," the diviner said.

The farm-people were in the house when the diviner knocked at the door, and they stopped whatever they were doing, the woman washing dishes and the old man stringing beans by the window, stopped without haste, without interest almost, and asked them at the door if they would have a piece of bread or a drink before setting out over the ground. But the diviner was thinking of the business he had to do, and he said they would take something later when the work was done. There was no reverence or respect in the woman's voice when she spoke to the diviner. She talked of the artesian well they wanted as they all walked out through the garden together, but there was no homage in her manner although the diviner alone had the knowledge of where the well would be.

They went past the rabbit-huts, talking; and the boy felt the walk in his legs now, and his mouth was dry. The sun was hot as summer, and he lingered behind in the shade and looked in at the rabbits in their separate nests of hay. They were all of one race, long, limber beasts, brown-coated and sleek, with flecks of yellow at the points of their hairs. He put his hand in quietly through the side of one box where the wire was parted, and the rabbit never stirred in her corner. Only her eye quivered, cool and dark and waking, as he drew his hand down the soft, loose velvet of her hanging ears.

Then he went on quickly after the farm people and the diviner, for this was the work he had to do now, and he must learn it word by word. The work had begun by the diviner taking the bit of fencing wire out of his pocket again and twisting it into the shape of a W. He carried it held out before him a little way, the apex of the letter turned up, and when the boy looked at his face he saw that it was altered: the eyes had given up their sight and the color was faded from under his skin, as if a veil had been drawn across. The farm people followed after him, the old man, and the woman, and her husband who had come up from the fields, not speaking, but still not hushed for any kind of wonder they felt, following him as he went slowly, as if blind, across the unresponding land.

They passed over a road packed hard by the feet of cattle, and they were almost at the tree-line along the meadow when suddenly it began. The diviner stopped as if he had been struck, and the first quiverings of declaration went through him; almost at once then, the wild surge of power began giving battle in his hand. There he stood rooted, and the others halted behind him, and the boy's breath went out of him at the sight of the W forcing itself inward and downward against the strong outward and upward warring of the man. He had taken his two hands to it now, and his mouth was shut tight against the onslaught of what this was. His body opposed it, his feet braced on the earth in anguish, and the veins stood out in his arms as if ready to burst through the skin.

The boy had scarcely seen it right when the struggle was over. The man seemingly bowed to the wire's will, and the apex of the letter was pointing earthward to the magnetic thing that passed them under the soil. The diviner moved off, holding the wire out again before him, but his face was quiet and certain now and he did not go far, only enough to feel the truth repeated. Step by step he covered the ground that lay close about, and how ever he turned, the wire turned in his hands to the chosen place, unswerving, as if thirsting itself for what ran secretly below.

It was so new to the boy that he did not know if he were living or dead, or whether or not there were people standing there in the open air before him. But when they began talking, he saw that it was a business to them, even to the diviner it was a business, as common as the stars moving or the shadow of the earth falling deeper night after night on the side of the moon. But still he could not open his mouth or shut it, but must leave it where it was until the diviner turned to him in a little while with the wire held out in his hand.

"Come along now," the diviner said, "we'll have to see if you have the power."

The boy took hold of the wire in his fingers, and suddenly the tears started running down his face. He knew he was not moving his hand, but the wire was turning, not towards the earth or in any earthward direction, but pointing straight to the center of life and blood where he had been taught his heart should be.

"Oh, come along now," said the diviner with a laugh, and the farm people as well began laughing at what they hoped to see. "Now take it easy," said the diviner, speaking with patience, as if he might be teaching a lad to put a sole on a boot or plane a piece of timber. "Wipe your face now and take hold of my hand. That'll fix it."

The boy wiped his nose with the back of his hand, and the diviner reached out and took hold of one end of the wire. He was holding the boy's spare hand in his, and before either of them could draw a breath the might of the water struck them. The boy went down under it, thrown as if from the back of a horse, flat on his back, with his mind wiped out for whatever next would come.

It is warm at this time of year in Australia, and the memory of the cold is something that happened at sometime when the continent was taking shape. They set out from it in the glacial time as penguins do from a breaking coastline in the spring, and for warmth they had drawn the Gulf Stream like a scarf around them.

"We were more than an hour on the road," the diviner said. "Can you fetch him some water from the house?"—as if this was any explanation.

MEDIEVAL PILGRIM'S BADGE

A MARVELOUS CATHEDRAL

FROM *The Cave of Cacahuamilpa*

GABRIELA MISTRAL

Man feels the breath of divinity in a cave, says Gabriela Mistral; it is a place where the day of creation is not done, a great cathedral with the stalagmites frozen altars and the sculptured limestone figures out of a Biblical world.

Gabriela Mistral was the noted Chilean poet and educator who won the Nobel Prize in 1945 for her *Sonnets of Death.* She was her country's only life consul, commissioned by special law "wherever she finds a suitable climate for her health and a pleasant atmosphere to pursue her studies." Three days of national mourning were decreed by President Ibanez of Chile when she died early in 1957.

She was part Indian and was deeply affected by the problems of the Indian masses of Latin America—which may well have influenced her simple, yet richly woven imagery, so marked in this selection from her prose.

THIS CAVE IS DEEP; ONE GEOGRAPHY BOOK SAYS IT IS ALMOST FIVE THOUSAND feet deep. When one touches the bottom the silence is overpowering, as though one had reached the roots of the earth. From the moment we enter we become aware of an *audible* desolation, almost more tragic than the *visual.* The only sound is that of our footsteps and the slow dripping of the drops of water which gives the cave a deep vibration.

The world has turned upside down before our eyes; outside, the sky is boundless, impalpable, and blue and holds the earth in an intangible embrace; the sky which covers us here is plastic and hard. But instead of the decoration of clouds, changing with every moment, what a sky we gaze upon here! Above our heads hang the hundred thousand whimsies of the water: wreaths, enormous inverted flower pistils, towers.

Through the centuries the lime filtration has peopled the bare heart of the cave until it has become this labyrinth of hallucinations.

The floor of the cave resembles its ceiling. ("Above it is like below," says Swedenborg.) In certain places the formations that hang down meet those that rise up. As I contemplate this contact a tremor runs through me; thus in prayer is the believer joined to the Creator.

The cave is a marvelous cathedral; but a cathedral that has altars not only against the walls, but scattered through the naves as well, and that might serve whole towns. There are thousands of human postures in the stalagmites that rise from the ground, like kneeling crowds whose backs cover the floor; at times they are wild masses, their arms contorted with anxiety. It is a community over which hangs a fateful hour; it resembles the loins of the sea when the wind lifts it up in a convulsive wave.

The valley of Jehosaphat comes to my mind, and the Scriptures become a living, possible thing to me. Here we come upon an immense striding figure, tall and grave, like a god; it might be Moses. A tightly knit mass of figures follows him. I turn a corner and the gaze of an anguished visage meets my eyes: Œdipus or King Lear. Its hair is disheveled by snow and wind, and from its mouth proceeds a cry which never quite emerges and which, in its immensity, would seem to unhinge the jaw. Across from this there is a countenance that is all dark; the only clearly formed thing about it is the eyes; we have to envisage all the rest around them.

We move ahead. . . .

Now the cave is the scene of a fantastic chase, like that of St. Julian the Hospitaler, in the tale of Flaubert: a buffalo rearing up to jump, deer that run lightly before it, and stags with branching antlers, all intermingled and turning upon one another, and crouching panthers and snakes which twist beneath our feet. . . . It is a palpitating bas-relief of the heart of the African jungle.

Or this group, from which I cannot tear my eyes away, with its innumerable figures that might be Adam surrounded by the beasts after the Fall. Creation has turned against him in anger; the animals mill about, looking at him, pressing in upon him. . . .

But in spots the sharp, clearly delineated forms predominate. Then the cave is not a place of violent fauna but of exquisite flora: waving ferns, firmly planted, meditative pines and cypresses, and beneath them a multitude of plants and bushes. Everything is covered over by a snowfall of many hours which gives the foliage a certain density. And before this quiet landscape I feel just as I felt in a snow-covered forest: the urgent need for a wind to come and unshroud the forest and liberate me from that hallucination compounded of whiteness and silence.

The air here is heavy, as in the heart of a tropical forest.

We go on in the rarefied atmosphere of a dream.

These forms rising from the floor of the cave seem at times a thousand arms filled with offerings; it is all one huge offertory raised to an unheeding god—propitiatory goblets, vases, thyrsi—like a judgment on cities that would not pray. One feels the profitless weariness of the slender arms and feels that at any moment one of them may fall, broken with fatigue.

In spite of the absolute quiet this does not seem for an instant a scene of death. Each of these beings is quick, but with a life different from our own. The Golden Legend tells the story of the Seven Young Sleepers whom a mountain covered, without harming them, like a light quilt. Centuries later they were brought to light by an excavation, seven white, undefiled bodies, still drowsy from their fabulous sleep. Their breasts rose and fell almost imperceptibly; there was no rigor of death in their bodies, and the kiss of the sun gently and quietly aroused them. In the same way the immobility of the stalagmites seems like restrained power; it is as though their vast breathing were being held within their bodies. As we leave each room we refrain from looking back; we feel as if the bodies all came to life as soon as we left, and that breasts, backs, and mouths breathe a sigh of relief as they move.

But if I had entered the cave alone, "as man by himself is pure," I would not hurry by in feverish haste like this, and the cavern would want to live for my adoring eyes. I would sit down before each group of figures; I would look upon them in silence hours and days until I had overcome their stubborn silence, and suddenly, as though warmed by my ardent gaze, the trees would emerge from their torpidness, the animals would complete their suspended leap, and from the lips would fall, like a full pregnant drop, the withheld word. The men would climb down their Jacob's ladder, and this moon-dwelling humanity would move about me. And, above all, I should like to be alone in the depths of the cave to hear that perfect silence which is its attribute, a silence unwounded even by the fall of the drops of water. (They only echo to reveal the miracle of the silence.) I would lave my ears of the impurities with which the agitation of the world has filled them and which has dulled them. It would be a silence like that of ten bandages swathing my head; better still, the silence of death within a body alive to sense it.

And when this complete silence had weighed down upon me, unbearably, like the mass of waters upon a submerged diver, I could also fill the depths of the cave with music. This world of forms can be translated into a symphony: those towers are the high, cold notes; this cupola, a severe sustained note; that clump of grass, a scherzo of tones. I would create a close forest of harmony when my soul had savored for years the heavenly taste of silence.

I go on observing the patiently carved out groups of figures. Which of those we have known in the other world has been forgotten? Not one. The water, with the creative power of a Shakespeare, has molded every type. And besides the creations of nature, the human inventions are here, too: this is a fine old armchair, there is a suggestion of the smokestacks of a factory. In this cave I have come to understand what is meant by the *imagination of nature*.

The cave, blind like Milton, dreamed the outside world and by its desire reproduced all the beings the water was forming in its vitals. I can believe that in this mass of beings not one is missing; I might even find my dead among them. If I were to stay here a few hours, my mother would come to me from that shadowy corner, and if I were to peer along the walls, clustered with faces, I would find my own there. Yes, this has been a fever-heated dream of the cave, and its days of creation are not done. The pulsation of the drops works on invisibly; that grave, slow pulsation which is everywhere, which seems to follow and mock us.

Electric lights brutally illuminate the stalactites. If the moon could only know the caves, how eagerly it would light them with its silvery blue, or its silvery gold, or its silvery silver.

The whiteness gives an austere chastity to the underground panorama. White and gray: we might be walking astounded through the landscape of another planet. We talk to hear the sound of our own voices, to keep from going mad with amazement.

Some day cities will spring up near this cave, and no matter how many temples are erected, those who are troubled in spirit will come here, to the frozen white interior of the cave, to feel more closely on their faces the breath of death. Perhaps their prayer will be the most perfect that contrite man has ever raised to God. Perhaps the greatest religious hymn of humanity will come to the tongue of man from these stalagmite altars. The sensation of divinity has come to me only in the abyss of the starry night and in this other depth which also makes the soul faint.

When I was a child and asked my mother what the inside of the earth was like, she said to me: "It is bare and horrible." Mother, I have looked upon the inside of the earth; it is like the swelling breast of a great flower, it is full of forms, and one walks breathless through its tremendous beauty.

We emerge from the cave, and the blue of noonday wounds our eyes, which, like those of a sick person, close, blinded. . . .

THE MIGHTY MIRACLE

FROM *The Wonder of Wonders at Windmill-Hill. Being the Invitation of John Lacy, Esq. And the Rest of the Inspired Prophets, to all Spectators, to Behold Dr. Emms Arise out of His First Grave.*

ANONYMOUS

Our least inhibited press agents today are the most candid and punctilious of men alongside this anonymous publicity man of 1708 who promised ticket buyers front-row seats to the resurrection of Dr. Emms. He brought the crowd out in the best traditions of the profession, but he could hardly blame himself for the unfortunate fact that Dr. Emms did not arise from the grave. There were compelling reasons for the ghostly reverend's reticence and these are explained in the persuasive advertisement which followed the event, addressed, we are afraid, to what must have been a somewhat skeptical public.

Being the invitation of John Lacy, Esq. and the rest of the inspired prophets, to all spectators, to come on Tuesday next, the 25th day of this instant May, where, to their exceeding astonishment, they may (without any prejudice to their eye-sight) behold Dr. Emms arise out of his first grave, and dress himself in his usual habit to all their view, and with a loud voice relate matters of moment, preaching a miraculous sermon, giving a strange account of past and future events; the like never seen or heard in England before, exceeding any wonder or show that ever was seen on Windmill-hill at any holiday-time. Licensed according to order.

THE TOWN HAVING BEEN BUSIED WITH APPREHENSIONS OF WARS IN THE NORTH, and the affairs of state, having almost suffered our late Doctor Emms to be buried in oblivion, as well as in his grave near Windmill-hill; and so, by consequence, he may rise alone, or, as we term it vulgarly, in hugger-mugger, without any to witness the wonder: But let me acquaint you, that, as such miracles are not common, it is fit they should be proclaimed aloud by fame's trumpet; neither have all men the gift of raising the dead, nor hath it been known for many ages. Esquire Lacy has published a relation of the dealing of God with his unworthy servant, since the time of his believing and professing himself inspired, which befel him, the first of July, 1707: His agitations coming upon him without the working of his imagination, upon what he saw in others, and proceeding from a supernatural cause, separate and distinct from himself, whereby his arm, leg, and head have been shaken, his limb twiched, the respiration of his breath has, for sundry days, beat various tunes of a drum, and his voice has been so strong, clear, and harmonious, that his natural one could never furnish: He has been carried on his knees several times round a room, swifter than he could have gone on his feet. Sir Richard Buckley has been cured of an hospital of diseases, by a promise thereof made through his mouth, under the operation of the spirit; and by the same means a man purblind has been cured, and a woman of a fever, Mr. Preston of a carbuncle, and another of a deep consumption. Therefore Esquire Lacy, with the rest of the inspired prophets, gives notice, for the satisfaction of the unbelieving, that, according to their former prophecy (who cannot err) that, on the twenty-fifth of May, they repair to Bunhill Fields, and there in that burying-place, commonly called Tindal's Ground, about the twelfth hour of the day, behold the wonderful doctor fairly rise; and in two minutes time the earth over his coffin will crack, and spread from the coffin, and he will instantly bounce out, and slip off his shroud (which must be washed, and, with the boards of his coffin, be kept as relicks, and doubtless perform cures by their wonderful operation) and there, in a trice, he dresses himself in his other apparel (which doubtless hath been kept for that intent ever since he was interred), and then there he will relate astonishing matters, to the amazement of all that see or hear him.

Likewise, for the more convenient accommodation of all spectators, there will be very commodious scaffolds erected throughout the ground, and also without the walls in the adjacent fields, called Bunhill Fields, exceeding high, during this great performance. The like may never be seen in England hereafter: And, that you may acquaint your children, and grandchildren, if you have any, that you have seen this mighty miracle, you are advised not to neglect this opportunity, since it is plainly evident, that, of all the shows or wonders that are usually seen on holiday-time, this must bear the bell; and there it is ordered to be published in all news, that the country may come in; the like never performed before. It is also believed that gingerbread, oranges, and all such goods exposed to publick sale in wheelbarrows, will doubtless get trade there, at this vast concourse; therefore, for the benefit of poor people, I give them timely notice, since it is a bad wind that blows none no profit. But, besides this admirable wonder of this strange and particular manner of his resurrection, he is to preach a sermon, and, lest it should not be printed, you are invited to be ear-witnesses thereof, as well as eye-witnesses to see his lips go, in the pronounciation thereof; all which will be matter of great moment, filling you all with exceeding amazement and great astonishment; his voice will be loud and audible, that all may hear him, and his doctrine full of knowledge; undoubtedly you will return home taught with profound understanding. Which miracle, if you chance to see or hear, you will not forget, and so by consequence, for the future, be endowed with sound judgment, and most excellent wisdom, most eloquent expressions, and what not: Then neglect not this great and most beneficial opportunity, but for that time set all your affairs aside: And take this advice from Mr. Lacy, and the inspired prophets, together with Mrs. Mary of Turnmill-street, a she prophetess, and the young woman who sells penny-pyes, who, in hopes of obtaining all your company, remains yours; not questioning but to give you all content with this rare show.

Esquire Lacy's Reasons why Doctor Emms was not raised from the dead, on the twenty-fifth day of May, according to the French Prophets Prediction.

We are not unsensible of the harsh censures and uncharitable reflexions that are cast upon us and our brethren, the prophets, in not raising from the dead our late spiritual brother Dr. Emms, on the precise time we foretold; therefore, to prevent, as much as in us lies, all further clamour and unnatural violence that may be occasioned thereby, we have thought fit to give our reasons for this omission, in the following order:

First, and principally, we were threatened with a popular rage and violence, which the laws of God and nature allows all mankind to avoid, having been practised by good and holy men in all ages of the world, even our Saviour himself, John x. 39, &c. who further confirms this truth, Matt. x. 33, by advising his disciples, when they were persecuted in one city, to flee into another. And, if it was lawful for the apostles and Christ himself to avoid the fury of their wicked and unbelieving adversaries, we hope no man can reasonably blame us from deferring the accomplishment of the said intended miracle. Jonah prophesied the destruction of Nineveh in forty days, but it was deferred near forty years, on their repentance.

Secondly, The secret decrees of the prophetical spirit are treasured up in the fountain of wisdom, and consequently past man's finding out, especially by a rebellious and gainsaying people.

Thirdly, Raising the dead, restoring the blind and lame to their sight and limbs, are great miracles, and only performed by faith, prayer, and fasting; but, where a rude, enraged and revengeful multitude is gathered together in defiance of heaven itself, all acts of devotion are obstructed, and even suspended till a more seasonable time.

Fourthly, Though prophetick periods do not always take place, according to the punctual warnings of the agitated spirit in the child of adoption, yet, like a great conqueror, who sometimes meets with difficulties and miscarriages in his march, in due time break through all obstruction, for the more glorious accomplishment of the promises.

Fifthly, and lastly. Had we been peaceably suffered to appear on the day and hour we predicted, it would then have been decided who were the cheats and impostors (names we have been notoriously loaded with) but when open rage, mob, fury, and even death itself not only threatened, but looked us in the face; such a time, we are sure, was inconsistent for the undertaking of any thing that related to a publick satisfaction; for, had the miracle really been wrought in such a confused medley of ungovernable rabble, instead of being acknowledged as such, we had run the hazard of being torn in pieces, and perhaps occasioned a fatal and general disorder among the people; for whose sake, more than for fear of our own lives, we prudently delayed attempting the said weighty undertaking till a more favourable opportunity; though we could freely have sacrificed our lives for the sake of spiritual truth, if such a dispensation had been either necessary or convenient; but (considering the madness of the age, the malice of the mob, and the rage of many male-contents against the present government, who, in all probability, would have took the advantage of such a confusion, in order to have promoted their long-wished for treasons and wicked designs) we preferred the publick peace and safety of the government before our own interest and reputation, which, however so much shaken in this particular, shall never discourage us from being loyal and obedient to our superiors, notwithstanding our being rendered obnoxious to them by spiteful and malicious agents, who are always fishing in troubled waters, to bring about their own notorious and pernicious purposes, though, to the scandal of themselves, and ruin of their Christian brethren, whom they hate for no other reason than being honester than themselves.

To conclude: Let men of carnal principles have what sentiments they please of us, we are resolved to act as the spirit of peace and love within us shall dictate and guide us, and as the supernatural agitations of Divine Inspiration shall enlighten our understanding.

THE BEST OF ALL POSSIBLE WORLDS

FROM *Candide*

VOLTAIRE

For Voltaire, every subject he touched on in his enormous body of varied writing served as a target for satirical dissection. An earthquake at Lisbon terrified the rest of Europe, and brought scores flocking to confess their large and small sins. For Voltaire it was an invitation to lampoon the beliefs of the orthodox and to deride philosophical optimism. In *Candide,* from which we have made this selection, he made full use of his opportunities.

His output of work was staggering—some sixty plays, treatises on history and physics, a huge correspondence, a mass of poetry whose titles alone fill forty octavo columns, pamphlets by the score—much of it superficial but all of it marked by his devastating irony and his cutting wit.

SCARCE HAD THEY . . . SET FOOT IN THE CITY, WHEN THEY PERCEIVED THE earth to tremble under their feet, and the sea, swelling and foaming in the harbour, dash in pieces the vessels that were riding at an anchor. Large sheets of flame and cinders covered the streets and public places. The houses tottered, and were tumbled topsy-turvy, even to their foundations, which were themselves destroyed; and thirty thousand inhabitants of both sexes, young and old, were buried beneath the ruins. The sailor, whistling and swearing, cried, "Damn it, there's something to be got here!" "What can be the 'sufficient reason' of this phenomenon?" said Pangloss. "It is certainly the Day of Judgment," said Candide. The sailor, defying death in the pursuit of plunder, rushed into the midst of the ruin, where he found some money, with which he got drunk, and after he had slept himself sober, he purchased the favours of the first good-natured wench that came in his way, amidst the ruins of demolished houses and the groans of half-buried and expiring persons. Pangloss pulled him by the sleeve: "Friend," said he, "this is not right; you trespass against the *universal reason,* and have mistaken your time." "Death and 'ounds!" answered the other, "I am a sailor and born at Batavia, and have trampled four times upon the crucifix in as many voyages to Japan; you are come to a good hand with your *universal reason.*"

In the meantime, Candide, who had been wounded by some pieces of stone that fell from the houses, lay stretched in the street, almost covered with rubbish. "For God's sake," said he to Pangloss, "get me a little wine and oil; I am dying." "This concussion of the earth is no new thing," replied Pangloss; "the city of Lima in America experienced the same last year: the same cause, the same effect; there is certainly a train of sulphur all the way underground from Lima to Lisbon." "Nothing more probable," said Candide; "but for the love of God a little oil and wine." "Probable!" replied the philosopher. "I maintain that the thing is demonstrable." Candide fainted away, and Pangloss fetched him some water from a neighbouring spring.

The next day, in searching among the ruins, they found some eatables, with which they repaired their exhausted strength. After this they assisted the inhabitants in relieving the distressed and wounded. Some whom they had humanely assisted, gave them as good a dinner as could be expected under such terrible circumstances. The repast, indeed, was mournful, and the company moistened their bread with their tears; but Pangloss endeavoured to comfort them under this affliction by affirming that things could not be otherwise than they were: "for," said he, "all this is for the very best end, for if there is a volcano at Lisbon, it could be in no other spot; for it is impossible but things should be as they are, for everything is for the best."

By the side of the preceptor sat a little man dressed in black, who was one of the *familiars* of the Inquisition. This person, taking him up with great complaisance, said, "Possibly, my good sir, you do not believe in original sin; for if everything is best, there could have been no such thing as the fall or punishment of men."

"I humbly ask your excellency's pardon," answered Pangloss, still more politely; "for the fall of man, and the curse consequent thereupon, necessarily entered into the system of the best of worlds." "That is as much as to say, sir," rejoined the *familiar,* "you do not believe in free-will." "Your excellency will be so good as to excuse me," said Pangloss; "free-will is consistent with absolute necessity; for it was necessary we should be free, for in that the will—"

Pangloss was in the midst of his proposition when the Inquisitor beckoned to his attendant to help him to a glass of port wine.

After the earthquake, which had destroyed three-fourths of the city of Lisbon, the sages of that country could think of no means more effectual to preserve the kingdom from utter ruin than to entertain the people with an *auto-da-fé,* it having been decided by the University of Coimbra that the burning a few people alive by a slow fire, and with great ceremony, is an infallible secret to prevent earthquakes.

In consequence thereof, they had seized on a Biscayner for marrying his godmother, and on two Portuguese for taking out the bacon of a larder pullet they were eating; after dinner, they came and secured Doctor Pangloss and his pupil Candide, the one for speaking his mind, and the other for seeming to approve what he had said. They were conducted to separate apartments, extremely cool, where they were never incommoded with the sun. Eight days afterwards they were each dressed in a *san-benito,* and their heads were adorned with paper mitres. The mitre and *san-benito* worn by Candide were painted with flames reversed, and with devils that had neither tails nor claws; but Doctor Pangloss's devils had both tails and claws, and his flames were upright. In these habits they marched in procession, and heard a very pathetic sermon, which was followed by an anthem accompanied by bagpipes. Candide was flogged to some tune while the anthem was singing; the Biscayner and the two men who would not eat bacon were burnt; and Pangloss was hanged, which is not a common custom at these solemnities. The same day there was another earthquake, which made most dreadful havoc.

Candide, amazed, terrified, confounded, astonished, all bloody and trembling from head to foot, said to himself, "If this is the best of all possible worlds, what are the others?"

PARIS, FRANCE

FROM *mehitabel in the catacombs*

DON MARQUIS

"It would be one on me," Don Marquis was reported to have told his close friends, "if I should be remembered longest for having created a cockroach character." Don Marquis was prophetic, even if unduly dispirited. There are not many personalities like Archie the Cockroach and Mehitabel the Cat whom readers have granted permanent residence with Alice's White Rabbit in that odd world of vocal and erudite fauna.

Casual readers of Don Marquis' newspaper column and the many thousands of theatregoers who saw his play *The Old Soak* knew him only as a humorist. His friends were always aware that he was giving a performance, a good one, in which his pessimism was overlaid with a sharp wit and a sardonic humor.

paris france
i would
fear greatly for the morals
of mehitabel the cat if she had any
the kind of life she
is leading is too violent
and undisciplined for words
she and the disreputable
tom cat who claims to have
been francois villon
when he was on earth
before have taken up their
permanent abode in the catacombs
whence they sally
forth nightly on excursions
of the most undignified nature
sometimes they honor
with their presence the cafes
of montparnasse and the boul mich

and sometimes they
seek diversion in the cabarets
on top of the butte
of montmartre
in these localities
it has become the fashion
among the humans
to feed beer to these
peculiar cats and they dance
and caper when they have
become well alcoholized
with this beverage
swinging their tails and
indulging in raucous feline
cries which they evidently
mistake for a song
it was my dubious
privilege to see them
when they returned to their
abode early yesterday morning
flushed as you might say
with bocks and still
in a holiday mood
the catacombs of paris are
not lined with the bones
of saints and martyrs
as are those of rome
but nevertheless these cats
should have more respect
for the relics of mortality
you may not believe me
but they actually danced and
capered among
the skeletons while the cat
who calls himself
francois villon gave forth
a chant of which the following
is a free translation

outcast bones from a thousand biers
click us a measure giddy and gleg

and caper my children dance my dears
skeleton rattle your mouldy leg
this one was a gourmet round as a keg
and that had the brow of semiramis
o fleshless forehead bald is an egg
all men s lovers come to this

this eyeless head that laughs and leers
was a chass daf once or a touareg
with golden rings in his yellow ears
skeleton rattle your mouldy leg
marot was this one or wilde or a wegg
who dropped into verses and down the abyss
and those are the bones of my old love meg
all men s lovers come to this

these bones were a ballet girl s for years
parbleu but she shook a wicked peg
and those ribs there were a noble peer s
skeleton rattle your mouldy leg
and here is a duchess that loved a yegg
with her lipless mouth that once drank bliss
down to the dreg of its ultimate dreg
all men s lovers come to this

prince if you pipe and plead and beg
you may yet be crowned with a grisly kiss
skeleton rattle your mouldy leg
all men s lovers come to this

TO DO AS ADAM DID

FROM *Men and Gardens*

NAN FAIRBROTHER

If Nan Fairbrother—we assume as a matter of course she is a gardener—has as elegant a hand with flowers as she has with prose, her gardens must be charming indeed. Miss Fairbrother is an erudite and most graceful historian of horticulture. In this selection from her book *Men and Gardens,* with the Bible, Chinese proverbs and the English poets as sources, she accounts for the reasons that move wise men to "that pleasantest work of human industry."

THE CHINESE HAVE A WISE SAYING WHICH I ONCE FOUND IN A BOOK OF PROVERBS —"If you would be happy for a week, take a wife: if you would be happy for a month, kill your pig: but if you would be happy all your life, plant a garden."

It is advice which reveals a high level of civilization with a low standard of living, but when I was a romantic young woman it seemed to me very shocking that the pleasures of eating should be considered four times as satisfactory as the pleasures of love. The Chinese, I felt, were wrong. But that was because I knew nothing about the eating. I had never known hunger as famine, but only as appetite between meals, and people who only know domestic cats are not really reliable judges of tigers.

Yet even in my privileged ignorance of the hungry facts of life, even in the most flowery days as a *jeune fille en fleur,* I never doubted the more lasting pleasures of gardening. Certainly for the time being there were more engrossing interests than planting roses; for a certain stretch of youth and expectancy one shuts the garden gate behind and goes off excited down the lane on other errands. Roses in those flowery years have no roots in earth but only in poetry; they are charms to wear in our hair.

Yet even the most eager and romantic settings-out were more like going off on holiday than leaving home for good. I knew I should come happily back again in the end, and I latched the garden gate carefully before I left.

If you would be happy . . .

And who would not? For all men, Pascal says, "seek happiness, all without exception; however different the paths they follow, they all seek the same goal. . . . It is the only motive of all actions of all men whatsoever, even of those who are going to be hanged." But there are less perverse ways to happiness than the gallows, and many Englishmen have felt, like the Chinese, that "Whoever understands and loves a Garden may have Content if he will." Nor is the "joy of Husbandmen a flash and so away, but it is a setled and habituall joy . . . a cleare shining beautifull affection."

If you would be happy all your life . . .

"I have never had any other desire so strong, and so like to covetousness, as that one which I have had always, that I might be master at last of a small house and large garden." Poor Abraham Cowley, who knew so well what the Chinese meant, yet still lived, he tells us, "disappointed . . . of that felicity . . . in a hired house and garden . . . without that pleasantest work of human industry, the improvement of something which we call our own."

But why have men found happiness in gardens? Why, in such different lands and different ages, have so many paths led to this green and quiet enclosure for growing plants? Certainly the pleasures of mankind are limited, there is no great variety from Adam to us or from king to beggar, but even so it is easier to see why human beings should delight in eating or sleeping or making love, in power or gold or glory, than why they should be happy labouring to make one plant grow instead of another.

For the old Christian gardeners the answer was very simple. "If we believe the Scripture," says Sir William Temple, "we must allow that God Almighty esteemed the life of a man in a garden the happiest He could give him, or else He would not have placed Adam in that of Eden." "God Almighty first planted a garden": it is a fact they are all agreed on, but whether gardening can therefore be considered the first of the arts, there is some argument. For surgeons too have claimed their own art as the most ancient because of the "operation of taking the Rib from Adam wherewith the Woman was made." However this may be, our first parents were happy in their "sweet gard'ning labour" until they were driven from Eden, "and no doubt Adam was exceedingly grieved to part with it," says one gardener with warm fellow-feeling. Whether Adam and Eve gardened in the wilderness we do not know, and equally the "Advances Gard'ning made from Adam's Expulsion to the General Deluge, is dubious, there being little left of it." And no one, surely, could make a more cautious statement of a profounder ignorance.

For the seventeenth century, the expulsion from Eden fully explains man's love of gardens, just as the legend of the single creature divided once explained the love between men and women. We long to return to our first Paradise, and though "it is impossible for us, Adam's Posterity" ever to make a garden as fair as Eden, "yet doubtless, by Industry and Pains Taking in that lovely, honest, and delightful Recreation of Planting, we may gain some little glimmering of that lost Splendour, although with much difficulty."

All Bliss
Consists in this,
To do as Adam did.

CERES, GODDESS OF HARVEST

FOUR SQUARE FEET OF JUNGLE

FROM *Jungle Life*

WILLIAM BEEBE

In an armful of moss and earth, a yard of jungle, William Beebe, naturalist, finds a teeming world, alive with shape and color, and wonders about that world, immeasurably multiplied by a thousand yards or a hundred thousand miles.

Of William Beebe, a fellow naturalist, Edwin Way Teale, whose work appears elsewhere in this book, wrote, "He stands very high indeed, on that ridge where literature and natural history meet."

ON THE LAST DAY OF MY STAY I WALKED SLOWLY UP THE TRAIL TOWARD THE *canela do mato*. For the last time I strained upward at the well-known branches, and with the very movement there came the voice of the swamp. Its tone was insistent, with a tinge of accusation, a note of censure. *Wh—y?* and after a little time, *Wh—y?*

I looked about me despairingly. What had I learned after all? Was there any clearing up of the mystery of the jungle? Had my week of scrutiny brought me any closer to the real intimacies of evolution? Or—evading these questions for the time—was there nothing I could do in the few precious moments left?

In five minutes I would turn my back on all this wildness, this jungle seething with profound truths and great solutions within arm's reach. I would pass to the ocean where monotony compels introspection, and finally to the great center of civilization where the veneer covers up all truths.

Even if my studies had taught only the lesson of the tremendous insurgence of life, could I not emphasize this, make it a more compelling factor to be considered in future efforts toward the frog's question and mine?

My eyes left the foliage overhead and sought the ground. Acting on impulse, I brought from my camping stores an empty war bag and scraped together an armful of leaves, sticks, moss, earth, mold of all sorts. Four square feet of jungle debris went into my bag, and I shouldered it.

Then I said adieu to my trail and my tree—a sorrowful leave-taking, as is always my misfortune. For the bonds which bind me to a place or a person are not easily broken. And, as usual, when the trail passed from view, the ideal alone remained. The thoughts of mosquitoes, of drenching, of hours of breathless, disappointed waiting, all sank in the memory of the daily discoveries, the mental delights of new research.

A week later, when the sky line was unbroken by land, when a long ground swell waved but did not disturb the deep blue of the open sea, I unlaced my bag of jungle mold. Armed with forceps, lens, and vials, I began my search. For days I had gazed upward; now my scrutiny was directed downward. With binoculars I had scanned without ceasing the myriad leaves of a great tree; now with lens or naked eye I sought for life or motion on single fallen leaves and dead twigs. When I studied the life of the great tree, I was in the land of Brobdingnag; now I was verily a Gulliver in Lilliput. The cosmos in my war bag teemed with interest as deep and as inviting as any in the jungle itself.

When I began work, I knew little of what I should find. My vague thoughts visualized ants and worms, and especially I anticipated unearthing myriads of the unpleasant "mucuims," or *bêtes rouges,* whose hosts had done all in their power to make life in the jungle unhappy.

Day by day my vials increased. Scores of creatures evaded my search; many others, of whose kind I had captured a generous number, I allowed to escape.

My Lilliputian census was far from the mere aggregation of ants and worms which I had anticipated, and a review of the whole showed that hardly any great group of living creatures was unrepresented.

As hinting of the presence of wild animals, a bunch of rufous hairs had in some way been tweaked from a passing agouti. Man himself was represented in the shape of two wads which had dropped from my gunshots sometime during the week. One had already begun to disintegrate and sheltered half a dozen diminutive creatures. Five feathers were the indications of birds, two of which were brilliant green plumes from a calliste. Of reptiles there was a broken skull of some lizard, long since dead, and the eggshell of a lizardling which had hatched and gone forth upon his mission into the jungle. A third reptilian trace may have been his nemesis—a bit of shed snakeskin. The group of amphibians was present even in this square of four feet—a very tiny, dried, black, and wholly unrecognizable little frog. Fishes were absent, though from my knees as I scraped up the debris, I could almost have seen a little *igarapé* in which dwelt scores of minnows.

As I delved deeper and examined the mold more carefully for the diminutive inhabitants, I found that this thin film from the floor of the jungle appeared to have several layers, each with its particular fauna. The upper layer was composed of recently fallen leaves, nuts, seeds, and twigs, dry and quite fresh. Here were colonies of small ants and huge, solitary ones; here lived in hiding small moths and beetles and bugs, awaiting dusk to fly forth through the jungle. The middle layer was by far the most important, and in it lived four fifths of all the small folk. The lowest layer was one of matted roots and clayey soil, and its animal life was meager.

Between the upper and the middle strata were sprouting nuts and seeds, with their blanched roots threaded downward into the rich dark mold, and the greening cotyledons curling upward toward light and warmth. Thus had the great bird-filled canella begun its life. In my war bag were a score of potential forest giants doomed to death in the salt ocean. But for my efforts toward the *Wh—y,* their fate might have been very different.

Some of the half-decayed leaves were very beautiful. Vistas of pale, bleached fungus lace trailed over the rich mahogany-colored tissues, studded here and there with bits of glistening, transparent quartz. Here I had many hints of a world of life beyond the power of the unaided eye. And here too the grosser fauna scrambled, hopped, or wriggled. Everywhere were tiny chrysalids and cocoons, many empty. Now and then a plaque of eggs, almost microscopic, showed veriest pinpricks where still more minute parasites had made their escape. When one contracted the field of vision to this world where leaves were fields and fungi loomed as forests, competition, tragedy lessened not at all. Minute seeds mimicked small beetles in shape and in tracery of patterns. Bits of bark simulated insects, a patch of fungus seemed a worm, while the mites themselves were invisible until they moved. Here and there I discovered a lifeless boulder of emerald or turquoise—the metallic cuirass of some long-dead beetle.

Some of the scenes which appeared as I picked over the mold, suddenly unfolding after an upheaval of debris, were like Aladdin's cave. Close to the eye appeared great logs and branches protruding in confusion from a heaped-up bank of diamonds. Brown, yellow, orange, and white colors played over the scene; and now over a steep hill came a horrid, ungainly creature with enormous proboscis, eight legs, and a shining, liver-colored body spotted with a sickly hue of yellow. It was studded with short, stiff, horny hairs—a mite by name, but under the lens a terrible monster. I put some of these on my arm, to see if they were the notorious "mucuims" which tortured us daily. Under the lens I saw the hideous creature stop in its awkward progress, and as it prepared to sink its proboscis, I involuntarily flinched, so fearful a thing seemed about to happen.

The lesser organisms defy description. They are nameless except in the lists of specialists, and probably most are of new unnamed forms. The only social insects were small twigfuls of ant and termite colonies, with from five to fifteen members. All others were isolated, scattered. Life here, so far beneath the sunlight, is an individual thing. Flocks and herds are unknown; the mob has no place here. Each tiny organism must live its life and meet its fate singlehanded.

Little pseudo scorpions were very abundant, and I could have vialed hundreds. They rushed out excitedly and, unlike all the other little beings, did not seek to hide. Instead, when they were disturbed, they sought open spaces, walking slowly and brandishing and feeling ahead with their great pincer-tipped arms, as long as their entire body. When irritated or frightened, they scurried backwards, holding up their chelae in readiness.

Mites were the most abundant creatures, equaling the ants in number, always crawling slowly along, tumbling over every obstacle in their path and feeling their way awkwardly. Their kinds were numerous, all villainous in appearance. Ticks were less common but equally repellent. Small spiders and beetles were occasionally found, and hundred-legged wrigglers fled to shelter at every turn of a leaf. The smallest snails in the world crawled slowly about, some flat-shelled, others turreted. Tiny earthworms, bright red and very active, crept slowly through fungus jungles until disturbed, when they became an amazingly active tangle of twisting curves, dancing all about. Simple insects, which we shall have to call *Collembola,* were difficult to capture. They leaped with agility many times their own length, and when quiescent, looked like bits of fungus. As for the rest, only Adam and a few specialists hidden in museums could call them by name. They were a numerous company, some ornamented with weird horns and fringes and patterns, others long of legs or legless, swift of foot or curling up into minute balls of animate matter.

One thing was evident early in my exploration: I was in a world of little people. No large insects were in any of the debris. The largest would be very small in comparison with a May beetle. And another thing was the durability of chitin. The remains of beetles, considering the rareness of living ones, were remarkable. The hard wing cases, the thorax armor, the segments of wasps, eyeless head masks still remained perfect in shape and vivid in color. Even in the deepest layers where all else had disintegrated and returned to the elements, these shards of death were as new.

And the smell of the mold, keen and strong as it came to my nostrils an inch away—it was pungent, rich, woody. It hinted of the age-old dissolution, century after century, which had been going on. Leaves had fallen, not in a sudden autumnal downpour, but in a never-ending drift, day after day, month after month. With a daily rain for moisture, with a temperature of three figures for the quicker increase of bacteria, and an excess of humidity to foster quick decay, the jungle floor was indeed a laboratory of vital work—where only analytic chemistry was allowed full sway, and the mystery of synthetic life was ever handicapped.

Before the vessel docked, I had completed my task and had secured over five hundred creatures of this lesser world. At least twice as many remained, but when I made my calculations, I estimated that the mold had sheltered only a thousand organisms plainly visible to the eye.

And when I had corked my last vial and the steward had removed the last pile of shredded debris, I leaned back and thought of the thousand creatures in my scant four square feet of mold. There came to mind a square mile of jungle floor with its thin layer of fallen leaves sheltering more than six billion creatures. Then I recalled the three thousand straight miles of jungle which had lain west of me, and the hundreds of miles of wonderful unbroken forest north and south, and my mind became a blank. And then from the mist of unnamable numerals, from this uncharted arithmetical census, there came to memory a voice, deep and guttural—and this time the slow enunciation was jeering, hopeless of answer, *Wh—y?* and soon afterwards, *Wh—y?* And I packed up my last box of vials and went on deck to watch the sunset.

SIX FEET DEEP

FROM *Listen for a Lonesome Drum*

CARL CARMER

There are still people in upstate New York who think the Cardiff Giant was a petrified man and you can't shake them an inch, says Carl Carmer in this report of an archaeological finding which had everybody from the Chancellor of the State University in Albany to P. T. Barnum involved back in 1869.

Carl Carmer is a collector of tales, some of them tall and some of them true, but all of them fascinating. Upstate New York is his particular preserve —its songs and folklore and its stories, both real and fancied.

STUB NEWELL NEEDED A WELL OUT BEHIND HIS BARN. HE TOLD GID EMMONS and Hank Nicholas about it and they said they were pretty busy but they would come over after supper if the moonlight was good and get it started. It turned out to be a clear night so they went over to Stub's place—it was near Cardiff on the Tully Center road—and fooled around with a hazel twig for a while in order to find a place where they would be sure to hit water, and then they began to dig. They had dug a hole about six feet deep when Gid's shovel brought up on something hard. He and Hank thought it was just a rock at first but pretty soon they realized it was a lot bigger than most rocks you find around there and they got sort of curious. In a little while they had dug all the dirt off the top and there in the moonlight, looking mighty white and strange, lay a naked man, a damn sight more of a man than either Gid or Hank had ever seen in their lives. He looked over ten feet tall and he was sort of scrooched up a bit at that, and everything about him was in the same proportion. His right arm was bent at the elbow so that his right hand rested on his belly and the back of that hand was at least an inch over half a foot across. But it was more than his size that was queer about this fellow. He was as hard as stone. By God, he *was* stone, so far as anybody could tell, although there wasn't any rock like what he was made of in York State.

Gid and Hank called Stub. He got pretty excited about it and somehow by morning most of the people round about had heard about it and came by to see what the stone man looked like. Stub said he might as well charge them

Dharmya: Black Star

Frederic Lewis

SUNLIGHT FLOODS THE FOREST

ROOTS

Black Star

Mauritus: Black Star

GRAVE OF AN AFRICAN CHIEFTAIN

right: GRAVE OF JOHN KEATS IN ROM

BURIAL PLACE OF ANNA TUTHILL SYMMES, FIRST WIFE OF JOHN CLEVES SYMMES, MOTHER-IN-LAW OF WILLIAM HENRY HARRISON AND GRANDMOTHER OF BENJAMIN HARRISON

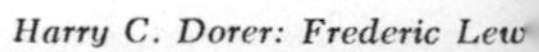

Harry C. Dorer: Frederic Lew

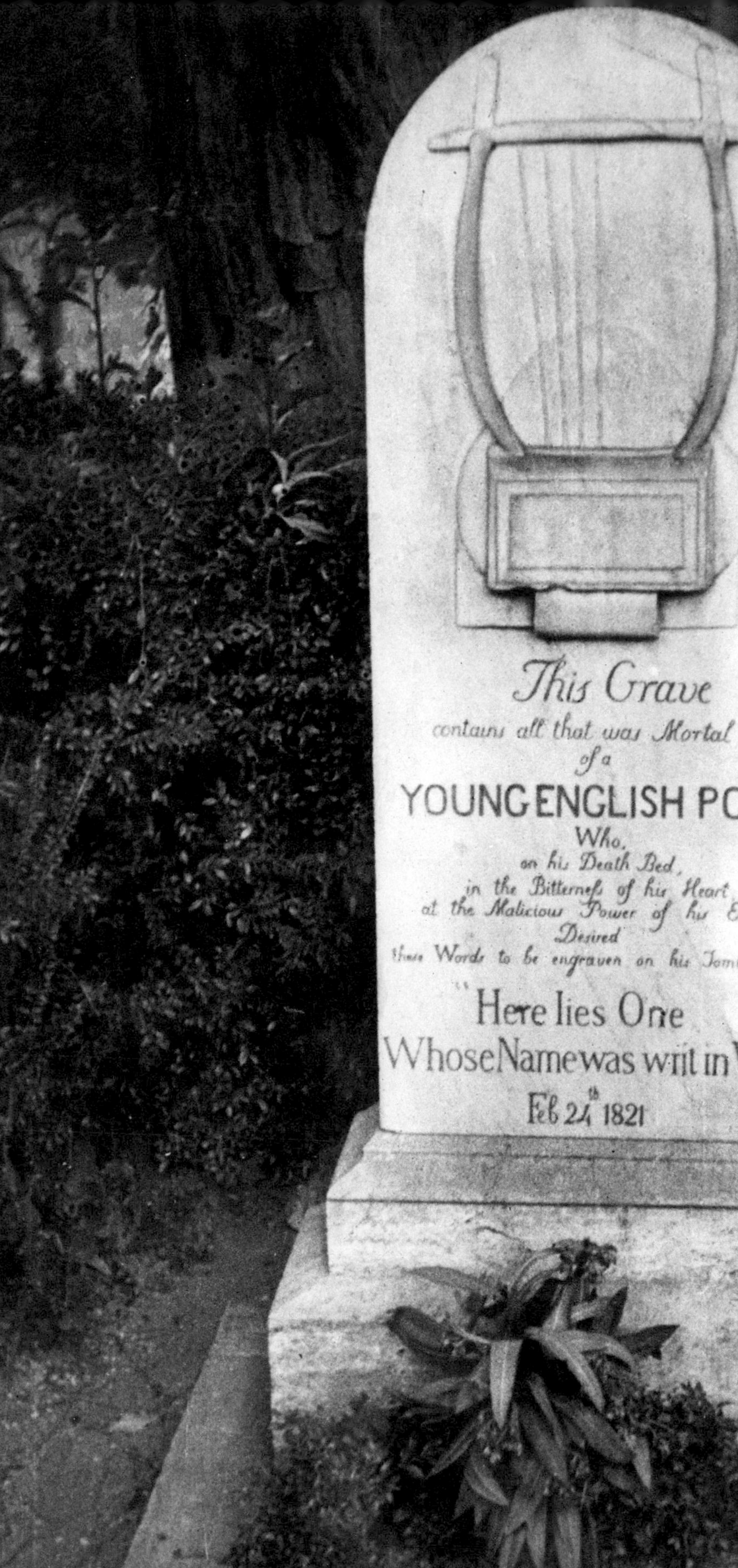
This Grave
contains all that was Mortal
of a
YOUNG ENGLISH POET
Who,
on his Death Bed,
in the Bitterness of his Heart
at the Malicious Power of his Enemies,
Desired
these Words to be engraven on his Tomb Stone
"Here lies One
Whose Name was writ in Water."
Feb 24th 1821

Pete Turner: FPG

right: BOY IN AN OPEN FIELD

below: DANDELION PICKER

Hirz: Frederic Lewis

Eric M. Sanford: FPG

NEW HAMPSHIRE APPLE ORCHARD IN SPRING

Davis: Monkmeyer

EARTH

a little something to look at it, seeing as how so many of them came that they kept him from working around the place, and it was only a little while before he was taking in over twenty-five dollars an hour.

Of course, people got to speculating about where the big fellow came from and what he was. Stub said he figured that giants must have lived in this section a long time ago before the Indians, and this was one of them that had died and got petrified somehow just like some shells do and pieces of wood. Almost everybody agreed with him until an Indian from the Reservation just a few miles away showed up and he said he had heard tell from his own father about stone giants that lived in these parts and made war on the Onondagas. The Indians used to dig pits and cover them over with foliage and leaves and then lie in wait until one of them came by. If he fell in the trap they did away with him quick enough. This Onondaga said he thought the stone man must have been killed that way and laid there in the pit ever since.

Then some students and teachers from the colleges near by began to arrive. One of the professors of geology began shouting around about the stone giant being a fake and a "preposterous imposition" and that made Stub sort of mad—so he said, "I'm goin' to get the leadin' authorities on this kind of thing down here and let them see it free of charge and ask them to say what they think about it."

So he asked Henry A. Ward, who had a museum of his own in Rochester, and Lewis Morgan, who knew more than anybody else about the history of York State Indians, and the Chancellor of the State University in Albany, and the Secretary of the same place, and the State Geologist, all of them to come have a look. They all came and Stub had everybody run out of the tent covering the exhibit. Then he sent all those experts in there and refused to let anybody else in for a whole quarter of an hour. When the five of them came out they all looked very serious and stroked their chins and teetered up and down on their toes. Chancellor Pruyn said he had nothing to say, but Secretary Woolworth said he was "gravely impressed with this probable creation of the Jesuit missionaries." Professor James Hall, the State Geologist, cleared his throat and said, "It is the most remarkable object yet brought to light in this country and although perhaps not dating back to the Stone Age, is nevertheless deserving of the attention of archeologists."

Everybody agreed that these reports made the giant pretty important even if they did not say anything very definite. Stub said they could never make him give up the theory that the big fellow was alive once and that his flesh had petrified. "Just look at the pores in his skin," he would say, "and the hairs on his leg. Nobody with a chisel could make those things." The crowds agreed with him, too, and they had become so big they were hard to handle.

Then a scholarly-looking young fellow from Harvard University named

Alexander McWhorter came by and looked the giant over with a magnifying glass. He got very excited at seeing some scratches under the big stone arm. He copied them down and said they were Phoenician words meaning "Tamur, god of gods" and that Phoenician explorers must have left this religious image there when they passed through Cardiff long before the days of Columbus.

About that time Stub got an invitation to bring his unexpected guest to Albany and set him up there in the Geological Hall. As soon as the details of how much they would charge at the door and how much of that Stub would get were settled the job of moving began. All of the men who could get their hands on the giant grunted and strained but they could not lift him. Finally they hoisted him with a block and tackle and he got a ride to Albany. The gate money doubled there and people came from most of the states in the Union to see the human giant that had turned to stone.

Mr. P. T. Barnum had heard of the giant by now and he went up to see Stub about buying him. He went as high as a hundred and fifty thousand dollars but Stub refused to sell. He had got a few fellows in on the deal with him, one of them being David Hannum over in Homer, and they planned to take the giant on a tour of the United States. So Mr. Barnum went away looking pretty sly.

When receipts began falling off a bit at the Geological Hall, Stub had the giant loaded on the Albany-to-New York Hudson River boat. There were crowds at every landing on the way down trying to get a look at the big passenger and the whole trip seemed like a triumphal procession.

When Stub and his party reached New York, though, they got a bad surprise, Mr. Barnum had gone off to Syracuse and got Professor Otto to make a plaster of Paris giant the same size as the stone one. He had had it shipped to New York and it was already on exhibition on Broadway at Wood's Museum as "the only original giant." Stub had his giant carted to Apollo Hall just two blocks away and hired a barker to outshout the one down the street. Then the fun began.

"We offer the magnanimous reward of a thousand dollars, ladies and gentlemen," Mr. Barnum's man shouted, "to anyone, man, woman or child, who can prove that ours is not the only simon-pure original giant. Beware of imitations, ladies and gentlemen. Do not be deceived by the calcareous humbug of the Albany showmen. Our claims are based on scientific fact alone. I appeal to you as intelligent Americans. Enter and behold the most stupendous contribution to the world's history ever discovered."

"Don't be fooled by counterfeits," Stub's barker yelled. "Enter and see the only petrified giant—lying there so natural you'd think he was alive. See the pores in his skin, the hairs on the back of his hand—all turned to stone.

See the grand old sleeper taking his nap of the centuries. The intelligent man and woman will not be deceived by spurious and cheap duplicates, ladies and gentlemen. See the only original stone giant just as he was found in the York State earth."

Both shows were doing a big business when an upstate professor named O. C. Marsh, who had been doing a little detective work on the kind of stone the big fellow turned into, found a man out in Fort Dodge, Iowa, who said he "got up that giant" out of a block of Iowa gypsum. The professor relayed the news and Stub said he guessed the jig was up. He said he had had the giant shipped east to Binghamton to his cousin, George Hall. He and George and a twelve-year-old boy had buried the big fellow in the middle of the night after he had been brought to Cardiff on a wagon drawn by four mules and four horses. Then York State folks began to laugh. They laughed and laughed while the professors and geologists got red in the face and looked straight ahead or tried to explain just what they had meant a few months before. Stub's giant got more popular than ever. Everybody wanted to see him—so they took him on a trip to let folks all over the United States laugh, too. The whole country bent just about double over Stub Newell's giant and how he fooled the professors—and six million people went to look at him.

The Cardiff Giant is still taking in the money after sixty-six years. For twenty-three of them he rested in a warehouse in his old home at Fort Dodge. Then some businessmen dusted him off and sent him on a tour of the Midwestern fairs. Last year the Syracuse, New York, chamber of commerce tried to "beg, buy, borrow or rent" him. He came back as a loan and spent the week of State Fair on exhibition just fourteen miles from where he was found that moonlit autumn night in 1869.

And around Cardiff and Pompey and Tully and Vesper there are still folks who think the giant was once human flesh and blood. Ask Ed Calkins who runs the hotel over at Jordan and was around when it was all going on.

"Stub Newell and the rest agreed to call him a fake when they found out they'd make more money that way," Ed says. "There's talk about him being made of gypsum. That's wrong. He's more like granite. He doesn't sound like gypsum when you hit him with a hammer and he weighs the same as he ever did. Gypsum would be light and porous by now. Mark my words, you haven't heard the last about his being a petrified human giant yet."

OF THE AMAZING THINGS WHICH THE IMCOMPARABLE DON QUIXOTE TOLD OF HAVING SEEN IN THE DEEP CAVE OF MONTESINOS, AN ADVENTURE THE GRANDEUR AND IMPOSSIBLE NATURE OF WHICH HAVE CAUSED IT TO BE REGARDED AS APOCRYPHAL

FROM *Don Quixote*

CERVANTES

Don Quixote, a world best seller for almost four centuries, seems now to have achieved that variety of reverent burial reserved for classics. Yet this burlesque of knight-errantry, which had as wide a vogue in the sixteenth century as do our best sellers today, is still too much alive for burial and too diverting for reverence. The reader will find proof in this selection which describes Don Quixote's descent into the enchanted caves of Montesino and the adventures which befell him there.

We know little of Cervantes. He was a soldier, he fought in the battle of Lepanto, he spent years as a slave of the Moors. Scholars today are inclined to believe that he did not, as some had thought, write his great book while in prison. But there is some evidence to indicate that he put aside work he thought much more important—his plays, poems, and pastoral novels—to turn out this burlesque because he needed money, believing the picaresque tale would have a wider appeal than his more serious works. And so it did. The book was hardly off the press when pirated editions appeared in large numbers all over the continent. This translation, by Samuel Putnam, is considered the best in English.

AT LENGTH, WHEN THREE DAYS HAD GONE BY, DURING WHICH TIME THEY HAD been feasted and entertained like royalty, Don Quixote asked the swordsman-licentiate to provide him with a guide who would conduct him to the Cave of Montesinos, as he had a great desire to enter it and see with his own eyes if the marvelous tales they told of it throughout that region were true or not. The bachelor replied that he would acquaint him with a first cousin of his, a notable student and very fond of reading books of chivalry, who would be delighted to conduct him to the mouth of the said cave and show him the Lakes of Ruidera, which were famous throughout La Mancha and all Spain as well. He assured the knight that the youth would be found to be entertaining company, since he knew enough to write books of his own, books that were printed and dedicated to princes.

The cousin finally arrived leading an ass in foal, with a packsaddle covered by a striped carpet or sackcloth; and Sancho thereupon proceeded to saddle Rocinante and get his gray ready, taking care to stuff his saddlebags to keep company with those the newcomer had brought with him. Being thus well provisioned, they commended themselves to God and, taking leave of all present, set out along the road that led to the celebrated cave.

On the way, Don Quixote inquired of the cousin what his pursuits were, his profession, and his studies. To this their companion replied that his profession was that of humanist, adding that his pursuits and studies had to do with composing books for the printers, all of them of great public utility and very entertaining. One of them, he stated, was entitled *The Book of Liveries,* in which were depicted seven hundred and three different liveries with their colors, mottoes, and ciphers, from which the gentlemen of the court might pick and choose the ones that suited them best for their feasts and revels without having to go begging for them from anyone or, as the saying has it, straining their wits to procure the costumes adapted to their purpose.

"For," he went on to say, "I provide the jealous, the scorned, the forgotten, the far-absent, with the garb that they should have and that becomes them very well. . . .

"I have another book which I call *Supplement to Virgilius Polydorus.*

It treats of the invention of things and is a very scholarly work and one that cost me much study. In it I set forth in a pleasing style, with due proof and explanation, certain things of great moment that Polydorus neglected to mention. He forgot to tell us who was the first man in the world to have a cold in the head, or the first to take unctions for the French disease, all of which I bring out most accurately, citing the authority of more than twenty-five authors. From this your Grace may see how well I have labored and may judge for yourself as to whether or not such a work should be useful to everyone." . . .

With this and other pleasing talk they spent the day, and when night came found lodgings in a little village which, as the cousin informed Don Quixote, was not more than a couple of leagues from the Cave of Montesinos; and their guide took occasion to remind the knight that if he was resolved to make the descent, he would have to find ropes with which to lower himself into the depths. To this Don Quixote's answer was that even if it was as deep as Hell, he proposed to see the bottom of it; and so they bought nearly a hundred fathoms of rope, and the following day, at two o'clock in the afternoon, they reached the cave, the mouth of which is broad and spacious, but clogged with boxthorn, wild fig trees, shrubs, and brambles, so dense and tangled an undergrowth as wholly to cover over and conceal the entrance. All three of them then dismounted, and Sancho and the cousin bound Don Quixote very stoutly with the ropes.

"Look well what you do, master," said Sancho as they were girdling him. "Don't go burying yourself alive or get yourself caught so you will hang there like a bottle that has been let down into the well to cool. If you ask me, I would say it is none of your Grace's affair to be prying into this cave, which must be worse than a dungeon."

"Keep on tying and keep still," Don Quixote admonished him. "It is just such an undertaking as this, Sancho, that is reserved for me."

The guide then addressed him. "Señor Don Quixote," he said, "I beg your Grace to view thoroughly and inspect with a hundred eyes what you find down there; who knows, maybe it will be something that I can put in my book on *Transformations*."

"Leave the tambourine," Sancho advised him, "to the one who knows how to play it."

By this time they had finished tying Don Quixote, passing the rope over his doublet, not over his battle harness.

"It was careless of us," said the knight, "not to have provided ourselves with a cattle bell to attach to the rope at my side so that you might be able to tell from the sound of it whether I was still descending and still alive.

However, there is nothing for it now. I am in God's hands and may He be my guide."

He knelt and prayed to Heaven in a low voice, imploring God to aid him and grant him success in this adventure, which impressed him as being a rare and dangerous one. Then he raised his voice:

"O lady who dost inspire my every deed and action, O most illustrious and peerless Dulcinea del Toboso! If it be possible for the prayers and entreaties of this thy fortunate lover to reach thine ears, I do beseech thee to hear them. What I ask of thee is nothing other than thy favor and protection, of which I so greatly stand in need at this moment. I am now about to sink, to hurl and plunge myself into the abyss that yawns before me here, simply in order that the world may know that there is nothing, however impossible it may seem, that I will not undertake and accomplish, provided only I have thy favor."

Having said this, he went up to the chasm and preceived that if he was to make a descent he would first have to clear an entrance by force of arm or by hacking away the underbrush; and accordingly, taking his sword, he began cutting and felling the brambles at the mouth of the cave, the noise of which caused a very great number of crows and jackdaws to fly out. There were so many of these birds and such was their velocity that they knocked Don Quixote down, and had he been as much of a believer in augury as he was a good Catholic Christian, he would have taken this as an ill omen and would have declined to bury himself in such a place as that. Finally, he arose and, seeing that no more crows or other night birds were emerging, such as the bats that flew out with the crows, he allowed himself to be lowered into the depths of the horrendous cavern, with Sancho and the cousin letting out the rope as the squire bestowed his benediction and crossed himself an endless number of times.

"May God be your guide," exclaimed Sancho, "and the Rock of France, along with the trinity of Gaeta, O flower, cream, and skimming of knights-errant! There you go, daredevil of the earth, heart of steel, arms of brass! Once more, may God be your guide and bring you back safe, sound, and without a scratch to the light of this world which you are leaving to bury yourself in that darkness that you go to seek!"

The cousin, meanwhile, was offering up practically the same prayers. Don Quixote then went on down, calling for them to give him rope and more rope, and they let it out for him little by little. By the time they could no longer hear his voice, which came out of the cave as through a pipe, they had let him have the entire hundred fathoms, all the rope there was, and were of a mind to pull him up again. They decided, however, to wait for half an hour, and then they once more began hauling in the line, with no effort whatever, for they could feel no weight on the other end, which led them to think that Don Quixote must have remained behind. Believing this to be the case, Sancho began weeping bitterly and started pulling with all his might in order to learn the truth of the matter; but when they had come to a little more than eighty fathoms, as it seemed to them, they once more felt a tug, which made them very happy indeed. Finally, at ten fathoms, they could see Don Quixote quite distinctly, and as he caught sight of him, Sancho cried out, "Welcome, master, we are glad to see you again. We thought you had stayed down there to found a family."

But Don Quixote said not a word in reply, and when they had him all the way up they saw that his eyes were closed and that, to all appearances, he was sound asleep. They laid him on the ground and untied him, but even this did not wake him. It was not until they had turned him over first on one side and then on the other and had given him a thorough shaking and mauling that, after a considerable length of time, he at last regained consciousness, stretching himself as if he had been roused from a profound slumber and gazing about him with a bewildered look.

"God forgive you, friends," he said, "you have taken me away from the most delightful existence mortal ever knew and the pleasantest sight human eyes ever rested upon. Now truly do I begin to understand how it is that all the pleasures of this life pass away like a shadow or a dream or wither like the flower of the field. O unfortunate Montesinos! O sorely wounded Durandarte! O unhappy Belerma! O tearful Guadiana! And you, hapless daughters of Ruidera, who in your waters display the tears your eyes once wept!"

The cousin and Sancho listened attentively to Don Quixote's words, which appeared to have been uttered in great pain, as though drawn from his entrails. They thereupon begged him to tell them the meaning of it all and what it was he had seen in that Hell he had visited.

"Hell do you call it?" said Don Quixote. "Do not call it that, for it does not deserve the name, as you shall see."

He then asked them to give him something to eat, as he was exceedingly hungry; and so they spread the cousin's sackcloth upon the green grass and laid out what fare the saddlebags could afford, and, sitting down together like the three good friends and companions that they were, they proceeded to make a meal of it, combining lunch and supper. When the sackcloth had been removed, Don Quixote de la Mancha spoke.

"Let no one arise," he said, "but both of you listen most attentively to what I have to say."

It was around four in the afternoon when the subdued light and tempered rays of the sun, which was now covered over with clouds, afforded Don Quixote an opportunity to tell his two illustrious listeners, without undue heat or weariness, what it was he had seen in the Cave of Montesinos. He began in the following manner:

"At a depth corresponding to the height of twelve or fourteen men, on the right-hand side of this dungeon, there is a concave recess capable of containing a large cart with its mules. A small light filters into it through distant chinks or crevices in the surface of the earth; and I caught sight of this nook just at a time when I was feeling tired and vexed at finding myself dangling from a rope in that manner as I descended into those dark regions without any certain knowledge as to where I was going. And so I decided to enter the recess and rest a little. I called to you, asking you not to give out any more rope until I told you to do so, but you must not have heard me. Accordingly, I gathered it in as you sent it to me and, making a coil or pile of it, I seated myself upon it, meanwhile thinking what I should have to do in order to let myself all the way down to the bottom, as I now had no one to hold me up.

"As I sat there lost in thought and deeply perplexed, suddenly and without my doing anything to bring it about a profound sleep fell upon me; and then, all unexpectedly and not knowing how it happened, I awoke and found myself in the midst of the most beautiful, pleasant, and delightful meadow that nature could create or the most fertile imagination could conceive. Opening my eyes, I rubbed them and discovered that I was not sleeping but really awake. Nevertheless, I felt my head and bosom to make sure it was I who was there and not some empty and deceptive phantom. And my sense of touch and feeling and the coherence of my thoughts were sufficient to assure me that I was the same then and there that I am here and now.

"It was at that moment that my eyes fell upon a sumptuous royal palace or castle, the walls and battlements of which appeared to be built of clear, transparent crystal. The two wings of the main gate were suddenly thrown open, and there emerged and came toward me a venerable old man clad in a hooded cloak of mulberry-colored stuff that swept the ground. Around his head and his bosom was a collegiate green satin sash, and on his head a black Milanese bonnet. His beard was snow-white and fell below his waist, and he carried no arms whatever, nothing but a rosary which he held in his hand, a string on which the beads were larger than fair-sized walnuts, every tenth one being as big as an ordinary ostrich egg. His bearing, his stride, the gravity of his demeanor, and his stately presence, each in itself and all of them together, filled me with wonder and astonishment. Upon reaching my side, the first thing he did was to give me a close embrace.

" 'It is a long time,' he said, 'O valiant knight, Don Quixote de la Mancha, that we in these enchanted solitudes have been waiting for a sight of you, that you might go back and inform the world of what lies locked and concealed in the depths of this cave which you have entered, the so-called Cave of Montesinos, an exploit solely reserved for your invincible heart and stupendous courage. Come with me, most illustrious sir, and I will show you the hidden marvels of this transparent castle of which I am the governor and perpetual guardian; for I am Montesinos himself, after whom the cave is named.'

"No sooner had he informed me that he was Montesinos than I asked him if the story was true that was told in the world above, to the effect that with a small dagger he had cut out the heart of his great friend Durandarte and had borne it to the lady Belerma as his friend at the point of death had requested him to do. He replied that it was all true except for the part about the dagger, for it was not a dagger, nor was it small, but a burnished poniard sharper than an awl."

"It must have been such a poniard," said Sancho at this point, "as that of Ramón de Hoces of Seville."

"I cannot say as to that," replied Don Quixote, "for Ramón de Hoces lived only yesterday and the battle of Roncesvalles, where this unfortunate affair occurred, was many years ago; and, in any case, it does not alter in any way the truth and substance of the tale."

"That is right," said the cousin. "Continue, Señor Don Quixote, for I am listening to your Grace with the greatest of pleasure."

"And mine in relating the story is no less," Don Quixote assured him. "And so, as I am saying, the venerable Montesinos took me into the crystal palace, where, in a low room that was made entirely of alabaster and very cool, I beheld a tomb fashioned out of marble with masterly craftsmanship, and upon it lay a knight stretched at full length. He was not a bronze knight, nor one of marble or of jasper, as you see on other tombs; he was of actual flesh and bone. His right hand, which seemed to me somewhat hairy and sinewy, a sign that its owner had been possessed of great strength —his right hand lay upon his heart; and before I could ask any questions, Montesinos, seeing how amazed I was, went on to explain.

" 'This,' he said, 'is my friend Durandarte, flower and mirror of the brave and enamored knights of his age. Merlin, that French enchanter, who they say was the devil's own son, holds him here under a spell as he does me and many other knights and ladies. How or why he did it to us, no one knows; but time will tell, and it is my belief that the time is not far off.

What astonishes me is the fact that it is as certain that Durandarte died in my arms as it is that it is now day; and there is likewise no doubt that after his death I took out his heart with my own hands. It weighed all of two pounds; for according to the naturalists he who has a large heart is endowed with greater valor than he who has a small one. And if it is true, then, that this knight really died, how is it that he still sighs and laments from time to time as though he were alive?'

"As Montesinos said this, the wretched Durandarte cried out in a loud voice:

'O my cousin Montesinos!
the last request I made of thee
was that when I should be lying
cold in death, thou wouldst favor me
by bearing this my captive heart
to fair Belerma where'er she be,
and ripping it from out my bosom
with knife or dagger, set it free.'

"Hearing these words, the venerable Montesinos knelt before the unfortunate knight and addressed him with tears in his eyes. 'Long since, O dearest cousin, Señor Durandarte, I did what you requested of me on that bitter day when we lost you. I took out your heart as well as I could, without leaving the smallest particle of it in your breast. I cleaned it with a lace handkerchief and set out for France with it, having first laid you in the bosom of the earth with enough tears to wash my hands of the blood that stained them after they had been in your entrails. What is more, beloved cousin, at the first village I came to after leaving Roncesvalles I put a little salt upon your heart so that it would not have an unpleasant odor but would remain, if not fresh, at least well preserved when I came to present it to the lady Belerma.

" 'That lady, like you and me and Guadiana your squire and the duenna Ruidera and her seven daughters and two nieces and many others among your friends and acquaintances, has been held here many a year through Merlin's magic art; and although more than five hundred years have passed, not a one of us has died. The only ones that are missing are Ruidera, her daughters and her nieces, for Merlin would seem to have taken pity on their tears and has transformed them into an equal number of lakes which today, in the world of the living and the province of La Mancha, are known as the Lakes of Ruidera. Seven of them belong to the King of Spain, and the two nieces to the knights of a very holy order called the Order of St. John.

" 'As for Guadiana, your squire, weeping for your sad fate, he was transformed into a river of the same name. When he came to the surface and beheld the sun of that other heaven, he was so grieved at thought of leaving you that he plunged down into the bowels of the earth once more; but inasmuch as he must needs yield to his natural current, he rises again from time to time where men and the sun may see him. The said lakes supply him with their waters, and with these and many others that reach him he enters Portugal with great pomp. But, for all of that, wherever he goes he is still sad and melancholy and does not pride himself upon breeding dainty fish of the kind that are sought after, but only coarse ones lacking in flavor, quite different from those of the Tagus with its golden sands.

" 'All this, O cousin, I have told you many times; and since you do not answer me, I am led to think that you do not believe me, or it may be you do not hear, all of which pains me, God only knows how much. But now I have some news to give you which, if it does not assuage your grief, will not add to it in any way. Know that here in your presence—you have but to open your eyes and you will see him—is that great knight of whom the wise Merlin prophesied so many things, I mean the famous Don Quixote de la Mancha, who once again and to better advantage than in past ages has undertaken to revive in this present age the long-forgotten profession of knight-errantry. It may be that, thanks to his favor and mediation, we shall be disenchanted; for great exploits are reserved for great men.'

" 'And even if it be not so,' replied the wretched Durandarte in a low, faint voice, 'and even if it be not so, O cousin, I say to you: patience, and shuffle.' And, turning on his side, he relapsed into his accustomed silence without uttering another word.

"At that moment a great outcry was heard, accompanied by the sound of weeping, profound sighs, and anguished sobs; and I turned my head and saw, through the crystal walls, a procession of exceedingly lovely damsels passing through another chamber. There were two rows of them, and they were all clad in mourning with white turbans on their heads after the Turkish fashion. At the end of the procession came a lady, as was to be seen from her dignified appearance, who wore a flowing white veil so long that it touched the ground. Her turban was twice as large as the largest of the others, her eyebrows were so close together that they met, her nose was somewhat flat and her mouth wide, but her lips were red; her teeth, when she displayed them, were seen to be few and uneven but white as peeled almonds. In her hands she carried a fine piece of cloth, and wrapped in it, so far as could be made out, was a mummified heart, all dried and withered.

"Montesinos informed me that all these people in the procession were the attendants of Durandarte and Belerma who had been enchanted along with their master and mistress, and that the last one, with the heart in her hands, was the lady Belerma herself, who with her damsels was accustomed to parade like this four days a week, singing, or rather weeping, dirges over the heart and body of his unfortunate cousin. He added that in case she impressed me as being somewhat ugly, or at any rate not as beautiful as report would have it, this was due to the bad nights and worse days that she spent as an enchanted being, as I could see for myself from the circles under her eyes and her sickly hue.

" 'And do not think,' continued Montesinos, 'that her sallowness and those circles are due to an affliction that is common to women at a certain period of the month, for it has been many months and even years since she has had that experience. It is, rather, the grief that she feels in her heart for that other heart she holds in her hands, which but serves to bring back to memory and revive the misfortune that befell her ill-starred lover. If it were not for that, even the great Dulcinea del Toboso, so famous in these parts and throughout the world, would scarcely equal her in beauty, grace, and dashing manner.'

" 'Hold there, Señor Don Montesinos!' said I at this point. 'Your Grace should tell your story in the proper way for, as you know, all comparisons are odious. There is no reason for comparing anybody with anybody. The peerless Dulcinea del Toboso is who she is and has been, and let the matter rest there.'

" 'Señor Don Quixote,' he replied to me, 'forgive me, your Grace. I confess that I was wrong in saying that Señora Dulcinea could scarcely equal Señora Belerma; for by some means or other I have learned that your Grace is her knight, and that is enough to make me bite my tongue out before comparing her with anything but Heaven itself.'

"And so the great Montesinos having given me this satisfaction, my heart recovered from the shock it had received when I heard my lady mentioned in the same breath with his."

"But," said Sancho, "I still can't help wondering why your Grace didn't jump on the old fellow and kick his bones to a pulp and pull his beard until there wasn't a hair left in it."

"No, friend Sancho," replied Don Quixote, "it would not have been right for me to do that, for we are all of us obliged to respect the aged, even though they be knights, and especially when they are under a magic spell. But I can tell you that we came off even in all the other questions and answers that passed between us."

The cousin now put in a word. "I do not understand, Señor Don Quixote," he said, "how your Grace in the short time you were down there could have seen so many things and done so much talking."

"How long has it been since I went down?" asked Don Quixote.

"A little more than an hour," Sancho told him.

"That cannot be," said the knight, "for night fell and day dawned, and it was day and night three times altogether; so that, according to my count, it was three whole days that I spent in those remote regions that are hidden from our sight."

"My master," averred Sancho, "must be speaking the truth; for since all the things that happened to him came about through magic, who knows? what seemed to us an hour may have been three days and nights for him."

"That is right," said Don Quixote.

"And did your Grace eat in all that time?" the cousin inquired.

"Not a mouthful," replied Don Quixote, "nor did I feel the least bit hungry."

"Then, those that are enchanted do not eat?" the student persisted.

"They neither eat nor are they subject to the major excretions," was Don Quixote's answer, "although it is believed that their nails, beard, and hair continue to grow."

"And do they sleep by any chance?" asked Sancho.

"No, certainly not," said Don Quixote, "or, at least, during the three days I was with them, none of them shut an eye, and the same was true of me."

"The proverb, 'Tell me what company you keep and I'll tell you what you are,' fits in here," observed Sancho. "Seeing your Grace has been keeping company with the bewitched, who fast and stay awake, it is small wonder if you didn't sleep either while you were with them. But forgive me, master, if I tell you that God—I was about to say the devil—may take me if I believe a word of your Grace's story."

"How is that?" asked the cousin. "Do you mean to say that Señor Don Quixote is lying? Why, even if he wished to, he had no opportunity to imagine and invent such a lot of falsehoods."

"I do not think that my master is lying," said Sancho.

"Well, then, what do you think?" Don Quixote wanted to know.

"I think," replied Sancho, "that Merlin or those enchanters that laid a spell on the whole crew you say you saw and talked with down there have put into your noddle or your memory all this rigmarole that you've been telling us, and all that remains to be told."

"Such a thing could be," said Don Quixote, "but it is not so in this case; for I have simply told you what I saw with my own eyes and felt with my own hands. Montesinos showed me countless other marvelous things which I will relate to you in due time and at leisure in the course of our journey, for this is not the place to speak of them. But what will you say when I tell you he pointed out to me three peasant lasses who were gamboling and disporting themselves like goats in those lovely meadows; and no sooner did I see them than I recognized one of them as being the peerless Dulcinea del Toboso and the other two as the same girls who had come with her and with whom we spoke upon the El Toboso road.

"I asked Montesinos if he knew them and he replied that he did not, but that he thought they must be some highborn ladies with a spell upon them. He added that they had arrived but a few days ago, which to me was not surprising in view of the fact that many other ladies of the present time as well as of past ages were to be found there in various strange and enchanted shapes, among whom he said he recognized Queen Guinevere and her duenna Quantañona, she who poured the wine for Lancelot 'when from Britain he came.' "

As he heard his master say this, Sancho Panza thought he would lose his mind or die of laughing. Knowing as he did the truth respecting Dulcinea's supposed enchantment, since he himself had been the enchanter and the concoctor of the evidence, he now was convinced beyond a doubt that the knight was out of his senses and wholly mad.

"It was an evil hour, my dear master," he said, "a worse season, and a sad day when your Grace went down into the other world, and an unlucky moment when you met that Señor Montesinos, who has sent you back to us like this. You would have been better off if you had stayed up here, with all your wits about you as God gave them to you, speaking in proverbs and giving advice at every step of the way, in place of telling us the most foolish stories that could be imagined."

"Knowing you as I do, Sancho," said Don Quixote, "I take no account of your words."

"Nor I of your Grace's," was the reply.

THE SAWING-OFF OF MANHATTAN ISLAND

FROM *All Around the Town*

HERBERT ASBURY

A hoax, by dictionary definition, "is a trick or deception practiced for the purpose of making sport or mischief, a practical joke." The hoaxer is a man with amateur status, he works for the pure joy of it. It is a moot question whether such eminent practitioners of the sport as Edgar Allan Poe with his newspaper report of a transoceanic balloon flight which never took place or Mark Twain with his discovery of the petrified man, can be classed as amateurs.

There is no doubt, however, of the status of carpenter Lozier and his crony, butcher DeVoe, who kept New York in a considerable flurry during the summer of 1824. Herbert Asbury, historian of the seamier side of American social life and author of *Gangs of New York,* reports on the project with his enviable facility for capturing the feel of a bygone period.

ONE OF THE MOST EXTRAORDINARY HOAXES EVER PERPETRATED IN NEW YORK originated a little more than a hundred years ago in the fertile imagination of a little dried-up old man named Lozier, who had amassed a competence as a carpenter and contractor and had then retired to enjoy life. For almost two months during the summer of 1824 Lozier's fantastic activities, which he carried on with the enthusiastic assistance of John DeVoe, a retired butcher better known as Uncle John, kept a considerable portion of middle- and lower-class New York in a veritable frenzy of excitement. . . .

In those early days, when the Present American metropolis was a comparatively small city of not more than 150,000 population, a favorite loafing-place was the old Centre Market at Grand, Baxter, and Centre Streets. A dozen long benches lined the Grand Street side of the Market, and every afternoon from spring to winter they were filled with amateur statesmen, principally retired butchers and other such small business men, most of whom combined scant knowledge with excessive gullibility. Chief among them were Lozier and Uncle John DeVoe, and of these two venerable jokesters, Lozier was the leader. He did most of the talking at the daily forums in front of the Market and was invariably able to produce a definite and apparently practicable remedy for every conceivable financial, political, or economic ill. He was always listened to with enormous respect, for he was wealthy, he possessed more education than his fellows and was therefore better able to express himself, and he was a recognized traveler, having made several voyages to Europe as a ship's carpenter. There was no lack of subjects to talk about, for those were wondrous times. The first great wave of Irish immigration had begun to beat against American shores as a result of the potato famine of 1822; Brazil and Mexico had thrown off the shackles of Portugal and Spain; the first steamship had crossed the Atlantic only a few years before; President James Monroe had just promulgated the Monroe Doctrine; and Mrs. Monroe had almost precipitated a revolution in New York and Washington society by announcing that as the First Lady of the Land she would no longer return social calls. The gifted Lozier professed to know the inside stories of all these momentous events, and so convincing was he that there were many who believed that he was high in the confidence not only of the President, but of foreign potentates as well.

Early in July 1824 Lozier was absent from his accustomed bench for several days, an unparalleled occurrence which aroused much comment. When he returned, he refused to join in the flow of conversation and even declined to settle arguments. He talked only to Uncle John DeVoe, and for the most part sat alone, brooding, obviously concerned with weighty matters. When his friends asked where he had been, and sought diligently to learn what mighty thoughts troubled his mind, he would at first divulge no information. At length, however, he admitted that he had been at City Hall in consultation with Mayor Stephen Allen. No one doubted the truth of this statement, which caused even more talk than had his absence. In those days the Mayor of New York was a personage of impressive dignity; he was not so approachable as now, and a man who had been summoned by His Honor automatically became a person of considerable importance. For almost a week Lozier kept his friends and admirers on tenterhooks of curiosity. Finally, on a day when all the Market benches were occupied and he was thus assured of an audience worthy of his talents, he made a full and complete explanation.

It appeared that Lozier and Mayor Allen had had a long conversation about Manhattan Island and had reached the conclusion that it was much too heavy on the Battery end, because of the many large buildings. The situation was rapidly becoming dangerous. Already the island had begun to sag, as was plain from the fact that it was all downhill from City Hall, and there were numerous and alarming indications that it might break off and sink into the sea, with appalling losses of life and property. Lozier and the Mayor had decided, therefore, that the island must be sawed off at Kingsbridge, at the northern end, and turned around, so that the Kingsbridge end would be where the Battery end had been for ages. The Battery end, of course, if it did not fall off in transit, would take the place of the Kingsbridge end. Once the turn had been made, the weaker end of the island would be anchored to the mainland, thus averting the danger of collapse.

When the conferences at City Hall began, it further appeared, Lozier and Mayor Allen were not in complete agreement as to the best method of accomplishing the mighty task. The Mayor thought that before Manhattan could be turned around it would be necessary to detach Long Island from its moorings and tow it out of the way, returning it later to its proper place. Lozier finally convinced him, however, that there was ample space in the harbor and the bay. It was at length decided, therefore, simply to saw Manhattan Island off, float it down past Governors and Ellis Islands, turn it around, and then float it back to its new position. For political reasons Mayor Allen wished the job to appear as a private undertaking and had turned the whole project over to Lozier, instructing him to employ the necessary labor and to superintend the work.

Such were the force of Lozier's personality, the power of his reputation, and the credulity of his generation that practically none who heard him thought of questioning the feasibility of the scheme. The few who were inclined to scoff were soon silenced, if not actually convinced, by his earnestness, and by the acclaim which had greeted the announcement of the project. Everyone realized at once that it was truly a gigantic plan, but they had Lozier's word for it that it could be accomplished. Moreover, as Lozier pointed out, the construction of the famous Erie Canal, which was then nearing completion, had once been called impossible even by competent engineers, and much derision had greeted the prediction that steam ships would one day cross the ocean. If man could run a river through the very heart of a mountain, and if he could cause a simple steam engine to propel a gigantic boat, why couldn't he saw off an island? Nobody knew the answer, and Lozier's story was swallowed *in toto,* hook, line, and sinker.

Sawing Manhattan Island off soon became the principal subject of argument and conversation at Centre Market, and elsewhere as news of the great project spread. Neither then nor later, however, did the few newspapers of the period pay any attention to Lozier's activities. It is doubtful if the editors ever heard of him, for in those days the only way of transmitting intelligence was by word of mouth, or by letter, which was even more uncertain. Important happenings in one part of the city did not become generally known for weeks or months, and frequently not at all. And

Grand Street then was as far uptown as the farthest reaches of the Bronx are today.

A few days after he had started the ball rolling Lozier appeared at Centre Market with a huge ledger, in which he proposed to record the names of all applicants for jobs, pending an examination to determine their fitness. This and other clerical work which developed during the progress of the hoax was the special care of Uncle John DeVoe, who ceremoniously set down the names, ages, and places of residence of all who applied. Work was none too plentiful that year, and laborers, many of them recently-arrived Irishmen, answered Lozier's call in such numbers that the big ledger soon bore the names of some three hundred men, all eager to begin the great work of sawing off Manhattan Island.

Lozier further aroused confidence in his scheme by notifying various butchers of his acquaintance to begin assembling the enormous herds of cattle, droves of hogs, and flocks of chickens which would be necessary to feed his army of workmen. He estimated that he would require at once five hundred head of cattle, an equal number of hogs, and at least three thousand chickens. He was especially anxious to obtain as many fowls as possible, for he had definitely promised that all who obtained jobs would have chicken dinners twice a week. There was great excitement among the butchers, the immediate effect of which was an increase in the prices of all sorts of meat. One enterprising butcher had in his pens fifty fat hogs awaiting slaughter, and to make certain of a sale to Lozier he drove them north and penned them near Kingsbridge, where he fed them for almost a month at considerable expense.

With his food-supply assured, Lozier engaged a score of small contractors and carpenters to furnish lumber and to superintend, under his direction, the building of the great barracks which were to house the workmen during the sawing operations. A separate building, to be constructed of the best materials, was ordered for the convenience of the twenty or thirty women, wives of laborers, who had been employed to cook and wash for the entire crew. Several of these contractors let their enthusiasm get the better of their judgment and actually hauled a dozen loads of lumber to the northern end of the island and dumped them near Kingsbridge. They implored Lozier to let them begin building, but he said that actual construction must wait until he had engaged all the men he would need and had assembled all his materials. It was his intention, he announced, to muster his workmen at a central meeting-place when everything was ready and march them in a body to Kingsbridge. He assured the contractors that by using a new method of building which he had devised, but which he declined to disclose in advance, they could easily erect the necessary buildings within a few hours.

The excitement was now at fever heat, and Lozier added fuel to the flame by producing elaborate plans for the various appliances which were to be used in the project. First, there were the great saws with which Manhattan Island was to be cut loose from the mainland. Each was to be one hundred feet long, with teeth three feet high. Fifty men would be required to manipulate one of these giant tools, and Lozier estimated that he would need at least a score. Then there were twenty-four huge oars, each two hundred and fifty feet long; and twenty-four great cast-iron towers, or oarlocks, in which the oars were to be mounted, twelve on the Hudson River shore and twelve on the East River. A hundred men would bend their backs at each oar, and row Manhattan Island down the bay after the sawyers had finished their work, then sweep it around and row it back. Great chains and anchors were to be provided to keep the island from being carried out to sea in the event that a storm arose. Lozier gave the plans and specifications of these Gargantuan implements to a score of blacksmiths, carpenters, and mechanics, who retired forthwith to their shops and feverishly began to estimate the cost, and the quantities of material that must go into their manufacture.

Lozier now turned his attention to the unskilled laborers whose names Uncle John DeVoe had set down as potential sawyers and rowers. He sent word for them to report at Centre Market for examination and announced that he would pay triple wages to those who performed the hazardous work of sawing off that part of the island which lay under water. The longest-winded men would be awarded these dangerous but desirable jobs. Laborers swarmed to the market, and every day for a week Lozier sat enthroned on a bench while man after man stepped forward and held his breath. As each displayed his prowess, Uncle John DeVoe timed them and entered the result in his ledger.

Lozier kept delaying the commencement of actual work by professing dissatisfaction with the estimates on the oars and towers and by insisting that he had not hired nearly enough men to do the job properly. At last, however, "the numbers became so thick and pressing," as DeVoe put it in *The Market Book,* that Lozier was compelled to fix a date for the grand trek northward. He hurriedly awarded the contracts for manufacturing the saws, oars, and towers and ordered them rushed to completion. He then instructed all who were to have a hand in the great work to report at the Bowery and Spring Street, where they would be met by a fife and drum corps which he had thoughtfully engaged to lead the march to Kingsbridge. The exact number who appeared at the rendezvous is unknown, of course, but DeVoe says that "great numbers presented themselves," and there were probably between five hundred and a thousand persons. Laborers were there by the score, many accompanied by their wives and children; the contractors and carpenters drove up in style, escorting wagons laden with lumber and tools; the butchers were on hand with cattle and hogs, and carts loaded with crated chickens. Practically everyone who had ever heard of the project was there, in fact, excepting Lozier and Uncle John DeVoe. When several hours had elapsed and they still had failed to appear, a volunteer delegation went to Centre Market in search of them. They found a message that both Lozier and Uncle John had left town on account of their health.

The crowd at Bowery and Spring Street milled about uncertainly for another hour or two, while the hogs grunted, the cattle mooed, the chickens cackled, the children squalled, and the fife and drum corps industriously dispensed martial music. At length, for the first time in weeks, if not in years, some of the more intelligent of Lozier's victims began to think, and the more they thought, the less likely it appeared that Manhattan Island would ever be sawed off. Gradually this conviction spread, and after a while the crowd began shamefacedly to disperse. A few of the more hot-headed went looking for Lozier, vowing that if they couldn't saw Manhattan off they could as least saw Lozier off, but they never found him. Lozier and Uncle John DeVoe had fled to Brooklyn as soon as Lozier had issued his final instructions, and had sought refuge in the home of a friend. There was much talk of having them arrested, but no one seemed willing to make a complaint to the authorities and so admit that he had been duped, and both Lozier and Uncle John went scot-free. However, it was several months before they again appeared at Centre Market, and when they did, Lozier found himself an oracle without a temple. The Centre Market statesmen had had enough.

COUSIN HATTIE'S RESTING PLACE

FROM *The Late George Apley*

JOHN P. MARQUAND

John P. Marquand, in *The Late George Apley,* from which this selection is taken, dissected the prides and prejudices of the Boston best families with so urbane a scalpel that at least one publisher refused the book as a rather feeble attempt at humorous fantasy. It would be interesting to know whether the publisher in question was a Bostonian. The book when it appeared was awarded the Pulitzer Prize as social satire of very high merit.

Marquand inherited the background which he describes with so devastating a blandness. Margaret Fuller, the famous New England bluestocking, was his aunt, and the farm in Newburyport, in the possession of the family for more than a century, was a favorite gathering place of the Boston Brahmins.

THE IMMINENCE OF WAR . . . WAS SUCCEEDED FOR GEORGE APLEY BY A CRISIS of a somewhat different nature, occasioned by the death and burial of Mrs. Henry Apley, a somewhat distant family connection. Her sons, entirely within their right, buried their mother in the Apley lot of the Mt. Auburn Cemetery—that gracious, well-endowed, and beautifully attended piece of ground where so many have found their final resting place and where others hope to, including the present writer. It was Apley's invariable custom to attend every funeral of the family, but on this occasion, being much pressed for time, he was not among those present at the grave, nor did he attend to the grave's location, although he was one of the trustees of the Apley lot. Instead, he entrusted these details to his second cousin, Roger Apley, greatly to his subsequent regret. His letters, however, are self-explanatory:—

Dear Roger:—

Yesterday, happening to be motoring with Catharine toward Concord, we stopped at Mt. Auburn Cemetery as is our habit whenever we pass by it. I was particularly anxious to see how the young arbor vitae which we decided, after so much debate, to plant on the southern border, were surviving the early summer heat. I was pleased to see that they were doing very well indeed and, in fact, was about to leave when I noticed that Cousin Hattie had been placed in that part of the lot which I had always understood, and which I believe everyone in the family has understood, was reserved for my particular branch. I refer to the part of ground around the oak tree which my father had ordered planted. This was a favourite place of his and has a peculiarly sentimental significance to me and to my children. As you know, these matters grow more important with the growing years. I cannot conceive what prompted you to allow Cousin Hattie to occupy this spot. Not only do I think she should not be there, but also her pink granite headstone with the recumbent figure on top of it, which I suppose represents an angel, makes a garish contrast to our own plain, white marble stones.

I admit that the Henry Apleys are connections of the family, though so distant that they might almost not be considered as such. I might also call to your attention that the Henry Apleys, due to their straitened circumstances, did not and have never contributed to the purchase and maintenance fund of our ground. Except for Thanksgiving dinner, I do not recall ever having seen Cousin Hattie except twice when she had difficulty in meeting her grandson's tuition bills. Under these circumstances it seems to me somewhat pushing and presumptuous, although I like neither of the words, of the Henry Apleys to preëmpt the place they did without at least consulting me. I may tell you confidentially that I was very much disturbed by the reaction of Adam, our chauffeur, who came with us, carrying some potted geraniums, slips from some which my mother had planted. It was clear to both Catharine and me that Adam was very much shocked, from his manner, if not from any words.

It is no use to embroider any further upon this, but I cannot forget that I left these arrangements to you, as a member of the trustees' committee. I feel very sure you did not realize how your decision would have affected me, and how it would affect my Uncle William who is planning to rest near that spot, I am afraid in the very near future. Uncle William, as you know, has a series of violent dislikes and among them was Cousin Hattie. I hesitate to tell him that she is there, and yet I am afraid I must do so because he has asked me to go with him next week to Mt. Auburn so that he may pick out the exact spot he desires. I dread the repercussions of his discovery so much that I think it is up to you to make representations to the Henry Apley branch and to arrange that Cousin Hattie be exhumed and placed near the arbor vitae trees on the other slope. This section of the lot is not occupied at present. Will you please let me know what you can do about this.

Dear Roger:—

I am very much gratified that you realize the seriousness of this situation. I agree with you it requires delicacy in handling, but I do not agree with you that it is too late to do anything about it. When the subway was built under Boston Common a great many bodies were exhumed from the old graveyard there and again buried. I note that you feel that you cannot see the Henry Apleys yourself, therefore you had better refer them to me. I shall write to Henry Apley today as you suggest. . . .

Dear Henry:—

Through a piece of mismanagement which I cannot believe is any fault of yours, your mother's remains have been placed in a spot in our family ground which I have always felt was tacitly at the disposal of our branch. I am afraid I must come to the point at once and ask that your mother be removed near the arbor vitae hedges on the opposite slope. I hope very much that you will agree with me when you consider the various implications involved, and believe me, I realize that my request may be trying to you in this period of your grief. I cannot avoid the feeling also that this accident has occurred because of my own pre-occupation in other matters, therefore I want you to realize that I, of course, shall defray all expenses. Please let me know at once about this as the matter is important. . . .

Dear Henry:—

I can ascribe much of your letter to the natural agitation which you must feel at such a time, but I see no reason for your final decision. The plot is family property until it is fully occupied. My one objection was regarding location. I do not feel that I have the slightest right in suggesting that your mother's remains be removed from the Apley plot, and I beg you to remember that I never did suggest it.

If, however, you feel that this removal is the most satisfactory solution of this difficulty and will relieve your own feelings, I shall not urge you not to do it. I repeat again that I stand ready to defray all expenses.

Such a contretemps, it will be recognized, bears no great novelty; rather it is a difficulty which has been faced by so many that nearly any reader may feel a sympathy for Apley's point of view and may comprehend as well the importance of such a negotiation. The consequence obviously foreshadowed a rift within the family and explains the reason for many breaches which are yet unhealed. At the time Apley was considerably surprised and not a little hurt by the unsympathetic, if not actually hostile, reactions of his own blood relations. He became aware for the first time that in spite of his most generous efforts certain of his own kin harbored for him a tacit resentment that bordered dangerously on dislike. It may only be added that he faced it with his usual composure in the belief that he had conscientiously done what was right.

Even his own uncle, Horatio Brent, who was suffering severely at the time from gout and from heart complications, saw fit in spite of his devotion to George Apley to remonstrate with his nephew's point of view. His letter, which is quoted here, is additionally useful in showing the impression that George Apley was making upon a certain segment of his own group. If this impression is neither true nor a welcome one to those who admired him most, it serves merely as another proof that no man of definite character can help but create opposition.

Dear George:—

Here I am at Pachogue Neck. I am sitting on the old piazza where you have been so often, with my foot swathed in bandages. Your aunt, who sends you her love, will not allow me to take stimulants and is arranging to have an elevator installed to pull me upstairs to bed. Old Bess, my pointer bitch, who you remember took first prize in the Dedham Field Trial six years back, is sitting here beside me creaky in her joints and I am afraid the vet will have to put her out of the way by autumn. Frankly, I wish we had vets instead of doctors, because I believe I should be put out of the way too quite as much as Bess.

It seems funny to see the whole world look as young as ever, to smell the salt air and to see the water sparkling on the bay, and to be so old myself. Frankly, George, it is damnably unpleasant. I think of all the good times we had together. I think of when your aunt and I took you to Paris with Henrietta to get you over that abortive romance. You can laugh at it now, I guess. I think of lots of things, because there is nothing else to do, and I hope you won't mind your uncle writing a few words to you because he is fond of you.

Of course I have heard about the Mt. Auburn Cemetery row. Everybody at Pachogue Neck has been talking about it for the past two weeks. I don't mind where Hattie is buried. I don't mind much where anyone is buried except that I do not like the idea of throwing around ashes, but I wonder if you see yourself the way other people see you. I don't like people outside of the family to be laughing at you, George. I don't like to have them say that you are exhibiting a sense of your own pompousness and your own importance, because I know that you are not. I know what the trouble is with you: it is the *galère* in which we have all had to live. We have all been told from the nursery that we are important and that we must do the right thing. Believe me you don't feel important when you have the gout. I want to tell you something that it won't hurt to remember. I know that I have forgotten it often enough myself, but here it is. Most people in the world don't know who the Apleys are and they don't give a damn. I don't intend this as rudeness but as a sort of comfort. I know it has been a comfort to me sometimes when talking with your aunt. Just remember that most people don't give a damn. When you remember it, you won't feel the necessity of taking the Apleys so seriously. I hope you know the way I mean it. . . .

GERMAN PEASANTS OF THE MIDDLE AGES

THE SONG OF THE EARTH

FROM *Johnny Appleseed and Aunt Mattie*

LOUIS BROMFIELD

Louis Bromfield, who achieved a large and popular literary reputation with his novels, was probably the most famous American farmer of this generation. He settled on a thousand-acre farm near his birthplace in Ohio which became one of the agricultural show places of America, drawing visitors from most countries of the world. Although he was a craftsman of distinction in his fiction, critics think that his more permanent writing came out of Malabar Farm itself, particularly in *Pleasant Valley*, a volume of autobiographical reminiscence, from which this warm, affectionate, and moving story of his Aunt Mattie and Johnny Appleseed is chosen.

MY EARLIEST MEMORIES OF JOHNNY APPLESEED ARE OF LISTENING TO MY GREAT-Aunt Mattie talk of him beneath the big catalpa tree on my grandfather's farm. Aunt Mattie was blind from the age of thirty and when I first remember her she was over eighty, a sprightly, very bright old lady with a crinkly mouth that was always curling up in a good-humored, faintly mocking smile. She was a witty, and at times a malicious, old lady and like so many blind people since the time of Homer, a great storyteller. I think that the stories were a kind of compensation for the darkness in which she spent more than half a century of her life. Now, nearly forty years after her death, I realize that you could not always take all her stories as gospel truth, but I also know that she was in her way a minor artist. If there were facts missing from one of her stories of frontier life, she supplied them out of her own imagination; if some fact did not suit one of her tales she modified and altered it to fit the artistic frame.

Aunt Mattie said she had known Johnny Appleseed. I do not know whether this was true or not. She was born in 1826 and by a curious combination of circumstances her presence and her stories brought me as a small boy very near to the eighteenth century for she was the child of my great-grandfather who had visited Voltaire at Ferney. She was born when he was seventy-two years old. But there were other elements which brought her very close to the strange little man who has become a legend and a kind of saint in our Middle Western country. She loved the woods and the streams and the wild birds and animals as Johnny Appleseed had done. My grandmother told me that when Aunt Mattie was a small child she had caused much anxiety through her trick of running off to spend whole days wandering through the swamps and forests of the still half-conquered Ohio frontier country. In those days there were occasional bears or wandering Indians about but no amount of bloodcurdling tales ever succeeded in instilling fears in Aunt Mattie as to what might happen to her. My grandmother said that, like Johnny himself, Aunt Mattie never seemed to have any fear of Indians or wild animals.

Even as a blind old woman she kept that love of the streams and forest and wild things. She had a remarkable talent for finding her way about the farm. Of course, she had been born there and until she lost her sight she knew it well and so even in all the fifty or more years of her blindness she must have known always exactly how it looked. But sometimes on long excursions she did not go off by herself, feeling with her small feet the roads and paths or guiding herself by the sound of the rustling leaves of the familiar landmark trees. Sometimes when she felt adventurous and wanted to make a long excursion down through the bottom pastures where the creek ran on into the thicket, she would ask one of the children to act as her guide. She would select a spot which she remembered beneath a tree on the edge of the creek and then tell us to come back for her two or three hours later. She did not like us playing about. She wanted to be left alone and at times, even as a child, you had the feeling that she had come there for a rendezvous and did not wish to be disturbed or spied upon. She would spend a whole afternoon listening to the sounds of fish jumping or birds singing or cattle lowing.

Since she knew that whole small world through touch and sound alone she undoubtedly understood it in a way none of the rest of us could ever do. She heard and interpreted sounds, small sounds—the symphony made by frogs and crickets and birds and cattle which we never heard at all. Sometimes you would come upon her sitting quietly beneath a tree beside the clear little stream, her head tilted a little in an attitude of listening. Like as not, the cattle would be lying all around close up to her, munching bluegrass and fighting flies.

The spirit of Johnny Appleseed haunted that same Valley. Once, long ago, he had roamed all the region, sleeping in the big sandstone caves or in Indian huts or settlers' cabins. He was welcome wherever he stopped among the Indians, the white settlers or the wild animals themselves.

With each year the figure of Johnny Appleseed grows a little more legendary; each year new stories and legends attach themselves to what has become in our country an almost mythical figure. A few facts are stated but few are known. It is said that Johnny's real name was John Chapman. Some say that he was born in New England, others that he was born at Fort Duquesne, later to be called Pittsburgh. It is pretty well accepted that he was a Swedenborgian by faith. It is also related that he died at last somewhere near the borders of Ohio and Indiana.

The truth is, of course, that Johnny Appleseed has attained that legendary status where facts are no longer of importance. Long before we returned to Pleasant Valley he had become a kind of frontier saint about whom had collected volumes of folklore and legend. In the natural process of things, it is the stories and legends and not the facts which have become important. I think Aunt Mattie understood this change of values which throughout all history has imperceptibly translated heroes into gods and hermits into saints.

She told us children that she remembered him well as an old man when he came to spend nights at her father's big farm. He was a small man, Aunt Mattie said, with a shriveled, weather-beaten face, framed by long ragged gray hair. His eyes were a very bright blue surrounded by fine little lines which came of living always in the open. He went barefoot winter and summer and for clothing wore strange garments fashioned out of a kind of sackcloth or of leather or skins given him by the Indians. His only baggage was a metal cooking pot with a handle, which did not encumber his movements since when traveling he wore it as a hat with the handle at the back. He always carried a "poke" swung over his shoulder in which he carried seeds and plants.

He would arrive in the evening and have supper with the family, although later on as he grew older and more solitary he would not eat in the house but only on the doorstep or in the woodshed. Sometimes in the evening he would preach a kind of sermon upon love of mankind and all Nature. As he grew older the Swedenborgian doctrines changed imperceptibly into a kind of pagan faith which ascribed spirits to trees and sticks and stones and regarded the animals and the birds as his friends. But the sermons never had the curse of the conventional doctrinal harangue; they were interspersed with wonderful, enchanting stories about the wild things, so that for the children, the opossum, the raccoon, the bear, the blue jay all came to have distinct personalities and a sense of reality which most people never understand. Aunt Mattie said that, like St. Francis, he had a habit of talking aloud to the birds and animals as he tramped barefooted through the woods. None of the children ever resented or avoided his "sermons." It is probable that Johnny's visits took the place in that frontier country of theater and talking pictures and comic strips all rolled into one.

He never accepted the hospitality of a bed but chose instead to sleep in the great haymows above the fat cattle and horses. Usually when the settler went to the barn in the morning Johnny had already vanished with his kettle on his head and his "poke" of apple and fennel seed thrown over his shoulder. I think every Indian, every settler, every trader in all that Ohio country must have known him well, much as my great-grandfather knew him.

A good many of the white men and their families humored him and were fond of him but looked upon him as half mad. Some of them owed their lives and the lives of their families to Johnny Appleseed. The Indians regarded him with awe and veneration, for in the way of primitive peoples, they looked upon his particular kind of "insanity" as God-given, an "insanity" which linked him to the trees, the rocks, the wild animals which were so much a part of the redskins' daily and hourly existence. Because of this veneration the Indians never harmed him and left him free to go and come as he liked, nor did they conceal their plans from him. More than once during the early days of the frontier Johnny slipped away with his kettle and "poke" out of an Indian encampment to journey miles through forest and marsh to warn some lonely family to leave their cabin for the safety of the nearest village or blockhouse until the raids were over. If the Indians knew he had used his friendship to betray their plans, they appeared to have borne him no ill will for he lived at peace among them, preaching brotherhood and good will until there were no longer any Indians left in all the region and Johnny died one night, an old man, in a hedgerow in Indiana. . . .

There is some disagreement concerning the way in which Johnny went about planting apple trees in the wild frontier country. Some say that he scattered the seeds as he went along the edges of marshes or natural clearings in the thick almost tropical forests, others that he distributed the seeds among the settlers themselves to plant, and still others claim that in the damp land surrounding the marshes he established nurseries where he kept the seedlings until they were big enough to transplant. My Great-Aunt Mattie said that her father, who lived in rather a grand way for a frontier settler, had boxes of apples brought each year from Maryland until his own trees began to bear and then he always saved the seeds, drying them on the shelf above the kitchen fireplace, to be put later into a box and kept for Johnny Appleseed when he came on one of his overnight visits.

Johnny scattered fennel seed all through our Ohio country, for when the trees were first cleared and the land plowed up, the mosquitoes increased and malaria spread from family to family. Johnny regarded a tea brewed of fennel leaves as a specific against what the settlers called "fever and ague" and he seeded the plant along trails and fence rows over all Ohio. Some people said that he carried flower seeds with him to distribute among the lonely women who lived in cabins in clearings in the vast forest and that today the great red day lilies which grow along the roadsides or on the sites of old cabins, long disappeared, were spread by Johnny. They say also that Johnny sometimes carried in his "poke" as gifts tiny seedlings of Norway spruce which he gave to frontier wives to plant before their cabins. Both stories may be true for in our part of Ohio there is nearly always a pair of Norway spruce well over a hundred years old in the dooryard of every old house, and the red day lilies have gone wild in fields, on roadsides and along hedgerows.

In the next county there is an ancient apple tree which, it is claimed, was one of those planted by Johnny. I do not know whether this is true or not but I do know that in our pastures, on the edge of the woods and in the fence rows there are apple trees which are the descendants of those planted by Johnny. They bear a wide variety of apples from those which are small and bitter to those, on one or two trees, which are small but of a delicious wild flavor which no apples borne on respectable commercial apple trees ever attain. Their blossoms have a special perfume, very sweet and spicy, which you can smell a long way off, long before you come upon the trees themselves. They have been scattered here and there long ago by squirrels and rabbits and muskrat and raccoon who fed on the fruit of the trees planted more than a century and a half ago on the edge of clearings out of Johnny Appleseed's "poke."

And in our Valley, Johnny Appleseed is certainly not dead. He is there in the caves and the woodland, along the edge of the marshes and in hedgerows. When in early spring there drifts toward you the perfume of a wild apple tree, the spirit of Johnny rides the breeze. When in winter the snow beneath a wild apple tree is crisscrossed with the delicate prints of raccoon or muskrat or rabbit, you know that they have been there gathering apples from the trees that would never have existed but for crazy Johnny and his saucepan and "poke" of seeds. He is alive wherever the feathery fennel or the flowering day lilies cover a bank. He is there in the trees and the caves, the springs and the streams of our Ohio country, alive still in a legend which grows and grows.

Sometimes when I am alone in the old bottom pasture, or the woods, the memory of blind Great-Aunt Mattie returns to me. I can see her again, sitting by the edge of the clear flowing stream where the children left her, surrounded by cattle and the wild birds, her head a little tilted, listening.

She has been dead for close to forty years and only lately have I begun to understand what it was she heard. It was the song of the earth and streams and forests of which Johnny Appleseed has become the patron saint in our country. It may be that while she sat there Johnny Appleseed was with her.

She had a verse which she used often to repeat to us children:

He prayeth well who loveth well
Both man and bird and beast
He prayeth best, who loveth best
All things both great and small
For the dear God who loveth us
He made and loveth all.

One hot summer afternoon when I was twelve years old we returned late to guide Aunt Mattie back to the farmhouse. As we approached the chosen spot the cattle were as usual lying in a circle about the place where we had left her. She was leaning against an ancient sycamore tree, her head thrown back a little, her eyes closed. My cousin and I thought she was asleep, but when we spoke to her she did not answer. It was my first sight of death and I felt no more terror than the cattle lying in the bluegrass in a protecting circle about her. It was all strangely a part of the Valley, of the whole cycle of existence and the most natural thing in the world. I remember that when I got back to the farmhouse I had an impulse to say, "Aunt Mattie has gone to join her friend Johnny Appleseed." But I was only a small boy and then it seemed silly. I only said, "Something has happened to Aunt Mattie."